J. C. Yu

12-4-78

THE STRUCTURE OF THE
CHEMICAL PROCESSING INDUSTRIES

BUILDING THE LITERATURE OF A PROFESSION

Fifteen prominent chemical engineers first met in New York more than 50 years ago to plan a continuing literature for their rapidly growing profession. From industry came such pioneer practitioners as Leo H. Baekeland, Arthur D. Little, Charles L. Reese, John V. N. Dorr, M. C. Whitaker, and R. S. McBride. From the universities came such eminent educators as William H. Walker, Alfred H. White, D. D. Jackson, J. H. James, Warren K. Lewis, and Harry A. Curtis. H. C. Parmelee, then editor of *Chemical and Metallurgical Engineering*, served as chairman and was joined subsequently by S. D. Kirkpatrick as consulting editor.

After several meetings, this committee submitted its report to the McGraw-Hill Book Company in September 1925. In the report were detailed specifications for a correlated series of more than a dozen texts and reference books which have since become the McGraw-Hill Series in Chemical Engineering and which became the cornerstone of the chemical engineering curriculum.

From this beginning there has evolved a series of texts surpassing by far the scope and longevity envisioned by the founding Editorial Board. The McGraw-Hill Series in Chemical Engineering stands as a unique historical record of the development of chemical engineering education and practice. In the series one finds the milestones of the subject's evolution: industrial chemistry, stoichiometry, unit operations and processes, thermodynamics, kinetics, and transfer operations.

Chemical engineering is a dynamic profession, and its literature continues to evolve. McGraw-Hill and its consulting editors remain committed to a publishing policy that will serve, and indeed lead, the needs of the chemical engineering profession during the years to come.

The Series

THE STRUCTURE OF THE CHEMICAL PROCESSING INDUSTRIES
Function and Economics

J. Wei
Department of Chemical Engineering
Massachusetts Institute of Technology

T. W. F. Russell
Department of Chemical Engineering
University of Delaware

M. W. Swartzlander
Union Carbide Corporation

McGraw-Hill Book Company

New York   St. Louis   San Francisco   Auckland   Bogotá   Düsseldorf
Johannesburg   London   Madrid   Mexico   Montreal   New Delhi   Panama
Paris   São Paulo   Singapore   Sydney   Tokyo   Toronto

THE STRUCTURE OF THE CHEMICAL PROCESSING INDUSTRIES

1234567890   DODO   78321098

This book was set in Times Roman.
The editors were B. J. Clark and Madelaine Eichberg;
the production supervisor was Leroy A. Young.
The drawings were done by Santype Ltd.
R. R. Donnelley & Sons Company was printer and binder.

Library of Congress Cataloging in Publication Data

Wei, James, date
    The structure of the chemical processing industries.

    (McGraw-Hill chemical engineering series)
    Includes bibliographies and index.
    1. Chemical industries. 2. Industrial organization (Economic theory)
I. Russell, T. W. F., date joint author. II. Swartzlander, M. W., joint author. III. Title
HD9650.5.W39   338.6   77-28209
ISBN 0-07-068985-7

CONTENTS

PREFACE

The Caliph of Baghdad in disguise saw three men working and asked them what they were doing. The first man said, "I work for the Caliph for a few dinars per day." The second man said, "I am an expert rock breaker." The third man said, "We are building a road from Baghdad to the seaport." The Caliph said to his Grand Vizier, "The first man is a clock watcher, who is only interested in his pay in *dinars*. The second man has pride in his *skill* and is the backbone and sinew of my realm. But the third man understands the goal of the *project* and may be able to contribute ideas on how to improve the road." The wise old Vizier replied, "The third man knows what we are doing but not why it should be done. An even wiser worker would have said that the broader *mission* is to improve transportation of goods and people, which improves the quality of life for all our subject prople. Our wisest worker would even consider whether flying carpets are better than roads to fulfill the mission. How few are those who understand the needs of the people and how to serve them!"

If the Caliph were to return today, he might exclaim that the workers now have wondrous machines and skills but that the progeny of the first worker is more numerous than ever. Even those with pride in their skills often do not fully know the purpose and worth of their work; their lives may be without meaning outside of technical accomplishments, and they may be unaware of their broader contributions. This book is designed to broaden the minds of the Caliph's workers and to produce more knowledgeable and productive chemical professionals, at all levels of specialization.

The book is concerned with the quantitative description and analysis of the production of chemicals and related products by firms in the chemical processing industries (CPI); the organization and use of the resources of manpower, capital, plant and equipment, technology, and innovation; the financial driving forces of market demand and competition; the sociopolitical restraining forces of governments and public opinion; and the future prospects. It is suitable for chemical engineers and chemists, both students and experienced professionals, who are interested in how chemical technology is mobilized to benefit society and how they can contribute effectively to it. The mathematics needed is covered by freshman calculus. Previous exposure to economics and accounting is helpful but not necessary.

From the very first day on the job, a chemical professional—chemical engineer or chemist—should know how the (CPI) serve society by anticipating and responding to its changing needs at acceptable costs. The chemical professionals should understand their role in the CPI and society. They should know the external and internal forces that represent threats and opportunities to the CPI, and they should know the factors affecting innovation and prosperity. To achieve this knowledge and skill, they need to stretch their mental horizons from scientific and technical matters to the broader economic and social issues. They need to learn the important economic and accounting concepts and tools, to become knowledgeable about the structure of the CPI, to practice analyzing economic studies and to use them for decision-making, to realize that there is seldom a single correct answer to a problem, to be able to find economic information, to consider many points of view before making up their own minds, and to be able to construct persuasive economic studies that alter the course of events.

In their first job, chemical professionals are assigned to specific projects, such as the improvement of an existing process or the development of a new product. Effective professionals must be skillful in problem solving. They must also understand financial accountability, i.e., that the benefits arising from the project should exceed the costs associated with the project. They should look beyond their immediate assignment and learn how their own work affects the project balance sheet. After about 10 years in industry, many chemical professionals change jobs from the technical speciality to the broader project responsibility. Again at this stage in their career, successful professionals should continue the learning process beyond the project responsibility to an understanding of how the project affects the company's performance and balance sheet. They should be working to build a more successful company. After 15 or 20 years, some move on to mission defining. Now effective chemical professionals are concerned not only with the company's performance but with how the company affects the prosperity of the nation and society. Prepared minds are needed for these transitions.

This book can be used in the classroom or for self-directed study. It contains all the concepts and tools needed, as well as much economic information and examples. Our students' comments, our in-class experience, and the comments of our teaching colleagues have prompted us to include a Reader's Guide, as Chap. 0, preceding the text itself. It shows the general reader, the in-class student, and the instructor how to enrich and update their study of the text. For instructors preparing a course, detailed suggestions are given in Sec. 0.2, Developing an Effective Course. Real understanding demands the habit of frequent review of information and concepts, the practice of using tools and finding information, the analysis and use of economic studies, and the construction of economic studies.

This book received its original influence from R. W. Schiessler of Mobil Corporation and from T. Leavitt of the Harvard Business School, who taught one of the authors (JW) about the true purpose of the modern corporation. As department chairman, A. B. Metzner was most encouraging and supportive of the course development, and as acting chairman, M. M. Denn was cooperative in manuscript preparation. Dean I. G. Greenfield provided funds to support the course development as part of his effort to encourage innovation in the college and supported the participation of his associate dean (TWFR).

Many industrial colleagues generously offered their comments and insights. We are particularly grateful to R. E. Heckert, of Du Pont, and H. J. Taufen, of Hercules, for their effective and dynamic guest lectures and for their interest and encouragement from the beginning. We have also greatly benefited from class presentations and discussions with J. J. Donnelly, of Mobil; T. T. Szabo, of Union Carbide; J. F. Dempsey, of Air Products and Chemicals; and R. J. Richardson, of Du Pont. E. A. Barr and H. L. Reichart, of Union Carbide, and P. H. Bailey, of Du Pont, contributed many useful comments.

This book was greatly facilitated by the efforts of P. M. Elliott, a political science student turned chemical engineer, who gathered and analyzed data, worked through rough drafts, and added his thoughts and criticisms to the text.

We are particularly thankful to the six classes of seniors and graduate students who took the course, worked the problems, provided much data collection and analysis, and helped the instructors to clarify the text material.

We are grateful to the secretarial staff in the Chemical Engineering Department and the Dean's office who prepared various drafts of the manuscript. Special thanks are due to Mrs. T. M. Holton, who prepared the final draft and effectively performed a great many other tasks associated with manuscript preparation.

J. Wei
T. W. F. Russell
M. W. Swartzlander

THE STRUCTURE OF THE
CHEMICAL PROCESSING INDUSTRIES

0

READER'S GUIDE

0.1 ENRICHING AND UPDATING

The usefulness of this text will be greatly enhanced if you supplement it with information from current periodicals, basic references, statistical collections, abstracting services, and indexes. This will allow you to update the data given in the text and—even more important—provide practice in finding the information chemical professionals need in day-to-day analysis and problem solving. The most important sources below are labeled with two asterisks and the next most important with one asterisk. If you are using the book for self-directed study, you should subscribe to the double-asterisk periodicals and regularly read the single-asterisk periodicals,[1] become familiar with the contents of the references with asterisks, locate a library with the Kirk-Othmer and SRI International references, and obtain a copy of the *Statistical Abstract of the United States* (Secs. 0.1.1 and 0.1.2).

0.1.1 Current Periodicals

Chemical and Engineering News**[2] The most important journal is this weekly publication of the American Chemical Society. Anyone seriously interested in the chemical industry should subscribe to it. Much of the statistical information in this text has been taken from. Facts and Figures issues of *Chemical Engineering*

---

[1] Subscription prices range from $15 to $50 per year.
[2] American Chemical Society, 1155 16th Street, N.W., Washington, DC 20036.

News to show you how easy it is to obtain the most recent statistics in a familiar and useful format. Of equal importance are the news items, detailed studies, and articles which appear throughout the year.

Chemical Week*[1] A subscription to this publication is very valuable. Like *Chemical and Engineering News*, it reports on the business, economic, and technical aspects of the chemical industry. It frequently publishes valuable longer studies on a particular product or situation. The annual Buyers' Guide lists about 1,500 companies and their addresses and the manufacturers of some 6,000 chemicals.

Chemical Engineering Progress[2] This monthly publication is particularly useful for information on new processes, capital and operating costs of processes, and new equipment in the chemical process industries (CPI). It also provides a current picture of issues important to chemical engineers.

CHEMTECH[3] This journal frequently contains articles with new and refreshing ideas about both the technical and business aspects of the CPI; it is published monthly.

Fortune[4] This twice monthly publication deals with major issues in economics and business and publishes annual directories of both foreign and United States companies (the famous "Fortune 500"), useful in showing the role of the chemical industry in the total business picture. In addition there are many articles on the CPI which will enliven and expand the material in this text.

Forbes[5] This monthly publication contains business articles written from an investor's viewpoint. Every year articles dealing with the CPI give insights not provided by other publications. One important feature of *Forbes* is that it frequently evaluates the operations of various companies. These critical evaluations provide more balanced information than the generally optimistic and self-congratulatory rhetoric of company reports.

Chemical Marketing Reporter*[6] This weekly newspaper contains the current market prices of chemicals as well as news articles about the chemical industry. It is the best source for chemical prices.

Chemical Engineering[7] This useful biweekly publication deals more with the technical than the business side of the chemical industry and is a good source of information about new processes.

---

[1] Subscription address: PO Box 970, Times Square Station, New York, NY 10036.
[2] American Institute of Chemical Engineers, 345 East 7 Street, New York, NY 10017.
[3] American Chemical Society, 1155 16th Street, N.W., Washington, DC 20036.
[4] Time, Inc., 541 North Fairbanks Court, Chicago, IL 60611.
[5] Forbes, Inc., 60 Fifth Avenue, New York, NY 10011.
[6] Schnell Publishing Company, Inc., 100 Church Street, New York, NY 10007.
[7] Subscription address: Fulfillment Manager, *Chemical Engineering*, PO Box 430, Hightstown, NJ 08520.

Hydrocarbon Processing[1] More technology- than business-oriented, this biweekly places more emphasis on petroleum refining and the oil industry than *Chemical Engineering* does.

Oil and Gas Journal[2] Written for the oil and gas industry, this biweekly contains useful statistics on production and prices as well as articles and petroleum industry news.

Economic Indicators[3] This monthly gives the most recent statistical data on total economic output, income, spending, employment, wages, business activity, prices, credit, and federal finance.

Survey of Current Business[3] This is also a monthly publication, prepared by the Bureau of Economic Analysis of the Department of Commerce. Like *Economic Indicators*, it contains statistical macroeconomic data and articles of general business interest.

The Wall Street Journal, Business Week, and *U.S. News and World Report* Providing daily and weekly business news, these three publications often contain articles pertaining to the chemical industry.

Chemical Age[4] A monthly publication, it is most useful for its international reporting. Of particular value is an annual directory of worldwide chemical companies and their key economic characteristics.

Economic Report of the President*[3] This annual report to the Congress on the state of the national economy is written by the Council of Economic Advisors. It covers major economic issues and contains valuable statistical tables.

Harvard Business Review[5] An outstanding and widely read monthly journal of business management, it presents timely articles and excellent business case studies.

Foreign Affairs[6] This leading quarterly journal of world events contains articles written by leaders in government, education, foundations, and business.

The Economist[7] A highly respected international business journal; it occasionally presents longer studies using statistics and analysis.

[1] Gulf Publishing Company, Box 2608, Houston, TX 77001.
[2] Petroleum Publishing Company, PO Box 1260, Tulsa, OK 74101.
[3] Superintendant of Documents, U.S. Government Printing Office, Washington, DC 20402.
[4] Morgan Granapian, Inc., 205 E. 42 Street, New York, NY 10017.
[5] PO Box 291, Cambridge, MA 01509.
[6] 428 East Preston Street, Baltimore MD 21202.
[7] 25 St. James Street, London SWIA 1HG, England.

Far Eastern Economic Review[1] This is a weekly business magazine specializing in the Far East.

0.1.2 Basic References

There are a number of good introductory texts in basic economics. The following ones are particularly helpful.

Paul A. Samuelson, "Economics," 10th ed., McGraw-Hill, New York, 1976.
C. E. Ferguson, "Microeconomic Theory," Irwin, Homewood, Ill.
G. J. Stigler, "The Theory of Price," Macmillan, New York, 1966.
Robert N. Anthony, "Management Accounting," Irwin, Homewood, Ill., 1964.
Myron, J. Gordon and Gordon Shillinglaw, "Accounting: A Management Approach," Richard D. Irwin, Homewood, Ill., 1974.
Sidney Davidson (ed.), "Standard Handbook for Accountants," McGraw-Hill, New York, 1970.

The following two books are available in paperback and worth having as part of a personal library:

Jules Backman, "The Economics of the Chemical Industry," Manufacturing Chemists Association, Washington, 1970. Valuable for historical perspective and analysis of the nature of the chemical industry although some of the statistics are now out of date.
American Chemical Society, "Chemistry in the Economy," Washington, 1974. Social and economic impact of chemistry, accomplishments of chemistry, and expected future developments considered in detail, with a good history of the development of most important industrial chemicals.

The following paperback should be purchased each year:

U.S. Bureau of the Census, *Statistical Abstract of the United States*,** Washington. The most valuable one-volume source of current statistics (population, vital statistics, labor force, income, and other types of information with which you should familiarize yourself); also available from Grosset & Dunlap, New York.

The following references should be available through a library:

SRI International: "Chemical Economics Handbook,"*. Menlo Park, Ca. An extremely important reference, presenting capacity, production, and sales data for chemicals in updated looseleaf albums.
H. F. Mark, J. J. McKetta, and D. F. Othmer, "Kirk-Othmer Encyclopedia of Chemical Technology," 2d ed., Interscience, New York, 1963. Out of date in some parts but still a useful place to begin searches (a new edition is scheduled for publication in 1978).
F. A. Lowenheim, and M. K. Moran, "Faith, Keyes, & Clark's Industrial Chemicals," 4th ed., Wiley-Interscience, New York, 1975. A one-volume summary of process technology with a history of sales volume and price.
R. N. Shreve, and J. A. Brink, Jr., "The Chemical Processing Industry,"* 4th ed., McGraw-Hill, New York, 1977. A summary of CPI process technology; despite some out-of-date material, often a useful book when you are starting a study of a chemical or process.

---

[1] 406–410 Marina House, PO Box 160, Hong Kong.

Douglas M. Considine (ed.), "Chemical and Process Technology Encyclopedia," McGraw-Hill, New York, 1974. Contains flow diagrams, process descriptions, some cost-of-production data, and some discussion of major use.

James A. Kent, "Riegel's Handbook of Industrial Chemistry," 7th ed., Van Nostrand Reinhold, New York, 1974.

"Moody's Handbook of Common Stock," Moody's Investor Service, New York, and "Standard and Poor's Stock Market Encyclopedia," Standard and Poor's Corporation, New York. Company financial data constantly updated.

John J. McKetta (ed.), "Encyclopedia of Chemical Processing Design," Dekker, New York, 1977.

Although written for a British audience, the following books are worth reading:

B. G. Reuben, and M. L. Burstall: "The Chemical Economy," Longmans, London, 1973.

F. B. Bradbury, and B. G. Dutton, "Chemical Industry: Social and Economic Aspects," Butterworths, London, 1972.

0.1.3 Statistical Collections

U.S. Industrial Outlook 19— with Projections to 19—, GPO, Washington. An annual publication with both a narrative and a statistical format.

Subscriber Services Section, Economics Statistics Administration, *1972 Census of Manufacturers*, Washington. Contains detailed financial data on manufacturing establishments, specific products, and specific industries organized by SIC sectors; includes industry reports on the CPI and related industries (irregular publication, 1972 being the latest).

Predicasts, Predicasts, Inc., Cleveland. A quarterly abstract dealing with market data for manufacturing industries arranged by SIC code.

U.S. Tariff Commission, *Synthetic Organic Chemicals*, GPO, Washington. An annual updated with monthly supplements providing statistics on the organic chemical industry.

0.1.4 Abstracting Services and Indexes

Standard sources like *Technical Abstracts*, *Chemical Abstracts*, *Applied Science and Technology Index*, and the *Engineering Index* will frequently be needed, and the following will be useful:

Chemical Market Abstracts, Predicasts, Inc., Cleveland. A monthly publication arranged by SIC code.

Chemical Industry Notes, Chemical Abstract Service, Columbus, Ohio. A weekly abstracting news items pertinent to the chemical industry.

F and S Index of Corporations and Industries, Predicasts, Inc., Cleveland. Annual, quarterly, and weekly editions covering companies, products, and other business data.

Many libraries also have available the Lockheed Retrieval Services, which is an on-line computer information-retrieval service. All the *Predicast* data bases and *Chemical Industry Notes* are searchable through this service.

Readers not enrolled in a formal course should read the next section, particularly the discussion on course objectives, skills to be developed, and problem assignments.

0.2 DEVELOPING AN EFFECTIVE COURSE

0.2.1 Instructor's Guide

This text provides the necessary fundamentals and required statistical information for developing a course. In this section we discuss other materials essential for making the course effective.

   The preparation and planning of this course differ from those of most engineering or science courses. Much of the material discussed needs to be current (no one today knows which problems will be the crucial issues tomorrow). This text contains the relatively timeless fundamental economic and accounting principles, examples of economic analysis, and a detailed discussion of the structure of the CPI in the United States. Experience has shown that one can develop a lively, interesting, up-to-date, and effective course by expanding upon and adding to the textual material in a number of ways.

Extensive use of current periodicals These are listed in Sec. 0.1.1. We recommend a personal subscription to at least *Chemical and Engineering News* and one other periodical on the list such as *CHEMTECH*. Both short news items and longer feature articles can be used to expand upon material in the text, to stimulate class discussion, and to generate effective homework assignments. For instance:

1. In 1975 many companies switched from FIFO (first in first out) to LIFO (last in first out) accounting to determine cost of goods sold. The news articles from a number of periodicals greatly enlivened the discussions in Chaps. 3 and 7, since company profits were significantly altered by this change.
2. A special *Chemical Week* report on Mideast Petrochemicals provided one class of intense discussion which expanded upon the material covered in Chap. 9. We have also used, at various times, the following features from *Chemical Week:* Catalysts, 1972; Dark Clouds on Sulfur's Horizons, 1971; and Methanol, 1974.
3. *Chemical and Engineering News* has a regular feature on Key Chemicals, in which updated production figures, price, major uses, new uses, and method of production are presented. This is very useful for expanding upon and updating material in Chaps. 5 and 6.
4. *Fortune* had a special article on methanol in 1975 which was most helpful in discussing the energy issue and illustrating how a report should be prepared.
5. An article in the June 15, 1976, issue of *Forbes* on Monsanto and its agricultural chemical business was the basis for a problem in Chap. 10.
6. The *Fortune* article Dupont "Gave Away" Billions—and Prospered, January 1973, illustrates the use of the experience curve (Chaps. 5 and 8), the competitive characteristics of the chemical industry (Chap. 8), and different ways of looking at a company's performance (Chap. 7).
7. Barbara Lawrence, Preliminary Project Evaluation: Any Technologist Can Do

It, *CHEMTECH*, November 1975, is studied by all our students to help them use the literature effectively.

In almost every class, we discuss or at least mention some item from one of the periodicals. We have subscriptions to most and have developed the habit of clipping articles for discussion. Some are brought to the attention of the class immediately, and some are filed until a particular topic is covered.

Use of case studies Case studies are a particularly effective way of meeting the objectives of the course and developing the student's skills, as outlined in Sec. 1.1. Case studies also serve as examples, good and bad, of how a problem should be handled. Critical analysis of case studies helps develop the student's ability to detect weaknesses, flaws in logic, and inappropriate interpretation of facts and events. There are three good sources for case studies.

Published case studies A comprehensive listing of published case studies is available in the "Intercollegiate Bibliography [of] 1974, Selected Cases in Administration."[1] Some of these case studies are well done and add greatly to the course. Unfortunately, there is no a priori way of determining which case studies will be useful. The instructor should order several case studies well in advance of the course in order to review them and choose which ones are to be used in class. We have used the following case studies with some success.

1. Industrial Chemicals, Inc. This Harvard Business School case examines research and development in a company by studying the personalities of the key people involved, how they interact with each other, and their career progression. This case study is well done and relatively timeless.
2. Mobil Chemical Company. This Harvard Business School case is somewhat outdated, but it shows the student what sort of information management and technical personnel need in order to embark on a new business. Top management was asked to decide whether to continue the development of a plastic milk container. A number of sharp questions will be asked, and equally sharp answers are needed before major funds can be committed. In a mock class session some of the students can be assigned the role of the top management committee and some the role of project advocates. Questions that must be included are: Why are plastic milk bottles needed? In what bottle size and what sales outlet does it have a competitive advantage over rival products? Is there a price or convenience advantage that housewives would perceive? How important is the handle? Does Mobil have any experience and advantage over other companies in marketing plastic milk bottles? How good is the Mobil technology in comparison with that of other companies? Is it lower in cost or more effective? Has research turned out excellent leads? How important is the ability

---

[1] Intercollegiate Case Clearing House, Soldiers Field, Boston, MA 02163.

to ship half-formed bottles? Does Mobil have advantages and experience in manufacturing or raw-material supply? Would the project be profitable, and can Mobil keep out imitations? What additional key data and information are needed before a clear decision can be made? How can the information be obtained? Should Mobil continue the development study or seek a partner? (Who, and with what special skills?) If the project is to continue, what questions must be resolved within a year for the next report to the top management committee?

3. Reichhold Chemicals, Inc. This University of Alabama case study deals with waste-water treatment problems of Reichhold's Tuscaloosa plant. Emphasis in the case study is on methods of treating waste water with a passing reference to some process improvements. This case provides a very good basis for class discussion on the economic and social issues involved in environmental problems. Points that should be raised include the following. Reichhold manufactures phenol by the benzene sulfonate process. What are the essential features of this process? (enough data for discussion are given in "Faith, Keyes, & Clark's Industrial Chemicals," Sec. 0.1.2). How can the process be modified to reduce pollution (an issue not considered in this case)? What other process can be used to manufacture phenol? Should Reichhold abandon this plant (only 6 percent of all phenol is made by the benzene sulfonate process) and build a more efficient pollution-free plant? What are the future prospects for phenol? What is the present plant worth?

Case studies prepared by industrial concerns There is no central index of such studies, many of which are prepared for internal use and not made public. Frequently, however, material can be presented in lectures by guest speakers from industry, who can discuss the case effectively.

Case studies prepared by the course instructor Many topics suggest themselves as one teaches a course and although it is not a trivial matter to do so, an instructor can prepare short case studies with the help of term papers and class assignments. If a research effort accompanies the classwork, one can prepare case studies of a sufficiently high quality to meet the thesis requirements of the master's degree.

Use of speakers from institutions outside the university This essential and rewarding part of the course allows students to hear and question people who are actually involved with the issues dealt with in the text, the supplementary sources, or the case studies. About 10 to 15 percent of the lecture time should be devoted to outside speakers. Industrial concerns and government agencies are most cooperative, especially if you talk to people at the highest level. The speaker and topic must be chosen to fit into the course structure. Request background material from the speaker in the form of handouts or published articles and make sure that the students are well read before the presentation. Time for questions and answers should be provided.

Assignment of student specialists After 2 years of experimentation, we have found that the following procedures greatly enliven class discussion, allow the more reticent student to participate more easily, and provide an effective means of motivating the students to become familiar with the basic references and to gain practice in researching the economic literature of the chemical industry.

Product specialist assignment Detailed instructions are given in the Sec. 0.2.2. The plan is to have each student be the course specialist on at least one chemical industry product and to prepare a comprehensive term paper. The products must be carefully selected by the instructor, who should have a plan for class discussion utilizing the detailed information collected by the student.

Typical product assignments used at the University of Delaware are shown in Table 0.1. (We normally do not include the products discussed in Chap. 6.) The 50 largest-volume chemicals from *Chemical and Engineering News* Fact and Figures issue are prime candidates for product-specialist assignments. High-market-value chemicals which are not necessarily in the largest-volume list also make good product assignments. Any chemicals which are particularly timely, e.g., Kepone, Red Dye No. 2, PCB, or DDT, make interesting product assignments. The instructor should always ask student specialists to comment when their products appear in the news.

Table 0.1 Typical product assignments

Precipitated calcium carbonate	Caustic soda	Carbon dioxide
Titanium dioxide	Ammonia	Nitrogen
Carbon black	Sulfuric acid	Oxygen
Yellow iron oxide	Nylon	DDT
Penicillin	Polyester fiber	Pesticides
Aspirin	Rayon	Herbicides
Vitamin C		

Company specialist assignment Detailed instructions are presented in Sec. 0.2.2. This assignment requires each student to become a class expert on a CPI company and to prepare a comprehensive term paper. The student is expected to provide both statistical and qualitative information on the company. The instructor must select the company assignments carefully, and it is essential to make use of the student's knowledge of the companies in both a planned and spontaneous fashion. For the past 2 years we have emphasized the smaller firms, and a typical set of assignments is shown in Table 0.2. Any of the firms listed in Appendix B make suitable assignments.

A list of both company and product specialists should be given to all students in the class and to invited speakers, who should be encouraged to call upon the student experts.

Table 0.2 Typical company assignments

Airco
Akzona
Becker Industries
Betz Laboratories
Borden
Cabot
Crompton-Knowles
General Foods
Oakite
Pfizer
Quaker Chemical
Stauffer
Sun
Texaco
Witco

Special-situation specialist This assignment may be made instead of a product or company assignment to one or more students, or it may be an additional term paper for some or all students. It can be a very satisfying type of assignment if the term papers are properly researched and clearly written. They can be the basis for a case study or may even lead to a graduate-level research program. Some of the topics which have been successfully reported on at the University of Delaware are listed in the Sec. 0.2.2.

If there is time, it is worthwhile to have students present term papers orally. We generally allot one or two class periods to this and evaluate the speaker's performance according to the following guidelines:

1. Oral presentation, 40%
    20%   *a.* Quality of the presentation (Is it clear, understandable, and well organized?)
    10%   *b.* Competence in using slides, graphs, tables, blackboard
    10%   *c.* Ability to answer questions (Does the speaker understand the material, satisfy the questioner, admit inability to answer, or try to bluff?)
2. Content, 60%
    15%   *a.* Comprehensiveness (Does the speaker cover all the points necessary?)
    15%   *b.* Critical analysis (Does the speaker merely report facts and opinions of others or is there active, independent criticism?)
    15%   *c.* Does the speaker use the concepts and financial and accounting criteria developed in the course?
    15%   *d.* Originality and scope (What general impression is made? What is the overall impact of the talk?)

Development and preparation of supplemental materials to augment the text Each student should be given a package of material at the start of the course which contains, as a minimum, the following:

1. Facts and Figures issue of *Chemical and Engineering News.* As explained earlier, much of the statistical material in the text is based on the tables presented in this issue.[1]
2. Two company reports and 10-K forms. These are essential for the accounting review and discussion in Chaps. 5 and 7. Enough copies can be obtained for each member of the class by writing to the treasurer's department of the company. Addresses for several firms are given in Chap. 7.
3. Case studies. Plan on three.
4. Reprints from current periodicals. These must be decided upon well before class begins and ordered from the specific publication. At least two will be needed.
5. *Statistical Abstract of the United States* As noted in Sec. 0.1.2, this is the standard summary of statistics on the political, economic, and social organizations of the United States. It needs to be used to keep sections of the book up to date.
6. Reprint of Barbara Lawrence, Preliminary Project Evaluation: Any Technologist Can Do It, *CHEMTECH*, November 1975.

Of course, there are many other sources for material. Government reports are particularly useful and are available from the Government Printing Office (GPO).

Industrial concerns, banks, and various other private agencies also produce material that can be useful in class, e.g., Shell Reports and reports by the Ford Foundation and the Chase Manhattan Bank.

The data in the text and in the above " evergreen package " can be overwhelming if the class is not given some chance to become familiar with them during or before the lecture. In Chaps. 5 to 7, where by necessity there are a large number of tables, we have included a section on Questions for Discussion, designed to make students more aware of the significance of the tabular data by requiring them to reorder the material, to compute new ratios, to compare one table with another, etc. By using the questions in this special section as homework or as a short in-class assignment the instructor can easily develop some significant discussion. For example, the class can be asked to rank the companies in Table 5.9 by return on investment and by profit margin. This simple exercise can easily generate 15 minutes of lively questions and discussion, which can be related to the material previously covered in Chap. 3 and to the various student company reports. Asking the class to find the companies in Table 5.10 with significant chemical sales can also generate some good class discussion.

Planning To prepare for a course we try to follow the schedule presented in Table 0.3. In the three-credit (42-h) course all 10 chapters can be adequately covered with time for guest speakers, case studies, and discussion of current problems of interest to the CPI. A flexible in-class schedule is given in Table 0.4.

---

[1] Reprints can be ordered from Special Issue Sales, ACS, 1155 16th Street, N.W., Washington, DC 20036.

Table 0.3 Planning schedule

Months before course begins	Phases to be completed	Comment
12–10	Collect articles which will expand upon and complement text; decide on reprints students should have	Begin to rough out in-class course schedule
6–4	Order text	Not knowing class registration can be troublesome; class enrollment should have an upper limit to ensure adequate class discussions and interaction
4–2	Order reprints, Facts and Figures issue of *Chemical and Engineering News*, case studies, company reports, etc.	
2	Decide upon companies and products to assign to student specialists; make a list in order of importance	In-class schedule should now be fairly well decided
$1\frac{1}{2}$	Invite outside speakers	The last bit of information needed to firm up the class schedule
1	Prepare package of supplemental material	

Table 0.4

Chap.	Hours	Chap.	Hours	Chap.	Hours
1	1–2	5	1–2	9	2–4
2	5–7	6	1–2	10	2–4
3	1–3	7	1–2	Guest speakers	3–5
4	2–4	8	4–6	Case studies	3–5

0.2.2 Student's Guide

This course should be studied differently from most engineering or science courses. The basic structure is more empirical and inductive, the kinds of information and skills you need to develop are different and more diverse, and there is seldom one correct answer to the problems posed. There must be active, informed, and well-thought-out discussion if you are to understand the economics of the complex CPI and the role chemical professionals now play and must learn to play in the years to come. Tomorrow's engineers and chemists *must* understand more of the overall picture. This *does not mean* that they should discard their technical and scientific skills. Without them they become one of those drones of society who can only *talk* about problems. Chemical professionals must strengthen their technical expertise by obtaining additional economic and sociopolitical skills. We need chemical professionals who can *solve* real problems in which the technical component may not be the crucial factor.

To develop the required skills you need to:

1. Read carefully the text, assigned case studies, reprints, journals, and references
2. Participate in class discussion both by listening and by talking
3. Do problems developed to demonstrate comprehension of concepts and important facts
4. Do problems using economic and accounting tools to analyze problems
5. Do problems giving practice in library research for economic data
6. Prepare two term papers which will develop your skills in data searching, logical analysis, and construction of convincing economic arguments
7. Take examinations which will test comprehension and analytical skill

Read Sec. 0.2.1 in order to understand the planning and scheduling for the course. Section 0.1 must constantly be consulted for appropriate sources.

Your contribution is needed both in and out of class in at least four ways.

As a product specialist Much can be learned about the chemical industry by studying the products it makes and the companies making up the industry. The task of the product specialist is to become a class expert on at least one important product of the chemical industry. Your instructor will assign the products to you based upon the overall plan for the course. You will be given approximately 2 to 3 weeks to prepare a term paper on the product. You will be graded by your ability to respond to class questions and discussion regarding your products as well as on the quality of the written report.

To become the kind of expert required, it is necessary but not sufficient to consider:

1. Total annual sales for the last decade
2. Selling-price structure over the last decade
3. Principal uses and percentages of product consumed by each use
4. Companies involved and as much information as possible on capacity and plant sites
5. Process flow diagram and technical details of major and alternative methods of manufacture
6. Some historical perspective

There should be at least three major sections to the term paper

1. *Marketing.* The following questions need to be answered. Who are the customers? What do they use the product for? What other products compete with it? What is the sales history? How much has been sold each year for the past 10 to 20 years? What is the price history? How is the product classified (Chap. 5)?

Are there any new uses or new markets to consider? What external threats exist? Can they be avoided?
2. *Manufacturing.* This is the technical section of the report. It must be quantitative and up to date. Answers are needed for the following questions. What process or processes are used? (A simplified process flow diagram with some basic mass and energy balances is necessary at the very least.) How old is the process? Have there been any recent innovations? What are the major capital costs? What are the major operating costs? Is the raw-material supply secure? Are alternate raw materials available? Can productivity be improved (new process, more control, more research and development)? Which companies manufacture the product? What are approximate plant capacities?
3. *Environmental impact.* Is a nuisance produced by the manufacturing process? Is there a problem in transportation? Do manufacture and use of the product cause environmental or health problems? Do the benefits outweigh any harm? Can any bad effects be controlled? What is the cost of such control?

As a company specialist You also will be required to become the class expert on one important company in the chemical industry. The instructor will make the assignment based on his course plan, but it is your responsibility to gather the kind of information which will provide active and informed class discussion. As a minimum, you must consider the following for your company term paper:

1. The company's financial structure: total sales, earnings per share, net income, stock price, assets, debts, etc.
2. The products made and their importance to the company's business
3. The company's planning for the future: expenditure for research and development, capital investment, innovations, and plans for dealing with a changing world

An annual report provides the minimum information needed. Financial data are also available from "Moody's" or "Standard and Poor's." Current periodicals often provide interesting insights into a company's operations (particularly *Forbes*).

A company term paper should consider the following questions:

1. What business is it in? What products does it make, and what customers do they serve? Will customers prosper in the future? Is there a mix of products? How vulnerable is the company to changes in market demand?
2. What is the image of the company? Is it an aggressive, growth-oriented company making unusual chemicals for a high price or a mature company making commodity chemicals in bulk for a low markup? Is innovation of new products, new markets, or new processes an important part of the company?
3. What is the past record? Look at its past 10 years' record of sales, earning per share, and stock price. What pattern do they present, rising or falling? What are the causes behind these changes, and how does this company compare with

other chemical companies, with industrial companies in general, with national GNP? Apply financial analysis.
4. What are the external threats and opportunities? What forces are gathering that may cause grief (a new process by a competitor, declining market for the product, regulation of pollution, price increase or unavailability of raw material) or prosperity?

Quantify your discussions as much as possible. Additional sources of information are brokerage houses and financial analysts, *The Wall Street Journal,* "Moody's Handbook," and company annual reports. Be critical and skeptical of your sources. Company reports tend to stress only the positive, anticompany critics tend to stress only the negative, and investor services such as " Moody's " and *Forbes* tend to be more neutral. You need to consider all these evaluations as a broad base for your own evaluations.

As a specialist on a specific situation or problem The instructor may or you may decide on an investigation of some special situation which affects the CPI. The possibilities are infinite, and much can be gained by both the student and the class if this type of term paper is well done.

Special-situation term papers must provide background information with as much quantitative data as possible. Be sure that both sides of any controversy are well represented. Principal arguments and logic should be analyzed. International data can be obtained in United Nations statistical tables, from major international or domestic banks operating in that nation, and often from the commerce attaché at the embassy or commercial officer at the consulate.

Topics which have been successfully prepared at the University of Delaware have included the following:

1. Environmental impact of synthetic vs. natural fibers
2. Chemical-plant buildup in the Middle East
3. The chemical industry of Brazil
4. Recycling waste oil
5. Experience curve for by-product chemicals
6. Fluorocarbon-ozone controversy
7. Pricing policy in the CPI

As a person informed by reading the current periodicals Sources of information on the chemical industry are listed in the Sec. 0.1. You should read at least two of the current periodicals on a regular basis and raise issues in class which you feel should be discussed.

Most of your work requires well-organized library research in sources outside the usual technical area. You will greatly broaden your professional skills by doing these assignments effectively and by reading the chemical-industry literature.

Obtain your information from as many sources as possible, to bring out different facets and interpretations. Every writer has prejudices and blind spots and cannot be depended upon to be comprehensive. The whole picture can emerge only after you look at the world through many pairs of eyes.

1

INTRODUCTION

1.1 GENERAL REMARKS

The chemical professionals, chemical engineers and chemists, devote most of their formal educational efforts to the study of technology and science. From courses in chemistry, physics, thermodynamics, kinetics, transport phenomena, unit operations, and design the engineer or chemist learns about the laws of nature and how to describe physical phenomena in useful ways. In order to function in a truly useful manner, however, today's chemical engineers and chemists must understand much more than science and technology. The dynamic chemical professional must also understand the complex economic and sociopolitical factors which affect the application of technical and scientific expertise.

Figure 1.1 graphically depicts the interactions between the decisive factors that affect the launching and success of a venture. We can use the diagram to illustrate the interactions in a typical problem facing our society today, the need to use our coal resources to become less dependent upon depletable crude-oil sources outside the United States. Suppose as a society we wish to manufacture a significant amount of synthetic oil or gas from coal. Solution of the major technical and scientific problems is a necessary first step before any economic issues can be considered. What is the basic chemistry, what are the kinetic, thermodynamic, and transport factors affecting equipment design, what are the engineering process

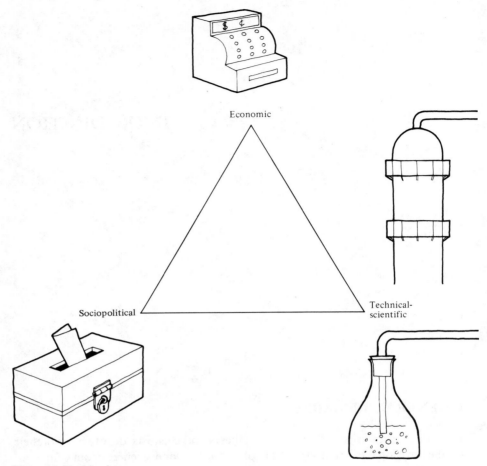

Figure 1.1 Decisive factors.

design problems, what materials of construction are needed, and what processes have already been tested and demonstrated?

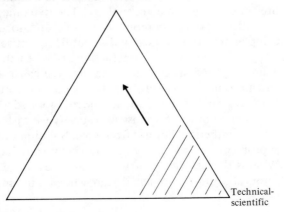

As a number of technical alternatives are developed, economic issues must be considered. At today's prices and availability of supplies, which process is more efficient in resource utilization? Are raw-material prices and availability likely to be stable or to change dramatically? What size plant should be built? Where should it be built? How many plants should be built?

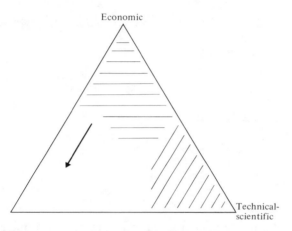

Solutions that are technically and economically feasible must be acceptable to society through the political process. The preference of the people is shaped by their hopes and fears and by their choices between economic efficiency and their quality of life. What environmental impact is acceptable to the public? What level of independence from imports strikes the people as the best balance between national security and consumer-price increases?

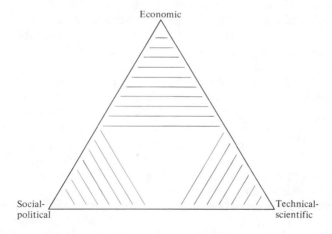

Today, most of the technical problems in coal conversion are solvable, and the operating- and capital-cost structures of coal process plants are reasonably well known. The problems which must now be solved are political and social, at both national and international levels. How will the price of a barrel of imported crude oil vary over the next 10 years? Can a safe supply of imported crude be

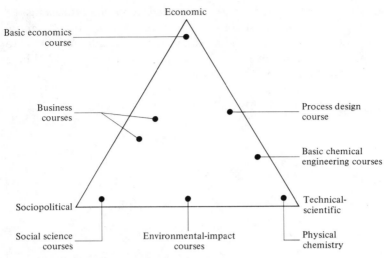

Figure 1.2 Decisive factors and university courses.

assumed? Will and should the United States government subsidize coal-conversion operations? Do we need a floor price on crude oil, and if so, what should it be? What political moves need to be made to achieve this?

We can also use the decisive-factors diagram to illustrate the structure of most educational programs. Marked on Fig. 1.2 are examples of the types of courses in a typical university program in chemical engineering or chemistry. In addition to the strictly technical and scientific courses, engineering students have a number of design-oriented courses which help them see the economic constraints affecting the application of technology. Process design courses usually show how to determine which combination of technologies should be used to perform a chemical transformation in the most economical manner.

The chemical professional student may also take some basic economic, social science, and business courses, which develop skills and give insight into economic and sociopolitical factors. This nontechnical knowledge should be related to the technical and scientific knowledge while the student is in school.

This text is written to help bridge the gap between the technical and nontechnical. The text material emphasizes those aspects along the technical-economic side of the triangular diagram, with frequent departures into the sociopolitical aspects. Case studies and outside readings will be used to illustrate interactions between all three decisive factors.

All professionals should know how these decisive factors affect the ventures in which they are involved. Recently graduated chemical professionals may have assignments that are mostly technical in nature. In 5 to 10 years, many professionals will begin to move to positions where economic factors play more decisive roles. After 15 to 20 years, some professionals will move to top positions where the main requirement is effective handling of sociopolitical issues. A typical career can be sketched on the decisive-factors triangle. A prepared mind is needed for these transitions in roles.

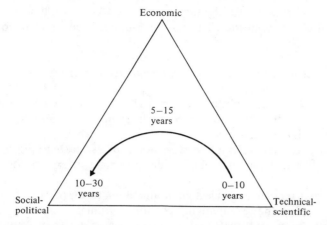

This text and the course based on it are designed to achieve the following *goals:*

1. To expand the mental horizon of the chemical professional beyond science and engineering and to show the economic purposes of the chemical process industries (CPI) and how the CPI benefit society.
2. To help chemical professionals understand how their work relates to the goals of their company and society.
3. To develop in the chemical professional an appreciation for the potential impact of new developments in technology, marketing, finance, politics, or international affairs as threats and opportunities.
4. To teach the chemical professional how to influence an organization to move in new directions by making fact-filled, comprehensive, and convincing economic studies.

To meet these objectives, certain *concepts and tools* should be mastered:

1. Basic economic and accounting principles are covered in Chaps. 2 to 4.
2. External and internal factors that affect the CPI and the companies within them are identified and discussed in Chaps. 4, 8, and 9.
3. Future factors which are threats and opportunities and which will affect innovation and growth are discussed in Chap. 10.

There are certain *facts* you must be familiar with if the objectives are to be attained:

1. The major products and some major technologies of the CPI are discussed in Chaps. 1, 5, and 6.
2. The major companies of the CPI are identified in Chap. 5, and some are discussed in more detail in Chap. 7.

3. The major markets and suppliers of the CPI are discussed in Chaps. 4 and 8.
4. Employment in the CPI is dealt with in Chaps. 1 and 8.
5. International manufacturing and trade are covered in Chap. 9.
6. The relation between the CPI and government is covered in Chaps. 2, 4, and 10.

The effective chemical professional needs to master certain *skills:*

1. The ability to read, analyze, and comprehend economic and accounting statements and studies, to understand their significance, and to use them as a rational basis for decisions
2. The ability to detect substantive weaknesses in a study, e.g., important facts and factors left out, flaws in logic, or inappropriate interpretations of facts and events
3. The ability to locate and select economic data, to supply appropriate logic and analysis, and to make convincing economic studies
4. The ability to grasp threats and opportunities, to devise imaginative and effective measures for thwarting the one and taking advantage of the other, and to convince key people and organizations to effect needed changes

If you are studying this book without being enrolled in a course, you must follow the current literature outlined in Sec. 0.1 and do many of the problems, which have been designed to help develop the skills listed above.

There are also certain *habits* that the chemical professional should develop to keep in touch with the important issues, events, and ideas being developed in the profession, the nation, and the world.

1. Regular reading of newspapers and journals that carry national and international news and developments in politics, economics, and social events
2. Regular reading of professional journals that carry news on the economics of the industry and on the development of new processes and products
3. Periodic attending of professional meetings, lectures, and symposia on broad issues that affect the profession
4. Periodic reading of current fiction and nonfiction to gain an insight into the changing values of society
5. Meeting people outside the profession in social and service capacities and paying particular attention to their concerns and their priorities

1.2 THE CHEMICAL PROCESSING INDUSTRIES

1.2.1 Definition

The CPI produce many different and unrelated products and serve a myriad of different markets. The CPI have been defined by some authors to include all

Table 1.1 The CPI as defined by *Chemical Engineering*

Industry segment	SIC code
1. **Chemicals (including petrochemicals):**	
Alkalies and chlorine	2812
Industrial gases	2813
Cyclic intermediates and crudes	2815
Industrial organic chemicals not elsewhere classified	2818
Industrial inorganic chemicals not elsewhere classified	2819
Synthetic rubber (vulcanizable elastomers)	2822
Gum and wood chemicals	2861
Chemicals and chemical preparations not elsewhere classified	2899
2. **Drugs and medicines:**	
Biological products	2831
Medicinal chemicals and botanicals	2833
Pharmaceutical preparations	2834
Perfumes, cosmetics, and other toilet preparations	2844
3. **Explosives and fireworks:**	
Ammunition, except for small arms, not elsewhere classified	1929
Small arms ammunition	1961
Ordnance and accessories not elsewhere classified	1999
Explosives	2892
4. **Fats and oils:**	
Cottonseed oil mills	2091
Soybean oil mills	2092
Vegetable oil mills, except cottonseed and soybean	2093
Animal and marine fats and oil, including grease and tallow	2094
Shortening, table oils, margarine, and other edible fats and oils not elsewhere classified	2096
5. **Fertilizers and agricultural chemicals:**	
Fertilizers	2871
Fertilizers, mixing only	2872
Agricultural pesticides and other agricultural chemicals not elsewhere classified	2879
6. **Foods and beverages:**	
Condensed and evaporated milk	2023
Wet corn milling	2046
Cane sugar, except refining only	2061
Cane sugar refining	2062
Beet sugar	2063
Malt liquors	2082
Malt	2083
Wines, brandy, and brandy spirits	2084
Distilled, rectified, and blended liquors	2085
Flavoring extracts and syrups not elsewhere classified	2087
Roasted coffee	2095
Food preparations not elsewhere classified	2099
7. **Leather tanning and finishing**	3111
8. **Lime and cement:**	
Cement, hydraulic	3241
Lime	3274
9. **Man-made fibres:**	
Cellulosic man-made fibers	2823
Synthetic organic fibers except cellulosic	2824
10. **Metallurgical and metal products:**	
Electrometallurgical products	3313
Primary smelting and refining of copper	3331
Primary smelting and refining of lead	3332
Primary smelting and refining of zinc	3333
Primary production of aluminum	3334
Primary smelting and refining of nonferrous metals not elsewhere classified	3339
Secondary smelting and refining and alloying of nonferrous metals and alloys	3341
Enameled iron and metal sanitary wear	3431
Electroplating, plating, polishing, anodizing, and coloring	3471
Coating, engraving and allied services not elsewhere classified	3479
11. **Paints, varnishes, pigments, and allied products:**	
Inorganic pigments	2816
Paints, varnishes, lacquers, enamels, and allied products	2851

(continued)

Table 1.1—*continued*

Industry segment	SIC code
12. **Petroleum refining and coal products:**	
Petroleum refining	2911
Paving mixtures and blocks	2951
Asphalt felts and coatings	2952
Lubricating oils and greases	2992
Coke and by-products [part of 3312, blast furnaces (including coke ovens), steelworks, and rolling mills]	3312
13. **Plastics materials, synthetic resins, and nonvulcanizable elastomers**	2821
14. **Rubber products:**	
Tires and inner tubes	3011
Rubber footwear	3021
Reclaimed rubber	3031
Fabricated rubber products not elsewhere classified	3069
15. **Soap, glycerin and cleaning, polishing, and related products:**	
Soap and other detergents except specialty cleaners	2841
Specialty cleaning, polishing, and sanitation preparations except soap and detergents	2842
Surface-active agents, sulfonated oils, and assistants	2843
16. **Stone, clay, glass, and ceramics:**	
Flat glass	3211
Glass containers	3221
Pressed and blown glass and glassware not elsewhere classified	3229
Brick and structural clay tile	3251
Ceramic wall and floor tile	3253
Clay refractories	3255
Structural clay products not elsewhere classified	3259
Pottery and related products	3261–3264, 3269
Gypsum products	3275
Abrasive products	3291
Asbestos products	3292
Steam and other packing and pipe and boiler covering	3293
Minerals and earth, ground or otherwise treated	3295
Mineral wool	3296
Nonclay refractories	3297
Nonmetallic mineral products	3299
17. **Wood, pulp, paper, and board:**	
Wood preserving	2491
Pulp mills	2611
Paper mills except building-paper mills	2621
Paperboard mills	2631
Paper coating and glazing	2641
Building-paper and building-board mills	2661
18. **Other chemically processed products:**	
Part of broad woven fabric mills, including dyeing and finishing	2231
Finishers of broad woven fabrics of cotton	2261
Finishers of broad woven fabrics of man-made fiber and silk	2262
Dyeing and finishing textiles not elsewhere classified	2269
Artificial leather, oilcloth, and other impregnated and coated fabrics except rubberized	2295
Glue and gelatin	2891
Printing ink	2893
Carbon black	2895
Carbon and graphite products	3624
Storage batteries	3691
Primary batteries (dry and wet)	3692
Part 2 of photographic equipment and supplies	3961
Lead pencils, crayons, and artists' materials	3952
Carbon paper and inked ribbons	3955
Linoleum, asphalted-felt-base, and other hard-surface floor coverings not elsewhere classified	3992
Candles and matches (part of 3999, manufacturing industries not elsewhere classified)	3999

Source: Chem. Eng. brochure, 1971.

industries in which a chemical reaction takes place. Using such an approach, the CPI would include wineries, paper mills, steel mills, tanneries, petroleum refineries, cane-sugar refineries, petrochemical plants, etc. *Chemical Engineering* takes this broad approach (Table 1.1).

An attempt to cover a group of such diverse activities as shown in Table 1.1 in detail would require many volumes. In this text we concentrate our efforts on Standard Industrial Classification (SIC) group 28, chemicals and allied products, and 29, petroleum refining and related industries.

The U.S. Bureau of the Budget defines SIC 28 as follows:

This major group includes establishments producing basic chemicals, and establishments manufacturing products by predominantly chemical processes. Establishments classified in this major group manufacture three general classes of products: (1) basic chemicals such as acids, alkalies, salts, and organic chemicals; (2) chemical products to be used in further manufacture such as synthetic fibers, plastics, materials, dry colors, and pigments; (3) finished chemical products to be used for ultimate consumption such as drugs, cosmetics, and soaps; or to be used as materials or supplied in other industries such as paints, fertilizers, and explosives.

Major SIC group 28 is broken into 8 three-digit groups:

SIC
- 28 Chemical and allied products
- 281 Industrial inorganic chemicals
- 282 Plastic materials and synthetic resins, synthetic rubber, synthetic resins, synthetic rubber, synthetic and other man-made fibers except glass
- 283 Drugs
- 284 Soap, detergents, and cleaning preparations, perfumes, cosmetics, and other toilet preparations
- 285 Paints, varnishes, lacquers, enamels, and allied products
- 286 Industrial organic chemicals
- 287 Agricultural chemicals
- 289 Miscellaneous chemical products

SIC group 29 is defined by the U.S. Bureau of the Budget as follows:

This major group includes establishments primarily engaged in petroleum refining, manufacturing paving and roofing materials, and compounding lubricating oils from purchased materials.

SIC group 29 is broken down into three groups with three-digits:

SIC
- 29 Petroleum refining and related industries
- 291 Petroleum refining
- 295 Paving and roofing materials
- 299 Miscellaneous products of petroleum and coal

Each of these three-digit subgroups is further subdivided into four-digit subgroups, such as 2891, adhesives and gelatins; 2892, explosives; 2893, printing ink;

Table 1.2 ESIC and SIC codes for chemicals and allied products

ESIC code	Title	SIC code
28	Chemicals and allied products	28
28.1	Industrial chemicals and synthetics	281, 282, 286
28.10	Industrial chemicals and synthetics	2812–2824, 2861–2869
28.3	Drugs	283
28.30	Drugs	2831–2834
28.4	Soap, cleansers, and toilet goods	284
28.40	Soap, cleansers, and toilet goods	2841–2844
28.5	Paints and allied products	285
28.51	Paints and allied products	2851
28.7	Agricultural chemicals	287
28.70	Agricultural chemicals	2873–2879
28.9	Miscellaneous chemical products	289
28.90	Miscellaneous chemical products	2891–2899

and 2895, carbon black. Likewise, the four-digit subgroups are broken into five-digit subgroups and so on. The complete SIC breakdown as used by the Census of Manufactures [1, 2],[1] is shown in Table A-1 in Appendix A. To obtain data for any n-digit SIC group, the statistics for the $(n + 1)$-digit groups included in that particular n-digit group are simply summed. For instance the volume of sales in SIC 29 is the sum of sales in SIC 291, 295, and 299.

The economic activities of many major corporations encompass operations in more than one SIC group. Exxon is engaged in oil and gas production (SIC 13), oil and gas transportation (SIC 40 to 46), oil refining, (SIC 29), oil marketing, (SIC 55), and petrochemicals (SIC 28). Many major companies that are not usually considered chemical companies have significant chemical production, e.g., U.S. Steel, General Electric, Borden, and Eastman Kodak.

In addition to the SIC code, where each plant or establishment receives an individual code, the federal government also uses the Enterprise Standard Industrial Classification (ESIC), where each company receives a single code according to the dominant activity of the firm. In this classification scheme the real estate transactions of firms like Shell Oil are all considered as ESIC 29, and the chemical operations of firms like Borden, General Electric, and Eastman Kodak will not be part of ESIC 28. This system is useful in compiling and analyzing financial and related data, e.g., income, expenses, and profits, that may be available only on a company basis. The existence of two systems requires care and discrimination in analyzing economic data. ESIC code numbers, titles, and relationships to SIC groups for chemicals and allied products are shown in Table 1.2.

Comparisons of economic data for chemicals and allied products with those for other industries are often made using the ESIC codes and titles. For future reference ESIC codes, titles, and relationships to the SIC codes for some pertinent industries are given in Table 1.3.

---

[1] Numbers in brackets refer to titles listed in References (Sec. 1.4).

Table 1.3 ESIC codes for other pertinent industries

ESIC code	Title	SIC code
26	Paper and allied products	26
26.2	Pulp, paper, and board mills	261–263, 266
26.20	Pulp, paper, and board mills	2611–2631, 2661
26.4	Miscellaneous converted paper products	264
26.40	Miscellaneous converted paper products	2641–2649
26.5	Paperboard containers and boxes	265
26.50	Paperboard containers and boxes	2651–2655
29	Petroleum and coal products	29, part of 13
29.1	Petroleum refining (including integrated)	291, part of 131
29.10	Petroleum refining (including integrated)	2911, part of 1311
29.9	Petroleum and coal products not elsewhere classified	295, 299
29.90	Petroleum and coal products not elsewhere classified	2951–2999
30	Rubber and miscellaneous products	30
30.5	Rubber products	301–306
30.50	Rubber products	3011–3069
30.7	Miscellaneous plastics products	307
30.79	Miscellaneous plastics products	3079
32	Stone, clay, and glass products	32
32.1	Glass products	321–323
32.10	Glass products	3211–3231
32.5	Structural clay products	325
32.50	Structural clay products	3251–3259
32.7	Concrete, gypsum, and plaster products	327
32.73	Ready-mixed concrete	3273
32.79	Concrete and gypsum products not elsewhere classified	3271, 3272, 3274, 3275
32.9	Nonmetallic metal products not elsewhere classified	324, 326, 328, 329
32.90	Nonmetallic mineral products not elsewhere classified	3241, 3261–3269, 3281–3299
33	Primary metal industries	33
33.1	Blast furnaces and steel mills	part of 331
33.12	Blast furnaces and steel mills	3312
33.2	Iron and steel foundries	part of 331, 332, 339
33.21	Gray-iron foundries	3321
33.23	Steel and malleable-iron foundries	3322–3325
33.29	Primary steel products not elsewhere classified	3313–3317, 3398, 3399
33.5	Nonferrous metals, except foundries	333–335
33.50	Nonferrous metals, except foundries	3331–3357
33.6	Nonferrous foundries	336
33.60	Nonferrous foundries	3361–336

Source: Enterprise Standard Industrial Classification Manual, 1974, GPO, Washington.

Table 1.4 Partial listing of input-output classifications, 1967

Industry number and title	Related Census–SIC codes (1967 edition)	Industry number and title	Related Census–SIC codes (1967 edition)
24 Paper and allied products except containers and boxes		**35 Glass and glass products**	
24.01 Pulp mills	2611.	35.01 Glass and glass products except containers.	3211, 3229, 3231.
24.02 Paper mills, except building paper	2621.	35.02 Glass containers	3221.
24.03 Paperboard mills	2631.	**36 Stone and clay products**	
24.04 Envelopes	2642.	36.01 Cement, hydraulic	3241.
24.05 Sanitary paper products	2647.	36.02 Brick and structural clay tile	3251.
24.06 Wallpaper and building paper and board mills.	2644, 2661.	36.03 Ceramic wall and floor tile	3253.
24.07 Converted paper, products, n.e.c., except containers and boxes.	2641, 2643, 2645, 2646, 2649.	36.04 Clay refractories	3255.
		36.05 Structural clay products, n.e.c.	3259.
		36.06 Vitreous plumbing fixtures	3261.
27 Chemicals and selected chemical products		36.07 Food utensils, pottery	3262, 3263.
27.01 Industrial inorganic and organic chemicals.	281 (excl. 28195.)	36.08 Porcelain electrical supplies	3264.
27.02 Fertilizers	2871, 2872.	36.09 Pottery products, n.e.c.	3269.
27.03 Agricultural chemicals, n.e.c.	2879.	36.10 Concrete block and brick	3271.
27.04 Miscellaneous chemical products	2861, 289.	36.11 Concrete products, n.e.c.	3272.
		36.12 Ready-mixed concrete	3273.
28 Plastics and synthetic materials		36.13 Lime	3274.
28.01 Plastics materials and resins	2821.	36.14 Gypsum products	3275.
28.02 Synthetic rubber	2822.	36.15 Cut stone and stone products	3281.
28.03 Cellulosic man-made fibers	2823.	36.16 Abrasive products	3291.
28.04 Organic fibers, noncellulosic	2824.	36.17 Asbestos products	3292.
		36.18 Gaskets and insulations	3293.
29 Drugs, cleaning and toilet preparations		36.19 Minerals, ground or treated	3295.
29.01 Drugs	283.	36.20 Mineral wool	3296.
29.02 Cleaning preparations	284 (excl. 2844.)	36.21 Nonclay refractories	3297.
29.03 Toilet preparations	2844.	36.22 Nonmetallic mineral products, n.e.c.	3299.
		37 Primary iron and steel manufacturing	
30 Paints and allied products		37.01 Blast furnaces and basic steel products.	331.
30.00 Paints and allied products	2851.	37.02 Iron and steel foundries	332.
		37.03 Iron and steel forgings	3391.
31 Petroleum refining and related industries		37.04 Primary metal products, n.e.c.	3399.
31.01 Petroleum refining and related products.	2911, 299.	**38 Primary nonferrous metals manufacturing**	
31.02 Paving mixtures and blocks	2951.	38.01 Primary copper	3331.
31.03 Asphalt felts and coatings	2952.	38.02 Primary lead	3332.
		38.03 Primary zinc	3333.
32 Rubber and miscellaneous plastics products		38.04 Primary aluminum	3334, 28195.
32.01 Tires and inner tubes	3011.	38.05 Primary nonferrous metals, n.e.c.	3339.
32.02 Rubber footwear	3021.	38.06 Secondary nonferrous metals	3341.
32.03 Reclaimed rubber and miscellaneous rubber products, n.e.c.	3031, 3069.	38.07 Copper rolling and drawing	3351.
32.04 Miscellaneous plastics products	3079.	38.08 Aluminum rolling and drawing	3352.
		38.09 Nonferrous rolling and drawing, n.e.c.	3356.
		38.10 Nonferrous wire drawing and insulating.	3357.
		38.11 Aluminum castings	3361.
		38.12 Brass, bronze, and copper castings	3362.
		38.13 Nonferrous castings, n.e.c.	3369.
		38.14 Nonferrous forgings	3392.

Source: *Surv. Curr. Bus.*, February 1974.

The federal government also uses a third system of classification for input-output analysis (Chap. 4). For future reference input-output classification numbers, titles, and relationship to the SIC code numbers are shown in Table 1.4 for chemicals and selected chemical products and several other industries.

On the international level, a single classification system has been proposed, the International Commodity Classification Code, but it is not expected to be operational until the mid-1980s. At present time two classification systems are in common use, the Brussels Tariff Nomenclature (BTN) and the United Nations Standard International Trade Classification (STIC). The U.S. Department of Commerce uses two additional systems to report statistics. Import statistics are reported using the Tariff Schedules of the United States (TSUS), and export statistics are reported using the Commerce Department schedule B.

1.2.2 The Purposes of a Firm

Why is a CPI firm needed by society? Modern chemical technology requires a high concentration of technical and managerial experts, a complex body of technological expertise, and large amounts of capital invested in equipment and plants. Furthermore, there must be an assurance of the firm's continuity beyond the mortality of the individual founders. A chemical firm can be a privately owned company, such as Monsanto, a semigovernment corporation, such as British Petroleum, or a government corporation, such as the Tennessee Valley Authority, as long as it is organized to provide economic goods and services through chemistry.

One of the purposes of a private firm is to make a profit, and the government corporation should at the very least minimize losses, which are burdens to the taxpayer. Some economists suggest that the firm's only purpose is to maximize profit. Although this view oversimplifies a complex issue, profit remains a useful measure of a firm's performance. Some economists suggest that the principal purpose of a firm is to survive and to continue to operate as an independent entity. While a firm sometimes serves society in the altruistic sense of contributions to charitable and humanitarian causes (donations to universities, museums, PBS television programs, and hospitals), its main purpose is to serve society by an exchange of goods and services with various groups of people and institutions. To appreciate the contributions of a firm, it is useful to consider how human needs could be satisfied if the chemical firm did not exist and what would have to be invented as replacement.

Employees The firm provides employment and paychecks, tools to work with, opportunities to learn skills, career development, personal fulfillment possibilities, and opportunities to participate in the production of useful goods and services. If modern firms did not exist, large-scale chemical activities would be impossible. Unemployment and unfulfilled careers, especially for chemists and chemical engineers, would be the result.

Stockholders and lenders The private firm receives savings from individuals and pension and insurance funds and returns dividends and interest, as well as stock appreciation. The government firm can return a surplus to the government treasury or constitute a burden to taxpayers. If the firm did not exist, this capital would have to be invested elsewhere (home mortgages, municipal bonds, finance companies' paper, federal paper, etc.).

Customers The firm delivers chemical goods and services needed for the customers to achieve their goals. If the firm did not exist, goods and services essential to the well-being and happiness of the customers would not be produced. Automobiles cannot be produced without tires, batteries, paints, etc. A lack of fertilizers and pesticides would mean a consequent reduction in food production and a threat to many lives.

Suppliers The firm pays its suppliers for delivered equipment, raw material, and services. If the firm did not exist, the suppliers would suffer a business decline and would have to find alternative buyers. Presumably no one buys such industrial goods as fluidized catalytic reactors and distillation columns except CPI firms.

Government The firm pays corporate income and excise taxes to the federal and local governments, increases the general economic activity and prosperity in the nation, and cooperates with the nation in extending power and influence abroad. If the chemical firm did not exist, lower payrolls would mean lower personal income tax revenues and lower exports would mean less ability to acquire resources from abroad. Lower government revenue would mean a decreased ability to carry out national goals—world peace and domestic security, improvement in the lot of the underprivileged, bettering the quality of life.

A firm in the CPI is organized to conduct large-scale economic activities through chemistry. Unlike such permanent establishments as the post office and state universities, a chemical firm is allowed to continue in existence only if it performs its functions well enough to satisfy all five segments of its public. An inefficient firm may have a work force that has low intelligence and dedication and a low morale due to the lack of adequate plants and facilities. The firm may produce high-cost low-quality goods by obsolete processes or goods that are not in demand. The firm may unwisely use the funds entrusted to it by investing in the wrong plants and by having too much or too little cash on hand to transact daily business. The firm may give the customers inferior goods and unreliable services. The firm may be unwise in its choice of suppliers or may alienate suppliers by unethical practices. The firm may offend the government and the people by illegal practices such as collusion and bribery or by damaging the environment and compromising the health of employees. When a firm loses the confidence of its public, all five segments can deal it punishing blows. Key employees may leave for better firms, and replacements may not be recruited. Investors may sell their stock and demand settlement on their bonds and loans. The company may not be able to raise new capital from Wall Street or the banks. Customers may turn to alternative sources of chemicals. Suppliers may demand cash payment on delivery of goods and services, instead of the usual time settlement. The government may intervene through regulations, injunctions, fines, and forced breakup.

The most visible indicator of efficiency in a firm is profit. All the other measures of performance make an impact on profit, sometimes swiftly but always eventually. Many mighty chemical firms, such as the Virginia Carolina Company and the American Viscose Company, which had unsatisfactory performances and profit have been absorbed by more efficient firms.

1.3 THE ROLE OF THE CHEMICAL PROFESSIONAL IN THE CPI

The chemical processing industries represent one of the most technically complex sectors of our society. To fulfill the purposes outlined in Sec. 1.2, the CPI needs both chemical engineers and chemists at all degree levels. These chemical professionals work in both fundamental and applied research, in product and process development, in design engineering, in production, in sales, and in administration

Table 1.5 Distribution by function (self-identified)

Chemical engineers†	Percent	Chemists‡	Percent
R & D	24.2	Basic research	9.6
Design	7.7	Applied research	29.1
Process	15.6	Research administration	14.6
Administration	10.6	General administration	8.7
Production	9.1	Education	19.4
Sales, marketing	5.3	Sales, marketing	5.0
Planning, economics	4.1	Production	6.8
Consulting	4.3	Consulting	1.1
Education	4.1	Other	5.7
Other	19.3		

† 1975 AIChE Survey Report.
‡ American Chemical Society, Office of Manpower Studies, " Professionals in Chemistry, 1975," Washington, 1976.

(often at the highest levels). A distribution of chemical professionals according to function is shown in Table 1.5.

There were approximately 200,000 chemical professionals in the United States in 1972, about 60,000 chemical engineers and about 140,000 chemists. In comparison, there were about 400,000 scientists and 1.1 million engineers in the 79-million-person labor force in the United States (1970). The numbers are approximate because of difficulties in defining a chemist or a chemical engineer. Statistics are gathered by the Department of Labor on the basis of self-identification. Some important studies by the National Science Foundation and the American Chemical Society are based on initial college degrees awarded. Since there are obvious difficulties with either of these approaches, care is needed in interpretation and use.

Almost without exception, chemical professionals start their careers in an institution of higher education. Table 1.6 shows the distribution of degrees

Table 1.6 Distribution of the chemical professional by academic degree (1950–1970)

Degree	Chemical engineers, %			Chemists, %		
	1950	1960	1970	1950	1960	1970
Bachelor's	84	79	72	81	77	73
Master's	13	16	20	12	12	13
Ph.D.	3	5	8	7	10	14

Source: American Chemical Society, "Chemistry in the Economy," Washington, 1973.

Table 1.7 Distribution of the chemical professional by academic degree (1975)

	Chemical engineer, %	Chemist, %
Bachelor's	56	55
Master's	26	17
Ph.D.	18	28

awarded over the past decade for both chemical engineers and chemists. A clear trend toward greater numbers completing Ph.D.s in both areas is evident, although more recent statistics indicate a reversal in this trend. The percentage of chemical engineers going to the master's level has also increased since 1949–1950, indicating that there is an expanding market for people holding this degree. Member surveys published in 1975 by both the AIChE and ACS showed a different distribution by degree level (Table 1.7). The discrepancy is probably due to the rather high percentage of bachelors who do not practice chemical engineering or chemistry. Those who proceed to the higher degree levels tend to stay in the profession and be more active in it. For comparison, about 5 percent of all engineers hold the Ph.D. degree, but almost 25 percent of all scientists hold a Ph.D.

Not all the 200,000 chemical professionals are employed in the CPI. Table 1.8 shows a distribution by sector in the United States economy. A higher percentage of chemists than chemical engineers works outside the CPI in such industries as mining, primary metals, and medical and dental laboratories. Within some selected CPI sectors the percentage of chemical engineers and chemists in the total work force is shown in Table 1.9. Petroleum refining is the only industry employing more chemical engineers than chemists.

Table 1.8 Distribution of the chemical profession by sector

	Percentage of total population	
Function	Chemical engineers	Chemists
CPI	62	45
Chemicals and allied products (SIC 28)	47	32
Petroleum refining and related industry (SIC 29)	8	2
Paper and allied products (SIC 26)	3	2
Rubber (SIC 30)	2	3
Stone, clay, and glass (SIC 32)	1	1
Food processing (SIC 20)	1	3
Other manufacturing	17	27
Nonmanufacturing	20	28

Source: Tomorrow's Manpower Needs, *U.S. Dep. Labor Bull.* 1737.

Table 1.9 The chemical professional as a percentage of total employment in various sectors

Sector	Percentage of those employed in the sector who are:	
	Chemical engineers	Chemists
Chemical and allied products	2.19	4.17
Synthetic fibers	0.94	2.81
Drugs and medicine	0.37	4.26
Paints and varnishes	1.73	4.80
Petroleum refining and coal	2.18	1.68
Food and kindred products	0.02	0.25
Other chemicals	2.81	4.31

Source: Tomorrow's Manpower Needs, *U.S. Dep. Labor Bull.* 1737.

Not all chemical professionals working in industry are employed by large companies. In fact, in a recent AIChE member survey over 60 percent reported that they worked for companies employing fewer than 5,000 people (Table 1.10).

The impact of chemical professionals in the industries in which they are employed has been profound. Table 1.11 lists some top executives who are chemical engineers, and similarly the top executives in many firms are chemists.

After receiving a bachelor's degree, a chemical professional in the CPI usually starts in a technical position as an apprentice to a more experienced engineer or chemist. A chemical professional's mental development needs to be a lifelong process, leading to greater opportunities and challenges and avoiding stagnation and obsolescence. One may elect to increase one's formal education by working toward an M.S. or Ph.D. in chemical engineering or chemistry or an M.B.A. or a law degree. There should be a continuing program to increase one's knowledge of technical and scientific subjects and sociopolitical subjects. A chemical professional may elect to climb the technical-scientific ladder, and through technical specialization become an expert or authority in a field. A great deal of specialized scientific and engineering knowledge must be absorbed and integrated with a growing and changing chemical technology. The managerial-ladder route requires an integrated knowledge of economics, business administration, and law, and one

Table 1.10 Size of company employing chemical engineers

Size of company	AIChE members, %
1–999	14.4
200–999	21.0
1,000–4,999	25.6
5,000 and over	39.1

Table 1.11 Chemical engineers as top executives in major North American Corporations, 1972

Company	Chairman	President
Du Pont	Charles B. McCoy	Charles B. McCoy
Du Pont of Canada	....	R. J. Richardson
Union Carbide	F. Perry Wilson	
Dow Chemical	Carl A. Gerstacker	C. B. Branch
Borden	Augustine R. Marusi	
PPG Industries	....	Joseph A. Neubauer
American Cyanamid	....	Clifford D. Siverd
International Minerals & Chemicals	Nelson C. White	
Universal Oil Products	Maynard P. Venema	
BASF Wyandotte	Robert B. Semple	
Texaco	M. F. Granville	J. K. McKinley
Gulf Oil	....	B. R. Dorsey
Gulf Oil Canada	....	Jerry McAfee
Standard Oil California	Otto N. Miller	
Standard Oil of Indiana	John E. Swearingen	Robert C. Gunness
Sun Oil	....	Robert H. Sharbaugh
Union Oil of California	....	Fred L. Hartley
Uniroyal	George R. Vila	George R. Vila
B. F. Goodrich	....	Harry B. Warner
American Biltrite Rubber	David W. Bernstein	
Kimberly Clark	....	Guy M. Minard
Alcoa	....	W. H. Krome George
American Can	William F. May	William F. May

Source: Chem. Eng. Prog., June 1972.

must keep up with business conditions, technological changes, and the sociopolitical environment. This dual ladder is shown in Fig. 1.3. Both ladders can be equal in intellectual challenge and professional satisfaction; the individual must choose his own route.

Whether they are in the plant, the laboratory, the engineering department, or the executive suite, the chemical professionals in the CPI play an important role. Some of what they have accomplished and the challenges they must face in coming years will be described in this book.

1.4 REFERENCES

1. *Standard Industrial Classification Manual, 1972*, GPO, Washington.
2. U.S. Department of Commerce, *Numerical List of Manufactured Products*, GPO, Washington, 1972.
3. *Enterprise Standard Industrial Classification Manual, 1974*, GPO, Washington.
4. A complete list of all input-output classification groups and relationships to the SIC code for the input-output tables of 1967 is given in *Surv. Curr. Bus.*, February 1974.

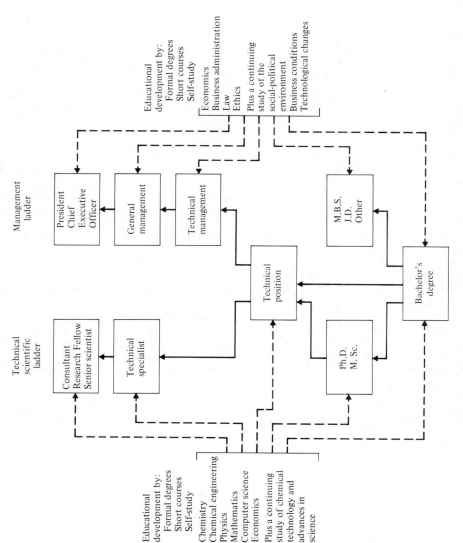

Figure 1.3 Developing a career.

1.5 PROBLEMS

1.1 Using Table 1.1 as a guide, prepare a list of 10 to 20 companies operating within a radius of 100 mi of you which could be classified as part of the CPI. From this list prepare another to include only those companies whose operations in your area could be classified as SIC 28 or SIC 29. (See Appendix A.)

1.2 Use a basic reference (" Moody's " or " Standard and Poor's "; Sec. I.1.2) to find the products made by each company. Find the SIC codes for each major product of the companies in your list regardless of whether they are made in your area or not.

1.3 Find the ESIC classification for each of the companies in your list by using the Facts and Figures issue of *Chemical and Engineering News* or the *Directory of Companies Filing Annual Reports with the Securities and Exchange Commission*, GPO, Washington.

1.4 Your neighbor tells you that he objects to the presence of local chemical plants or oil refineries. Can you explain why the plant is needed and who needs it? What alternatives to the plant can you suggest? How would the local people be affected in terms of employment, safety, additional tax revenue, etc.? Can you estimate whether the costs to your local society are greater than the benefits?

1.5 Some critics say that the goods provided by the CPI are not truly needed and should not be produced. Examples of supposedly unnecessary products often cited are synthetic fibers (vs. wool or cotton), plastic containers and disposable products such as throwaway diapers, artificial colorings or flavors in foods, food preservatives, and fertilizers. Since these products are purchased, there must be some utility to the consumer. Does the public have such appalling judgment and taste that the critics need to dictate what it should do? Select three products and list their potential advantages or disadvantages to our society as a whole.

1.6 Examine the job functions listed in Table 1.5. What types of skills and knowledge might be of particular value in administration or sales and marketing? How might one obtain such skills? For your personal use, write down a potential career path that might suit your own goals, including what you might like to be doing 5, 10, and 20 years from now.

1.7 Investigate the backgrounds of the two top people of several of the largest CPI companies in the United States (Table 5.14). Specifically, what were their majors in college? What backgrounds might you expect for the top people in RCA, General Motors, Boeing, Chase Manhattan Bank, and Pacific Gas and Electric? Company annual reports, " Moody's," and " Standard and Poor's " will yield the names of company officials. References like " Who's Who in America " and "American Men and Women of Science " are appropriate places to start investigating backgrounds.

1.8 Are more chemists than chemical engineers engaged in research? What are the approximate percentages? Why are more chemists engaged in education than chemical engineers?

1.9 Is it worthwhile financially to obtain a master's degree in chemical engineering or chemistry? A Ph.D.? (Salary data are reported at least once a year in *Chemical and Engineering News*.) What noneconomic factors influence such decisions?

2

BASIC ECONOMICS

Economics is concerned with the most efficient allocation of scarce resources to various uses and with the creation and distribution of wealth. The complete economic picture can best be understood by first discussing how the individual consumer or household chooses to allocate a limited budget and how these individual choices subsequently lead to demand for a product. A review of some important aspects of consumer economics is presented in Sec. 2.1.

When a product is in demand, numerous firms attempt to produce the product at a profit. What processing unit should be built to produce the product and how the unit should be operated in order to make a profit are important aspects of a subject known as the *economics of the firm*. Portions of this important subject relevant to the CPI are discussed in Sec. 2.2.

The design of a chemical processing unit to meet a specific consumer demand and the comparison of alternative process costs (by return-on-investment and discounted-cash-flow analysis) are well covered in texts on process economics and will not be treated in this text.

The financial well-being of the firm depends upon the economic performance of the countries in which it operates. Selected parts of national and international economics are discussed in Sec. 2.3.

2.1 ECONOMICS OF THE CONSUMER

The individual consumer ultimately determines what is produced by the chemical industry (Fig. 2.1). Some products made by the chemical industry, e.g., antifreeze, plastic food wrapping, tires, drugs, and cleaning agents, satisfy the *direct demand*

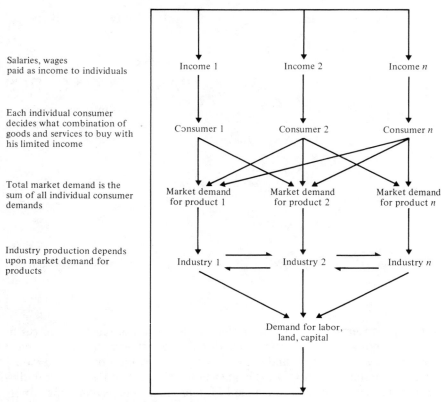

Salaries, wages
paid as income to individuals

Each individual consumer
decides what combination of
goods and services to buy with
his limited income

Total market demand is the
sum of all individual consumer
demands

Industry production depends
upon market demand for
products

Figure 2.1 Derivation of demand and flow of dollars.

of consumers. Many other products of the chemical industry contribute indirectly to final products made for the consumer. These satisfy the *derived* demand of the consumer. Examples of chemical products which satisfy derived demand include (1) all chemical intermediates, e.g., monomers eventually used in polymer products; (2) fertilizers for growing food; (3) synthetic fibers for making textiles and carpets; (4) pulping chemicals and dyes ultimately required for making books and newspapers; the list is almost endless. But whether the demand is direct or derived, it is always the consumers' needs which determine the well-being of the CPI. It is fitting that we begin with an analysis of consumer economics in our consideration of the economic structure of the CPI.

Economists maintain that a consumer derives a certain amount of *utility* from each final product he buys. Utility is a relative measure of the physical and psychological satisfaction a person derives from a final product. Things urgently needed to maintain life, e.g., emergency health care, may provide the consumer with the most utility at some particular time. The consumer needs a mix of numerous products to sustain a satisfactory life, and doubling any one of them does not necessarily double satisfaction or utility. The functionality can only be expressed in a general way:[1]

$$U = U(q_1, q_2, q_3, \ldots, q_n) \tag{2.1}$$

where U is total utility and $q_1, q_2, q_3, \ldots, q_n$ are the quantities of final products which the consumer purchases. The rational consumer, aware of all options available to him, is assumed to purchase a combination of products in such a way as to maximize U. Of course, this maximization must be done within the constraint of a limited budget, stated as

$$I = \sum_{i=1}^{n} p_i q_i \tag{2.2}$$

where I = consumer's income available for purchases
  p = price of product
  n = total number of products bought

It is extremely difficult to design an experiment for the individual consumer which would generate sufficient data to determine the functional relationship between utility U and quantity of products $q_1, \ldots, q_n$. Nevertheless, the concept of utility is useful since it permits us to describe a reasonably complicated problem with the shorthand of mathematical symbols and significantly extends our ability to describe the economics of the consumer.

As Leavitt [5] explained, the firm supplying the consumer must focus on human needs or utility rather than the product lines which satisfy the need. If people need transportation, they can take electric street cars or they can buy bicycles. While human needs are relatively constant, the product lines needed to satisfy those needs may change rapidly as substitutions are found.

2.1.1 Consumer Demand Curve

The amount of any one product q_i a consumer will buy is a function of his income I and the prices of all products $p_1, \ldots, p_n$:

$$q_1 = D_1(p_1, \ldots, p_n, I) \tag{2.3}$$

This functional relationship is referred to as the *consumer's demand function*, and in theory it can be derived from a utility-function-maximization analysis.

As an illustrative example, consider the simple case in which the consumer can only buy two products, both of which are necessary to him, say food and housing. It may reasonably be assumed that his utility will be zero if either of the products is not available. The utility function for this simple situation can be

---

[1] Notation for Chap. 2 is summarized in Sec. 2.5.

represented by $U = q_1 q_2$. His budget constraint is $I = p_1 q_1 + p_2 q_2$. Thus, it is necessary to maximize

$$U = q_1 q_2$$

subject to

$$I = p_1 q_1 + p_2 q_2$$

This can be done using the Lagrange-multiplier procedure for determining the maximum value of a function with constraints. A function V is created as follows:

$$V = U + \lambda(I - p_1 q_1 - p_2 q_2) = q_1 q_2 + \lambda(I - p_1 q_1 - p_2 q_2)$$

where λ is an undetermined parameter. Taking the partial derivative of V with respect to q_1, q_2, and λ gives

$$\frac{\partial V}{\partial q_1} = q_2 - \lambda p_1 = 0 \qquad \frac{\partial V}{\partial q_2} = q_1 - \lambda p_2 = 0 \qquad \frac{\partial V}{\partial \lambda} = I - p_1 q_1 - p_2 q_2 = 0$$

Solving for q_1 and q_2 yields the functional form for Eq. (2.3) (the consumer's demand function):

$$q_1 = \frac{I}{2p_1} \qquad q_2 = \frac{I}{2p_2}$$

Thus, with the function $U = q_1 q_2$ the consumer will maximize his utility by spending half his income on each product. The quantity of each product bought is inversely proportional to its price and directly proportional to income. In this case, the demand for product 1 depends only on p_1.

For example, a consumer with several teenaged drivers in the family considers their utility for transportation to be equal to the number of vehicles times the miles which the family can drive; that is, q_1 is miles, and q_2 is the number of vehicles the family owns. The cost of fuel, depreciation, and maintenance p_1 is 20 cents per mile. The cost of a secondhand vehicle p_{2a} is \$2,000 per unit, and that of a new car p_{2b} is \$4,000 per unit. If the family has \$8,000 to spend on transportation, it can maximize its utility by using the procedure described above:

$$q_1 = \frac{I}{2p_1} = \frac{8,000}{2 \times 0.20} = 20,000 \text{ mi}$$

$$q_{2a} = \frac{I}{2p_{2a}} = \frac{8,000}{2 \times 2,000} = 2$$

$$q_{2b} = \frac{I}{2p_{2b}} = \frac{8,000}{2 \times 4,000} = 1$$

The utility U is the product of q_1 and q_2:

$$U_{2a} = q_1 q_{2a} = 40,000 \qquad U_{2b} = q_2 q_{2b} = 20,000$$

This family would decide to buy two secondhand cars and drive them a total of 20,000 mi.

If the consumer's income I and all other prices $p_2, \ldots, p_n$ may be assumed to remain constant, the demand function of Eq. (2.3) simplifies to

$$q_1 = D_1(p_1) \tag{2.4}$$

At a given price, the sum of all the consumers' demands gives the market demand for the particular product at that price. If all the consumer demand functions were known, they could be added to give the *total market demand function*. The total market demand curve is a plot of price p vs. total amount of a given product required by all consumers Q. This function is usually negatively sloped; the lower the price the greater the quantity demanded.

Total market demand When the market demand curve for a particular product is developed, it will take any of several downward-sloping forms (Fig. 2.2). If the demand for a product is relatively independent of price, the demand is *inelastic*; if demand is highly dependent on price, the demand is *elastic*. This property is measured by the *price elasticity E*, which is simply the percent change in demand for a product divided by the percent change in the price causing the change in demand Q:

$$\text{Price elasticity } E = -\frac{dQ/Q}{dp/p} = -\frac{p\,dQ}{Q\,dp} \tag{2.5}$$

with this definition E is almost always a positive number.

The price elasticities E shown in Fig. 2.2 are determined at the point w. Note that when a linear relationship is assumed between p and Q, $p = aQ + b$. Then

$$E = -\frac{aQ + b}{aQ} = -1 - \frac{b}{aQ}$$

$$p = aQ + b$$

$$E = -\frac{p}{Q}\frac{dQ}{dp} = -\frac{p}{Q}\frac{1}{a}$$

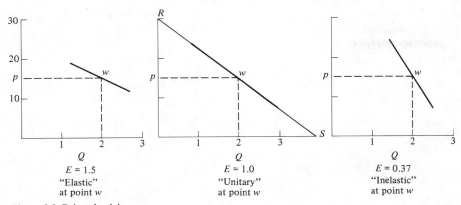

Figure 2.2 Price elasticity.

For the unitary case ($E = 1.0$ at point w), the elasticity is ∞ at point R ($Q \to 0$) and 0 at point S ($Q \to +b/a$). In practice we find linearity between p and Q only over a limited range of Q. The only function with a constant elasticity is $Q = ap^{-n}$, where $E = n$.

One important determinant of price elasticity is the effect of availability of a reasonable substitute for the product. If consumers consider plastic milk cartons and paper milk cartons as close substitutes for each other, with almost equal utility, the price elasticity for either product will be large ($E > 1$) when the price of the other product remains the same. Gasoline, on the other hand, has no readily available substitutes, so that price changes have only a small effect on demand in the short run.

If the price of gasoline were to stay high for a long time, consumers could switch to smaller cars, develop a public transportation system, or learn to drive less. Short-run price elasticities are generally small because no alternative courses of action are readily available. Established equipment and entrenched production habits limit flexibility. However, long-run price elasticities may be much greater. Old equipment deteriorates, and habits change, allowing alternatives to be developed.

Total revenue to an industry is given by TR $= pQ$. The effect of a price change on revenue can be computed as follows:

$$\frac{d(\text{TR})}{dp} = p\frac{dQ}{dp} + Q = Q\frac{p}{Q}\frac{dQ}{dp} + Q = (1 - E)Q \tag{2.6}$$

Thus, for an elastic product, $E > 1$, a price increase would lead to a loss of revenue. For an inelastic product, $E < 1$, a price increase would lead to an increase of revenue. If E is 1 (unitary elasticity), changing price will have no effect on revenue.

Some products are complementary and are used jointly, so that a decrease in price for one product may increase the demand for another. For example, automobiles and antifreeze are complementary products. Other products are substitutes, so that an increase in price for one product may increase the demand for the other. For example, nylon and polyester shirts are substitute products. The influence of one product's price P_y on another product's demand Q_x is measured by the *cross elasticity*:

$$\text{Cross elasticity CE} = \frac{dQ_x/Q_x}{dp_y/p_y} = \frac{p_y}{Q_x}\frac{dQ_x}{dp_y} \tag{2.7a}$$

For substitute products CE is positive; for complementary products CE is negative.

The effect of personal-income fluctuations on the demand for a product is measured by income elasticity:

$$\text{Income elasticity IE} = \frac{dQ_x/Q_x}{dI/I} = \frac{I}{Q_x}\frac{dQ_x}{dI} \tag{2.7b}$$

Luxury items, e.g., travel abroad for pleasure, usually have high IE values, while common things, e.g., salt have low IE values. Inferior items, e.g., cheap cuts of meat, may have negative IE values.

2.1.2 Determination of Total Market Demand

It is impractical to build up a total-market-demand curve for a product by estimating and then adding each individual consumer demand. However, a qualitative understanding of utility and elasticities combined with statistical analysis of past market behavior, projected consumer incomes, and sales of major items does permit total demand for a particular product to be estimated. The ability to arrive at such an estimate is a crucial step in projecting the profitability of a business venture in the CPI. Two approaches may be used to derive a total-market-demand curve:

1. *Using past market data.* For many existing products, the historical price–quantity-sold information is available and can be analyzed to derive total market demand vs. price. For example, the amount of electricity sold per household vs. price collected from various parts of the country can be used to construct a crude market-demand curve for electricity (Fig. 2.3).
2. *Using projected market and sales data.* Considerable effort must be expended to make a sales forecast and to establish a selling price. There is much more art than science in this task.

Sales forecasting should begin with an estimation of consumer purchasing power as measured by gross national product (GNP) and disposable personal

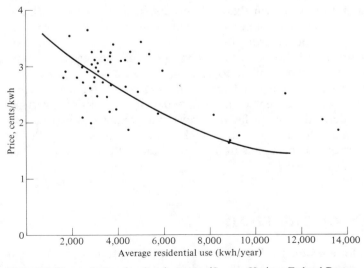

Figure 2.3 Demand curve for electric power. (*Source:* Various Federal Power Commission Reports.)

income. An end-use study, particularly if the product is a new one, must be made. For each end use a value-in-use analysis must be carried out as an essential first step in estimating total sales and selling price. Value in use is the price the user must pay for the best alternative product plus any associated costs to derive the same performance or utility. For example, if the product is a new paint requiring only one coat in applications currently requiring two coats, the value in use for the new paint is equal to the cost of two coats of the old paint *plus* the cost for additional labor, etc. Knowing the value in use allows one to assume a selling price and to determine the market opportunity for which the product is both technically and economically advantageous. When the price of a product drops below the value in use of a potentially important customer, this product becomes the preferred one to buy. Lowering the price will broaden the market, and raising the price will price it out of the reach of many customers. The demand curve (p vs. Q) can be built up by estimating total possible sales Q over a range of selling prices p. The fraction of the market which can be penetrated by any specific firm is affected by several nonprice factors:

1. Product information and awareness of the customer
2. Reluctance of satisfied old customers to change
3. Ability of the seller to deliver in a timely and regular manner
4. Ability of the seller to provide technical services and continued product improvement to the customer
5. Competition

An understanding of these factors is necessary to estimate q, the individual firm's share of the market.

For the most part the CPI are not concerned with meeting final demand of consumer goods but with supplying other industries, who, in turn, furnish products to final demand. For the intermediate CPI products, or *industrial goods*, any demand is a *derived demand*. Consumer satisfaction enters the picture for such products several stages removed from the CPI. For example, consumers may demand garbage removal and choose garbage bags; the result is a derived demand for ethylene. Consumers may demand automobiles; the result is derived demand for steel, which, in turn, causes derived demand for oxygen to make the steel and hydrochloric acid to pickle the steel. Citizens may demand government service; the result may be a derived demand for highways and bombers, which in turn leads to a derived demand for asphalt and jet fuel. It is therefore necessary first to estimate the final demand of consumers in order to estimate the resulting derived demand for CPI products.

2.2 ECONOMICS OF THE FIRM

Consumer demand for a product will generally be met by a business firm if it can make a reasonable profit by supplying the product without violating the law or arousing negative public opinion. As the product price increases, the firm will be willing to expand production by using higher-cost methods, e.g., inefficient older equipment, inexperienced new labor, and overtime premium for old labor, and by operating a process beyond the optimum capacity for best efficiency. The total-market-supply curve is the sum of individual supply curves of the various producers and generally increases with increasing price. These supply curves, or production functions, can be generated from engineering and technical data.

A supply curve for natural gas, for instance, is determined by analyzing each field to determine production costs. The cost is low for a large shallow field near a city. The cost is high for a small deep field in the arctic. As the price increases, more fields of higher production costs are opened. A detailed example illustrating the development of a supply curve for a simple chemical processing unit is given later, in Example 2.2.

Supply curves can be classified with regard to elasticity. Three situations of price elasticity of supply

$$E_s = \frac{p}{Q}\frac{dQ}{dP} \qquad (2.8)$$

are illustrated in Fig. 2.4. Here Q is the total industry output. In a perfectly inelastic situation $(E_s \to 0)$ the supply remains constant regardless of market price. The elasticity of supply of helium, which is a by-product of natural-gas processing, is inelastic. Regardless of the market price of helium, its production is limited by the production of the natural gas. Some petroleum products provide examples of a

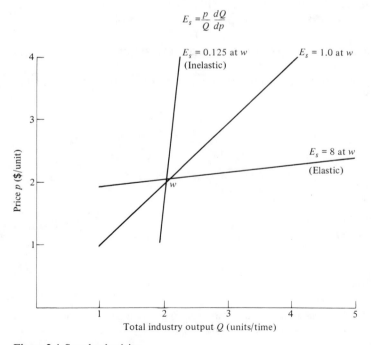

Figure 2.4 Supply elasticity.

large elasticity of supply. A refinery is designed to take several different cuts from the barrel of crude oil. The processing equipment is versatile enough to vary the proportion of oil going to any particular cut. Thus, if the market price of gasoline increases in the summer because people drive more then, refineries can quickly switch to producing more gasoline and less fuel oil. They reverse the operation in winter, when more home heating oil is needed.

Human need is infinite and can never be completely satisfied by the finite productive capacity of any economy. A free market is efficient in regulating supply and demand, so what is produced just meets what is demanded with "hard dollars." Since the market allocates a limited resource to those who can pay the price, some needs will not be satisfied. The free market differs from a centrally planned economy, where the government allocates a limited resource not according to individual purchasing power but according to centralized political goals. Neither the free market nor the centrally planned economy can satisfy all needs.

A typical supply-demand situation for an industry where there is perfect competition is qualitatively illustrated in Fig. 2.5a. The supply and demand curves intersect at an equilibrium price, representing a stable situation in which supply equals demand. If supply temporarily exceeds the equilibrium value, the market price will have to be lowered in order to sell off any excess product (step 1 in Fig. 2.5b). This lowered price in turn will cause production Q to decrease in the next time period (step 2). A decrease in Q below the equilibrium point will cause a shortage and induce the price to rise (step 3), which will cause total production to increase in the next period (step 4). But this increase will in turn cause a drop in demand. This postulated "cobweb" process will continue until the equilibrium is reestablished. The adjustment process requires the existence of:

1. Marginal producers who would either curtail production or go out of business when the price drops
2. Marginal consumers who would reduce consumption or do without entirely when the price rises

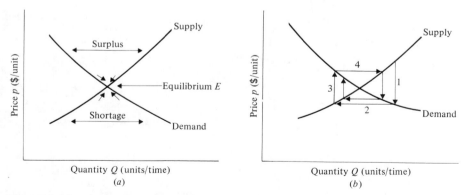

Figure 2.5 (a) A supply-demand relationship. For the demand curve Q is total demand. (b) Reestablishment of equilibrium for a small change in supply. For the supply curve Q is total industry output.

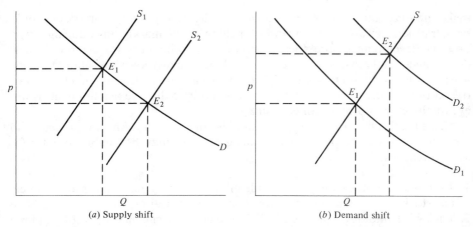

Figure 2.6 Qualitative illustration of shifts in supply and demand curves. For the demand curve Q is total demand. For the supply curve Q is total industry output.

If the price is such that firms supplying the product make more than a "normal" profit, new firms will be induced to shift their investments to enter the market, causing the supply curve to shift from S_1 to S_2, as illustrated in Fig. 2.6a. A new, lower price will then be established at the equilibrium point E_2. The lower price may cause some marginally profitable suppliers to stop making the product, and the supply curve will shift back to the left. Under ideal conditions, the profits for every product would be the same "normal" profit, so that there is no incentive for any firm to enter or leave a market.

Shifts in the demand curve can also cause the equilibrium price to change. When a new use is found for the product, the demand curve may move from D_1 to D_2, as shown in Fig. 2.6b. If the demand shift causes the equilibrium price to shift upward, new firms may be attracted into the industry or existing firms may increase production capability, causing a supply shift and readjustment of price downward. Alternatively, a decrease in demand (causing the equilibrium price to shift downward) may cause firms to withdraw from the industry and the price to readjust upward.

The time necessary to complete supply or demand shifts depends upon the product and the industry. In a technologically simple industry, readjustments toward equilibrium may take place over a few months. In a complex and capital-intensive industry like the CPI, in which it takes several years to plan, design, and construct a plant, changes leading to equilibrium may take several years. In the short run, both supply and demand tend to be inelastic, as it is not easy to find substitutes, shift suppliers, modify and build plants, and increase production rapidly. In the long run, all these adaptive movements can be accomplished, so that supply and demand both become more elastic.

The free entrance of firms into the production of an item of extraordinary profit and the exit of firms from the production of an item of low profit tend to make the long-run profit of any industry stable. An especially high profit should be a transient reward for innovation (opening a new market, introducing a new product, developing a more efficient process) until other firms learn about the new development and move in to lower profits. A particularly low profit should also be a transient pheomenon. Marginal firms will have to phase out or close down operations, supply will dwindle, and price will rise, so that the remaining firms will eventually enjoy normal profits again.

This ideal is limited by the problem of *barriers to entry*. An entrepreneur who sees an extraordinary profit in producing an item may be unable to enter for several reasons:

1. Lack of a resource supply, e.g., crude oil for a refinery, natural gas for chemical feedstocks, or a diamond mine for a jewelery operation.
2. Lack of technology, e.g., that needed for a complex chemical operation or for a nuclear power plant.
3. Lack of capital. In the CPI enormous plants are often required. Units which produce 1 billion pounds per year, as for ethylene and methanol, are not uncommon. Plants of this size cannot be built unless a firm can raise substantial sums of money.
4. Exclusion by patent protection, e.g., in many chemical processes or instant photography.
5. Exclusion by contract, e.g., a soft-drink bottling franchise.
6. Lack of a government franchise, e.g., that needed for a pipeline, telephone, or television broadcasting operation.

Many economists believe that the barriers to entry are bad since they restrict the free movement and most efficient use of resources. Some economists believe that some barriers to entry are good, since innovators need a few years of extraordinary profit, free from competition, to justify the risk and expenditure in sticking their necks out in a new area.

Similarly there is a *barrier to exit* for marginal and inefficient producers. Ignorance and bad advice, stubborness and pride, political pressure to keep workers employed and regional economies from declining, singly or in combination, may keep a firm in production beyond the point where a reasonable profit can be made.

The conceptual analysis of a firm is similar in a number of respects to the conceptual analysis of the consumer, but while a consumer attempts to maximize utility, it is usually the basic assumption that the firm attempts to maximize total profit, a quantity much easier to determine than utility. Some economists believe that an owner-manager of a small enterprise may try to maximize profit but that a hired manager of a giant corporation is more interested in increasing his power and prerogatives by increasing the size of his organization. Thus it may be more accurate to say that modern corporations try to maximize sales subject to adequate profit. For a firm to determine its profit for making any particular product it must know (1) the relation between production cost and quantity produced and (2) the relation between market price of product and quantity produced. The first item, the *production function*, can be estimated by engineering and cost analysis. The second item is determined by the market-concentration power of the firm.

2.2.1 Determining Cost of Production

An analysis of the production of a firm must begin with a study of both capital and production costs. The term *cost* is often used in a different sense by economists, engineers, and accountants. Cost to an economist means all the costs of producing a product that an engineer or accountant would consider *plus* a reasonable return for the capital needed to build (fixed capital) and operate (working capital) the production facilities.

The total annual cost of producing a product is traditionally considered to have two components, fixed cost and variable cost. A list of such costs is provided by Peters and Timmerhaus [4]. Fixed cost FC does not depend on the rate of production in the time period. The major components of any fixed cost are:

1. Fixed charges on plants and property
   a. Depreciation
   b. Property taxes
   c. Insurance
   d. Rent paid to others
2. Overhead costs: medical, safety and protection, general plant overhead, payroll overhead, cafeteria, recreation, control laboratories, supervision
3. Administrative expenses: executive salaries, engineering salaries, research and development, general office expense

Variable costs are those costs associated with producing and selling the product which depend upon the rate of production. The major components of the variable cost VC are:

1. Direct production costs
   a. Raw materials
   b. Operating labor
   c. Power and utilities
   d. Maintenance
   e. Operating supplies, i.e., catalysts, solvents, etc.
   f. Laboratory charges
2. Distribution and marketing expenses: sales offices, salesperson wages and expenses, shipping, advertising, marketing, and technical sales

In the short run many costs are fixed. In the long run all costs are variable. Short-range fixed costs such as executive salaries, engineering salaries, research and development salaries and expenses may be reduced in a prolonged business decline.

Variable costs usually increase sharply with production rate as plant design capacity is reached and exceeded. Chemical conversions and yields may sharply decrease, utility and labor costs may increase, and special operating measures may have to be undertaken.

It is frequently useful to express the variable cost VC as a function of the plant annual production rate q. A useful functional relationship often used is

$$VC(q) = aq + bq^n \tag{2.9}$$

where the second term on the right-hand side represents those variable costs which increase faster than if they were directly proportional to q.

The total cost of production TC for producing a particular amount q of a product is simply the sum of the fixed and variable costs at that production rate:

$$TC = FC + VC(q) \tag{2.10}$$

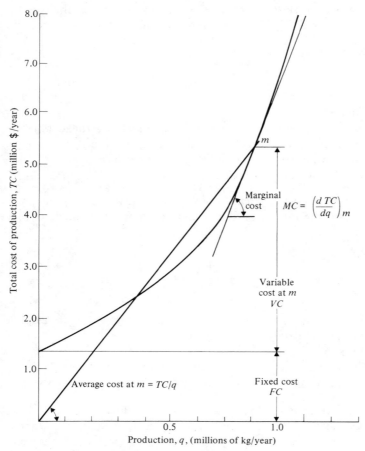

Figure 2.7 Total cost of production vs. production.

The total cost of production is usually computed on an annual basis. A typical relationship between TC and q is shown in Fig. 2.7; this curve was obtained by analyzing a chemical processing operation and is typical of the shape of curves for processing operations in the CPI. Both the average or unit cost AC and the marginal cost MC are shown in Fig. 2.7. The average cost is defined as

$$AC(q) = \frac{TC}{q} \qquad (2.11)$$

The marginal cost MC is the incremental cost of producing 1 additional unit

$$MC(q) = \frac{d}{dq} TC \qquad (2.12)$$

The essential elements of a production cost analysis can be illustrated with a simple example. In particular we will show how production costs are related to the chemistry, the reactor analysis, and the process design.

Example 2.1 Suppose that laboratory bench-scale experiments have shown that it is feasible to manufacture a specialty chemical, Delos, by the simple isomerization of a readily available raw material, Algol. The chemistry is

$$Algol \longrightarrow Delos$$

Enough laboratory experimentation and analysis have been carried out to determine that the rate at which Algol reacts to form Delos can be represented by the kinetic rate expression

$$r_A = kC_A$$

where k is the reaction rate constant in min^{-1} and C_A is the concentration of Algol in mol/l. At the processing temperature of interest (150°C) k has a value of 0.005 min^{-1}.

The process to produce Delos is simple yet effective. The two key pieces of equipment are a well-stirred tank-type reactor and a separation column. A simplified flow diagram is shown in Fig. 2.8. The reactor performance is described by the following mass-balance relationships:

Algol mass balance: $\qquad 0 = WC_{AF} - WC_A - kC_A L \qquad (2.13)$

Delos mass balance: $\qquad 0 = -WC_D + kC_A L \qquad (2.14)$

where C_{AF} = concentration of Algol in reactor feed
$\quad C_A, C_D$ = concentration of Algol and Delos in reactor effluent
$\quad\quad W$ = process flow rate, l/min
$\quad\quad L$ = reactor volume, l

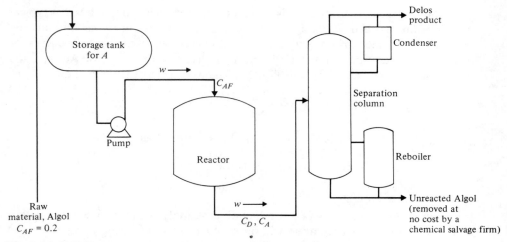

Figure 2.8 Simplified process flow diagram for manufacture of Delos.

Equations (2.13) and (2.14) can be rearranged to yield various process operating parameters of interest:

1. Relationship between concentrations

$$C_{AF} = C_A + C_D \tag{2.15}$$

2. Concentration of Algol in the reactor effluent C_A as a function of Delos produced WC_D and reactor volume L:

$$C_A = \frac{WC_D}{kL} \tag{2.16}$$

$$C_A = \frac{C_{AF}}{1 + kL/W} \tag{2.17}$$

where L/W is the reactor holding time.

3. Process unit throughput W in terms of the reactor volume L and Delos produced WC_D:

$$W = \frac{WC_D}{C_{AF} - WC_D/kL} \tag{2.18}$$

The separation column design and operation are more complex and cannot be summarized as readily. The column height is essentially determined by the relative volatilities of Algol and Delos and any inert material present. The diameter of the column is set by total unit throughput W as is the design of the reboiler and condenser. To meet the purposes of this example it is not necessary to consider in detail the column design, and we will assume that its capital and operating costs can be directly related to the reactor design. Product Delos is distilled overhead, and the unreacted Algol is produced as a bottom product and removed at no cost by a chemical salvage firm.

The total production cost can be computed with the following assumptions:

1. The cost of the raw material, Algol, is $RC per mole.
2. Algol is available at a concentration C_{AF} of 0.2 mol/l.
3. Variable production costs such as utilities, power, operating supplies, and operating labor are assumed proportional to unit throughput W and equal to $PC per liter.
4. Fixed costs, the most important of which are depreciation on the storage tank, pump, reactor, separation column, reboiler, and condenser, are assumed to be proportional to the reactor volume L and equal to $45L$ per year.

Total production cost on an annual basis can be obtained using Eq. (2.10):

$$TC = 45L + VC(q)$$

The variable costs on an annual basis VC are related to q, the total amount of Delos produced, by using reactor design analysis. For the process being considered there are two components of the variable cost, raw-material costs and variable production costs.

Delos has a molecular weight of 100. With a 350-day (504,000-min) operating year for the process, q is related to the process parameters as follows:

$$q = WC_D \text{ mol/min} \times 504{,}000 \text{ min/year} \times 0.10 \text{ kg/mol} = 50{,}400WC_D$$

Raw-material cost can be expressed as a function of q using Eq. (2.18):

$$\text{Raw-material cost} = WC_{AF}(RC)(504{,}000)$$

$$= \frac{WC_D C_{AF}}{C_{AF} - WC_D/kL}(RC)(504{,}000)$$

$$= 10(RC)\frac{q}{1 - q/B}$$

where $B = 50{,}400C_{AF}kL$.

For a specific reactor design, parameter B is constant. Raw-material costs increase faster than q when $q/B > 0.1$. This is caused by increased feed rate W and increased unconverted Algol in the effluent.

The variable production cost can also be expressed in terms of the annual Delos production q:

$$\text{Variable operating cost} = PC(W)(504{,}000)$$

$$= (PC)\frac{WC_D(504{,}000)}{C_{AF} - WC_D/kL}$$

$$= 10\frac{PC}{C_{AF}}\frac{q}{1 - q/B}$$

Total annual cost becomes

$$TC = 45L + \frac{10q}{1 - q/B}\left(\frac{PC}{C_{AF}} + RC\right) \tag{2.19}$$

This expression, derived directly from the process design parameters, can be rearranged into a form similar to Eq. (2.9) if the term $|[1 - q/B]^{-1}$ is approximated by the series expansion

$$\left(1 - \frac{q}{B}\right)^{-1} \cong 1 + \frac{q}{B} + \left(\frac{q}{B}\right)^2 + \left(\frac{q}{B}\right)^3 + \cdots + \left(\frac{q}{B}\right)^n$$

$$TC = 45L + 10q\left(\frac{PC}{C_{AF}} + RC\right)\left[1 + \frac{q}{B} + \left(\frac{q}{B}\right)^2 + \left(\frac{q}{B}\right)^3\right]$$

The approximation including the cubic term is valid to within 10 percent of the correct cost if q/B is less than 0.5.

Figure 2.7 was prepared using Eq. (2.19) for a reactor volume $L = 30{,}000$ l. For operating costs $PC = 0.01$ and for raw-material cost $L = 30{,}000$ l, for $RC = 0.15$

$$TC = 45L + 2\frac{q}{1 - q/B} \tag{2.20}$$

The cost curve shown in Fig. 2.7 is specific for a particular plant at some particular time. The same processing unit can be made more efficient as operating experience is gained, leading to lower total costs at some later time. A firm may also build additional processing units which will generally have a lower cost

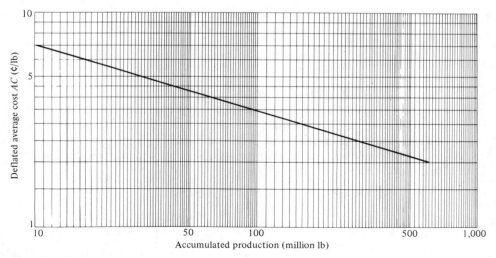

Figure 2.9 Typical experience curve.

function, due to economies of scale and/or economies of experience. This phenomenon of decreasing cost due to increased experience can be presented in the form of a *learning curve* of unit cost vs. time or as an *experience curve* of unit cost (corrected for inflation) vs. a firm's accumulated production (defined as the sum of all production of the chemical up to a particular time). A log-log plot of deflated cost vs. total accumulated production for a chemical often shows a linear decline in cost as accumulated production increases (Fig. 2.9).

2.2.2 Optimizing a Firm's Profit

As an essential first step toward optimizing profit, a firm must decide how much product to sell and at what price. The income from sales or total revenue TR of a firm for selling a product is simply pq. The marginal revenue MR is $d(\text{TR})/dq$. The profit π is the difference between the firm's total revenue and total cost:

$$\pi(q) = \text{TR} - \text{TC} \tag{2.21}$$

Assuming that the firm wishes to maximize profit, we have

$$\frac{d\pi}{dq} = \frac{d(\text{TR})}{dq} - \frac{d(\text{TC})}{dq} = \text{MR} - \text{MC} = 0 \tag{2.22}$$

Thus, to maximize profit, a firm will set production so that $\text{MR} = \text{MC}$. This means that in order to maximize profit a firm will increase (or decrease) production until the revenue from one additional unit sold equals the additional cost of making it. The value of FC has no influence on the optimal production level once the plant is designed and built. It is thus considered *sunk cost*.

The marginal cost MC of production is the incremental cost of producing the product and is defined by Eq. (2.12) and shown in Fig. 2.7:

$$\text{MC} = \frac{d(\text{TC})}{dq}$$

The average or unit cost of production AC, as defined by Eq. (2.11), is plotted vs. production q in Fig. 2.10 for a 30,000-L reactor producing Delos. ($C_{AF} = 0.2$, $PC = 0.01$, $RC = 0.15$).

To maximize the profit for any type of operation the expression for total revenue for the operation, $\text{TR} = pq$, is substituted into Eq. (2.22) and an expression relating price p the operation's production q and the marginal cost MC is obtained:

$$\frac{d\pi}{dq} = \frac{d(pq)}{dq} - \text{MC} = p + q\frac{dp}{dq} - \text{MC}$$

To maximize profit with respect to production $d\pi/dq$ must be equal to zero:

$$p + q\frac{dp}{dq} - \text{MC} = 0 \tag{2.23}$$

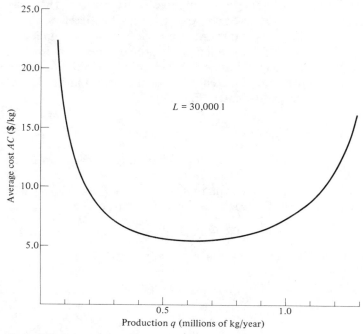

Figure 2.10 Average cost of production vs. production.

In using Eq. (2.23) one must take into consideration the relationship between p and q. This depends on the type of competition in the industry. It is necessary to identify three extreme cases of competition:

1. *Perfect or atomistic competition.* In this situation the output of a product from each firm is a very small part of the total supply, and production decisions by any one firm have no influence on total supply and the product's market price $(dp/dq = 0)$. The firm may decide to produce and to sell at any volume, but it has no influence on price.
2. *Monopoly.* In this situation one firm supplies all of a product $(q = Q = \text{total}$ industry production). Its decisions with regard to output have a decisive effect on price $(dp/dq = dp/dQ$, which is the slope of the total demand curve).
3. *Oligopoly.* In this intermediate situation a few firms supply most of a product, and a single firm's decision on production volume has some effect on price $(dp/dq$ not necessarily zero). The exact relationship between p and q is very difficult if not impossible to predict, since a price increase by one firm may be matched or ignored by the other firms.

Atomistic, or perfect, competition If there is perfect competition, the amount produced by the atomistic firm will not affect p; $dp/dq = 0$. Then

$$\frac{d\pi}{dq} = p - \text{MC} = 0 \tag{2.24}$$

To maximize profit, the firm will produce the quantity of product at which the marginal cost equals the externally determined price, $MC = p$. In cases of perfect competition, the extra revenue derived from an additional unit of production is simply the market price ($MC = MR = p$). This is not affected by the action of the individual atomistic firm.

As an example, assume the following relationships:

$$FC = \$60$$
$$VC = \$(0.25 \times 10^{-6}q^4)$$
$$p = \$1 \text{ per unit of } q \text{ sold}$$
$$TC = FC + VC = \$(60 + 0.25 \times 10^{-6}q^4)$$

To maximize profit

$$MC = \frac{d(TC)}{dq} = 10^{-6}q^3 = p$$

Therefore, the amount to produce is

$$q^3 = 10^6 p = 10^6 \times 1 \qquad q = 100 \text{ units}$$

Figure 2.11 illustrates this example. When q is below the break-even point, profit

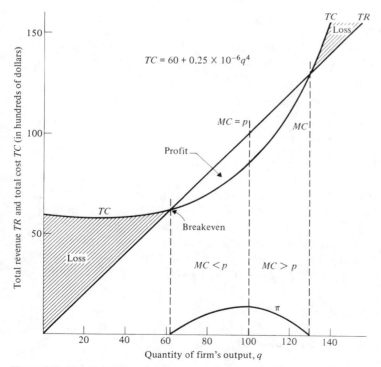

Figure 2.11 Determining production to maximize profit for the atomistic firm.

is negative, when q is at the optimum level; the profit $\pi = pq - \text{TC}$ is $15. A small firm in plastics processing may approach this ideal case.

Monopoly In a monopolistic situation one firm supplies all of a product: $q = Q$. The firm also sets the price p, and the total market demand function provides the Q in response. Thus, dp/dQ is not zero in Eq. (2.23). One needs the function relating p and Q to determine the optimum p for maximizing profits.

To illustrate the operation of the monopoly firm, we assume the same total cost function as before but assume that for some reason all firms but one have dropped out of business. We also assume the following relationship for the demand curve:

$$p = 2 - 10^{-2}Q$$

Since the monopolistic firm is the sole producer $(q = Q)$, Eq. (2.23) becomes

$$\frac{d\pi}{dQ} = \text{MR} - \text{MC} = 0$$

Differentiating the demand-curve relationship and substituting gives

$$\text{MR} = p + Q\frac{dp}{dQ} = p\left(1 + \frac{Q}{p}\frac{dp}{dQ}\right) = p\left(1 - \frac{1}{E}\right)$$

$$= 2 - 10^{-2}Q + Q(-10^{-2}) = 2 - 2 \times 10^{-2}Q$$

For an elastic demand, the marginal revenue MR is positive, and for an inelastic demand the MR is negative. Finding the equation for marginal cost gives

$$\text{MC} = \frac{dC}{dQ} = \frac{d}{dQ}(60 + 0.25 \times 10^{-6}Q^4) = 10^{-6}Q^3$$

and setting MC = MR leads to

$$10^{-6}Q^3 = 2 - 2 \times 10^{-2}Q$$

A solution to this equation yields $Q = 76.6$. At this production rate $p = 1.24 per unit and $\pi = 25.6. Figure 2.12 illustrates the example. The optimum in an unregulated monopoly yields a lower production level but a higher price and profit than under atomistic competition. In reality, government-sanctioned monopolies, such as an electric utility, have regulated prices. Such firms often try to maximize efficiencies and to increase market size but do not emphasize profit maximization.

Oligopoly Production of many CPI products takes place in an oligopolistic situation. Often, three or four firms produce over 50 percent of a chemical. The oligopoly has a set of characteristics which are not as easily defined as for perfect competition or monopoly.

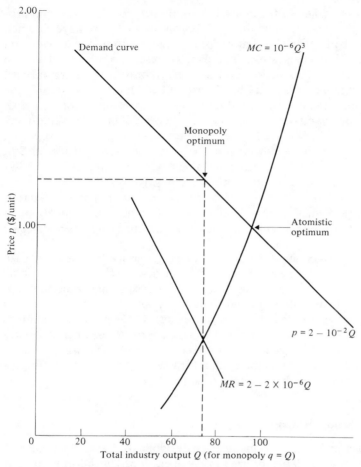

Figure within plot labels:

2.00

Demand curve $MC = 10^{-6}Q^3$

Monopoly
optimum

Price p ($\$$/unit)

1.00

Atomistic
optimum

$p = 2 - 10^{-2}Q$

$MR = 2 - 2 \times 10^{-6}Q$

0   20   40   60   80   100

Total industry output Q (for monopoly $q = Q$)

Figure 2.12 Determining production to maximize profit of a monopoly.

Equation (2.23) can be used to compute the profit of any firm:

$$\text{MR} = p + q\frac{dp}{dq} = \text{MC}$$

While the atomistic firm has no influence on price and the monopolistic firm can set price unilaterally, the oligopolistic firm may announce a price increase and set a production figure and then wait for the response of other firms. If the other firms do not follow with a similar price increase, this firm may find all its customers defecting and will have to rescind the price increase; if the price increase is followed by the other firms, the market shares will remain the same in a shrunken market. If the oligopolistic firm starts a price war by decreasing the price in an effort to capture a larger market share, the other firms may or may not follow suit. The value of dp/dq is determined by the business strategy of the other firms.

Capital allocation and design In the analysis leading to expressions for total production cost and strategies for maximizing the profit of a firm, we have assumed that the operating plant exists and that firms are required to make decisions on production volume. The already existing plant represents a sunk cost due to irreversible past decisions. Production level is governed only by the marginal cost. In the example of this section if the fixed cost FC is $100 instead of $60, the optimum production remains at $q = 100$ units but the profit π becomes $-\$45$. Closing the plant down would be worse. The fixed cost FC must be paid in any case, and the profit becomes $-\$100$ (an even worse loss). Because of past errors, the best strategy now is to operate at $q = 100$ units and accept a loss of $45. However, nothing would induce one to make a new plant investment of a similar nature again unless there were a sufficiently large positive profit.

Projected return on investment (ROI) is one of the most important determinants of new plant investment. A firm must make sufficient ROI to justify plant expansion, and a firm with a risky investment would require even higher projected ROI to proceed with a new plant.

A firm has an annual capital investment budget, generated from internal cash flow of profit, depreciation, external borrowing and new stock sales. A rational firm ranks all capital project proposals according to descending projected ROI and probable risk, and funds all projects with sufficient ROI subject to the budget constraint. An aggressive firm may have far more meritorious projects than funds available, so that many would stay on the planning board. A less aggressive firm with more funds than good projects may lend excess funds to other companies. In each case, a company tries to maximize its return on investment by putting its funds in investments with the highest return with safety.

2.2.3 Developing a Supply Curve

A supply curve for a particular product can be developed if the engineering and technical information is available for each firm's operation. This information can often be generated and a supply curve estimated for CPI products by a chemical professional.

The process for obtaining the supply curve is most conveniently demonstrated by expanding upon Example 2.1. The following steps are taken:

1. From the process design an analytical or graphical relationship between total cost TC and production q for each operating unit must be developed.
2. Using Eq. (2.23), one determines the production rate q at which each firm will operate at a given price p for an expected range of prices:

$$\mathrm{MC} = \frac{d(\mathrm{TC})}{dq} = p + q\frac{dp}{dq}$$

Unless dp/dq is known, this part of the analysis may be carried out assuming $dp/dq = 0$ (the perfect-competition situation).

3. The supply curve, a plot of price p vs. total product production Q, is made by summing all the individual firm productions q at one particular price.

Example 2.2 If we consider that the Delos business consists of 10 firms each operating with a 30,000-l reactor, 10 firms each operating with a 40,000-l reactor, and 10 firms each operating with a 50,000-l reactor, a supply curve can be generated using the simple reactor design and process economic parameters developed in Sec. 2.2.1. The total cost for any one firm is given by

$$TC = 45L + \frac{10q}{1 - q/B}\left(\frac{PC}{C_{AF}} + RC\right) \qquad (2.19)$$

$$B = 50{,}400C_{AF}kL$$

For the industry under consideration in our example we can obtain a cost for each of the firms in the groups if we assume that C_{AF} is 0.2 and k is 0.005 for all firms.

These restrictions can easily be removed at the expense of some additional arithmetic, and the effect of different values for C_{AF} and k can be examined. It would also be easy to examine the effect of different raw-material and operating costs for different firms since they are reflected in the PC and RC terms in Eq. (2.19).

The simplified equation for TC when PC is 1 cent per liter and RC is 15 cents per mole is

$$TC = 45L - \frac{2q}{1 - q/B}$$

The TC for the various groups are:

Group I: $\qquad L_{\mathrm{I}} = 30{,}000$

$$TC_{\mathrm{I}} = 1.35 \times 10^6 + \frac{2q}{1 - q/B} \qquad B = 1.51 \times 10^6$$

Group II: $\qquad L_{\mathrm{II}} = 40{,}000$

$$TC_{\mathrm{II}} = 1.81 \times 10^6 + \frac{2q}{1 - q/B} \qquad B = 2.02 \times 10^6$$

Group III: $\qquad L_{\mathrm{III}} = 50{,}000$

$$TC_{\mathrm{III}} = 2.25 \times 10^6 + \frac{2q}{1 - q/B} \qquad B = 2.52 \times 10^6$$

Figure 2.13 shows a plot of the total cost for a typical company in each group TC vs. the company's production q.

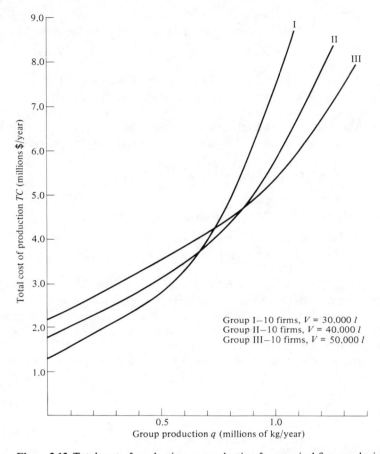

Figure 2.13 Total cost of production vs. production for a typical firm producing Delos.

Any group's production can be obtained at any group total cost simply by multiplying the firm's q or TC by 10.

Equation (2.19), giving the total cost TC in terms of reactor volume L and production rate q, can be differentiated to obtain the marginal cost MC (for $C_{AF} = 0.2$)

$$\frac{d(TC)}{dq} = \frac{d}{dq}\left(45L + \frac{2q}{1 - q/B}\right) = MC$$

$$MC = \frac{2}{(1 - q/B)^2} \tag{2.25}$$

The marginal cost is related to the price p, as shown before [Eq. (2.23)]:

$$MC = p \quad \frac{2}{(1 - q/B)^2} = p$$

$$q = B\left(1 - \sqrt{\frac{2}{p}}\right) \tag{2.26}$$

$$q = 50{,}400 C_{AF} k L\left(1 - \sqrt{\frac{2}{p}}\right)$$

For $C_{AF} = 0.2$ and $k = 0.005$

$$q = 50.4 L\left(1 - \sqrt{\frac{2}{p}}\right) \tag{2.27}$$

Equation (2.27) gives the optimal production rate of a firm producing Delos for any price p. Note that when $p \leq 2$, there is no production.

The industry supply curve is generated by obtaining the functional relationship between total Delos production of the 30 firms Q and p.

$$Q = \sum q_i$$

$$= 50.4[10(30{,}000) + 10(40{,}000) + 10(50{,}000)]\left(1 - \sqrt{\frac{2}{p}}\right)$$

$$= 60.48 \times 10^6\left(1 - \sqrt{\frac{2}{p}}\right) \tag{2.28}$$

A plot of p vs. Q is shown in Fig. 2.14. This is the supply curve for Delos. Its intersection with a demand curve establishes the production rate for each firm manufacturing Delos. For example if the price is $10 per kilogram, 33.4 million kilograms of Delos will be produced. The production rate for each firm can be established using Eq. (2.27):

Group I: $q = 0.836 \times 10^6$ kg/year

Group II: $q = 1.11 \times 10^6$ kg/year

Group III: $q = 1.39 \times 10^6$ kg/year

Table 2.1 shows the profit for each firm in the various groups as a function of price for PC = 1 cent per liter and RC = 15 cents per mole:

$$\pi = pq - 45L - \frac{2q}{1 - q/B} \tag{2.29}$$

At the price of about $5.57 all firms will have a zero profit. With the simple cost functions used in this example no one firm can make a profit while

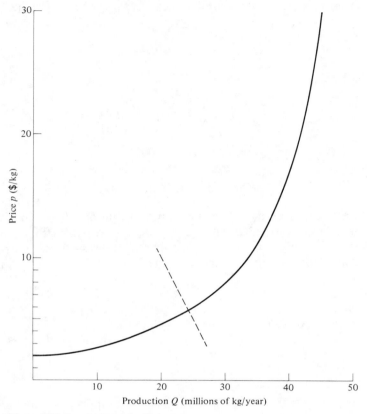

Figure 2.14 Supply curve for Delos.

another loses money. In reality this may not always be the case, as can easily be shown if we assume some economy of scale for fixed cost:

$$FC = 45L^{0.8}$$

This expression for fixed costs assumes that there is an advantage to building a larger reactor. The profit equation now becomes

$$\pi = pq - 45L^{0.8} - \frac{2q}{1 - q/B} \tag{2.30}$$

At a price of $3.03 per kilogram and with the above economic constraints, each firm in the three respective groups makes the profit shown in Table 2.2. The firms in Group III with the larger reactors (50,000 l) are able to make a small profit at this price, thanks to economy of sale, while firms in Group I and II lose money.

Table 2.1 Profit of firms manufacturing Delos

$$q = 50.5L\left(1 - \sqrt{\frac{2}{p}}\right) \qquad \pi = pq - 45L - \frac{2q}{1 - q/50.4L}$$

Price per kilogram	Group I ($L = 30{,}000$)		Group II ($L = 40{,}000$)		Group III ($L = 50{,}000$)	
	Production q, 10^3 kg/yr	Profit π \$ (thousands)	Production q, 10^3 kg/yr	Profit π \$ (thousands)	Production q, 10^3 kg/yr	Profit π \$ (thousands)
\$ 2	0	\$ $-1{,}350$	0	\$ $-1{,}800$	0	\$ $-2{,}250$
4	442	-831	591	$-1{,}108$	738	$-1{,}385$
5	556	-328	741	-438	926	-548
6	639	270	852	360	1,065	450
8	756	1,674	1,008	2,232	1,260	2,790
10	836	3,270	1,114	4,360	1,393	5,450

Table 2.2 Profit for FC $= 45L^{0.8}$

Group	Production q, 10^3 kg/yr	Profit π
I	294	\$ $-11{,}000$
II	378	$-1{,}000$
III	473	10,000

2.3 ECONOMICS OF A NATION

The well-being of the chemical industry depends upon the economic performance and buying power of the nation in which it operates. To determine a nation's economic performance, the flow of goods, services, and money between consumers, government, business, and foreign interests must be known. In the United States, the Department of Commerce has the responsibility of maintaining the national accounts. The economy of the United States is complex; the collection of data and the estimation of various important quantities such as GNP and national income is a difficult and nontrivial task. Some idea of the complexity of the national accounts as well as some of the key concepts used in the bookkeeping operation can be seen in Fig. 2.15. The cash flows between blocks show where the money comes from and goes to. These are summed to give the measured quantity in the block. For example, personal income is the sum of compensation of employees, proprietors' income, interest, dividends, rental income of persons, transfer payments, and government and consumer interest payments. Personal income is distributed as personal savings, personal outlays, and personal tax and nontax (social security, etc.) payments.

A one-figure indication of the health of a nation's economy is provided by the GNP, the most common measure of economic activity, which has been widely used for many years. It is defined as the flow rate of final goods and services

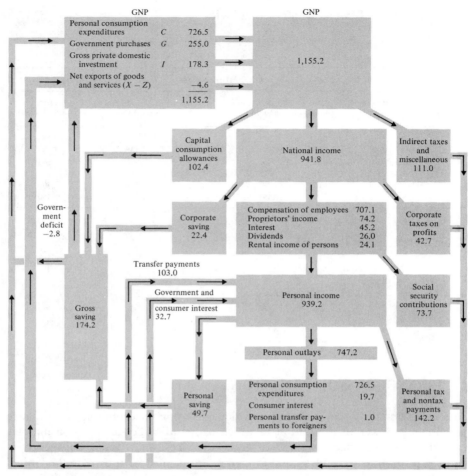

Figure 2.15 Flow of income and expenditures in the United States in 1972. (*Source:* SRI International, Menlo Park, Ca.)

produced by a nation in any one year, or the rate at which money is spent in any one year. It is usually measured in terms of the market value of such production per year. The GNP can be computed as follows:

$$GNP = C + G + I + (X - Z) \tag{2.31}$$

where C = expenditure by consumers for final goods and services
 G = market value of all government purchases
 I = market value of investment goods produced by nation
 $X - Z$ = market value of exports minus imports from one nation to other countries

Consumer goods and services make up the largest part of GNP. These can be consumer durables (automobiles, major appliances, furniture, etc.); nondurables (food, clothing, and fuel); and services (medical, insurance, garbage collection, etc.). The purchase of goods and services by government serves as a measure of the productive economic activity consumed in the public sector. Investments include capital equipment and building construction by businesses, new house construction, and all business-inventory changes. The GNP and its individual components, as flow of goods and services for the United States, are presented for selected years from 1929 to 1976 in Table 2.3.

The National Income Division of the Department of Commerce computes the GNP regularly, and a monthly summary of the National Income Accounts is provided by *Economic Indicators*, a publication issued by the GPO. Data for computing GNP are provided by (1) periodic censuses, (2) payroll and employment statistics as developed from social security information, (3) tax information collected by the Internal Revenue Service, and (4) fiscal records of the federal government. More detail on sources of information and methods of estimation are given in Refs. 1 to 3.

The GNP values shown in Table 2.3 are expressed in dollars for the year calculated. By using current dollars to measure economic activity, real growth is obscured by the effects of inflation, which decrease the real worth of the dollar. To correct the GNP for inflationary effects, price indexes using 1972 prices as the base year are computed by the Department of Commerce. The components of GNP are then converted into constant 1972 dollars by using the appropriate price index. In Table 2.4 the GNP has been corrected for the effects of inflation. The GNP deflator is an implicit price deflator derived from the rate of inflation.

In 1976, the Department of Commerce replaced the 1958 constant-dollar deflator with a 1972 constant-dollar deflator. Both deflators are reported in the Table 2.4 for comparison. In addition, in 1976 the Department published a GNP table using a different procedure to calculate the GNP for the current year and previous years; consequently, comparisons of tables prepared before 1976 with tables prepared later will show small discrepancies in annual GNP values.

Table 2.3 GNP and its major components for the United States, selected years, 1929–1974 (billions)†

	1929	1930	1940	1950	1960	1970	1974	1975	1976
GNP	$103.4	$90.7	$100.0	$286.2	$506.0	$982.4	$1,413.2	$1,516.3	$1,692.4
By type of expenditure:									
Personal consumption C	77.3	69.9	71.0	192.0	324.9	618.8	887.5	973.2	1,078.6
Government purchases G	8.8	9.5	14.2	38.5	100.3	218.9	303.3	339.0	365.8
Investment goods I	16.2	10.2	13.1	53.8	76.4	140.8	215.0	183.7	241.2
Net exports X−Z	1.1	1.0	1.7	1.9	4.4	3.9	7.5	20.5	6.9

† Figures may not add exactly to the totals given because of rounding.

Source: Economic Report of the President, 1977, table B-1; U.S. Bureau of the Census, *Statistical Abstract of the United States: 1976*, 97th ed., table 628.

Table 2.4 United States GNP corrected for inflation (billions)

| Period | GNP in constant dollars | | Deflators | |
	1958 dollars	1972 dollars	1958 = 100	1972 = 100
1929	203.6	314.7	50.64	32.87
1933	141.5	222.1	39.29	25.13
1940	227.2	343.6	43.87	29.10
1950	355.3	533.5	80.16	53.64
1958	447.3	679.5	100.0	66.06
1960	487.7	736.8	103.29	68.67
1970	722.5	1,075.3	135.24	91.36
1972	792.5	1,171.1	146.12	100.0
1974	821.1†	1,214.0	170.11†	116.41
1975		1,191.7		127.25
1976†		1,265.0†		133.79†

† Projected.

The GNP can also be estimated by a procedure based on how the money is earned:

GNP = personal income + social security contributions + corporate saving + capital consumption allowances + corporate taxes on profits + indirect taxes and miscellaneous

Table 2.5 National income of the United States (billions)

	1929	1940	1950	1960	1970	1974	1975	1976†
National income	$84.8	$79.7	$236.2	$412.0	$798.4	$1,135.7	$1,207.6	$1,349.4
Employee compensation	51.1	52.1	154.8	294.9	609.2	875.8	928.8	1,028.4
Proprietors' income	14.9	12.9	38.4	47.0	65.1	86.9	90.2	96.7
Rental income	4.9	2.7	7.1	13.8	18.6	21.0	22.4	23.5
Corporate profit‡	10.5	9.8	37.6	48.9	66.4	87.8	103.1	
Net interest	4.7	3.3	2.3	9.8	37.5	67.1	74.6	82.1
Capital consumption	9.7	9.0	23.9	47.7	90.8	137.7	161.4	179.8
Indirect tax	7.1	10.1	23.4	45.4	94.0	128.4	138.7	149.7
GNP	103.4	100.0	286.2	506.0	982.4	1,413.2	1,516.3	1,692.4

† Projected.
‡ Profits with inventory valuation adjustment and without capital consumption adjustment.
Source: Economic Report of the President, 1977, tables B-17 and B-19.

Table 2.6 National income for the United States, selected years, 1950–1974, and contribution by selected industrial sectors (billions)

	1950	1960	1970	1974
National income	$242.8	$418.0	$804.4	$1,157.5
Contribution by:				
Chemical and allied products (SIC 28)	4.9	9.1	16.0	21.6
Petroleum and coal products (SIC 29)	3.4	4.4	6.6	12.9
Rubber and miscellaneous				
plastic products (SIC 30)	1.3	2.8	5.8	8.3
Stone, glass, and clay (SIC 32)	2.8	4.6	6.9	9.7

Source: U.S. Bureau of the Census, *Statistical Abstract of the United States: 1976,* 97th ed., table 640.

Another measure of economic health is the national income, the amount of money paid to the owners of economic resources (land, labor, capital) in return for supplying the services of these resources. It can be computed by subtracting indirect taxes and some minor charges and capital consumption charges (depreciation) from GNP (Fig. 2.15). It can also be derived by adding all compensation of employees, proprietors' income, interest, dividends, rental income of persons, corporate taxes on profits, and corporate saving. The past record of GNP in the United States, as a flow of earnings, is shown in Table 2.5. Using this approach, one can estimate the contribution to the national income by individual industrial sectors. The United States national income for 1950 to 1974 and the contribution to it by the chemical industry is shown in Table 2.6.

Table 2.7 Income per person, United States, selected years 1929–1975

Year	Personal income per person		Disposable income per person	
	Current dollars	Constant 1972 dollars	Current dollars	Constant 1972 dollars
1929	$696	$1,943	$675	$1,884
1930	618	1,768	598	1,711
1940	589	1,914	569	1,849
1950	1,491	2,626	1,355	2,386
1960	2,212	3,084	1,934	2,696
1970	3,911	4,228	3,348	3,619
1973	5,002	4,742	4,285	4,062
1974	5,443	4,656	4,639	3,968
1975	5,852	4,632	5,062	4,007

Source: Surv. Curr. Bus., July 1976.

Table 2.8 Personal consumption expenditures per person, United States, selected years, 1929–1975

Year	Durable goods		Nondurable goods		Services	
	Current dollars	1972 dollars	Current dollars	1972 dollars	Current dollars	1972 dollars
1929	76	176	$309	$805	$249	$788
1930	58	138	276	759	233	726
1940	59	165	280	908	198	672
1950	203	286	648	1,067	415	876
1960	239	291	836	1,153	723	1,064
1970	415	434	1,292	1,380	1,314	1,451
1973	588	579	1,587	1,470	1,674	1,599
1974	574	530	1,775	1,432	1,839	1,620
1975	617	524	1,916	1,433	2,025	1,650

Source: Surv. Curr. Bus., July 1976.

Individual households derive income from working or from selling (or lending) raw materials, land, and capital. The economic health of the household sector can be measured by personal income per person and by disposable income per person (Fig. 2.15). Personal income is simply the total current income before taxes of all persons (Fig. 2.15). It equals national income *minus* social security tax, corporate taxes on profits, and corporate saving *plus* transfer payments made by the government (social security payments, welfare, etc.) and interest payments. Disposable income is what remains of personal income after taxes have been paid. These quantities are shown per person for the United States consumer, 1929 to 1974, both in current and constant dollars in Table 2.7. The United States consumer's income has grown at a steady pace since the 1930s. Income per person in constant dollars has nearly doubled in 25 years.

After providing for savings, the consumer uses his disposable income to buy services and goods (collectively termed *final products*). The consumer's personal consumption expenditures per person for durable goods, nondurable goods, and services are shown in Table 2.8.

To help you understand foreign economic activities and buying power, GNP values for other countries are shown in Table 2.9 for 1974. Also shown is GNP per person. There is a tremendous range of GNP per capita from $8,449 for Kuwait to $71 for Rwanda, or more than a hundredfold difference in material wealth and comfort. The wealthy nations tend to be the industrial nations in temperate climates, and the poor nations tend to be those with an agricultural economy in tropical climates. Mineral resources are the basis of wealth for Kuwait, Qatar, and the United Arab Emirates. Among industrial nations, the per capita wealth of the United States is surpassed by that of Sweden and Switzerland.

Table 2.9 Estimates of GNP for foreign countries, 1974, current United States dollars

Nation	GNP Total (millions)	Per capita	Nation	GNP Total (millions)	Per capita
Algeria	$7,730	$504	Lebanon	2,841	874
Angola	2,980	492	Liberia	417	248
Argentina	61,385	1,246	Libya	6,230	2,984
Australia	52,160	3,998	Luxembourg	1,829	5,226
Austria	27,900	3,710	Madagascar	1,258	174
Bangladesh	7,730	100	Malaysia	6,565	554
Belgium	45,740	4,686	Mali	397	73
Bolivia	1,014	202	Malta	353	1,096
Brazil	77,220	750	Mexico	48,650	870
Cambodia	627	81	Morocco	5,012	286
Canada	118,900	5,372	Mozambique	2,905	334
Central African Republic	302	176	Netherlands	59,670	4,440
Chad	350	88	New Zealand	11,710	3,930
Chile	7,640	777	Nicaraqua	1,065	503
China (Taiwan)	10,226	663	Niger	525	125
Colombia	9,968	413	Nigeria	14,802	250
Congo	425	423	Norway	18,750	4,735
Costa Rica	1,461	775	Pakistan	8,340	126
Cyprus	963	1,459	Panama	1,418	904
Denmark	27,350	5,342	Paragua	979	402
Dominican Republic	2,378	509	Peru	9,080	617
Ecuador	2,496	371	Philippines	10,330	246
Egypt	9,100	259	Portugal	11,200	1,308
El Salvador	1,335	344	Rhodesia	2,493	406
Ethiopia	2,240	83	Qatar	511	5,938
Finland	17,060	3,661	Rwanda	280	71
France	255,060	4,851	Saudi Arabia	7,520	1,299
Germany, West	348,170	5,618	Sierra Leone	4,455	162
Ghana	2,857	287	Singapore	4,283	1,929
Greece	16,290	1,780	South Africa	26,125	1,077
Guatemala	2,545	454	Spain	60,230	1,728
Guinea	575	137	Sudan	2,300	135
Guyana	294	380	Swaziland	140	310
Haiti	694	143	Sweden	50,100	6,155
Honduras	869	291	Switzerland	40,870	6,346
Hong Kong	5,998	1,435	Syria	2,379	345
Iceland	1,025	4,835	Tanzania	1,834	127
India	71,000	117	Thailand	9,180	232
Indonesia	15,370	115	Tunisia	2,515	459
Iran	25,598	762	Turkey	22,036	576
Iraq	6,680	645	Uganda	1,715	161
Ireland	6,560	2,165	United Arab Emirates	1,425	6,736
Israel	8,950	2,732	United Kingdom	174,800	3,120
Italy	138,270	2,520	United States	1,294,900	6,155
Jamaica	1,714	868	Upper Volta	450	79
Japan	413,070	3,812	Uruguay	2,585	865
Jordan	575	286	Venezuela	16,120	1,357
Kenya	2,249	172	Yemen, South	175	110
Korea, South	12,380	376	Yemen, North	500	80
Kuwait	7,165	8,449	Zaire	3,129	147
Laos	320	100	Zambia	2,425	503

Source: Institute for International Development.

2.4 REFERENCES

1. S. Rosen, "National Income and Other Social Accounts," Holt, New York, 1972.
2. National Income Supplement, pt. III, U.S. Income and Output, 1954, GPO, Washington.
3. *Surv. Curr. Bus.*, August 1965.
4. M. S. Peters and K. D. Timmerhaus, "Plant Design and Economics For Chemical Engineers," McGraw-Hill, New York, 1968.
5. Theodore Leavitt, Marketing Myopia, *Harvard Bus. Rev.*, July-August 1960.

2.5 NOTATION

a, b	parameters in variable cost [Eq. (2.9)]
AC	average cost, TC/q
C	concentration of component, mol/l
CE	cross elasticity $= \dfrac{p_y}{Q_x}\dfrac{dQ_x}{dp_y}$ [Eq. (2.7)]
E	price elasticity $= -\dfrac{p}{Q}\dfrac{dQ}{dp}$ [Eq. (2.5)]
E_s	supply elasticity $= \dfrac{p}{Q}\dfrac{dQ}{dp}$
FC	fixed production cost
I	consumers' income
IE	income elasticity $= \dfrac{I}{Q_x}\dfrac{dQ_x}{dI}$ [Eq. (2.7b)]
L	reactor volume, l
MR	marginal revenue $d(\text{TR})/dq$
p	price of product, dollars per unit produced
PC	production costs
q	(1) with number subscript, quantity of product desired by consumer; (2) with letter subscript or with no subscript, quantity of product produced by single firm
Q	total demand for product or total amount supplied by firms engaged in manufacturing product (at equilibrium supply equals demand)
RC	raw-material costs
TC	total annual production cost
TR	total revenue for industry pQ, or for firm pq
U	consumers' utility
VC	variable production cost
W	process flow rate, l/min
π	profit

2.6 PROBLEMS

2.1 List the five most important products or services which influence your utility function. What qualities do these products possess that affect your utility function? How could these qualities be measured? Would it be satisfactory to use price to define your utility? Will the same products be important in determining your utility next year, in 5 years, by age 65?

2.2 Propose a functional form for U and two products different from that in Sec. 2.1.1. Justify the functional form with a paragraph of discussion.

2.3 If $U = q_1 q_2$, find the consumer's demand functions if the usual budget constraint applies.

2.4 Most customers of firms in the CPI are other firms. For instance a manufacturer of ethanolamines needs ethylene oxide and ammonia. It is a trivial matter to determine the required amounts of these raw materials if the total pounds of ethanolamines needed is known. Of course ethylene oxide is also used for a number of other products. What information must you obtain to construct a demand curve for ethylene oxide?

2.5 For the following total market demand functions, develop relationships for the price elasticity E. How does E depend on p? Plot P vs. Q and E vs. p for each case.

(a) $P = aQ + b$ (b) $P = aQ^b$ (c) $P = ae^{-bQ}$

2.6 A study prepared by the Ford Foundation and MITRE Corporation, a strategy study center, entitled Nuclear Power: Issues and Choices, claims that the income elasticity of demand for energy was between 0.8 and 0.9 for the United States in 1975.

(a) Between 1950 and 1975 per capita income in the United States just about doubled. By how much should the United States energy consumption have increased? How would you expect the value for the income elasticity to change over the next few years?

(b) The same report predicted that price elasticity of demand for energy would shortly reach 0.35. If the United States wished to reduce energy consumption by 25 percent, how much would the price have to rise?

2.7 The total annual cost TC of Delos production depends upon several factors, including the fixed cost FC (Sec. 2.2.1). Show the effect of changes in fixed cost on the total annual cost by varying the fixed costs over a range of ± 30 percent for a company with a reactor of 30,000 l. Assume that the price for Delos is \$5.50 per kilogram, the production cost PC is 1 cent per liter, the raw material cost RC is 15 cents per mole and the functional form of FC remains as a constant multiplied by L.

(a) Suppose you, as a Delos producer, have reason to question your stability with respect to production costs. Show the dependence of the total annual Delos cost on production cost PC, if PC varies up or down by as much as 30 percent.

(b) Leading economic indicators have just revealed that a price increase for the raw material Algol is anticipated, but information about its magnitude is not available. As a concerned Delos competitor, prepare a plot to show the effect of a raw-material price fluctuation of about ± 30 percent on the total annual production cost.

2.8 The following questions are based on The Last Word, *CHEMTECH*, August, 1972.

(a) What is the price elasticity of salt in this story?

(b) Why does Sheik El Wadi receive more benefit than Abdullah in this new route innovation even when he has done nothing to deserve it?

(c) It takes time and effort to teach villagers to use salt for food preservation. Does this effort benefit Abdullah exclusively, or does it benefit all salt sellers?

(d) Would it be desirable for the Sultan to grant Abdullah and progenies a perpetual monopoly for the new route as a reward?

2.9 Old Smooky McCarthy is the last of the dipstick artists in wildcatting, or looking for oil in unpromising places. After a year with his faithful dipstick, he found the oilfield which he named Thornberry. All told, the cost of finding, drilling, and connecting, was \$200,000. Thornberry is a good well and flows at a steady rate of 200 bbl/day. In the last few years each barrel that flows contains more water and less oil. Old Smooky has to pay for hired help, utility, upkeep of his pump, "severence tax" to the county, all of which sums to \$120 per day. It does not take a college education (Old Smooky got through third grade) to figure out that with oil selling at a steady \$3 per barrel and the oil yield dropping steadily, the day will come when it pays to plug and abandon the well. But when? Professor Sharppencil was called in to consult.

After a bit of digging into Smooky's records, which amount to a few scraps of paper and some scribbles on the back of an envelope, Professor Sharppencil did some thinking before reporting back.

Sharppencil: Despite the fact that you had 200 bbl/day all these years, only a declining fraction is oil. The fraction f can be represented by $f = 0.800 - 0.60t$, where t is the number of years since first production.

Old Smooky: Since I was knee high to a grasshopper, I hated all them revenooers. I ain't gonna pay no dime to no Feds, so you can forget all about depletion allowance and income tax. Just tell me when to quit producing and start for the hills with my trusty dipstick again.

Sharppencil: According to sound financial policy, you should continue to produce till the day when your marginal cost per barrel of oil equals your marginal revenue. On the other hand, a sound accounting practice is to depreciate your capital cost of $200,000 evenly over the life of the well; so if the well lasts 20 years, your depreciation cost would be $10,000 per year.

Old Smooky: Say, young fella. I heard a wild rumor a week ago that the price of oil may be going up, might even hit five. You reckon I could maybe squeeze a few more barrels?

Sharppencil: The answer to your question is in the affirmative.

Old Smooky: You sure talk smart!

Sharppencil: At $1,000 per day consulting fee, I better talk smart.

(f) What is the average cost of a barrel of oil produced over the life of the well?

(g) Assuming straight-line depreciation of the capital cost, what is the annual profit in year 1?

(h) What is the annual profit in the last year?

(i) If the price of oil goes to $4 per barrel, what would be the new value of t at which to plug and abandon?

(j) At $4 per barrel, how much more oil would be produced?

(k) What is the price elasticity of supply for this well?

(l) The asset value at t is $200,000. Forgetting the time value of money, if Old Smooky wants to sell Thornberry at $t = 0$, what would a reasonable customer who knows all the facts be willing to pay?

2.10 In 1973, all the automobiles in the United States are manufactured by the Universal Motor Company. This monopoly is concerned about recent clamor for putting antipollution devices on cars, costing as much as $500 per car. Mr. Bigelow, the president, is wondering whether he can pass along this extra cost to the customers or whether he will have to take this extra cost out of his profit. Thus, he called in his favorite economics consultant, Professor Sharppencil.

Bigelow: In my job, there is a new headache every month. I can't wait till I reach retirement age next year. What do you think about splitting the $500 fairly with the consumers: we swallow $50 and increase the sticker price by $450. After all, we have to do our share for clean air too.

Sharppencil: Things are a lot more complicated than you think, Mr. Big!

Bigelow: I was afraid you'd say that.

Sharppencil: Now you are selling 10 million cars a year at $3,000 a car. If you set the new car price at $3,500, you won't sell 10 million. There'll be a lot of cheapskates who would say that with this price rise they'll stretch that old jalopy another year. Fortunately, I did a consumer study last year, and I can now say with confidence that the sales will drop to 8 million.

Bigelow: That's horrible! You're not suggesting that we leave the price at $3,000 and take the $500 out of my hide!

Sharppencil: In that case, your profit would drop from $5 billion a year to zero. I figured all this out on a formula that even your vice-president on manufacturing does not know about:

Total cost = 2.5 billion + $2,000Q + \frac{1}{4} \times 10^{-18} Q^4$ (before + $500)

New TC = 2.5 billion + $2,500Q + \frac{1}{4} \times 10^{-18} Q^4$ (after + $500)

where Q is the number of cars sold per year.

Bigelow: Don't keep me guessing. What should I do?

Sharppencil: I'll go home and do a few calculations and give you the pricing strategy to yield the maximum profit. Y'd also like to know the new price, the forecast of volume, and your new profit picture. I'll throw in other goodies, such as the price elasticity of demand, the cost elasticity of production, the average cost formula, the marginal cost formula. . . . .

Bigelow: No formulas please, just the facts next week.

Sharppencil [to himself]: My students love to grind out formulas. I'll turn in the formulas to Bigelow anyway. He may not understand mathematics, but he is easily impressed.

Provide the analysis Sharppencil promised.

2.11 The supply curve for Delos is defined by Eq. (2.28). If the demand curve can be defined as $p = 30 - 10^{-6}Q$, find the profit for each company in each of the groups.

2.12 Suppose all the companies in group I producing Delos set up a cooperative research effort which results in an increase in the reaction rate constant k of 50 percent. Determine the new supply curve and the new profit for each company. Determine market share and compare both profit and market share with that when k is the same for all firms (0.005 min^{-1}). How much should each firm in group I be willing to pay for the research effort?

2.13 Suppose all the firms producing Delos can obtain their raw material at a concentration 50 percent greater than 0.2 mol/l and at the same price. Determine the new supply curve, the new share of market, and the new profit for each firm.

2.14 If just one firm in group I can reduce its cost of raw material by 50 percent, how will its profit be affected?

2.15 Using the data from Table 2.3, determine the percentage growth in personal consumption C and government purchases G for each of the years shown. What conclusions can you draw?

2.16 Compare the disposable personal income in both current and 1958 dollars with total national income and prepare a graph showing disposable income as a percentage of total income vs. year.

2.17 As the United States grows more affluent, has the investment for the future I become a larger or smaller percentage of the total GNP since 1929? Has the share of net income for employee compensation or corporate profit been growing?

2.18 Table 2.9 shows that per capital GNP varies from \$8,444 (Kuwait) to \$71 (Rwanda) in a ratio of over 100. What can account for this huge disparity of productive capabilities? Is it land, resources, capital, technology, labor, or luck which is accountable? Do you believe these differences will or should continue? How might they be narrowed?

2.19 The definition of product in the legal sense may differ from the everyday sense. In 1956, the Supreme Court ruled that Du Pont does not have a monopoly in cellophane, since the relevant product market under question is the "flexible packaging material market," in competition with many other materials. There is high enough cross elasticity to prevent a monopoly. According to this definition, indicate which of the following chemical products have reasonable substitutes and could be included in larger market definitions: gasoline, sulfuric acid, titanium dioxide, aspirin, vitamin C. Discuss.

2.20 A factory[1] produces a product by a series of machine operations. The operators are paid at a piece rate of 20 cents per unit produced. The operation has an efficiency that depends on the production rate, creating rejects that have no commercial value. The relation between production and required feed rate is $f = q^{1.3}$, where f and q are in units per hour. Per unit of feed, the raw material cost is 20 cents per unit, and the power cost is 1 cent per unit. The plant operates 24 h/day, 7 days/week, and 52 weeks/year. The first cost of plant and machines is \$33,000. Annual fixed charges (interest, taxes, depreciations, etc.) are 32 percent of first cost. Heating and light is \$500 per year, and general overhead is \$3,000 per year.

(*a*) What is the fixed cost per FC per year, variable cost VC per year as a function of q, and total cost TC per year as a function of q?

(*b*) At a given price, ranging from zero to \$1 per unit, what is the optimum production volume, the total cost TC per year, the total revenue TR per year, and the profit per year?

(*c*) At what selling price would it pay to shut down the plant?

[1] This problem is based on one of W. K. Lewis for an economics course 1927 to 1930; private communications from H. C. Hottel.

3

BASIC ACCOUNTING

Some basic knowledge of accounting is necessary before you can develop the concepts and obtain the data needed to analyze a firm's operations, discover whether or not the firm is making a profit, and predict whether a company will continue to make a profit. It is also essential to know how the firm's operations are reported to determine its role in a particular industry or in the national economy. Financial reports of the individual firm are one of the most important sources of data for the national accounting summaries presented in Chap. 2 and for the input-output tables discussed in Chap. 4.

The conventions governing accounting are fairly simple, but their detailed application is complex, requiring years of study and experience. In this chapter we illustrate the basic conventions and the doctrines governing their application with a simple example and by analyzing a standard company report.

Accounting systems have as input business transactions in their original form (receipts and invoices). These business events are first entered chronologically in a *journal* and then classified and posted in an appropriate account in a *ledger*. Periodically (sometimes once a month but at least once a year) the accounts are closed and a summary is issued in the form of an *income statement* and a *balance sheet*. Data from these financial statements are used by management, owners, creditors, and others interested in the firm as well as by local, state, and federal governments. The flow of information is shown in Fig. 3.1.

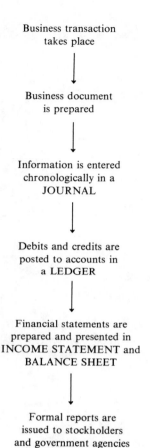

Business transaction
takes place

Business document
is prepared

Information is entered
chronologically in a
JOURNAL

Debits and credits are
posted to accounts in
a LEDGER

Financial statements are
prepared and presented in
INCOME STATEMENT and
BALANCE SHEET

Formal reports are
issued to stockholders
and government agencies

Figure 3.1 Flow of information through an accounting system.

3.1 ACCOUNTING CONCEPTS AND CONVENTIONS

Various accounting texts deal with the fundamental concepts of accounting. Anthony[1] lists seven concepts and some concise definitions which are well-suited to ourpose.

The dual-aspect concept This can best be stated by one of the following equations:

$$Assets = Equities$$

$$Assets = Liabilities + Owners' Equity$$

[1] Robert N. Anthony, "Management Accounting," Irwin, Homewood, Ill., 1964.

BALANCE SHEET

ASSETS	LIABILITIES AND STOCKHOLDERS EQUITY
Current assets: Cash Marketable securities Accounts and notes receivable Inventories	*Current liabilities:* Accounts payable Notes payable Accrued tax
Fixed assets: Equipment Buildings Land	*Long-term liabilities* Long-term bank loans Bonds
	Stockholders' equity
TOTAL	TOTAL

Figure 3.2 A typical balance sheet.

Assets are economic resources which are owned by the firm and are expected to benefit future operations. They are generally classified on income statements as follows:

1. Current assets:
    a. Cash
    b. Marketable securities
    c. Accounts and notes receivable
    d. Inventories
2. Fixed assets or plants and equipment
3. Other assets, e.g., investments

Liabilities are outside claims against assets of the firm. They are obligations to convey assets or perform services and require settlement in the future. By deducting the liabilities from the assets, the amount actually belonging to the firm's owners is found. All balance sheets are designed to show the dual-aspect concept (Fig. 3.2).

Money measurement concept Accounting records show only facts that can be expressed in monetary terms.

Business-entity concept Accounts are kept for business entities as distinguished from persons associated with those entities. Usually the accounting entity is the same as a legal entity (corporation, estate, or trust).

Going-concern concept The accounting entity is assumed to continue its operation for an indefinite period of time sufficient to carry out its commitments. This allows assets to be valued not according to distress liquidation value but according to acquisition cost minus depreciation.

Cost concept Assets are ordinarily entered on the accounting records at the price paid to acquire them. Intangibles such as good will or patents are evaluated at the cost of buying these rights and must be amortized over a period of years.

Accrual concept Income is measured as the difference between revenues and expenses rather than the difference between cash receipts and disbursements. *Revenue* is the income from goods sold and services rendered during a given time and increases owner's equity resulting from operation. Not all cash receipts represent revenue. Borrowing from the bank increases cash, but since this is offset by an identical increase in liabilities, the owners' equity is not changed. Likewise, collection of an account receivable increases the asset cash, but this is matched by an identical decrease of another asset, accounts receivable. These two operations simply swap one set of assets for another set of assets. *Expenses* are the cost of the goods and services used in the process of obtaining revenue. Expenses decrease the owners' equity. Just as revenues and cash receipts are not one and the same, expenses and cash payments are not identical. An expenditure or cash payment may be an expense, or it may be used to acquire an asset which turns into an expense much later as depreciation or as cost of goods sold (COGS). Profit, or increase in owner's equity, is produced when revenue exceeds expense.

Realization concept Revenue is realized at the time of sale of goods or services rendered.

Three important conventions govern the application of the basic accounting concepts.

Consistency The application of the consistency doctrine implies that a particular accounting method, once adopted, will not be changed from period to period. Consistency is emphasized in a company report by the accountant's statement: "... in conformity with generally accepted accounting principles, applied on a basis consistent with that of the previous year." Of course, management with approval from its accountants can change an accounting procedure, but it must be reported, showing the dollar effect of the change. Table 3.1 illustrates this point.

Conservatism Conservatism is the convention of selecting those accounting options which produce a lower net income and a less favorable financial position. For instance, research and development is counted as an expense rather than as an acquisition of an asset and thus decreases profit immediately.

Table 3.1

Opinion of Independent Public Accountants

THE DOW CHEMICAL COMPANY

We have examined the consolidated balance sheet of The Dow Chemical Company and its subsidiary companies as of December 31, 1976 and 1975, and the related consolidated statements of income, retained earnings, capital surplus, and changes in financial position for the years then ended. Our examinations were made in accordance with generally accepted auditing standards and, accordingly, included such tests of the accounting records and such other auditing procedures as we considered necessary in the circumstances.

In our opinion, the financial statements referred to above present fairly the financial position of The Dow Chemical

Company and its subsidiary companies as of December 31, 1976 and 1975, and the results of their operations and the changes in their financial position for the years then ended, in conformity with generally accepted accounting principles applied on a consistent basis after restatement for the changes, with which we concur, in the methods of accounting for contingencies and translation of foreign currencies as described in Note A to the financial statements.

Haskins & Sells

Detroit, Michigan, February 18, 1977

Source: Dow annual report, 1976.

Materiality This convention allows the accountant to be primarily concerned with significant information and to ignore insignificant matters. An item is usually considered as material if there is a reasonable expectation that knowledge of it would influence the decisions of prudent users of the financial statement.

The basic concepts of accounting and the conventions governing their application have remained unchanged for a fairly long period of time, probably because they are stated in such general terms. The accounting procedures, or methods of pragmatic application of the concepts and conventions, are changed more frequently. Procedures may be changed to take advantage of advances in electronic computation, to respond to changes in the law, and sometimes to respond to pressure from various groups for additional information.

The accounting procedures which are used to determine depreciation, for example, are extremely important to individual firms within the CPI and to the understanding of transactions of the CPI with other segments of the economy. *Depreciation* is the dollar figure representing the allocation of the cost of a plant asset to an expense in the period during which services are received from that asset. The two major causes of depreciation are physical deterioration and obsolescence.

The simplest and most widely used method of computing depreciation is to reduce the asset by equal amounts in equal periods of time (*straight-line method*). For example, if a piece of equipment is bought at a cost of $7,000, has a life of 7 years, and has no salvage value at the end of 7 years, it would be depreciated at a rate of $1,000 annually under straightline depreciation. Accelerated methods of computing depreciation lead to larger values for depreciation in the early year of the life of an asset and lower values in the later years. Two accelerated methods are in common use:

1. *Fixed percentage, or declining-balance, method.* This is an accounting procedure in which the depreciation is calculated as a fixed fraction of the remaining book value of the asset.

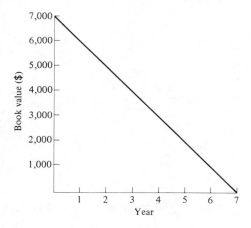

Figure 3.3 Straight-line depreciation.

2. *Sum-of-the-years-digit method.* The depreciation rate used in this procedure is a fraction in which the numerator is remaining years of useful life and the denominator is the sum of the digits of the years over which the asset is depreciated. For example, an asset being depreciated over 10 years is depreciated at a rate of $10/(1 + 2 + 3 + \cdots + 10) \approx 18$ percent during the first year.

In the CPI the useful life of many pieces of equipment is shortened because of rapid changes in technology; 10 years of life is usually assumed, but 7 years is common. The following example illustrates the three methods of depreciation for an asset of $7,000 expected to have a 7-year life.

Straight-line depreciation Depreciation rate is constant and equal to $\frac{1}{7} = 0.143$ annually. The book value of the asset drops (Fig. 3.3) at a constant rate each year until it is zero at the end of the seventh year (Table 3.2).

Table 3.2 Depreciation, straight-line

n	Depreciation rate on original value	Depreciation	Book value
1	0.143	$1,000	$6,000
2	0.143	1,000	5,000
3	0.143	1,000	4,000
4	0.143	1,000	3,000
5	0.143	1,000	2,000
6	0.143	1,000	1,000
7	0.143	1,000	0
	1.000	$7,000	

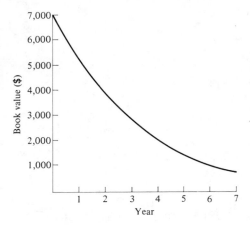

Figure 3.4 Declining-balance depreciation.

Declining-balance method Depreciation is a fixed percentage of the remaining book value of the asset. The U.S. Internal Revenue Service allows a company to use a double-declining-balance method, in which twice the straight-line rate is applied to each year's declining balance. The example assumes that the depreciation rate is one-fourth the book value annually (Table 3.3). Note that this method yields a nonzero book value at the end of year seven (Fig. 3.4). This is usually avoided by switching to straight-line depreciation in the later years of an asset's life. 3.3).

Sum-of-the-years-digit method Asset depreciates at a rate of $(j + 1 - n)/\sum\limits_{i=1}^{j} i$ during year n, where j is the life of the asset (Table 3.4). A graphical representation is shown in Fig. 3.5.

Table 3.3 Depreciation, declining-balance

n	Depreciation rate on original value	Depreciation rate on remaining book value	Depreciation	Year-end book value
1	0.2500	0.25	$1,750	$5,250
2	0.1873	0.25	1,312	3,938
3	0.1407	0.25	985	2,953
4	0.1054	0.25	738	2,215
5	0.0791	0.25	554	1,661
6	0.0593	0.25	415	1,246
7	0.0444	0.25	311	934
	0.8667			

Table 3.4 Depreciation, sum-of-the-years digit

n	Depreciation rate on original value	Depreciation rate on remaining book value	Depreciation	Year-end book value
1	0.250	0.2500	$1,750	$5,250
2	0.2143	0.2857	1,500	3,750
3	0.1786	0.3333	1,250	2,500
4	0.1429	0.4000	1,000	1,500
5	0.1071	0.5000	750	750
6	0.0714	0.6667	500	250
7	0.0357	1.0000	250	0
	1.000		$7,000	

The depreciation rate may frequently be revised to reflect changes in estimates of an asset's life. If this is necessary, the depreciation program is corrected by spreading the undepreciated cost of the asset over the newly estimated useful life. Such changes must, of course, be reported, and the dollar effect on earnings must be stated (convention of consistency). Management may change the method of computing depreciation, e.g., from accelerated to straight line. These changes must also be reported. If a piece of equipment suddenly becomes obsolete and is sold for scrap, it is necessary to write down the asset in the balance sheet. It is also necessary to include an expense in the income statement as loss on sale or as extraordinary write-off.

Depreciation policy for financial reporting need not be the same as depreciation policy for determination of taxable income (and usually is not). It is perfectly legal and moral to keep two sets of books.

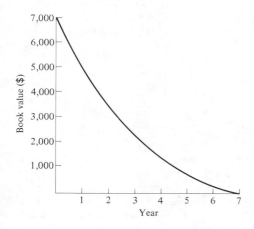

Figure 3.5 Sum-of-the-years-digit depreciation.

3.2 A SIMPLE EXAMPLE: DELCHEM INC.

The basic concepts of accounting can be illustrated by an example. In the following simplified illustration, the flow of information from journal to ledger to financial statement is shown.

Example 3.1 On Jan. 1, 1977, three people agree to start a business to manufacture a specialty solvent which they have named Cleansolv. The three, Armstrong, Bigelow, and Custer, name the company Delchem, and their contributions to its formation are as follows:

Armstrong: $5,000
Bigelow: $5,000
Custer: basic process development, small reactor and mixing vessels, and raw
 materials

The three decide to distribute 1,000 shares of stock in the following way:

Armstrong: 300 shares
Bigelow: 300 shares
Custer: 400 shares

All transactions are recorded in a general journal of the form shown in Table 3.5.

Table 3.5
DELCHEM CORPORATION
General Journal   Page 1

Date	Account titles and explanation	LP†	Debit	Credit
1/1	Cash	10	5,000	
	Stockholders' Equity	50		5,000
	Capital invested by Armstrong			
1/1	Cash	10	5,000	
	Stockholders' Equity	50		5,000
	Capital invested by Bigelow			
1/1	Raw Materials	11	1,000	
	Stockholders' Equity	50		1,000
	Raw materials from Custer			
1/1	Equipment	12	3,000	
	Stockholders' Equity	50		3,000
	Reactor and mixing vessels from Custer			

† The ledger page (LP) column is used as a cross-reference between the general journal and the various ledger accounts. The number in the column indicates the account to which the debit or credit has been transferred.

The process of transferring journal entries to the ledger is called *posting*. For an *asset* or an *expense* account, a debit entry is an addition and a credit entry is a deduction. In the case of a *liability* or a *revenue* account, the opposite is true. Separate ledger accounts are maintained for each major type of transaction. Each debit entry to a ledger account is matched by a credit entry to another account. *There is a one-to-one correspondence between journal entries and entries to the ledger;* hence the use of ledger page (LP) as a cross-reference.

The ledger in Table 3.6 contains the accounts necessary to record the transactions of Jan. 1, 1977.

Note that each journal transaction appears twice, once as a credit and once as a debit. Accounts 10, 11, and 12 are asset accounts and show a debit balance. Account 50 is a liability account and shows a credit balance, $14,000. For example, the $1,000 worth of raw materials contributed by Custer represents an addition to the corporation's assets and is recorded in the Raw Materials account as a debit. It represents an increase in equity of the corporation to Custer. It must also be recorded as a credit to the Owners' Equity account.

The number of accounts in the ledger depends on the information management needs to make decisions. If the owners need to know each partner's

Table 3.6
DELCHEM CORPORATION
Ledger

Date		JP†	Debit	Credit
	Asset accounts			
1/1	Cash (10)‡	1	5,000	
			5,000	
	Ending balance		10,000	
1/1	Raw Materials Account (11)‡	1	1,000	
	Ending balance		1,000	
1/1	Equipment Account (12)‡	1	3,000	
	Ending balance		3,000	
	Liability accounts			
1/1	Stockholders' Equity (50)‡	1		5,000
		1		5,000
		1		1,000
		1		3,000
	Ending balance			14,000

† Journal page.
‡ Ledger page.

Table 3.7
DELCHEM CORPORATION
Consolidated Balance Sheet
January 1, 1977

Assets		Liabilities and Stockholders' Equity	
Cash (10)..............................	$10,000		
Inventory		Current Liabilities	$ 0
(raw materials) (11)	1,000	Stockholders'	
Plant and		Equity (50).........................	14,000
Equipment (12)	3,000		
	$14,000		$14,000

share at any time, it would be necessary to maintain three equity accounts instead of the single account now shown.

As the firm grows, more accounts are needed to extract the necessary information for business decisions.

Today most data for large firms are stored and manipulated electronically, and manual ledgers are not kept.

The company's balance sheet as of Jan. 1 appears as shown in Table 3.7. Notice that on the balance sheet

Assets = Liabilities + Stockholders' Equity

Each ledger account balance is closed or transferred to the balance sheets. The number next to each balance-sheet entry indicates the ledger account(s) which contributed to that entry.

In January Delchem Corporation has a number of transactions, and these are recorded in the general journal (Table 3.8).

The ledger must now be enlarged to account for the new types of transactions being made and recorded. The following new asset accounts are created: Finished Goods (14), Prepaid Expense (15), and Accumulated Depreciation (13). The following new liability accounts are also created: Accrued Wages Payable (22), Accounts Payable (24), Bank Loan (21), and Interest Payable (23). Transferral of assets, such as cash, to other assets, like raw materials, simply involves the exchange of one asset for another. An example is the transfer of $5,000 in raw materials to $5,000 of finished goods.

Revenue (income) and expense accounts are *temporary* accounts which are used to classify changes affecting the Stockholders' Equity. Three expense accounts have been created: Legal Expense (40), Depreciation Expense (41), and Interest Expense (42). A revenue account is not needed for this period. A special account, Income Summary (55) is also created. These accounts are used to prepare the income statement. The balances of revenue and expense accounts are cleared (reduced to zero) through the Income Summary account at the end of each period.

The general ledger of Delchem Corporation now takes the form shown in Table 3.9.

Table 3.8
DELCHEM CORPORATION
General Journal

Date	Account titles and explanation	LP	Debit	Credit
1/3	Legal Expense	40	1,000	
	Cash	10		1,000
	Paid lawyer to set up corporation			
1/4	Finished Goods	14	1,000	
	Accrued Wages Payable	22		1,000
	Hired Davis as production labor and promised to pay him $1,000 on 2/1†			
1/4	Prepaid Expenses	15	2,000	
	Cash	10		2,000
	Cash down payment on equipment to be delivered later			
1/10	Raw Materials	11	10,000	
	Cash	10		4,000
	Accounts Payable	24		6,000
	Purchased raw materials, paid $4,000, balance of $6,000 due in February			
1/17	Cash	10	2,000	
	Bank Loan	21		2,000
	Obtained year loan from bank, interest at 12% per year			
1/26	Finished Goods	14	5,000	
	Raw Materials	11		5,000
	5,000 l of Cleansolv manufactured using $5,000 of raw materials†			

Adjusting entries

Date	Account titles and explanation	LP	Debit	Credit
1/31	Depreciation Expense: Equipment	41	25	
	Equipment	12		25
	$3,000 \times \frac{1}{10} \times \frac{1}{12} = \$25$ per month			
1/31	Interest Expense	42	20	
	Interest Payable	23		20
	To record bank loan interest for January			
1/31	Income Summary	55	1,045	
	Legal Expense	40		1,000
	Depreciation Expense: Equipment	41		25
	Interest Expense	42		20
	To close the expense and revenue accounts for the period			
1/31	Stockholders' Equity	50	1,045	
	Income Summary	55		1,045
	To close the income summary and transfer the gain (or loss) to the equity account			

† Notice that we have now in the inventory 5,000 l of Cleansolv, incorporating $1,000 of labor and $5,000 of raw materials. Thus the inventory value of this batch of Cleansolv is $6,000/(5,000 l) or $1.20 per liter.

Table 3.9
DELCHEM CORPORATION
Ledger

Date		JP	Debit	Credit
	Asset accounts			
	Cash (10)			
1/1	Starting balance	1	10,000	
1/3		2		1,000
1/4		2		2,000
1/10		2		4,000
1/17		2	2,000	
	Ending balance		5,000	
	Raw Materials (11)			
1/1	Starting balance	1	1,000	
1/10		2	10,000	
1/26		2		5,000
	Ending balance		6,000	
	Equipment (12)			
1/1	Starting balance	1	3,000	
1/31		2		25
	Ending balance		2,975	
	Finished Goods (14)			
1/1	Starting balance		0	
1/4		2	1,000	
1/26		2	5,000	
	Ending balance		6,000	
	Prepaid Expenses (15)			
1/1	Starting balance		0	
1/4		2	2,000	
	Ending balance		2,000	
	Liability accounts			
	Bank Loan (21)			
1/1	Starting balance			0
1/17		2		2,000
	Ending balance			2,000
	Accrued Wages Payables (22)			
1/1	Starting balance			0
1/4		2		1,000
	Ending balance			1,000
	Interest Payable (23)			
1/1	Starting balance			0
1/30		2		20
	Ending balance			20
	Accounts Payable (24)			
1/1	Starting balance			0
1/10		2		6,000
	Ending balance			6,000
	Stockholders' Equity (50)			
1/1	Starting balance	1		14,000
1/31		2	1,045	
	Ending balance			12,955

Table 3.9 (*continued*)

Date		JP	Debit	Credit
	Expense accounts			
	Legal Expense (40)			
1/1	Starting balance		0	
1/3		2	1,000	
1/31		2		1,000
	Ending balance		0	
	Depreciation Expense: Equipment (41)			
1/1	Starting balance		0	
1/31		2	25	
1/31		2		25
	Ending balance		0	
	Interest Expense (42)			
1/1	Starting balance		0	
1/31		2	20	
1/31		2		20
	Ending balance		0	
	Income Summary (55)			
1/1	Starting balance			0
1/31		2	1,000	
1/31		2	25	
1/31		2	20	
1/31		2		1,045
	Ending balance			0

The ledger is set up to show asset accounts, the liability accounts, the revenue accounts, and the expense accounts.

With the corporation operational, an income statement (Table 3.10) showing the results of its operation for the period can now be prepared.

The consolidated income statement is prepared from the revenue and expense accounts. For this month Delchem has no revenue. Its expenses are directly shown on the income statement. There is a one-to-one correspon-

Table 3.10
DELCHEM CORPORATION
Consolidated Income Statement
Jan. 1–31, 1977

Revenue	$0	
Legal Expenses		$1,000
Depreciation Expense: Equipment		25
Interest Expense		20
Earnings (loss)		($1,045)

Table 3.11
DELCHEM CORPORATION
Consolidated Balance Sheet
Feb. 1, 1977

Assets		Liabilities and Stockholders' Equity	
Cash (10)	$ 5,000	Accrued Wages (22)	$ 1,000
Prepaid Expense (15)	2,000	Short-Term Borrowing:	
Inventory:		Accounts Payable (24)	6,000
Raw Materials (11)	6,000	Bank Loan (21)	2,000
Finished Goods (14)	6,000	Interest Payable (23)	20
Plant and		Total Liabilities	$ 9,020
Equipment (12)	2,975	Stockholders' Equity	$12,955
		Total Liabilities and	
Total Assets	$21,975	Stockholders' Equity	$21,975

dence between the statement and the accounts in the ledger. The Income Summary account is used to record the net effect of the revenue and expense accounts.

The balance sheet is prepared as before (Table 3.11). Note that in this month there are a number of new entries. The asset accounts all have debit balances and are shown on the left-hand side on the balance sheet. The right-hand side of the balance sheet shows the credit balance of each liability account, including stockholders' equity.

The stockholders' equity declined from $14,000 to $12,955, which agrees with the loss of $1,045 shown in the income statement.

The income statement shows the accural and realization concepts in practice. During the period there were a number of disbursements of cash:

1. $1,000 paid to lawyer
2. $2,000 paid on equipment purchase
3. $4,000 paid for raw material

Of these, only the lawyer's fee is considered as an expense on the income statement. The value of the lawyer's service is not entered as an asset of the company in accordance with the principle of conservatism. The raw material and equipment purchases increased the assets of the company by increasing inventory, plants, and properties. These cash disbursements are expenditures. The raw materials will be counted as expenses when the goods are sold. The equipment will become expense as it is depreciated.

As of Feb. 1, the partners agree that since the business is now operating, Custer should receive a $1,500 per month salary, to be paid at the end of each month for services rendered. The journal entries in Table 3.12 show the business transactions for Delchem during February.

Table 3.12
DELCHEM CORPORATION
General Journal

Page 3

Date	Account titles and explanation	LP	Debit	Credit
2/1	Accrued Wages Payable	22	1,000	
	Cash	10		1,000
	Finished Goods	14	1,000	
	Accrued Wages Payable	22		1,000
	Back wages to Davis, owe for February			
2/7	Equipment	12	5,000	
	Prepaid Expense	15		2,000
	Cash	10		3,000
	Equipment arrives, $3,000 balance paid in cash			
2/10	Accounts Payable	24	6,000	
	Cash	10		6,000
	Pay outstanding raw materials account upon delivery			
2/20	Finished Goods	14	4,000	
	Raw Materials	11		4,000
	Make 5,000 l of Cleansolv using $4,000 of raw materials†			
2/25	Cash	10	2,000	
	Bank Loan	21		2,000
	Take out another $2,000 loan at 12% interest; promise to pay back after 1 year			
2/26	Cost of Goods Sold	44	1,000	
	Finished Goods	14		1,000
	Cash	10	3,000	
	Revenue	30		3,000
	Sell 1,000 l of Cleansolv at $3 per liter‡			
2/28	Salaries Expense	43	1,500	
	Salaries Payable	26		1,500
	Owe Custer his salary			
	Adjusting entries			
2/28	Depreciation Expense: Equipment	41	66.67	
	Equipment	12		66.67
	$8,000 \times \frac{1}{10} \times \frac{1}{12} = \$66.67$ per month			
2/28	Interest Expense	42	40.00	
	Interest Payable	23		40.00
	To record bank loan interest for February			
2/28	Revenue	30	3,000.00	
	Income Summary	55		3,000.00
	To close the revenue account			

(*continued*)

Table 3.12 (*continued*)

Date	Account titles and explanation	LP	Debit	Credit
	Adjusting entries			
2/28	Income Summary	55	2,606.67	
	Salaries Expense	43		1,500.00
	Depreciation Expense: Equipment	41		66.67
	Interest Expense	42		40.00
	Cost of Goods Sold	44		1,000.00
	To close the expense accounts			
2/28	Income Summary	55	393.33	
	Stockholders' Equity	50		393.33
	To close out the income summary			

  † The book value of the second batch of finished goods is \$5,000/(5,000 L) or \$1 per liter.
  ‡ This firm uses the LIFO method, where the goods sold are evaluated at the cost of the last batch manufactured, or \$1 per liter. So the credit side of the Finished Goods account shows a withdrawal of 1,000 l at \$1 per liter. The debit side of the Cost of Goods Sold account records the \$1,000 cost of the 1,000 l.

Note that a new expense account, Cost of Goods Sold (44), has been created to account for the costs of manufacturing Cleansolv sold. Revenue from this sale is accounted for in a new revenue account (30).

Posting the journal entries to the ledger produces Table 3.13.

Table 3.13
DELCHEM CORPORATION
Ledger

Date		JP	Debit	Credit
	Asset accounts			
	Cash (10)			
2/1	Starting balance	2	5,000.00	
2/1		3		1,000.00
2/10		3		6,000.00
2/7		3		3,000.00
2/25		3	2,000.00	
2/26		3	3,000.00	
	Ending balance		0	
	Raw Materials (11)			
2/1	Starting balance	2	6,000.00	
2/20		3		4,000.00
	Ending balance		2,000.00	
	Equipment (12)			
2/1	Starting balance	2	2,975.00	
2/7		3	5,000.00	
2/28		3		66.67
	Ending balance		7,908.33	

Table 3.13 (*continued*)

Date		JP	Debit	Credit
	Asset accounts			
	Finished Goods (14)			
2/1	Starting balance	2	6,000.00	
2/1		3	1,000.00	
2/20		3	4,000.00	
2/26		3		1,000.00
	Ending balance		10,000.00	
	Prepaid Expenses (15)			
2/1	Starting balance	3	2,000.00	
2/7		3		2,000.00
	Ending balance		0	
	Liability accounts			
	Bank Loan (21)			
2/1	Starting balance	2		2,000.00
2/25		3		2,000.00
	Ending balance			4,000.00
	Accured Wages Payable (22)			
2/1	Starting balance	2		1,000.00
2/1		3	1,000.00	
2/1		3		1,000.00
	Ending balance			1,000.00
	Interest Payable (23)			
2/1	Starting balance	2		20.00
2/28		3		40.00
	Ending balance			60.00
	Accounts Payable (24)			
2/1	Starting balance	2		6,000.00
2/7		3	6,000.00	
	Ending balance			0
	Salaries Payable (26)			
2/1	Starting balance	2		0
2/28		3		1,500.00
	Ending balance			1,500.00
	Stockholders' Equity (50)			
2/1	Starting salary	2		12,955.00
2/28		3		393.33
	Ending balance			13,348.33
	Revenue accounts			
	Revenue (30)			
2/1	Starting balance	2		0
2/26		3		3,000.00
2/28		3	3,000.00	
	Ending balance			0

(*continued*)

Table 3.13 (*continued*)

Date		JP	Debit	Credit
	Expense accounts			
	Depreciation Expense: Equipment (41)			
2/1	Starting balance		0	
2/28		3	66.67	
2/28		3		66.67
	Ending balance		0	
	Interest Expense (42)			
2/1	Starting balance		0	
2/28		3	40.00	
2/28		3		40.00
	Ending balance		0	
	Salaries Expense (43)			
2/1	Starting balance		0	
2/28		3	1,500.00	
2/28				1,500.00
	Ending balance		0	
	Cost of Goods Sold (44)			
2/1	Starting balance		0	
2/26		3	1,000.00	
2/28		3		1,000.00
	Ending balance		0	
	Income Summary (55)			
2/1	Starting balance		0	
2/28		3		3,000.00
2/28		3	40.00	
2/28		3	1,500.00	
2/28		3	1,000.00	
2/28		3	66.67	
2/28		3	393.33	
	Ending balance		0	

Table 3.14
DELCHEM CORPORATION
Consolidated Income Statement
Feb. 1 to 28, 1977

Revenue		$3,000.00
Cost of Goods Sold		$1,000.00
Selling, Administration, and General Expense		1,500.00
Depreciation Expense		66.67
Interest Expense		40.00
Earnings		$393.33

Table 3.15
DELCHEM CORPORATION
Consolidated Balance Sheet
Mar. 1, 1977

Assets		Liabilities and Stockholders' Equity	
Cash	0	Accrued Wages	$ 1,000.00
Inventory:		Salaries Payable	1,500.00
Raw Materials	$ 2,000.00	Short-Term Borrowing:	
Finished Goods	10,000.00	Accounts Payable	0
Plant and Equipment	7,908.33	Bank Loans	4,000.00
		Interest Payable	60.00
		Total Liabilities	$ 6,560.00
		Stockholders' Equity	$13,348.33
		Total Liabilities and	
Total Assets	$19,908.33	Stockholders' Equity	$19,908.33

The financial statements appear as shown in Tables 3.14 and 3.15.

Notice that the Stockholders' Equity has increased from $12,955 to $13,348.33, reflecting the February earnings of 393.33. The transactions for Delchem during March are given in problem 3.2.

3.3 ANALYSIS OF THE COMPANY REPORT

A company report is easily obtained by writing to the executive offices of a firm. More detailed financial information is available in any company's annual report to the Securities and Exchange Commission (form 10-K). In reading this chapter, it would be useful to have one or two reports of some company in which you have an interest.

A company report contains a good deal of information other than financial data, and such matters will be dealt with in Chap. 7. In this chapter we consider only the financial information. Each company reports in its own way, but there are certain more or less standard methods of presenting financial statements. Every report contains an income statement and a balance sheet. Various other summaries are usually included, e.g.,

1. Statement of stockholders' equity
2. Statement of changes in financial position
3. Sources and uses of working capital
4. Investment in property, plant, and equipment
5. Distribution of revenue

Some typical income statements are shown in Table 3.16. Although they contain more and varied entries, the form of each is basically similar to those shown in Sec. 3.2.

Table 3.16 Examples of consolidated income statements

UNION CARBIDE

	Millions of Dollars (Except Per Share Figures)	
	Year Ended Dec. 31, 1976	Year Ended Dec. 31, 1975
Net Sales	$6,345.7	$5,665.0
Operating Costs and Expenses		
Cost of Sales and Distribution	4,337.2	3,839.3
Research and Development	142.4	120.2
Selling, Administrative, and Other	756.1	638.7
Depreciation	301.0	269.8
	5,536.7	4,868.0
Income from Operations	809.0	797.0
Plus: Other Income—Net	37.7	48.7
Less: Interest on Long-Term and Short-Term Debt	120.2	100.2
Income Before Provision for Income Taxes	726.5	745.5
Provision for Income Taxes	266.4	343.2
Income of Consolidated Companies	460.1	402.3
Less: Minority Stockholders' Share of Income	27.9	28.4
Plus: UCC Share of Income of Companies Carried at Equity	9.0	7.8
Net Income	441.2	381.7
Retained Earnings at January 1*	2,411.3	2,178.9
	2,852.5	2,560.6
Dividends Declared	153.8	146.9
Retained Earnings at December 31	$2,698.7	$2,413.7
Per Share		
Net Income**	$7.15	$6.23
Dividends Declared	$2.50	$2.40

*Includes an adjustment of ($2.4) million for companies with which business combinations were effected on a pooling of interests basis ($0.6 million in 1975).

**Based on 61,703,340 shares (61,268,981 shares in 1975), the weighted average number of shares outstanding during the year.

The Notes to Financial Statements on pages 31 through 35 are an integral part of this statement.

EXXON

Revenue	1976	1975
Sales and other operating revenue	$51,626,149,000	$47,795,477,000
Dividends, interest and other revenue	958,672,000	965,115,000
	52,584,821,000	48,760,592,000
Costs and other deductions		
Crude oil and product purchases	26,776,289,000	21,701,723,000
Operating expenses	4,690,849,000	4,310,416,000
Selling, general and administrative expenses	2,718,677,000	2,628,276,000
Depreciation and depletion	1,448,369,000	1,524,098,000
Exploration expenses, including dry holes	423,625,000	382,292,000
Income, excise and other taxes	13,507,802,000	15,325,798,000
Debt-related costs	264,594,000	261,864,000
Income applicable to minority interests	113,652,000	123,112,000
	49,943,857,000	46,257,579,000
Net income	$ 2,640,964,000	$ 2,503,013,000
Per share, after adjustment for stock split	$5.90	$5.60

Table 3.16 (*continued*)

DOW

	Year Ended December 31	
	1976	(Restated) **1975**
Products and Services		
Net sales	**$5,652,069,729**	$4,888,114,202
Operating costs and expenses:		
Cost of sales	**4,133,570,435**	3,404,473,577
Selling and administrative	**431,917,397**	413,670,368
	4,565,487,832	3,818,143,945
Operating income	**1,086,581,897**	1,069,970,257
Non-Products and Services		
Investment and financial:		
Profit on investment turnover	**11,589,156**	20,836,713
Income from sundry investments	**808,851**	716,482
Equity in earnings of non-consolidated subsidiaries	**7,142,286**	3,864,220
Administrative expenses	**(1,290,789)**	(1,343,528)
	18,249,504	24,073,887
Equity in earnings of associated companies and minority investments exceeding 20%	**52,215,773**	50,528,579
Interest expense — net	**(149,833,874)**	(96,796,234)
Sundry income — net	**33,755,977**	66,493,157
Non-products and services income (loss)	**(45,612,620)**	44,299,389
Income Before Provision for Taxes on Income	**1,040,969,277**	1,114,269,646
Provision for Taxes on Income	**421,600,000**	476,027,661
Income Before Minority Interests	**619,369,277**	638,241,985
Minority Interests' Share in Income	**6,602,692**	5,856,564
Net Income	**$ 612,766,585**	$ 632,385,421
Earnings per Share	**$3.30**	$3.41

The first entry in the income statement is always *sales* or *revenue*. Sometimes if there is significant income from sources other than the main business of the company such as interest or dividends from investments, it is shown separately from operating revenue. *Expense*, the next item on the income statement, is almost always broken down into the following categories.

Operating costs and expenses These are plant expenses of the operating divisions. The category may be subdivided into direct material, or the cost of raw material and utilities that appear in the finished goods; direct labor, or the cost of production labor; and plant overhead, which includes any manager's salary, quality control, security guards, and other plant expenses that must be allocated.

Selling, administrative, and general expenses These are headquarter expenses of top management, expenses of staff functions of finance and control, research and development, engineering and construction, advertising and sales, public relations, patents and licenses, and new business development. For income-statement

Table 3.17 Examples of balance statements

UNION CARBIDE

	Millions of Dollars	
	Dec. 31, 1976	Dec. 31, 1975
Assets		
Current Assets		
Cash	$ 112.6	$ 90.1
Time Deposits and Short-Term Marketable Securities	293.0	495.0
	405.6	585.1
Notes and Accounts Receivable	1,038.1	913.7
Inventories		
Raw Materials and Supplies	395.6	354.3
Work in Process	360.6	283.0
Finished Goods	609.2	511.7
	1,365.4	1,149.0
Prepaid Expenses	100.4	76.7
Total Current Assets	2,909.5	2,724.5
Fixed Assets		
Property, Plant, and Equipment	6,836.3	6,038.2
Less: Accumulated Depreciation	3,460.8	3,253.7
Net Fixed Assets	3,375.5	2,784.5
Investments and Advances		
Companies Carried at Equity	136.9	106.3
Other	60.0	45.6
Other Assets	139.7	79.9
	$6,621.6	$5,740.8
Liabilities and Stockholders' Equity		
Current Liabilities		
Accounts Payable	$ 351.4	$ 277.2
Short-Term Debt	225.5	176.5
Payments Due Within One Year on Long-Term Debt	47.2	37.8
Accrued Income and Other Taxes	186.2	168.0
Other Accrued Liabilities	436.0	410.6
Total Current Liabilities	1,246.3	1,070.1
Long-Term Debt	1,574.1	1,277.5
Deferred Credits	560.6	473.5
Minority Stockholders' Equity in Consolidated Subsidiaries	185.5	171.7
UCC Stockholders' Equity	3,055.1	2,748.0
	$6,621.6	$5,740.8

EXXON

	1976	1975
Assets		
Current assets		
Cash, including time deposits of $972,148,000 and $639,376,000	$ 1,278,578,000	$ 876,017,000
Marketable securities, at cost, which approximates market	3,795,259,000	3,773,361,000
Notes and accounts receivable, less estimated doubtful amounts of $95,810,000 and $99,838,000	5,354,462,000	5,098,154,000
Inventories		
Crude oil, products and merchandise	3,794,454,000	3,596,672,000
Materials and supplies	439,833,000	399,086,000
Prepaid taxes and other expenses	389,361,000	261,544,000
Total current assets	15,051,947,000	14,004,834,000
Investments and advances	1,563,211,000	1,515,203,000
Property, plant and equipment, at cost, less depreciation and depletion	18,671,208,000	16,152,137,000
Deferred charges and other assets	1,044,980,000	1,167,224,000
Total assets	36,331,346,000	32,839,398,000
Liabilities		
Current liabilities		
Notes and loans payable	1,859,844,000	1,598,099,000
Accounts payable and accrued liabilities	7,714,068,000	6,486,280,000
Income taxes payable	947,529,000	1,260,640,000
Total current liabilities	10,521,441,000	9,345,019,000
Long-term debt	3,696,798,000	3,451,146,000
Annuity and other reserves	646,668,000	609,313,000
Deferred income tax credits	2,149,931,000	1,621,369,000
Other deferred credits	71,630,000	77,878,000
Equity of minority shareholders in affiliated companies	774,526,000	710,262,000
Total liabilities	17,860,994,000	15,814,987,000
Shareholders' equity		
Capital	2,608,591,000	2,583,480,000
Earnings reinvested	15,861,761,000	14,440,931,000
Total shareholders' equity	$18,470,352,000	$17,024,411,000

DOW

LIABILITIES

	December 31	
	1976	**(Restated) 1975**
Current Liabilities		
Notes payable	$ 429,333,755	$ 268,555,708
Long-term debt due within one year	64,442,984	76,694,456
Accounts payable	671,257,052	544,496,606
United States and foreign taxes on income	129,605,717	224,502,007
Accrued and other current liabilities	403,861,128	368,859,024
	1,698,500,636	1,483,107,801
Long-Term Debt	1,878,474,304	1,563,218,709
Other Liabilities		
Minority interests in subsidiary companies	50,492,093	46,495,814
Deferred employee benefits	32,037,121	40,973,833
Deferred income taxes	324,149,467	260,042,919
Other		1,582,183
	406,678,681	349,094,749
Stockholders' Equity		
Common stock	495,698,354	492,239,386
Capital surplus	428,790,235	384,959,169
Retained earnings	2,198,514,993	1,762,004,778
	3,123,003,582	2,639,203,333
Less—Treasury stock at cost	257,993,234	190,435,778
	2,865,010,348	2,448,767,555
TOTAL	$6,848,663,969	$5,844,188,814

ASSETS

	December 31	
	1976	**(Restated) 1975**
Current Assets		
Cash	$ 40,936,787	$ 25,097,234
Marketable securities and interest-bearing deposits (at cost—approximately market)	91,309,394	349,813,988
Accounts and notes receivable:		
Trade, less allowance for doubtful receivables (1976, $37,600,735; 1975, $39,244,744)	881,278,343	754,735,444
Miscellaneous	374,996,841	242,686,381
Deferred income tax benefits	67,053,981	73,283,069
Inventories:		
Finished and in process	646,330,736	527,192,992
Materials and supplies	352,547,640	287,382,772
	2,454,453,722	2,260,191,880
Investments		
Capital stock—at cost plus equity in accumulated earnings (less reserves—1976, $2,867,316; 1975, $4,157,316):		
Banking and insurance subsidiaries	69,120,943	63,379,544
Associated companies (50% owned)	299,435,741	260,995,026
Other	80,801,558	73,105,850
Sundry—at cost (less reserves—1976, $2,100,857; 1975, $2,192,028)	26,837,328	29,147,266
Noncurrent receivables (less reserves—1976, $1,276,858; 1975, $7,598,268)	131,508,597	121,305,324
	607,704,167	547,933,010
Plant Properties	5,987,278,500	4,933,165,822
Less—Accumulated depreciation	2,433,358,376	2,146,104,313
	3,553,920,124	2,787,061,509
Unexpended Pollution Control Funds	67,503,406	98,538,901
Goodwill	83,588,887	84,467,970
Deferred Charges and Other Assets	81,493,663	65,995,544
TOTAL	$6,848,663,969	$5,844,188,814

purposes they are not prorated against any of the chemical products produced. Union Carbide provides research and development as a separate entry. Dow and Exxon include research and development as part of selling and administrative expense.

Depreciation and obsolescence As discussed in Sec. 3.1, this is very important to the chemical professional responsible for design and capital expenditure. Note that only Union Carbide and Exxon report this item as a separate line. Dow includes depreciation as part of cost of sales.

The format for the income statement varies greatly, as can be seen from Table 3.16. All statements show interest expense, but Dow has a very detailed analysis. Net income before and after tax is generally shown. There is always an entry entitled provision for income tax. Income tax payment is a matter for extensive negotiation with the IRS, and when most company reports are made, this item is not known with a high degree of certainty. Large companies with subsidiaries in which there is a minority interest will include an item to reflect the minority interest in earnings (the most prevalent accounting practice is to include the subsidiaries' total expenses and revenues in the parent firms' figures and then subtract out the minority share). The net income, dividends on preferred stock, the amount earned on common stock, and earnings per share of common stock are usually part of the income statement.

Typical consolidated balance sheets are shown in Table 3.17. A company's current assets consist of cash, marketable securities, accounts and notes receivable, inventories, and various other items specific to the operation of a particular firm, such as prepaid taxes and prepaid expenses.

A company's fixed assets are reported by subtracting depreciation charges from the acquisition cost of all property, plant, and equipment. Sometimes only the net figure is shown; sometimes all three entries are included. Other intangible assets of the firm, such as good will, patents, and trademarks, are shown as separate entries. They are included only when a significant sum is paid to acquire them from another firm and must be amortized over a period of time.

Long-term debt is included as a special entry, as are deferred income taxes and items such as deferred investment tax credit, equity of minority shareholders, and reserve for employee pensions.

The shareholders' equity is the item which balances the equation

$$\text{Assets} = \text{Liabilities} + \text{Shareholders' Equity}$$

Most reports have a section entitled Notes to Financial Statements or Summary of Significant Accounting Policies. They are useful in defining the company's practices regarding entries in the income statement and balance sheet. These notes should be consulted frequently as one analyzes a company report.

A record of financial data for several years (usually 5 to 10 years) is often included in a report, providing historical perspective. Typical examples of several such records are shown in Table 3.18. Sudden changes or discontinuities in these series are often indications of trouble and need explanation.

Table 3.18 Examples of financial records

UNION CARBIDE

For The Year	Dollars in Millions — Except Per Share Figures									
	1976	1975	1974	1973	1972	1971	1970	1969	1968	1967
Net Sales	$6,345.7	$5,665.0	$5,320.1	$3,938.8	$3,261.3	$3,037.5	$3,026.3	$2,933.0	$2,685.9	$2,545.6
Less: Cost of Sales and										
Distribution	4,337.2	3,839.3	3,497.9	2,575.9	2,137.1	2,016.4	2,002.9	1,914.2	1,738.2	1,609.8
Research and Development	142.4	120.2	94.2	76.8	69.6	78.3	78.0	75.6	82.7	85.3
Selling, Administrative, and										
Other	756.1	638.7	531.3	426.2	376.8	368.7	360.3	334.3	324.1	322.5
Depreciation	301.0	269.8	248.3	245.2	245.2	229.3	236.4	250.0	230.8	230.8
Income from Operations	809.0	797.0	948.4	614.7	432.6	344.8	348.7	358.9	310.1	297.2
Plus: Other Income—Net	37.7	48.7	25.6	0.5	10.3	7.3	6.7	33.2	3.6	11.8
Less: Interest on Long-Term and										
Short-Term Debt	120.2	100.2	69.8	60.6	56.1	60.9	58.5	50.9	47.1	41.9
Income before Provision for										
Income Taxes	726.5	745.5	904.2	554.6	386.8	291.2	296.9	341.2	266.6	267.1
Provision for Income Taxes	266.4	343.2	375.4	245.0	164.3	126.9	130.4	149.1	100.9	92.3
Income of Consolidated Companies .	460.1	402.3	528.8	309.6	222.5	164.3	166.5	192.1	165.7	174.8
Less: Minority Share of Income ..	27.9	28.4	30.7	25.0	17.8	15.7	13.3	10.5	9.8	10.0
Plus: UCC Share of Income of										
Companies Carried at Equity ..	9.0	7.8	27.0	12.6	3.5	4.4	4.1	4.6	1.1	5.9
Income before Extraordinary Items ..	441.2	381.7	525.1	297.2	208.2	153.0	157.3	186.2	157.0	170.7
Extraordinary Items	—	—	—	—	(2.2)	(0.2)	—	—	—	—
Net Income	441.2	381.7	525.1	297.2	206.0	152.8	157.3	186.2	157.0	170.7
Net Income Per Share	7.15	6.23	8.61	4.89	3.40	2.52	2.60	3.08	2.60	2.82
Dividends	153.8	146.9	132.6	126.1	121.3	121.1	121.0	121.0	120.9	120.9
Dividends Per Share	2.50	2.40	2.175	2.075	2.00	2.00	2.00	2.00	2.00	2.00
Capital Expenditures	964.5	862.2	516.6	288.7	243.9	335.2	393.7	322.2	347.1	478.7
Market Price Range Per Share										
High	76¾	66½	46	51¾	52	50⅜	40½	47¼	50⅛	59
Low	55⅝	40⅛	31¾	29¼	41⅞	38⅝	29½	35¼	40⅛	45⅛

At Year-End										
Working Capital	1,663.2	1,654.4	1,347.0	1,205.0	997.3	870.7	789.3	870.5	811.1	871.8
Total Assets	6,621.6	5,740.8	4,879.2	4,163.4	3,711.3	3,546.3	3,563.8	3,355.9	3,208.6	3,088.3
Invested Capital	4,901.9	4,239.8	3,607.7	3,196.6	2,956.4	2,893.3	2,976.3	2,787.1	2,698.7	2,644.3
UCC Stockholders' Equity	3,055.1	2,748.0	2,502.4	2,106.4	1,929.4	1,839.5	1,804.6	1,766.7	1,701.2	1,665.0
Per Share	49.45	44.80	41.01	34.60	31.77	30.37	29.84	29.22	28.14	27.54
Shares Outstanding (Thousands) ...	61,787	61,336	61,016	60,868	60,732	60,568	60,479	60,479	60,465	60,454
Number of Employees	113,118	106,475	109,566	109,417	98,114	99,181	102,144	104,411	100,448	99,794

Other Financial Data										
Current Ratio	2.3	2.5	2.2	2.5	2.6	2.6	2.2	2.7	2.7	3.1
Debt as Percent of Invested Capital ..	37.7	35.2	30.6	34.1	34.7	36.4	39.4	36.6	37.0	37.0
Net Income as Percent of:										
Sales	7.0	6.7	9.9	7.5	6.3	5.0	5.2	6.3	5.8	6.7
Assets (Average)	7.1	7.2	11.6	7.5	5.7	4.3	4.6	5.7	5.0	5.8
Invested Capital (Average)	9.7	9.7	15.4	9.7	7.0	5.2	5.5	6.8	5.9	6.9
UCC Stockholders' Equity										
(Average)	15.2	14.5	22.8	14.7	10.9	8.4	8.8	10.7	9.3	10.4
Dividends as Percent of Net Income..	34.9	38.5	25.3	42.4	58.9	79.3	76.9	65.0	77.0	70.8

Net income per share is based on weighted average number of shares outstanding during the year.

Invested capital consists of short-term debt, long-term debt including current installments, and UCC stockholders' equity.

Market price ranges through January 1976 are as reported on the New York Stock Exchange; thereafter on the Composite Tape.

(continued)

Table 3.18 (continued)

EXXON

Consolidated statement of income	1976	1975	1974	1973	1972
Sales and other operating revenue					
Petroleum and natural gas					
Petroleum products	$36,867	33,040	31,597	20,681	16,072
Crude oil	8,474	9,548	8,488	3,985	3,177
Natural gas	1,509	1,262	903	748	646
Other	1,260	1,114	1,099	924	788
Total	48,110	44,964	42,087	26,338	20,683
Chemical products	3,238	2,594	2,787	1,563	1,258
Other	278	238	147	121	130
Total sales and other operating revenue	51,626	47,796	45,021	28,022	22,071
Dividends, interest and other revenue	959	965	772	454	365
Total revenue	52,585	48,761	45,793	28,476	22,436
Costs and other deductions					
Crude oil and product purchases	26,776	21,702	18,607	7,456	6,022
Operating expenses	4,691	4,311	4,279	3,805	3,001
Selling, general and administrative expenses	2,719	2,628	2,439	2,277	2,104
Depreciation and depletion	1,448	1,524	1,265	1,136	1,059
Exploration expenses, including dry holes	423	382	360	255	265
Income, excise and other taxes					
Income	5,190	7,279	7,848	3,739	2,345
Excise, duties and other	8,318	8,047	7,419	6,856	5,750
Debt-related costs	265	262	420	374	248
Income applicable to minority interests	114	123	126	127	83
Total deductions	49,944	46,258	42,763	26,025	20,877
Net income	$ 2,641	2,503	3,030	2,451	1,559
Net income per share, after adjustment for stock split	$ 5.90	5.60	6.77	5.47	3.48
Cash dividends per share, after adjustment for stock split	$ 2.725	2.50	2.50	2.125	1.90
Earnings to average shareholders' equity (percent)	14.9	15.3	20.6	18.8	13.1
Earnings to total revenue (percent)	5.0	5.1	6.6	8.6	6.9
Property, plant and equipment, less reserves	$18,671	16,152	14,838	13,462	12,645
Total additions to property, plant and equipment	$ 4,098	3,558	2,910	2,235	1,984
Working capital	$ 4,531	4,660	5,241	3,534	2,398
Ratio of current assets to current liabilities	1.43	1.50	1.55	1.56	1.51
Long-term debt	$ 3,697	3,451	3,052	2,671	2,617
Shareholders' equity	$18,470	17,024	15,634	13,740	12,284
Shareholders' equity per share, after adjustment for stock split	$ 41.22	38.05	34.95	30.69	27.39
Average number of shares outstanding (thousands)	447,744	447,315	447,540	448,179	448,310
Number of shareholders at year-end (thousands)	684	689	707	720	755
Research and development expenditures	$ 202	187	174	124	106
Wages, salaries, and employee benefits	$ 2,661	2,694	2,232	1,862	1,679
Average number of employees (thousands)	126	137	133	137	141

See Note 2 on page 35 for explanation of an accounting change in 1976. There was no effect on
years prior to 1976 from this change because it was adopted prospectively from January 1, 1976.

Table 3.18 (*continued*)

DOW

Financial Condition
(in millions)

Current Assets:	1976	1975	1974	1973	1972	1966	1956
Cash and marketable securities	$ 132.3	$ 374.9	$ 423.3	$ 317.7	$ 162.5	$ 127.2	$ 72.4
Receivables (less reserves)	1,323.3	1,070.7	1,039.2	744.8	595.4	254.9	77.2
Inventories	998.9	814.6	722.6	497.5	423.9	195.2	104.5
Total current assets	2,454.5	2,260.2	2,185.1	1,560.0	1,181.8	577.3	254.1
Current Liabilities:							
Notes payable	429.3	268.6	220.7	214.0	269.6	58.8	
Accounts payable and accruals	1,269.2	1,214.5	1,349.9	791.1	528.4	229.6	110.7
Total current liabilities	1,698.5	1,483.1	1,570.6	1,005.1	798.0	288.4	110.7
Working Capital .(A)	756.0	777.1	614.5	554.9	383.8	288.9	143.4
Net Property .(B)	3,553.9	2,787.0	2,233.2	1,778.4	1,649.7	849.7	376.5
Other Assets .(C)	840.3	797.0	674.0	557.7	481.2	311.9	23.0
Investment (A) plus (B) plus (C) .(D)	5,150.2	4,361.1	3,521.7	2,891.0	2,514.7	1,450.5	542.9
Long-Term Indebtedness	1,878.5	1,563.2	1,304.9	1,225.9	1,094.9	552.3	159.7
Other Liabilities	406.7	349.2	262.2	130.6	85.3	.8	1.5
Total .(E)	2,285.2	1,912.4	1,567.1	1,356.5	1,180.2	553.1	161.2
Common Stockholders' Equity (D) minus (E)	$2,865.0	$2,448.7	$1,954.6	$1,534.5	$1,334.5	$ 897.4	$ 381.7

Income
(in millions)

	1976	1975	1974	1973	1972	1966	1956
Net sales	$5,652.1	$4,888.1	$4,938.5	$3,067.9	$2,403.7	$1,309.7	$ 565.3
Cost of sales	4,133.6	3,404.5	3,398.3	2,229.4	1,760.8	977.5	400.6
Selling and administrative expenses	431.9	413.6	405.6	330.3	284.9	130.3	45.6
Operating income	1,086.6	1,070.0	1,134.6	508.2	358.0	201.9	119.1
Investment and sundry income—net	104.2	141.1	41.5	58.3	51.8	25.4	2.4
Interest expense	(149.8)	(96.8)	(79.6)	(83.4)	(85.8)	(17.6)	(4.7)
Non-products and services income (loss)	(45.6)	44.3	(38.1)	(25.1)	(34.0)	7.8	(2.3)
Taxes on income	421.6	476.0	527.0	202.6	127.1	81.3	54.6
Minority interests' share in income	6.6	5.9	5.6	9.3	7.9		.4
Income before extraordinary items and cumulative effect of accounting change	612.8	632.4	563.9	271.2	189.0	128.4	61.8
Extraordinary items—net of tax			11.7	4.4	.2		
Cumulative effect of accounting change—net of tax			(41.7)				
Net income	612.8	632.4	533.9	275.6	189.2	128.4	61.8
Per share of common stock (in dollars) (*):							
Income before extraordinary items and cumulative effect of accounting change	3.30	3.41	3.05	1.47	1.03	.71	.39
Extraordinary items			.06	.02			
Cumulative effect of accounting change(**)			(.22)				
Net income per share	3.30	3.41	2.89	1.49	1.03	.71	.39
Cash dividends declared	.95	.75	.60	.49	.45	.33	.17
Average common shares outstanding (thousands)	185,412	185,205	185,022	184,228	182,648	180,044	159,895

Other Statistics
(in millions)

	1976	1975	1974	1973	1972	1966	1956
Additions to property	$1,186.2	$ 921.5	$ 870.0	$ 401.7	$ 359.0	$ 241.5	$ 61.0
Depreciation	404.2	347.4	327.2	263.1	234.9	122.6	73.9
Research and development expenses	187.5	167.4	148.7	118.4	104.7	71.3	34.7
Taxes (major)	596.6	635.7	613.6	314.3	218.0	118.3	67.2
Wages and salaries paid	908.3	810.1	738.7	611.6	516.4	302.1	140.3
Cost of employee benefits	199.3	170.9	149.0	101.8	85.4	28.8	13.5
Number of employees at year-end (thousands)	53.0	53.1	53.3	49.8	48.8	35.0	25.2
Market closing price on December 31 (in dollars) (*)	43.38	45.81	27.50	28.75	25.38	10.27	10.13

Years prior to 1976 have been restated for the changes in the methods of accounting for contingencies and translation of foreign currencies.

(*) *Adjusted for stock splits and stock dividends*

(**) *If the accounting change is applied retroactively, pro forma net income per share would be:1974,$3.11; 1973,$ 1.44; 1972,$.99.*

Certain ratios are often used to compare financial performance. Some of the most widely used and their definitions are given below.

Profit margin This is the ratio of net income to total sales expressed as a percentage of sales. Some sources quote a pretax profit margin, which is the ratio of profit before interest and taxes to sales. We will use the first definition, which is a good measure of management efficiency in a given industry. The ratio varies widely among industries.

Return on owners' equity This is the ratio of net income to owners' or stockholders' equity, usually expressed as a percentage. It reflects the ability of management to put stockholders' money to good use.

Current (or working-capital) ratio This is simply the ratio of current assets to current liabilities. A 2 : 1 ratio is about standard. A ratio close to unity indicates little margin for uncertainties and possible instability.

Long-term debt to equity As the name suggests, this is the ratio of long-term debt to owners' equity. Since debt interest must be paid on time, a high ratio could lead to postponement of dividends or even insolvency in a year of low profit.

Sales per employee Total annual sales divided by the number of employees in a firm gives some idea of that firm's investment in labor-saving plants and research.

Earnings per share This is the net income divided by the number of shares of common stock. A related measure is ratio of stock price to earnings per share. This indicates the stock market confidence in the future performance of the company.

Percent retained earnings Net income minus the amount paid to stockholders yields the retained earnings. This money is reinvested in the business for expansion and other purposes. A high percentage of retained earnings indicates a growth company rather than a current-income-producing company.

3.4 PROBLEMS

3.1 Derive an algebraic expression showing the fraction undepreciated at the end of year n for each of the following means of calculating depreciation:
    (a) Straight line
    (b) Double declining balance
    (c) Sum-of-the-years digits
Let r = rate of depreciation.

3.2 From the following transactions for Delchem Corp. construct the journal ledger, balance sheet, and income statement for March. Do not forget to include previous commitments (interest, depreciation, Custers salary, etc.).

DELCHEM CORPORATION
March

Date	Account titles and explanation
3/1	Pay $1,000 to Davis, give him a raise, owe him $1,500 for March
3/10	Pay $360 for advertisement in a chemical trade journal
3/11	Buy $5,500 of raw materials, pay $4,000 now, owe $1,500 due in April
3/15	Borrow $5,000 from bank at 12% interest, promise to pay back after 1 year
3/15	Sell 3,000 l of Cleansolv at $3.50 per liter

3.3 In April the price of Cleansolv drops to 50 cents per liter. Delchem decides not to sell anything, but continues to produce Cleansolv at 1,000 l/month. To keep everything running, Custer makes a deal with a bank to borrow $5,000 a month on a continuous basis. Would the income and balance statements look very bad? What kind of troubles would Delchem eventually encounter?

3.4 Old Smooky McCarthy was drilling wildcat holes in northern Michigan when he struck oil. The find is estimated at 3 million barrels of oil. The cost of drilling the well was $1.5 million; royalty to the land owner is $2 per barrel plus a bonus of $5,000 for signing the agreement last year. Oil currently sells at $11 per barrel. What should the asset value of this property be on the balance sheet?

3.5 Chuck Adamson built a new indigo plant at a cost of $2 million to capitalize on the worldwide craze for blue denim. He managed to convince the IRS that the craze would last for only 2 years so that he should be allowed to depreciate the plant in 2 years by straight line, even though the plant will physically last 15 years. However, the blue-denim craze continued strongly into the third year. Will Adamson operate without a plant listed on the balance sheet? Will he have no capital depreciation expenses on his product cost? Can he undersell any would-be newcomers into the market?

3.6 Sharppencil & Associates, Inc., is a consulting firm operating from rented office space and furniture. It spent $200,000 in the past 2 years developing a set of computer programs for the control of coal-gasification plants, which it hopes to sell to the federal government, General Electric, and a number of foreign firms. How should the firm list this set of programs on the balance sheet? Suppose two buyers, each paying $500,000, could be found each year for the next 3 years. How should these transactions be listed in the books? Should the firm amortize the programs over a period of time? On the other hand, suppose no buyers can be located for 3 years. How would the programs be entered then?

3.7 Inflation has suddenly doubled the cost of all Cleansolv raw materials and tripled machinery costs. How should this affect Delchem's evaluation of assets under raw materials, plants, and finished goods? The price of Cleansolv has also doubled. What will happen to the profit margin? Should the firm use LIFO or FIFO accounting? Is it dangerous and unrealistic to keep depreciation charges at the original machine cost since replacement machinery cost has tripled?

3.8 From a recent annual report of a chemical company (preferably the company for which you are the class expert), answer as many of the following questions as possible:
   (a) What was the year's net income?
   (b) What was net income as a percentage of sales?
   (c) What was income tax as a percentage of pretax income?

(*d*) What percentage of the cost of plants and properties was shown as depreciation and obsolescence?

(*e*) What percentage of sales was shown as depreciation and obsolescence?

(*f*) What percentage of sales was selling, general, and administrative expenses?

(*g*) What was the total revenue from net sales and other income?

(*h*) What percentage of total revenue was spent for materials and services?

(*i*) What percentage of total revenue was spent for wages, salaries, and related expenses?

(*j*) What percentage of total revenue was paid out as dividends?

(*k*) How much was retained for use of the business, including depreciation "set asides"?

(*l*) How much did it cost to construct (or acquire in other ways) the company's existing plants and properties?

(*m*) How much of the cost of plants and properties costs had been charged to date as an operating cost?

(*n*) What percentage of the cost of plants and properties has been charged to cost?

(*o*) What percentage of total assets is in cash, marketable securities, accounts receivable, and inventories?

(*p*) What were the total liabilities, excluding stockholders' equity?

(*q*) What was the total stockholders' equity?

(*r*) How much cash and marketable securities were on hand at the beginning of the year?

(*s*) During the year, the cash and marketable securities increased and decreased; what was the increase due to the sum of net income and depreciation?

(*t*) What were dividends as a percentage of net income plus depreciation?

(*u*) What were construction expenditures as a percentage of net income plus depreciation?

(*v*) How much cash and marketable securities were left at the end of the year?

4

INPUT-OUTPUT ANALYSIS

The ultimate goal of all economic activity is to supply final products (including goods and services) for consumption. The GNP is the value measured in dollars of all such production for any particular year. To produce a final product, input by several industries is often required. *The net contribution to production* by a particular industry is termed *value added.* This can be measured as the difference between the industry's total sales and the cost of the goods and services it purchases from other industries. Summation of all value-added contributions made by all industries as well as by individuals and the government equals the GNP.

The *net contribution to ultimate consumption* by a particular industry is termed *final demand.* This can be measured as the difference between the industry's total sales and the industry's sales to other industries. This difference directly benefits ultimate consumption—by individual households, by governments, by capital investors, and by exports. The summation of all final demands made by all industries as well as by individuals and the government also equals the GNP (Table 4.1).

The role of the CPI is usually more one of supplying other industries with intermediate products than of supplying the ultimate consumer directly. The significance of the interindustry flow of CPI products would be lost if we were to consider only one economic measurement, such as GNP. To account for interindustry interaction and to segregate the value-added contribution to GNP by industry, the very powerful bookkeeping technique of *input-output analysis* has been developed.

Although the idea of input-output analysis dates back to eighteenth-century France, the modern version of such analysis was pioneered in the 1930s by

Wassily Leontief at Harvard University. During the Second World War the Bureau of Labor Statistics of the U.S. Department of Labor became interested in input-output analysis and applied it to the United States economy. Since then the National Economics Division of the Department of Commerce's Office of Business Economics has been given responsibility for updating the analysis for the United States economy periodically.

Input-output analysis can be applied to a wide variety of problems, but its major contribution is that it allows the repercussion of changes in final demand to be measured quantitatively for a great many industrial sectors. For instance, the CPI can determine the effect on their output of an increase in automobile sales by using input-output analysis. The techniques of input-output analysis can also be used to determine the effect on the CPI of increasing the amount of plastics in cars and decreasing the amount of steel. The effect of changes in the GNP on the CPI and on any other sector also can be estimated with input-output analysis. Most recently the economic impact of energy shortages and their serious implications have been studied by input-output analysis. The basis of input-output analysis is a set of three tables, to be described. Readers who want to understand this technique better should consult the suggested reading list (Sec. 4.6).

4.1 THE TRANSACTIONS TABLE

The total dollar *output* (sales) of any particular industry can be broken down into sales to other industries and sales to final demand:

$$X_k = (X_{k1} + X_{k2} + X_{k3} + \cdots + X_{kn}) + F_k \qquad (4.1)$$

where X_k = total dollar output of industry k
X_{kj} = sales of industry k to industry j
n = total number of industries
F_k = sales of industry k directly to final demand (personal consumption, government expenses, investment, and export)

For each industry of interest such an equation can be written:

$$X_1 = (X_{11} + X_{12} + X_{13} + \cdots + X_{1n}) + F_1$$
$$X_2 = (X_{21} + X_{22} + X_{23} + \cdots + X_{2n}) + F_2 \qquad (4.2)$$
$$\cdots\cdots\cdots\cdots\cdots\cdots\cdots\cdots\cdots\cdots\cdots\cdots\cdots$$
$$X_n = (X_{n1} + X_{n2} + X_{n3} + \cdots + X_{nn}) + F_n$$

The *output* X_{kj} from industry k to industry j is also the *input* from k to j necessary for j to make its products. Equations (4.2) can be presented in tabular form (Table 4.1), which illustrates once again the principle of double-entry bookkeeping (total output is equal to total input). Summing all industrial inputs X_{ik} to any industry k in a column yields the total cost of all intermediate inputs I_k required by industry k to produce its total output X_k. The difference between the

Table 4.1 Transaction equations written in tabular form

Output from	Input to				Intermediate output O	Final demand F	Total output
	1	2	3	n			
1	X_{11}	X_{12}	X_{13}	X_{1n}	O_1	F_1	X_1
2	X_{21}	X_{22}	X_{23}	X_{2n}	O_2	F_2	X_2
3	X_{31}	X_{32}	X_{33}	X_{3n}	O_3	F_3	X_3
n	X_{n1}	X_{n2}	X_{n3}	X_{nn}	O_n	F_n	X_n
Intermediate input I	I_1	I_2	I_3	I_n			
Value added V	V_1	V_2	V_3	V_n	$\cdots$	W	
Total input	X_1	X_2	X_3	X_n	$\cdots$		

cost of all intermediate inputs to industry k and its total sales measured by its total output X_k is the value added to total gross production by industry k:

$$X_k = (X_{1k} + X_{2k} + \cdots + X_{nk}) + V_k = I_k + V_k \tag{4.3}$$

Summing all industry outputs X_{kj} from any industry k in a row yields the cost of all intermediate outputs O_k sold to customers in other industries. The difference between the total sales X_k and intermediate output O_k is the final demand of industry k:

$$X_k = (X_{k1} + X_{k2} + \cdots + X_{kn}) + F_k = O_k + F_k \tag{4.4}$$

Another item W of nonindustry contribution to the GNP represents transactions such as government payroll to cabinet ministers and garbage collectors. The GNP is the sum

$$\text{GNP} = \sum_1^n V_j + W \tag{4.5}$$

or

$$\text{GNP} = \sum_1^n F_i + W \tag{4.6}$$

A simplified four-sector transactions table (Table 4.2) approximately represents the United States economy for 1965. The GNP is shown as \$600 billion and is the sum of value added [Eq. (4.5)] or final demand [Eq. (4.6)].

The sector designated as the consumer industry sells \$60 billion worth of goods to itself, \$7 billion to the basic industry sector, nothing to the energy sector, \$19 billion to the service sector, and \$180 billion to final demand. Its total output is \$266 billion [Eqs. (4.3) and (4.4)]. The consumer industry sector buys \$60 billion of goods and services from itself, \$80 billion from the basic industry sector, \$2 billion from the energy sector and \$26 billion from the service sector. Its net contribution to production or its value added is \$98 billion.

Table 4.2 Transactions table for a four-sector economy (billions of dollars)

	Consumer industry	Basic industry	Energy industry	Service	Final demand	GNP	Total output
Consumer industry	$ 60	$ 7	$ 0	$ 19	$180		$ 266
Basic industry	80	102	1	23	39		245
Energy industry	2	7	23	11	22		65
Service	26	28	12	115	271		452
Value added	98	101	29	285	87	$600	
GNP					$600		
Total output	$266	$245	$65	$452			$1,028

As would be expected, final demand is a high percentage of total output for the consumer-industry sector, and value added is a high percentage of total output for the service sector. Basic industry sells most of its output to itself and also buys more from itself than from the other sectors. This pattern is repeated for all sectors except the consumer industry sector, which buys more from basic industry than from itself. W is $87 billion.

The Department of Commerce prefers to create *special industries* to represent the nonindustry sectors of individual households, government, investment, and export. For an economy with m special industries, the transactions table is as shown in Table 4.3. Now $\sum_{n+1}^{n+m} V_k$, $\sum_{n+1}^{n+m} F_k$, and $\sum_{n+1}^{n+m} X_k$ are all equal to W of Table 4.1. In this case

$$\text{GNP} = \sum_{1}^{n+m} V_j = \sum_{1}^{n+m} F_i \tag{4.7}$$

Table 4.3 Transactions table including special industries

	Input to						Intermediate output	Final demand	Total
Output from	1	2	3	n	$n+1$	$n+m$	O	F	output
1	X_{11}	X_{12}	X_{13}	X_{1n}	0	0	O_1	F_1	X_1
2	X_{21}	X_{22}	X_{23}	X_{2n}	0	0	O_2	F_2	X_2
3	X_{31}	X_{32}	X_{33}	X_{3n}	0	0	O_3	F_3	X_3
n	X_{n1}	X_{n2}	X_{n3}	X_{nn}	0	0	O_n	F_n	X_n
$n+1$	0	0	0	0	0	0	0	F_{n+1}	X_{n+1}
$n+m$	0	0	0	0	0	0	0	F_{n+m}	X_{n+m}
Intermediate input I	I_1	I_2	I_3	I_n	0	0			
Value added V	V_1	V_2	V_3	V_n	V_{n+1}	V_{n+m}		GNP	
Total input	X_1	X_2	X_3	X_n	X_{n+1}	X_{n+m}			

Transactions tables for the United States economy have been developed by the federal government for 1947, 1958, 1963, and 1967. In addition, tables for 1961 and 1966 have been derived from the 1958 and 1963 tables.

It is not a trivial matter to prepare these transactions tables. Data and statistics from a great many diverse sources are needed, and a good deal of guided estimation must be done. The construction of the table is approached on an industry-by-industry basis. Output data for an industry form the basis for each industry analysis. A complete technological analysis of the industry must be undertaken to estimate inputs of raw materials, energy, etc. Other inputs required are also estimated and if possible checked with limited output data from various sources. Marketing data and analyses are used in estimating outputs for an industry. Some valuable insights into the problems of constructing the transactions table are given in Ref. 1. The most recently completed transactions table (1967) is presented in Table 4.4. The United States economy is subdivided into 87 industries. The input-output CPI sectors are related to SIC code by Table 1.4. Relationship of other input-output industries to SIC code can be found in Ref. 2. For a particular industry each row shows the dollar value of the goods and services (output) going to each of the 87 industries and to final demand. Each column shows the dollar value of an industry's consumption (inputs) of intermediate goods and services from every industry and its value added. The 87 industries can be grouped into 13 categories, as shown in Table 4.5. The categories require some additional explanation. The dummy industries include business travel, entertainment, and gifts (81); office supplies (82); scrap, and used and second-hand goods (83). These industries were defined to monitor goods and services transferred to and from industries 1 to 80. For example, business travel (81) includes inputs from transportation (65), hotel services (22), and sports and amusements (76). Business travel (81) supplies all industries, especially trade (69), finance (20), and business service (73).

Special industries include government industry (84); rest of the world industry (85); and household industry (86). Industry 84 measures the income originating in federal, state and local government, excluding such government enterprises as the TVA in 78 and 79. Note that 84 has no output to other industries. Its output goes only to final demand and mainly reflects employee compensation. Rest-of-the-world industry (85) mostly reflects United States income originating in foreign nations. Industry 86 measures income originating in households, e.g., employee compensation of domestic servants. Industries 85 and 86 also have no outputs to other industries.

The transactions table breaks value added into three components:

1. Employee compensation (EC)
2. Indirect business taxes (IBT)
3. Property-type income (PTI)

Property-type income is a composite of several factors, including proprietor's income, rental income of persons, corporate profits, inventory-valuation adjustment, net interest, business-transfer payments, surplus of government enterprises

Table 4.4 Transactions table for the United States economy, 1967 (millions of dollars)†

Industry No.	For the distribution of output of an industry, read the row for that industry. For the composition of inputs to an industry, read the column for that industry.	1 Livestock and livestock products	2 Other agricultural products	3 Forestry and fishery products	4 Agricultural, forestry and fishery services	5 Iron and ferroalloy ores mining	6 Nonferrous metal ores mining	7 Coal mining	8 Crude petroleum and natural gas	9 Stone and clay mining and quarrying	10 Chemical and fertilizer mineral mining	11 New construction	12 Maintenance and repair construction	13 Ordnance and accessories	14 Food and kindred products
1	Livestock and livestock products	5,610	1,448	96	160										19,777
2	Other agricultural products	8,379	905	105	507							80		3	6,882
3	Forestry and fishery products			34											423
4	Agricultural, forestry and fishery services	603	1,335	45								161	19		
5	Iron and ferroalloy ores mining					92	4	(*)							
6	Nonferrous metal ores mining					33	213				5	3			
7	Coal mining	4	1		(*)	(*)	1	400		(*)	6	(*)		3	39
8	Crude petroleum and natural gas							1	374						
9	Stone and clay mining and quarrying	2	119			4	5	3		63	7	670	261		8
10	Chemical and fertilizer mineral mining		12			5	3			2	61				4
11	New construction														
12	Maintenance and repair construction	233	370			30	16	23	476	18	8	26	4		257
13	Ordnance and accessories													768	
14	Food and kindred products	3,694		24	44									24	14,828
15	Tobacco manufactures														
16	Broad and narrow fabrics, yarn and thread mills		9			1		13				18	3	7	3
17	Miscellaneous textile goods and floor coverings	10	29	59	46	1	(*)	2	5	2		204	(*)	6	17
18	Apparel											49	4	6	46
19	Miscellaneous fabricated textile products	(*)	43	(*)	5			3		11		1		7	77
20	Lumber and wood products, except containers	3	3			4	11	22			1	4,550	396	78	
21	Wooden containers		105		13										110
22	Household furniture											343	8	(*)	
23	Other furniture and fixtures											222	9	(*)	
24	Paper and allied products, except containers	15	1	(*)	(*)			1		21	4	247	45	5	873
25	Paperboard containers and boxes	2	3		123	(*)	(*)	(*)	(*)	(*)	1	1		70	1,704
26	Printing and publishing	6	10	(*)	(*)	(*)	(*)	(*)	1			3	(*)	2	504
27	Chemicals and selected chemical products	75	2,297	3	21	28	50	50	164	48	27	136	18	240	403
28	Plastics and synthetic materials													10	43
29	Drugs, cleaning and toilet preparations	54									(*)				268
30	Paints and allied products			3						9		456	868	2	4
31	Petroleum refining and related industries	167	905	36	5	4	5	35	33	74	3	1,400	624	26	219
32	Rubber and miscellaneous plastics products	37	165	5	(*)	15	9	27	34	29	9	641	108	88	688
33	Leather tanning and industrial leather products														(*)
34	Footwear and other leather products				1										1
35	Glass and glass products	9										163	92	2	1,001
36	Stone and clay products	6	25	(*)	(*)	1	3	11	83	119		6,177	67	15	1
37	Primary iron and steel manufacturing					42	41	42	120	51	18	1,456	296	523	13
38	Primary nonferrous metal manufacturing	1	1			4	1	8		5	2	2,155	209	298	5
39	Metal containers	15	9	39											1,980
40	Heating, plumbing and structural metal products				(*)	(*)		1	48	3	2	7,796	1,294	5	
41	Stampings, screw machine products and bolts	26				2	6	42		(*)		1,531	19	121	194
42	Other fabricated metal products	32	45	9	11	2	4	13	63	13	1	1,583	384	146	228
43	Engines and turbines			2	3	4	9	14	49	24	1	91	(*)	6	
44	Farm machinery and equipment	8	299											8	(*)
45	Construction, mining and oil field machinery					26	23	101	57	21	11	129	18	15	
46	Materials handling machinery and equipment						1	1	1	8	1	420	130	1	10
47	Metalworking machinery and equipment	1				1	1	1	5	1	1	2	(*)	95	64
48	Special industry machinery and equipment														107
49	General industrial machinery and equipment				(*)	(*)		5	86	17	(*)	170	38	25	62
50	Machine shop products	5	5		(*)	1		51	80	4	5	42	6	106	(*)
51	Office, computing and accounting machines													(*)	(*)
52	Service industry machines											602	193	15	
53	Electric industrial equipment and apparatus					1	1		162	6	2	440	51	2	
54	Household appliances											146	178	17	
55	Electric lighting and wiring equipment	2	2	(*)		(*)	(*)	8	3	(*)	(*)	1,246	285	1	5
56	Radio, television and communication equipment											63	50	251	
57	Electronic components and accessories								2					252	
58	Miscellaneous electrical machinery, equipment and supplies	12	38	2		1		1	(*)			44	7	4	2
59	Motor vehicles and equipment	7	7			6						3	1	50	4
60	Aircraft and parts													1,260	
61	Other transportation equipment	(*)	7	16	1	(*)	2	(*)			(*)	1	(*)	4	
62	Scientific and controlling instruments			(*)		(*)	(*)		9			279	24	94	11
63	Optical, ophthalmic and photographic equipment					(*)	(*)							83	2
64	Miscellaneous manufacturing	2	2	4		(*)	1	(*)	(*)	(*)	(*)	111	91	5	9
65	Transportation and warehousing	690	452	40	27	103	65	28	146	26	15	2,135	478	89	2,592
66	Communications; except radio and TV broadcasting	75	71			2	3	5	12	1	4	294	45	103	297
67	Radio and TV broadcasting														
68	Electric, gas, water and sanitary services	97	205	1	2	49	41	69	172	74	44	64	9	53	633
69	Wholesale and retail trade	1,333	1,527	48	28	18	28	68	175	51	16	6,503	1,723	267	3,286
70	Finance and insurance	257	314	16	2	9	31	32	93	25	9	572	86	29	335
71	Real estate and rental	475	2,062	13	79	133	43	160	2,420	89	40	599	101	46	744
72	Hotels; personal and repair services except auto													15	162
73	Business services	76	1,231	(*)	(*)	62	22	81	242	75	31	4,382	529	263	3,100
74	Automobile repair and services	124	132	5	1	2	2	6	17	17	1	365	60	16	193
75	Amusements														
76	Medical, educational services and nonprofit organizations	183	17			1	1	2	6	(*)	2	84	13	16	45
77	Federal Government enterprises	3	4	(*)	(*)	1	1	2	6	1	2	28	4	13	62
78	State and local government enterprises	2											3	1	18
79	Directly allocated imports				36							88	13		1,310
80A	Transferred imports	182	333	505		540	318		1,076	111	90			60	1,338
80B	Business travel, entertainment and gifts	28	40	15	13	3	6	8	87	10	6	532	163	147	362
81	Office supplies	1	1	1	1	(*)		7		2	(*)	26	4	13	60
82	Scrap, used and secondhand goods				7		7		18	86	2	(*)	9	6	(*)
83	Government industry														
84	Rest of the world industry														
85	Household industry														
86	Inventory valuation adjustment														
I.	Intermediate inputs, total	22,552	14,587	1,126	1,146	1,238	1,029	1,319	6,420	1,034	430	48,033	9,672	5,874	65,459
V.A.	Value added	8,086	13,953	819	1,524	506	611	1,844	8,611	1,321	597	31,856	13,719	4,859	23,993
E.C.	*Employee compensation*	*1,211*	*2,169*	*118*	*718*	*452*	*483*	*1,837*	*882*	*733*	*186*	*25,090*	*11,763*	*4,097*	*15,182*
I.B.T.	*Indirect business taxes*	*768*	*937*	*11*	*62*	*49*	*56*	*69*	*735*	*46*	*22*	*483*	*97*	*73*	*4,403*
P.T.I.	*Property-type income*	*6,108*	*10,847*	*695*	*744*	*205*	*193*	*598*	*6,994*	*542*	*390*	*6,278*	*1,890*	*689*	*6,408*
T.	**Total**	**30,638**	**28,540**	**1,945**	**2,670**	**1,744**	**1,640**	**3,163**	**15,031**	**2,355**	**1,027**	**79,889**	**23,391**	**10,733**	**89,451**
TR.	*Transfers*	*228*	*408*	*750*	*500*	*654*	*392*	*4*	*1,898*	*258*	*109*			*1,401*	*2,898*

Table 4.4 (*continued*)

Tobacco manufactures	Broad and narrow fabrics, yarn and thread mills	Miscellaneous textile goods and floor coverings	Apparel	Miscellaneous fabricated textile products	Lumber and wood products, except containers	Wooden containers	Household furniture	Other furniture and fixtures	Paper and allied products, except containers	Paperboard containers and boxes	Printing and publishing	Chemicals and selected chemical products	Plastics and synthetic materials	Drugs, cleaning, and toilet preparations	Paints and allied products	Petroleum refining and related industries	Rubber and miscellaneous plastics products	Leather tanning and industrial leather products	Footwear and other leather products	Industry No.
15	16	17	18	19	20	21	22	23	24	25	26	27	28	29	30	31	32	33	34	
1,423	101	159												12				15		1
	1,154	24										36				58				2
			165		1,002							13		2		1				3
																				4
																				5
												47								6
2	14	2	3	1	3	(*)	2	1	70	1	1	71	30	4	(*)	11,556	10	2	(*)	7
	(*)				2				57			49				63	7			8
1									26			60	1	3	18		11			9
												608	12							10
																				11
7	51	11	25	4	64	1	18	11	120	26	79	161	53	49	12	363	50	2	6	12
					1		7	9				11				2				13
1	32	14	(*)		(*)				134	1	1	194	50	306	77	31	6	256	6	14
1,664																				15
	5,170	820	5,662	1,758	11		254	14	151		43	2	45	3	1		328		123	16
	458	294	94	410	7		101	47	53	5	44	6	1	1	1		452		124	17
2	39	66	4,654	78	13	1	15	8	10	7	18	5	3	4	1	3	28	1	46	18
1	45	56	374	3	1	1	17	17	17	(*)	13	17	(*)	(*)			11		45	19
6	4	1		8	3,492	198	702	170	1,186	13	5	55	4	6	6	2	41	(*)	47	20
	(*)	5			33	17	2	1	1	(*)							1		(*)	21
	(*)			7	29	4	78	55	1	1		(*)					3		7	22
				1	8		16	70	1		4						7		1	23
53	6	29	52	34	67	2	8	7	2,683	2,444	230	257	91	6	85	138	5	31		24
57	80	15	101	65	24	3	65	34	338	109	116	84	337	22	75	169	2	59		25
34	2	9	1		3				139	34	2,431	5	28	1	8	3				26
14	389	65	54	1	160		10	5	622	141	406	4,407	2,928	1,368	613	516	55	6		27
85	1,524	751	444	25	15		13		193	24	43	676	235	74	276	4	2,276	1	2	28
16	18	3	5	5	(*)		77	34	15	4	5	302	49	675	29	83	17	39	6	29
(*)	8	1	1	2	58	4	7	4	102	30	15	79	49	36	19	23	(*)		1	30
2	21	6	21	2	106	1	226	111	305	28	40	1,800	119	54	46	1,831	21	3	4	31
49	42	77	30	81	61	(*)	4	1	98		98	95	197	393	6	58	562	3	368	32
(*)		1	67	14	2	(*)			4	1		1				1	7	119	772	33
	(*)	10	2		2			1			1						25	4	112	34
66		4	1		18	(*)	32	26	1		2	11	5	193		38				35
14	14				85	2	30	7	33			61	1	22	10	58	65	2		36
		2		1	97	2	250	27	3	32	10	184	4	12	12	8	44			37
					43	(*)	35		3	20	40	322	27	2	31	41	16		1	38
1		2			3				4		162	240	8	196		169	88	6		39
				39	15		12	(*)		1	2	2					10		25	40
				50	50	1	20	50			1		1	46			2		60	41
16	7	2	24	6	179	5	285	128	189	34	68	80	6	168	19	16	204	1		42
								3									3			43
							4		4			(*)					2			44
												1								45
(*)	3	(*)	21	10	9	(*)	1	7	16	1	1	23	3	1	(*)	18	6	(*)	11	46
6	6	21	18	8	15	2	11	10	18	42	13	15	16	8	2	67	3	8	47
1	87	18	8		18	1	5		26	4	20	228	19			17	(*)		48
1	2	(*)			11		5		54	2		70	14	2		65	13	(*)	49
					14				5			19	19	5	3		20	1	50
									2		1	3					1		51
	2			1	3	1	13		1			1					1		52
					3		1					19					2		53
(*)	1	(*)	5	(*)	6	(*)	1	3	8		2	5	2		1	12	8	4	54
					1		5	10	4		1		1	1		9	5		55
		11						2				(*)		(*)		5	2		56
1		(*)			4							1		(*)		(*)	2		57
												1		(*)		(*)			58
	2				5	(*)			1			16	1	2		3	15			59
				1	6		4		12		1	2		1			51	1	60
				1	1		12										1		61
(*)	1		13	20	1	(*)	16	22	16	2		4	1	53	(*)	17	10	(*)	8	62
	1		3	1	1		1	1	16		178	11	1	12	2	8	1	6	63
	1	18	312	34	1		16	1	9	2	36	20	3	12	2	92	1	(*)	41	64
35	253	106	148	30	429	20	111	40	575	227	255	611	177	162	81	1,389	238	31	35	65
	30	11			2	2	23	16	49	49	76	52	17		25	62	3	18	66
																				67
12	175	36	97	23	124	5	32	19	349	45	121	699	120	51	16	462	152	9	21	68
57	486	161	661	115	441	24	223	80	535	151	550	543	260	369	101	303	440	90	143	69
16	49	14	106	19	79	3	33	20	75	17	134	100	35	60	13	250	56	8	26	70
50	122	56	311	41	109		68	37	219	96	965	543	166	387	67	630	170	14	60	71
18	5	4	6	6			3	2	25	18	36	17	10	55	14	15	18	(*)	7	72
360	178	72	366	50	197	8	125	64	359	133	921	681	130	2,066	102	770	436	13	116	73
1	8	2	21	3	57	1	7	4	13	7	55	22	8	10	4	11	13	1	4	74
																				75
																				76
1	5	2	14	2	5		4	2	8	4	44	17		21	7	9	1		5	77
13	2	4	51	6	7	6	6	4	12	5	278	35	4	21	4	6	12	1	13	78
(*)		(*)	4		7		(*)	4	4			8		4	(*)	5	1			79
8	29	24	9		2				2			3		21		2	5	1		80A
18	390	384	50	1	758		31		1,366		3	637	124	114	1	1,018	197	70	22	80B
41	48	12	114	15	34	4	36	14	62	3	261	130	70	169	45	27	120	3	7	81
2	11	2	22	1	7			5	11	5	16	16	4	10		11	11	1	82
1		39	(*)						239		(*)	33			36	11	16		83
																				84
																				85
																				86
																				87
4,080	*11,155*	*3,439*	*14,216*	*3,034*	*8,075*	*324*	*2,860*	*1,548*	*10,540*	*3,813*	*11,127*	*14,642*	*5,494*	*7,751*	*1,971*	*20,085*	*7,632*	*768*	*2,410*	I.
3,860	*4,811*	*1,229*	*8,349*	*1,249*	*4,830*	*219*	*2,262*	*1,273*	*6,193*	*2,218*	*10,991*	*8,540*	*2,929*	*4,832*	*943*	*6,890*	*6,178*	*322*	*1,831*	V.A.
693	*3,585*	*798*	*6,806*	*902*	*3,084*	*155*	*1,674*	*985*	*3,881*	*1,677*	*8,224*	*4,890*	*1,989*	*2,461*	*643*	*8,896*	*4,006*	*234*	*1,479*	E.C.
2,154	*86*	*24*	*96*	*17*	*112*	*4*	*37*	*20*	*170*	*48*	*162*	*211*	*71*	*85*	*26*	*5,044*	*570*	*6*	*19*	I.B.T.
1,103	*1,340*	*413*	*1,447*	*350*	*1,684*	*62*	*551*	*389*	*2,192*	*495*	*2,606*	*4,069*	*875*	*2,246*	*275*	*1,579*	*1,601*	*83*	*333*	P.T.I.
7,940	*15,966*	*4,668*	*22,566*	*4,283*	*12,905*	*543*	*5,122*	*2,822*	*16,733*	*6,031*	*22,118*	*23,182*	*8,424*	*12,582*	*2,914*	*26,975*	*13,809*	*1,090*	*4,240*	T.
24	*758*	*705*	*168*	*860*	*1,219*	*96*	*128*	*251*	*1,776*	*158*	*429*	*5,935*	*1,052*	*884*	*106*	*1,969*	*1,073*	*91*	*112*	TR.

(*continued*)

Table 4.4 (continued)

Industry No.	For the distribution of output of an industry, read the row for that industry. / For the composition of inputs to an industry, read the column for that industry.	Glass and glass products 35	Stone and clay products 36	Primary iron and steel manufacturing 37	Primary nonferrous metals manufacturing 38	Metal containers 39	Heating, plumbing and structural metal products 40	Stampings, screw machine products and bolts 41	Other fabricated metal products 42	Engines and turbines 43	Farm machinery and equipment 44	Construction, mining and oil field machinery 45	Materials handling machinery and equipment 46	Metalworking machinery and equipment 47	Special industry machinery and equipment 48
1	Livestock and livestock products														
2	Other agricultural products														
3	Forestry and fishery products														
4	Agricultural, forestry and fishery services														
5	Iron and ferroalloy ores mining		10	1,497	5					1					
6	Nonferrous metal ores mining		12	57	1,052										
7	Coal mining	2	56	644	12	(*)	1	3	3	2	3	2	1	1	1
8	Crude petroleum and natural gas														
9	Stone and clay mining and quarrying	42	797	66	4		1		2						
10	Chemical and fertilizer mineral mining	4	42	26	3				7						
11	New construction														
12	Maintenance and repair construction	32	99	291	70	2	40	36	38	12	13	22	6	28	18
13	Ordnance and accessories			2		(*)	12	4	15	24	4	7	1	2	13
14	Food and kindred products		6	1		8	1		1						
15	Tobacco manufactures														
16	Broad and narrow fabrics, yarn and thread mills		46		10										5
17	Miscellaneous textile goods and floor coverings		24		1		(*)								
18	Apparel	5	9	21	10	2	10	8	11	2	3	4	2	7	4
19	Miscellaneous fabricated textile products		1	1	1	(*)	3	4	3	(*)		1	1	1	1
20	Lumber and wood products, except containers	33	32	74	76	4	30	35	48		10	8	3	8	27
21	Wooden containers	5		5	10		9	9	3		2	1	1	1	1
22	Household furniture	17	(*)				2		6	12	1		(*)		(*)
23	Other furniture and fixtures	(*)	(*)	2	(*)		2	2	15		4		1	1	(*)
24	Paper and allied products, except containers	28	197	9	17	8	25	30	63	1	2	2	1	3	3
25	Paperboard containers and boxes	198	66	18	16	45	54	61	126	13	7	5	2	8	5
26	Printing and publishing	1	3	4	13	137	2	2	12	(*)	1	1	(*)	1	7
27	Chemicals and selected chemical products	88	205	392	184	5	14	29	138	2	2	1	(*)	10	4
28	Plastics and synthetic materials	4	58	(*)	155			9	17	1				1	2
29	Drugs, cleaning and toilet preparations	4	5		2		2	3	9	4				(*)	2
30	Paints and allied products	19	8	14	11	91	102	21	69	4	12	11	3	13	2
31	Petroleum refining and related industries	7	104	116	48	3	34	17	44	15	11	20	5	43	26
32	Rubber and miscellaneous plastics products	92	122	33	59	5	26	59	210	8	130	98	31	72	45
33	Leather tanning and industrial leather products		3	2	6			2	2			1			1
34	Footwear and other leather products		(*)	1	(*)			1	2			(*)	(*)	(*)	1
35	Glass and glass products	242	3	2	1		56	4	19					(*)	4
36	Stone and clay products	64	1,231	113	40	10	38	22	57	33	11	42	8	85	29
37	Primary iron and steel manufacturing		125	6,917	340	1,238	3,018	2,208	2,200	384	655	951	268	695	484
38	Primary nonferrous metal manufacturing	28	26	859	6,723	136	874	524	872	195	62	58	83	231	159
39	Metal containers		12		2										6
40	Heating, plumbing and structural metal products	1	11	68	7	2	298	22	90	13	13	40	33	30	99
41	Stampings, screw machine products and bolts	1	3	210	45	50	278	176	210	74	105	54	33	306	47
42	Other fabricated metal products	3	114	455	184	13	339	116	442	43	72	72	67	169	74
43	Engines and turbines	9	(*)	33	6	6	29	8	11	13	283	294	129	32	6
44	Farm machinery and equipment		(*)	33	1	8	8	11	11	25	228	58	20	8	4
45	Construction, mining and oil field machinery		71	18	1	42	4	21	10	143	96	301	107	19	30
46	Materials handling machinery and equipment	1	6	48	14	1	28	4	15	1	3	75	132	8	23
47	Metalworking machinery and equipment	12	81	297	156	27	64	169	187	49	38	119	38	612	138
48	Special industry machinery and equipment		11	35	2	4	21	10	31	13	9	10	9	47	388
49	General industrial machinery and equipment	4	31	344	89	1	131	14	93	139	319	359	149	230	250
50	Machine shop products		11	205	103		119	117	73	100	42	38	50	70	22
51	Office, computing and accounting machines		5		(*)	1								1	8
52	Service industry machines	(*)	4	1	3		164	16	37		2		11	14	11
53	Electric industrial equipment and apparatus	1	14	289	120	6	38	18	23	81	24	74	91	265	203
54	Household appliances	(*)	1	4	6	7	36	15	6		13			5	5
55	Electric lighting and wiring equipment	6	23	19	22	1	8	24	28	(*)	1	3	1	8	9
56	Radio, television and communication equipment	(*)	2	4	13		3	3	3	6			1	6	43
57	Electronic components and accessories	(*)	(*)	9	103		(*)		2	2				1	1
58	Miscellaneous electrical machinery, equipment and supplies	(*)	(*)	1	9			(*)		1	74	40	10	5	2
59	Motor vehicles and equipment	14		121	46	(*)	51	228	74	89	31	65	28	78	27
60	Aircraft and parts		1	1		4	41	7	11	151	1	24	5	21	21
61	Other transportation equipment			12	1	1	57	3	8	35	7	29	2	(*)	11
62	Scientific and controlling instruments	7	5	50	6	1	67	20	34	6	14	33	12	14	13
63	Optical, ophthalmic and photographic equipment	1	1	2	1	(*)	2	3	3	(*)	1	(*)		1	6
64	Miscellaneous manufacturing	7	41	11	17		3	21	26		4	3	2	10	4
65	Transportation and warehousing	108	650	1,420	539	74	201	142	142	32	65	59	20	59	45
66	Communications; except radio and TV broadcasting	13	57	95	44	6	75	35	58	16	18	30	17	47	35
67	Radio and TV broadcasting														
68	Electric, gas, water and sanitary services	136	358	822	427	25	95	82	121	19	24	40	11	56	27
69	Wholesale and retail trade	118	290	934	746	83	409	179	300	129	173	201	79	267	206
70	Finance and insurance	20	90	182	116	15	84	41	65	7	37	34	13	38	32
71	Real estate and rental	72	208	80	153	32	173	95	149	28	46	81	39	129	178
72	Business services	4	7	14	3		2	5	12	3	6	5	3	8	3
73	Hotels; personal and repair services except auto	111	283	841	279	83	243	147	277	63	143	117	63	164	90
74	Automobile repair and services	4	33	27	11	2	16	6	13	4	5	7	3	9	7
75	Amusements														
76	Medical, educational services and nonprofit organizations	3	10	11	11	1	10	6	9		3	3		3	8
77	Federal Government enterprises	4	10	19	9	1	11	6	11	1	5	6	3	8	6
78	State and local government enterprises	(*)	8	6	3	(*)	1	1	1	1	(*)	(*)	(*)	6	(*)
79	Directly allocated imports														
80A															
80B	Business imports	95	176	1,420	1,984	6	54	114	293	77	267	83	22	275	290
81	Business travel, entertainment and gifts	25	68	95	52	87	133	33	83	34	30	34	17	81	62
82	Office supplies	4	10	19	8	1	11	4	10	3	4	5	2	7	6
83	Scrap, used and secondhand goods	8	3	841	871			32			16				14
84	Government industry														
85	Rest of the world industry														
86	Household industry														
	Inventory valuation adjustment														
I.	Intermediate inputs, total	1,692	6,002	19,336	15,156	2,185	7,909	5,031	7,002	2,457	3,140	3,448	1,538	4,307	3,295
V.A.	Value added	2,109	5,025	12,387	5,715	1,170	4,601	4,262	5,517	1,368	1,686	2,526	1,001	4,369	2,386
E.C.	*Employee compensation*	1,414	3,581	9,176	3,453	753	3,436	3,079	3,686	1,004	1,249	1,787	789	3,291	1,892
I.B.T.	*Indirect business taxes*	33	125	558	155	31	86	75	65	27	55	55	18	72	97
P.T.I.	*Property-type income*	662	1,319	2,654	2,106	387	1,079	1,108	1,806	337	408	743	193	1,005	457
T.	**Total**	3,801	11,026	31,723	20,870	3,355	12,510	9,293	12,519	3,825	4,826	5,974	2,538	8,676	5,681
TR.	*Transfers*	199	571	2,332	2,682	90	1,012	792	2,090	688	528	476	305	1,200	726

Table 4.4 (*continued*)

General industrial machinery and equipment	Machine shop products	Office, computing and accounting machines	Service industry machines	Electric industrial equipment and apparatus	Household appliances	Electric lighting and wiring equipment	Radio, television and communication equipment	Electronic components and accessories	Miscellaneous electrical machinery, equipment and supplies	Motor vehicles and equipment	Aircraft and parts	Other transportation equipment	Scientific and controlling instruments	Optical, ophthalmic and photographic equipment	Miscellaneous manufacturing	Transportation and warehousing	Communications; except radio and TV broadcasting	Radio and TV broadcasting	Electric, gas, water and sanitary services	Industry No.
49	50	51	52	53	54	55	56	57	58	59	60	61	62	63	64	65	66	67	68	
													9		10	41				1
																2				2
																				3
																				4
				1															(*)	5
2	1	1	1	3	2	1	2	1	1	16	2	2	(*)		2	7	(*)	(*)	895	6
													3			26			-2,521	7
													3						(*)	8
													4						(*)	9
														1					(*)	10
																				11
27	10	15	13	32	17	11	46	28	8	105	65	22	18	20	23	1,307	567	6	1,137	12
1	2	1	1	19	(*)	6	161	2	(*)	20	406	28	21	1	5	166				13
		1	1										13		17				(*)	14
																			(*)	15
4	5		1	2	4	15	4	3	2	12	21	(*)	40	75	141				2	16
6	4	3	3	4	7	4	3	11	8	137	5	18	14	7	25	35	19	5	7	17
(*)	(*)	(*)		3				(*)	2	596	7	3	8	6	11	92			8	18
22	2		6	13	9		4	9	6	43	11	299	9	1	148	2			1	19
3	(*)		9	3	15			26		7	3	(*)	1		8					20
			9	5	1			270	8	2		30	9		9					21
(*)	3	9	4	67	(*)		24	1	79	43	52	5	10	70	3	5			(*)	22
4	2	33		2	4		42		1	55	10	15	15	84	153	71	21	(*)	34	23
14	15	9	24	99	78		33	37	24	47	10	3	3	27	266	26	50	41	5	24
1	1	94	1		(*)		15	1		1	15	1	1		35	50	41	1	3	25
13	1	1	18	66	23		15	109	63	61	11	2	20	208	53	46	1		56	26
1	7	2		41	33		46	63	28	21	29		21	36	219				2	27
2		6	1	5	1			8				30	8		15	5				28
1	1		20	46	17	8	8	1	1	153	16	29	4	2	43	64	1	(*)		29
30	43	7	11	44	8	86	27	12	3	73	90	13	11		28	1,999	65	1	275	30
41	21	60	53	246	86		115	160	59	899	85	139	119	63	363	287	24	1	23	31
4			1	1						(*)					16					32
(*)	(*)	(*)	1	7	1	1	(*)			1		23	12	48	39					33
1				20	125	44	232	1	23	353		12	35		33	11	(*)			34
85	31	6	49	103	40	13	45	69		98	41	12	890	166	25				1	35
843	335	82	311	411	252	95	279	318		1,239	452	1	166	20	246	261	10		41	36
308	144	92	265	605	266	100	283			673	732		206	193	371	66			11	37
2										3			12							38
															6				(*)	39
126	8	21	128	1	24	18	7	8	7	29	8	281	10	(*)						40
56	50	80	107	164	239	112	278	165	37	2,898	396	53	113	55	87	19			(*)	41
195	47	62	192	94	189	60	144	120	66	1,239	353	63	129	76	180	206	1		27	42
73	8		5	120						251	63	284			65				2	43
19	2	(*)	2		5	10	(*)			20	4	31	8	(*)	12				1	44
58	3	1	11	15				7		63	1	26	3							45
20	1	(*)	18	12	(*)	49	26	1	69	22	5	2	69	3	1	2				46
156	101	75	41	134			105		37	409	337	83	4	5	4	6				47
87	6	4	12	1		52	16	3	38	6	4	1	3	12	5					48
514	58	34	70	70	8	8	62	20		297	177	285	31	12	4	135			37	49
65	217	70	5	22	19		119	64		439	662	36	30	5	14	(*)				50
(*)	(*)	881	2	6						1	6	(*)	8		22					51
49	1	1	327	154	2		9		64	442	2	10	15	1	4	4	(*)		40	52
253	24	145	410	287	147	157	21	(*)	4	145	78	84	163	37	47	39	6			53
3	(*)		568	75	(*)		13	2		13	2	34	(*)		16					54
6	8	159	33	163	65	136	148	33	77	253	1	24	35	6	20	9	1	3	29	55
3	1	81	178	1	2	12	1,086	285	16	149	615	1	143	26	20	1	213	10	1	56
4	(*)	720	1	257	16	19	3,211	1,141	43	35	146	2	157	82	28	35	26	29	2	57
	50			50		99	18	16	173	521	68		21	5	4	46	2		5	58
41	27	2	90	38	40	18		2	140	12,157	318	143	46		16	71	3		3	59
61	2	2	70	11	7	3	212	2	2	49	4,652	14	47	5	313					60
18	4		14	84	3	(*)				2	440		6	1	18	403				61
26	2	18	69	113	145	5	55	11	14	161	347	13	459	8	14	42				62
1		4	2	6	1	10	12	16	9	3	10	1	78	306	1	8	(*)	3	(*)	63
1	1	6	5	80	38	3	31	4	1	16	9	23	30	12	589	16	4		563	64
71	28	29	48	66	43	20	95	55	29	716	97	122	38	34	135	5,228	41	2	100	65
48	20	42	23	63	20	20	144	64	14	80	183	29	46	31	46	505	143	129		66
																		812	87	67
52	41	19	24	68	43	37	77	64	22	195	108	46	32	21	49	342	135	44	6,888	68
257	98	246	206	325	179	120	490	260	101	926	442	309	226	144	421	1,627	144	53	202	69
32	19	40	15	44	18	10	55	39	19	114	66	30	25	23	58	781	142	17	219	70
100	116	255	61	198	98	81	228	109	54	192	340	86	100	78	151	1,360	323	146	155	71
6	3	2	1	9	3	3	11	10	6	25	64	5	8	5		60	212		52	72
169	82	149	126	185	331	103	478	217	71	631	555	103	250	158	343	862	631	136	287	73
10	4	7	5	13	4	5	31	10	3	659	39	6	8	4	9	795	101	(*)	48	75
											6				19	46	19		13	76
8	3	6	4	3	3	3	22	10	2	22	43	5	8	5	10	1,446	80	3	639	78
9	3	7		8	9	4	26	8	1	43	24	6	10		20	1,446	6	4	4,971	79
							(*)			40		4	1	(*)	181	896	133	1		80A
197	2	168	13	189	10	60	677	151	94	595	660	170	142	183	446	1,363			145	80B
86	49	157	54	143	44	40	151	129	26	116	270	61	103	38	85	248	131	111	128	81
7	3	7	4	8	3	3	22	8		19	21	5	9	4	13	78	70	3	31	82
10						2	(*)			212						6	(*)			83
																				84
																				85
																				86
																				87
4,336	1,758	3,932	3,606	5,361	3,507	2,194	9,519	4,504	1,830	30,342	12,521	4,922	3,367	2,096	5,586	21,829	3,299	1,604	19,609	I.
3,464	2,182	2,750	1,673	4,543	1,943	1,924	7,812	3,643	1,306	13,398	9,472	2,889	2,625	2,683	3,771	30,996	16,029	1,580	17,712	V.A.
2,570	1,636	2,000	1,151	3,352	1,345	1,800	6,314	3,119	973	8,453	8,673	2,490	1,859	1,419	2,719	20,929	6,498	1,060	4,004	E.C.
61	27	33	28	73	34	27	96	46	24	1,696	231	55	48	83	63	1,869	8,464	33	2,111	I.B.T.
833	519	716	495	1,138	564	698	1,401	477	509	2,949	666	346	620	1,241	988	8,858	(*)7,067	487	10,696	P.T.I.
7,800	3,940	6,682	5,279	9,903	5,450	4,118	17,331	8,147	3,136	43,740	21,993	7,811	6,191	4,779	9,357	52,825	19,328	3,183	37,321	T.
1,023	183	720	1,048	1,087	249	336	1,520	810	423	1,354	958	443	887	375	1,060	2,774	1		5,947	TR.

(*continued*)

Table 4.4 (continued)

Industry No.	For the distribution of output of an industry, read the row for that industry. For the composition of inputs to an industry, read the column for that industry.	Wholesale and retail trade	Finance and insurance	Real estate and rental	Hotels; personal and repair services except auto	Business services	Automobile repair and services	Amusements	Medical, educational services and non-profit organizations	Federal Government enterprises	State and local government enterprises	Gross imports of goods and services	Business travel, entertainment and gifts	Office supplies	Scrap, used and second-hand goods
		69	70	71	72	73	75	76	77	78	79	80A & 80B	81	82	83
1	Livestock and livestock products			1,127				52	17				31		
2	Other agricultural products	10		1,200	7			203	27	389	2		115		
3	Forestry and fishery products			2					(*)				50		
4	Agricultural, forestry and fishery services	139		159				25			1				
5	Iron and ferroalloy ores mining	(*)		4											
6	Nonferrous metal ores mining	1		10											
7	Coal mining	3	1	37	6	1	(*)	(*)	10	72	70				
8	Crude petroleum and natural gas			165											
9	Stone and clay mining and quarrying	5		28											
10	Chemical and fertilizer mineral mining			6							4				
11	New construction														
12	Maintenance and repair construction	526	135	7,150	188	259	33	104	739	60	1,711				
13	Ordnance and accessories	38		11	1								16		28
14	Food and kindred products	892		138	2				502	121			2,960		
15	Tobacco manufactures	9		8									187		10
16	Broad and narrow fabrics, yarn and thread mills	20		22	21				7	2					60
17	Miscellaneous textile goods and floor coverings	53		22	12	9	(*)		(*)	1					
18	Apparel	134		51	93		7		33		5		8		9
19	Miscellaneous fabricated textile products	80		3	108	(*)	10		22	14	2				3
20	Lumber and wood products, except containers	92		29	11								4	(*)	
21	Wooden containers	107		1											
22	Household furniture	24		7											
23	Other furniture and fixtures	26		1											
24	Paper and allied products except containers	1,006	251	41	109	101	5	8	94	8	10		7	528	17
25	Paperboard containers and boxes	571		4	33	1		1	24	2	(*)				38
26	Printing and publishing	379	445	126	13	9,361	(*)	21	673	29	26		14	1,485	74
27	Chemicals and selected chemical products	215	1	301	63	149	4	39	54	5	122		2	13	
28	Plastics and synthetic materials	23		30											
29	Drugs, cleaning and toilet preparations	274		101	473	101	7		1,140	17	21		78		
30	Paints and allied products	51		15	14	7	37	1	1	(*)			(*)		
31	Petroleum refining and related industries	1,375	92	720	232	131	174	18	212	45	96				12
32	Rubber and miscellaneous plastics products	714	14	134	197	405	238	3	150	13	28		4	12	10
33	Leather tanning and industrial leather products	2		1	14				(*)						5
34	Footwear and other leather products	39		6	201			6		2			39		(*)
35	Glass and glass products	130		18	5	27	109		5	1	2		4	1	
36	Stone and clay products	138		37	65	76	94	3	12	(*)	5		3		
37	Primary iron and steel manufacturing	37		62	4	7				(*)	8				206
38	Primary nonferrous metal manufacturing	42		37	6					1				5	156
39	Metal containers	107		8		36									29
40	Heating, plumbing and structural metal products	180		45						(*)					40
41	Stampings, screw machine products and bolts	62		13	80	305	949		9	4	4			(*)	119
42	Other fabricated metal products	154		22	139	255	165		6	1	8		6	4	40
43	Engines and turbines	17		28	61	15			(*)		13				12
44	Farm machinery and equipment	34		10	56					1					7
45	Construction, mining and oil field machinery	50		37	301				(*)		9				5
46	Materials handling machinery and equipment	32		16											23
47	Metalworking machinery and equipment	68		24	10	29	2		5	(*)	1			(*)	4
48	Special industry machinery and equipment	80		139										(*)	8
49	General industrial machinery and equipment	69		22		90					1			(*)	31
50	Machine shop products	35		48	23	131	319				4				6
51	Office, computing and accounting machines	88		247		156				2				13	2
52	Service industry machines	49		18	9	157	67			(*)					19
53	Electric industrial equipment and apparatus	55		64	29	120	4	1			5				21
54	Household appliances	62		25	125	11			1				52		12
55	Electric lighting and wiring equipment	65	6	28	10	1	23	3	29	1	13				10
56	Radio, television and communication equipment	78		78			60			(*)			88	(*)	22
57	Electronic components and accessories	71		34	339	14	−3		8	(*)					18
58	Miscellaneous electrical machinery, equipment and supplies	95	2	11	7	9	243	(*)	5		4				13
59	Motor vehicles and equipment	99		116	5	39	1,259			8	7				99
60	Aircraft and parts	66		32		(*)			1						23
61	Other transportation equipment	31		29	11	21		1	1	4					18
62	Scientific and controlling instruments	106		32	18	28	5		289	(*)	1		16		12
63	Optical, ophthalmic and photographic equipment	121	2	30	163	263		63	163	1	1		40		4
64	Miscellaneous manufacturing	246	2	35	364	524	4	34	181	1			74	176	19
65	Transportation and warehousing	1,235	115	1,096	144	383	113	78	736	245	67		4,629	369	57
66	Communications; except radio and TV broadcasting	1,769	973	212	170	1,279	89	67	574	20	43				
67	Radio and TV broadcasting			18		3,053			19						
68	Electric, gas, water and sanitary services	2,415	392	436	367	201	84	86	1,498	132	1,136				
69	Wholesale and retail trade	3,382	598	1,612	660	1,090	1,469	200	951	78	110		748		1
70	Finance and insurance	2,474	8,701	3,574	398	365	203	108	389	87	173				5
71	Real estate and rental	8,608	1,961	3,654	1,441	2,149	392	716	2,704	186	161				
72	Hotels; personal and repair services except auto	457		519	582	345	14	6	237	3	5		1,418		6
73	Business services	8,466	3,957	3,109	601	2,541	155	398	1,262	199	346				
75	Automobile repair and services	1,764	144	169	337	505	26	31	327	43	30				
76	Amusements	184		209	2	173		1	31	6			187		
77	Medical, educational services and nonprofit organizations	230	562	95	68	118	8	22	665	1	13		71		
78	Federal Government enterprises	1,791	851	411	55	594	7	41	333	2	13				
79	State and local government enterprises	590	128	923	11	9	155	3	50	2	6				
80A 80B	Directly allocated imports	46	81			6		68	2		342				
	Transferred imports		20										356		690
81	Business travel, entertainment and gifts	2,045	807	105	299	1,151	69	224	780	28	48				
82	Office supplies	340	610	54	34	184	6	14	160	6	15				
83	Scrap, used and secondhand goods	10	1	(*)	(*)	(*)	38	(*)	1		(*)				
84	Government industry														
85	Rest of the world industry														
86	Household industry														
87	Inventory valuation adjustment														
I.	Intermediate inputs, total	45,101	20,853	29,181	8,203	27,369	6,656	4,624	14,610	3,075	4,405		11,206	2,607	1,991
V.A.	Value added	118,265	26,899	84,053	12,412	29,076	8,101	5,020	33,897	4,616	5,242				
E.C.	Employee compensation	69,812	19,471	1,880	7,075	16,636	3,785	2,875	23,536	5,785	1,070				
I.B.T.	Indirect business taxes	22,889	1,913	18,253	280	413	205	736	245	67					
P.T.I.	Property-type income	25,563	5,515	63,939	5,057	12,686	4,110	1,409	10,116	−1,234	5,172				
T.	Total	163,365	47,752	113,253	20,805	56,444	14,756	9,644	48,507	7,691	9,647		11,206	2,607	1,991
TR.	Transfers[1]	5,717	188	11,996	2	13,743	147	69					11,206	2,607	1,991

Table 4.4 (continued)

(84) Government Industry	(85) Rest of the world industry	(86) Household Industry	(87) Inventory valuation adjustment	Intermediate outputs, total	Personal consumption expenditures	Gross private fixed capital formation	Net inventory change	Net exports[2]	Federal Govt. Purchases — Total	Defense	Nondefense	State & Local Govt. Purchases — Total	Education	Other	Total final demand	Total[3]	Transfers[3]	Industry No.
				28,620	1,811		129	55	8	5	4	15	1	13	2,018	30,638	2,453	1
				21,691	3,756		1,031	3,184	-1,195	7	-1,202	73	16	57	6,849	28,540	2,182	2
				1,696	449		2	47	-255	5	-260	5	1	4	249	1,945	52	3
				2,486	136			14	11	10	1	24	17	7	185	2,670	14	4
				1,660			25	122	-66	-65		(*)			82	1,744	10	5
				1,467			12	35	126	58	67				173	1,640	36	6
				2,545	121		125	306	43	36	7	22	15	7	618	3,163	42	7
				14,692			257	82							339	15,031	1,138	8
				2,304	4		12	84	-2	-1	-1	-47		-47	51	2,355	95	9
				838	2		8	149	(*)	(*)		31		31	189	1,027	237	10
					54,338			15	3,475	975	2,501	22,061	6,176	15,885	79,889	79,889		11
				17,696	1,657		147	309	1,458	973	480	4,241	772	3,470	5,695	23,391	825	12
				24,540	60,974		899	1,906	655	207	448	477	68	409	64,911	89,451	4,181	13
				1,881	5,270		189	601				-1		-1	6,059	7,940	217	14
				14,908	592		114	250	74	73	1	27	9	18	1,058	15,966	980	15
				2,958	1,406	89	107	89	20	14	6	(*)	(*)	-1	1,710	4,668	282	16
				5,698	16,247		281	169	127	96	31	43	2	41	16,867	22,566	289	17
				1,824	1,983	7	49	74	336	323	13	17	5	12	2,459	4,283	171	18
				12,118	259		121	367	30	21	8	4	3	1	787	12,905	254	19
				513				3	24	21	3				30	543	30	20
				939	3,861	165	49	24	56	26	31	28	21	8	4,183	5,122	182	21
				570	174	1,632	41	19	89	40	50	297	235	62	2,251	2,822	178	22
				14,060	1,502		228	649	116	62	55	179	98	82	2,673	16,733	1,251	23
				5,841	73		39	24	34	29	5	21	12	9	191	6,081	174	24
				16,358	4,119		297	252	228	180	49	864	144	720	5,760	22,118	11,338	25
				18,797	504		305	1,710	1,752	1,286	466	113	15	99	4,385	23,182	1,674	26
				7,644	18		26	670	65	65	(*)				779	8,424	980	27
				3,913	7,294		221	435	192	121	71	527	145	383	8,669	12,582	872	28
				2,754	52		54	48	4	3	1	3	2	1	160	2,914	185	29
				14,105	10,194		541	765	1,078	939	139	292	146	146	12,870	26,975	2,510	30
				10,481	2,269	30	142	323	392	355	37	172	45	128	3,320	13,809	823	31
				1,047			-6	43	6	5	2				43	1,090	27	32
				522	3,659		21	20	16	14	2	3		3	3,718	4,240	134	33
				3,228	317		39	145	18	10	8	53	22	31	573	3,801	69	34
				10,438	244		127	177	26	23	4	13	9	4	588	11,026	512	35
				30,395	4		514	519	290	286	4	(*)	(*)	2	1,328	31,723	2,048	36
				19,752	15	34	336	726	8	42	-34	(*)	(*)		1,119	20,870	1,105	37
				3,255	11		61	16	13	13	(*)				100	3,355	322	38
				10,878	66	933	128	284	222	179	43				1,633	12,510	904	39
				8,406	374		86	274	139	108	31	13	23	-10	886	9,293	843	40
				10,479	774	337	198	435	263	226	37	33	27	6	2,039	12,519	976	41
				2,073	144	735	55	394	415	366		49		9	1,752	3,825	410	42
				959	36	2,942	409	419	29	25	4	30		21	3,868	4,826	367	43
				1,854		2,428	58	1,270	307	295	13	57		57	4,120	5,974	737	44
				1,163		1,108	36	132	99	82	17	1		1	1,376	2,538	283	45
				4,300	88	3,461	167	486	116	406	23	14	9	4	4,376	8,676	568	46
				1,516	22	3,205	90	791	46	32	14	11	11	1	4,165	5,681	568	47
				4,844		1,888	125	627	303	243	60	13		13	2,956	7,800	710	48
				1,659	112	3,352	156	710	533	242	291	125	106	19	4,988	6,647	296	49
				2,433	404	1,729	126	359	103	96	7	160	119	42	2,881	5,314	521	50
				5,430	28	2,886	132	558	799	679	119	126	105	20	4,529	9,903	488	51
				1,494	3,538	127	103	149	14	11	3	71	18	53	4,002	5,450	869	52
				3,153	557	67	58	169	48	35	13	25	13	12	965	4,118	914	53
				3,609	3,646	2,937	600	580	5,837	5,179	657	67	55	12	13,722	17,831	400	54
				6,712	171	18	139	372	720	617	103	14	4	10	1,435	8,147	1,426	55
				1,855	626		210	162	223	196	27	26	4	22	1,281	3,136	830	56
																	423	57
																		58
				15,464	15,822	9,054	-310	1,976	1,002	847	155	731	182	549	28,276	43,740	1,674	59
				7,199	7,840	1,918	196	1,809	8,649	7,840	810	2		2	14,794	21,993	1,782	60
				1,336	1,078	3,430	195	207	1,547	1,327	220	18		18	6,475	7,811	423	61
				2,909	601	1,132	109	568	718	586	133	154	25	130	3,282	6,191	677	62
				1,853	1,030	920	78	322	430	356	74	146	65	81	2,926	4,779	612	63
				3,665	4,417	533	147	332	98	59	40	164	142	23	5,692	9,357	1,388	64
				32,172	11,396	829	228	3,891	3,324	2,996	329	985	633	353	20,653	52,823	6,795	65
				9,237	7,837	1,096		140	544	405	138	475	136	340	10,091	19,328	688	66
				3,176								7	7		7	3,183	3,071	67
				21,370	13,935			74	344	295	49	1,599	1,054	545	15,952	37,321	188	68
				42,551	109,367	6,544	508	-615	1,397	1,142	255	384	-88	472	120,815	163,365	3,431	69
				21,934	25,267		4	-1	90	54	37	403	173	231	25,818	47,711	1,772	70
				38,798	70,868	2,100		577	292	129	163	618	168	450	74,456	113,253		71
				4,660	15,472			3	616	511	105	74	-159	234	16,165	20,805	2,197	72
				47,156	4,590			458	2,689	1,866	824	1,551	631	920	9,289	56,444	909	73
				6,471	8,069				64	55	9	152	43	110	8,285	14,756	89	74
				3,587	5,571			-57	-7	-7		23	24	-1	6,057	9,644	555	75
				2,684	41,112			332	2,227	1,085	1,142	2,480	138	2,342	45,819	48,507	141	76
				5,840	1,223			106	281	225	57	230	27	203	1,841	7,691	1,805	77
				8,414	935				286	6	280	23		-14	1,233	9,647	7,962	78
				3,826	9,870	658	-100		3,964	2,877	1,087	3	(*)	3				79
				22,570			-18,221	-22,570							-22,570			80
	1,763						-22,570										22,570	80 A
				11,206											11,206	11,206		80 B
				2,137				176	99	77		294	143	151	470	2,607		81
				2,613	1,287	-2,921	-121	580	-304	-219	-85	857	22	835	-622			82
								35,205	27,126	8,080	46,449	26,982	19,467		81,654	81,654		83
					-2,047				-861						-861	6,280		84
					4,701			9,188							4,701	4,701		85
							-1,843								-1,843			86
																		87
81,654	4,517	4,701	-1,843					-1,843								795,388		I.
81,654	45	4,701																V.A.
																471,090		E.C.
																70,859		I.B.T.
																854,060		P.T.I.
81,654	6,280	4,701	-1,843		490,660	110,443	10,034	5,132	90,804	71,333	19,471	88,315	39,512	48,803	795,388			T.
	1,769																	TR.

† * = less than $1 million.

Source: Surv. Curr. Bus., February 1974, p. 38.

Table 4.5 Input-output classifications

Category	Industries included
Agriculture	1–4
Mining	5–10
Construction	11, 12
Manufacturing	13–64
Transportation, communication, electric, gas, and sanitary services	65–68
Trade	69
Finance, insurance, and real estate	70, 71
Services	72–77
Government enterprises	78, 79
Imports	80
Dummy industries	81–83
81 Business travel, entertainment, gifts	
82 Office supplies	
83 Scrap, used, and second-hand goods	
Special industries	84–86
84 Government industry	
85 Rest-of-the-world industry	
86 Household industry	
Inventory-valuation adjustment	87

less subsidies, and capital consumption allowances (depreciation, depletion, and amortization). As expected, property-type income is highest for sector 71, real estate and rental. The depreciation part of property-type income accounts for the moderately high values for some of the CPI sectors (27, 29). The depletion part of property-type income accounts for the moderately high values of sector 8, crude petroleum and natural gas.

Because depreciation needs to be a part of value added, the flow of capital expenditures in the transactions table requires special consideration. As shown in Sec. 2.1, gross private domestic investment is a component of the GNP. In order to make the summation of the final demand inputs equal to the GNP it is necessary to consider output of capital goods from any industry k as input to final demand and not as input to the industry to which the capital goods actually go.

The final demand in Table 4.4 is broken into several components, including gross private fixed capital formation, to account for capital goods and output from each industry. As a consequence, interindustry flows of capital goods are not explicitly given by the transactions table. For example, if a firm in the chemicals and selected chemical products sector (27) buys a compressor from sector 43, engines and turbines, the amount paid appears as part of the final-demand figure in row 43 of Table 4.4. The depreciation on the compressor becomes part of column 27's value added under property-type income. For estimates of capital-goods transactions between industries for 1967, see the transaction table in Ref. 3. In this capital-goods transaction table the compressor sale would be recorded as an output of sector 43 and an input to sector 27.

In addition to gross private fixed-capital formation a number of other components of final demand are shown in Table 4.4:

1. Personal-consumption expenditures
2. Net inventory change
3. Net exports
4. Federal government purchases
   a. Total
   b. Defense
   c. Nondefense

Table 4.6 Sales of CPI and related industries to intermediate consumers and to final demand, 1967

Industry	Sales to intermediate consumers (millions)	Sales to final demand (millions)	Total sales going to final demand, %
Crude petroleum and natural gas (8)	$14,692	$ 339	2
Chemical and fertilizer mineral mining (10)	838	189	18
Paper and allied products, except containers (24)	14,060	2,673	16
Chemicals and selected chemical products (27)	18,797	4,385	19
Plastics and synthetic materials (28)	7,644	779	9
Drugs, cleaning and toilet preparations (29)	3,913	8,669	69
Paints and allied products (30)	2,754	160	5
Petroleum refining and related industries (31)	14,105	12,870	48
Rubber and miscellaneous plastics products (32)	10,481	3,329	24
Glass and glass products (35)	3,228	573	15
Primary iron and steel manufacturing (37)	30,395	1,328	4
Primary nonferrous metal manufacturing (38)	19,752	1,119	5

Table 4.7 Derived demand for chemicals and selected chemical products

Seller	Total sold (millions)	Major buyers	Total bought from seller (millions)
Chemicals and selected chemical products (27)	$23,182	Chemicals and selected chemical products (27)	$4,407
		Plastics and synthetic materials (28)	2,928
		Other agricultural products (2)	2,297
		Drugs, cleaning and toilet preparations (29)	1,368
		Petroleum refining and related industries (31)	623
		Paper and allied products except containers (24)	622
		Paints and allied products (30)	613
		Total final demand	4,385
Plastics and synthetic materials (28)	8,424	Rubber and miscellaneous plastic products (32)	2,276
		Broad and narrow fabrics, yarn and thread mills (16)	1,524
		Miscellaneous textile goods and floor coverings (17)	751
		Chemicals and selected chemical products (27)	676
		Apparel (18)	444
		Paints and allied products (30)	276
		Plastics and synthetic materials (28)	235
		Total final demand	779
Other agricultural products (2)	28,549	Livestock and livestock products (1)	8,379
		Food and kindred products (14)	6,882
		Tobacco manufactures (15)	1,423
		Real estate and rental (71)	1,200
		Broad and narrow fabrics, yarn and thread mills (16)	1,154
		Other agricultural products (2)	905
		Agricultural, forestry, and fishery services (4)	507
		Total final demand	6,819
Drugs, cleaning and toilet preparations (29)	12,582	Medical, educational services, and nonprofit organizations (77)	1,140
		Drugs, cleaning and toilet preparations (29)	675
		Hotels; personal repair services except auto (72)	473
		Chemicals and selected chemical products (27)	302
		Wholesale and retail trade (69)	274
		Real estate and rental (71)	101
		Business services (73)	101
		Total final demand	8,669

Table 4.7 (*continued*)

Seller	Total sold (millions)	Major buyers	Total bought from seller (millions)
Petroleum refining and related industries (31)	26,975	Petroleum refining and related industries (31)	1,831
		Chemicals and selected chemical products (27)	1,800
		New construction (11)	1,400
		Wholesale and retail trade (69)	1,375
		Other agricultural products (2)	905
		Real estate and rental (71)	720
		Maintenance and repair construction (12)	624
		Total final demand	12,870
Paper and allied products, except containers (24)	16,733	Printing and publishing (26)	3,314
		Paper and allied products, except containers (24)	2,683
		Paperboard containers and boxes (25)	2,444
		Wholesale and retail trade (69)	1,006
		Food and kindred products (14)	873
		Office supplies (82)	528
		Plastic and synthetic materials (28)	257
		Total final demand	2,673
Paint and allied products (30)	2,914	Maintenance and repair construction (12)	868
		New construction (11)	456
		Motor vehicles and equipment (59)	153
		Heating, plumbing, and structural metal products (40)	102
		Metal containers (39)	91
		Chemicals and selected chemical products (27)	79
		Household furniture (22)	77
		Total final demand	160

5. State and local government purchases
   a. Total
   b. Education
   c. Other

The 87 × 87 matrix in Table 4.4 contains a wealth of information useful to the chemical professional. It is helpful when one is extracting data to be presented in summary tables. Tables 4.6 to 4.8, which illustrate several important aspects of the sales pattern within the United States, are typical examples. There is wide variation among industries in the proportion of total output going directly to final demand. Some industries, e.g., new construction (11), food and kindred products

(14), apparel (18), and household furniture (22), sell most of their products directly to final demand. Other industries, e.g., stone and clay mining (9), wood containers (21), iron and ferroalloy ores mining (5), and metal containers (39), sell practically all their output to intermediate consumers. The CPI and related industries fit mostly into the latter category (Table 4.6).

With the notable exception of industry 29, drugs and cleaning and toilet preparations, the connection between production and final demand of all industries shown in Table 4.6 can be traced only through intermediate sales to other industries.

Table 4.7 illustrates this point for industry 27, chemicals and selected chemical products. The first column of this table shows the sales to the seven industries buying the largest amounts (in dollar value) from industry 27. Also shown is the amount sold to final demand. Note that the largest industrial buyer is industry 27 itself.

Table 4.8 Diversity of sales distribution patterns of the CPI and related industries, 1967

Industry	Number of industrial buyers†	Percent of total sales sold to the largest buyer
Crude petroleum and natural gas (8)	7	76
Chemical and fertilizer mineral mining (10)	19	59
Paper and allied products except containers (24)	75	20
Chemicals and selected chemical products (27)	78	19
Plastics and synthetic materials (28)	42	27
Drugs, cleaning and toilet preparations (29)	42	9
Paints and allied products (30)	63	30
Petroleum refining and related industries (31)	80	7
Rubber and miscellaneous plastics products (32)	80	7
Glass and glass products (35)	49	26
Primary iron and steel manufacturing (37)	62	19
Primary nonferrous metal manufacturing (38)	19	32

† Buyers of $1 million or more annually.

The next six largest industrial buyers, all in the CPI, are plastics and synthetic materials (28), other agricultural products (2), drugs, cleaning and toilet preparations (29), petroleum refining and related industries (31), paints and allied products (30), and paper and allied products, except containers (24). In the column headed major buyers, the seven industries buying the largest amounts from the six industries listed in the seller column are given. Several of the major buyers, e.g., new construction, food and kindred products, apparel, household furniture, and motor vehicles and equipment, are major suppliers to final demand. The demand for industry 27's products is thus derived through supplying other industries' needs.

There is great diversity in intermediate sales-distribution patterns. This is especially true for the CPI and related industries (Table 4.8). For example, both chemicals and selected chemical products (27) and petroleum refining and related industries (31) have sales of over $1 million to over 75 industries. However, 19 percent of total sales of 27 goes to its largest buyer industry, while 7 percent of total sales of 31 goes to its largest buyer industry. Plastics and synthetic materials (28) and drugs, cleaning and toilet preparations (29) both sell to 42 industries. But 28 sells 27 percent of its total output to its largest buyer industry while 29 sells only 9 percent of its total output to its largest buyer.

4.2 THE DIRECT-REQUIREMENTS TABLE

The dollar-flow matrix in Tables 4.2 and 4.4 can be normalized to yield a table of coefficients which represent the fractions of a dollar required by a sector to produce a dollar of output. This is done as follows: the division of any element X_{kj} in the transaction table by the output of a sector gives the dollar input from industry k required for $1 of output from industry j. This is defined as the direct coefficient

$$D_{kj} = \frac{X_{kj}}{X_j} \tag{4.8}$$

Equations (4.2) can be thus rewritten as

$$X_1 = (D_{11}X_1 + D_{12}X_2 + D_{13}X_3 + \cdots + D_{1n}X_n) + F_1$$
$$X_2 = (D_{21}X_1 + D_{22}X_2 + D_{23}X_3 + \cdots + D_{2n}X_n) + F_2 \tag{4.9}$$

$$\cdots\cdots\cdots\cdots\cdots\cdots\cdots\cdots\cdots\cdots\cdots\cdots\cdots\cdots\cdots\cdots\cdots\cdots$$

$$X_n = (D_{n1}X_1 + D_{n2}X_2 + D_{n3}X_3 + \cdots + D_{nn}X_n) + F_n$$

In vector notation Eq. (4.9) are

$$\mathbf{X} = \mathbf{D}\mathbf{X} + \mathbf{F} \tag{4.10}$$

where boldface letters are vectors and $\mathbf{D}$ is a matrix.

Table 4.9 Direct-requirements table (four-sector economy)†

	Consumer	Basic	Energy	Service	Final demand
Consumer	0.226	0.029	0.000	0.042	0.300
Basic	0.301	0.416	0.015	0.051	0.065
Energy	0.008	0.029	0.354	0.024	0.037
Service	0.098	0.114	0.185	0.254	0.452
Value added	0.368	0.412	0.446	0.628	0.147
Total	1.00	1.00	1.00	1.00	

† Figures may not total 1.00 because of rounding.

In tabular form the direct coefficients of an entire economy are referred to as a *direct-requirements table*. Table 4.9 shows the direct-requirements table for the four-sector economy illustrated in Table 4.2. Each column shows the inputs to the industry named at the top of the column required from the industry named at the left of each row to produce $1 of column industry output.

	Industry *j*
Industry *k*	Dollar input from *k* needed to produce $1 output from *j*

Table 4.9 is readily obtained by using Eq. (4.8). For example, the direct requirement of the energy industry for service is 0.185, which is obtained by $12 billion of service industry input divided by the total output of the energy sector, $65 billion. Table 4.9 shows that in addition to service costs of 18.5 cents, the energy sector needs 35.4 cents of input from itself, 44.6 cents from value added (mostly employee compensation), and 1.5 cents from basic industry to produce $1 of output.

Table 4.10, is the direct-requirements table of the United States economy for 1967. Note that the special industries 84 to 87 are not listed. Except for the larger number of sectors, Table 4.10 is completely analogous to Table 4.9.

For example, to produce $1 of output the plastics and synthetic materials industry (28) requires input from 58 industries. It requires the most input from chemicals and selected chemical products (34.7 cents); paper and allied products, except containers (3 cents); and wholesale and retail trade (3 cents). Table 4.11 lists the five largest suppliers of sectors 8, 10, 24, 27, 28, and 29 in terms of dollar of direct input per total dollar output.

The direct-requirements table permits estimation of the changes in output directly required of any industry *k* due to changes in total output of industries supplied by industry *k*. Assuming that the direct coefficients remain constant, this is accomplished as follows:

$$\Delta X_k = \sum_{j=1}^{n} D_{kj}\, \Delta X_j \tag{4.11}$$

Table 4.10 shows that the motor vehicles and equipment sector (59) requires $0.00139 of input from chemicals and selected chemical products (27) to produce $1 of output.

$$D_{27,\,59} = 0.00139$$

If final demand for sector 59 increases by $10 million, we can estimate the change in the direct requirements for sector 27 as follows:

$$\Delta X_{59} = \Delta F_{59} = \$10{,}000{,}000$$
$$\Delta X_{27} = 0.00139 \times 10{,}000{,}000 \qquad [\text{Eq. (4.11)}]$$
$$= \$13{,}900$$

If other industries which are supplied by sector 27 increased their output, the total direct effect could be estimated by summing the individual amounts [Eq. (4.11)].

4.3 THE TOTAL-REQUIREMENTS TABLE

Although useful, the direct-requirements table does not enable one to calculate directly the total-input requirement for an industry given a change in final demand. The direct coefficient is the dollar value of products bought *directly* from one industry for $1 of output from another. It does not include the value of products required *indirectly* via the input from other industries. Returning to the previous example, the $13,900 increase of input required from sector 27 for a change of $10 million in total output to final demand from sector 59 represents only those products bought directly from sector 27; but automobile production requires direct input from rubber and miscellaneous plastic products (32), plastics and synthetic products (28), paints and allied products (30), glass and glass products (35), primary iron and steel manufacturing (37), and so on. These industries, in turn, require input from chemicals and selected chemical products. Moreover, these industries will require additional motor vehicles and equipment (59), raising the demand for such products even higher that the initial $10 million change. Thus the increase in total output from a change in final demand is equal to

$$\Delta X = \Delta F + (\mathbf{D}\,\Delta F) + (\mathbf{D}\mathbf{D}\,\Delta F) + (\mathbf{D}\mathbf{D}\mathbf{D}\,\Delta F) + \cdots$$

where the first term, $\Delta \mathbf{F}$ is the initial change in final demand, the second term, $\mathbf{D}\,\Delta \mathbf{F}$, is the first-round increase in production computed by the direct requirement, the third term, $\mathbf{D}\mathbf{D}\,\Delta \mathbf{F}$, is a new round of increase in production brought about by the need of the supplying industries to purchase goods and services to cover the needs of the increase in production, etc.

To take into account both the *direct* and *indirect* requirements of input by one industry needed for a dollar's worth of output to final demand of another industry,

Table 4.10 Direct requirements, 1967 (dollar input per total dollar output)

For the composition of inputs to an industry, read the column for that industry.

Industry No.	Industry	1 Livestock and livestock products	2 Other agricultural products	3 Forestry and fishery products	4 Agricultural, forestry and fishery services	5 Iron and ferroalloy ores mining	6 Nonferrous metal ores mining	7 Coal mining	8 Crude petroleum and natural gas	9 Stone and clay mining and quarrying	10 Chemical and fertilizer mineral mining	11 New construction
1	Livestock and livestock products	0.18312	.05074	.04951	.06344							
2	Other agricultural products	.27350	.03170	.05308	.18086							0.00100
3	Forestry and fishery products			.01753								
4	Agricultural, forestry and fishery services	.01969	.04677	.02303								.00202
5	Iron and ferroalloy ores mining					.05270	.00268	.00009			.00117	
6	Nonferrous metal ores mining					.01904	.12969			.00195	.00273	
7	Coal mining	.00013	.00003		.00015	.00017	.00037	.12636	.00002	.00234	.00029	
8	Crude petroleum and natural gas							.00035	.02487			
9	Stone and clay mining and quarrying	.00006	.00117			.00229	.00274	.00101		.02692	.00711	.00838
10	Chemical and fertilizer mineral mining		.00013			.00275	.00152			.00072	.05948	
11	New construction											
12	Maintenance and repair construction	.00761	.01296			.01726	.00951	.00737	.03168	.00764	.00818	.00032
13	Ordnance and accessories											
14	Food and kindred products	.12058		.01219	.01651							
15	Tobacco manufactures											
16	Broad and narrow fabrics, yarn and thread mills		.00032			.00010		.00408				.00023
17	Miscellaneous textile goods and floor coverings	.00032	.00101	.03044	.01704	.00075	.00006	.00070	.00032	.00093		.00255
18	Apparel											.00061
19	Miscellaneous fabricated textile products	.00001	.00152	.00015	.00169			.00095		.00463		.00001
20	Lumber and wood products, except containers	.00009	.00009			.00206	.00658	.00692			.00107	.05695
21	Wooden containers		.00367		.00476							
22	Household furniture											.00429
23	Other furniture and fixtures											.00277
24	Paper and allied products, except containers	.00050	.00004	.00005	.00001	.00008	.00006	.00006	.00006	.00870	.00380	.00309
25	Paperboard containers and boxes	.00006	.00012			.00011	.00024	.00006	.00001	.00013	.00049	
26	Printing and publishing	.00020	.00036	.00015	.00007	.00006	.00012	.00003	.00004	.00001	.00010	.00093
27	Chemicals and selected chemical products	.00245	.08047	.00139	.00768	.01577	.03073	.01591	.01090	.02242	.02619	.00170
28	Plastics and synthetic materials											
29	Drugs, cleaning and toilet preparations	.00175									.00010	
30	Paints and allied products			.00120				.00059				.00570
31	Petroleum refining and related industries	.00545	.03172	.01835	.00187	.00247	.00329	.01107	.00220	.03151	.00243	.01753
32	Rubber and miscellaneous plastics products	.00119	.00577	.00257	.00004	.00832	.00524	.00854	.00227	.01214	.00837	.00802
33	Leather tanning and industrial leather products											
34	Footwear and other leather products	.00030			.00030							
35	Glass and glass products	.00018										.00204
36	Stone and clay products	.00007	.00086	.00021	.00007	.00052	.00171	.00360	.00582	.05066		.06732
37	Primary iron and steel manufacturing					.02386	.02518	.01334	.00796	.02157	.01752	.01823
38	Primary nonferrous metal manufacturing	.00004	.00001			.00218	.00061	.00253		.00225	.00156	.02698
39	Metal containers	.00049	.00033	.01985								
40	Heating, plumbing and structural metal products					.00011	.00006	.00032	.00322	.00132	.00201	.09759
41	Stampings, screw machine products and bolts	.00085				.00126	.00335	.01331		.00013	.00019	.00063
42	Other fabricated metal products	.00105	.00157	.00183	.00536	.00120	.00226	.00108	.00416	.00553	.00097	.01916
43	Engines and turbines				.00008	.00229	.00105	.00537	.00436	.00323	.01019	.00114
44	Farm machinery and equipment	.00025		.01018								
45	Construction, mining and oil field machinery					.01497	.01421	.03206	.00381	.00887	.01100	.00161
46	Materials handling machinery and equipment						.00049			.00318	.00049	.00526
47	Metalworking machinery and equipment					.00075	.00079		.00032	.00012	.00019	.00003
48	Special industry machinery and equipment											
49	General industrial machinery and equipment				.00021	.00017	.00024	.00142	.00570	.00718	.00029	.00213
50	Machine shop products	.00016	.00019			.00031	.03110	.00259	.00532	.00174	.00467	.00053
51	Office, computing and accounting machines											.00754
52	Service industry machines											.00551
53	Electric industrial equipment and apparatus					.00040	.00073		.01075	.00234	.00156	
54	Household appliances											.00183
55	Electric lighting and wiring equipment	.00006	.00007	.00015		.00006	.00018	.00262	.00017	.00017	.00019	.01360
56	Radio, television and communication equipment								.00033			.00078
57	Electronic components and accessories								.00011			
58	Miscellaneous electrical machinery, equipment and supplies	.00039	.00133	.00077					.00022			.00055
59	Motor vehicles and equipment		.00022	.00026								.00004
60	Aircraft and parts											
61	Other transportation equipment	.00001	.00023	.00817	.00026	.00006	.00134	.00009			.00039	.00001
62	Scientific and controlling instruments			.00010		.00011	.00024		.00062			.00349
63	Optical, ophthalmic and photographic equipment											
64	Miscellaneous manufacturing	.00007	.00007	.00221		.00017	.00037	.00009	.00002	.00013	.00029	.00138
65	Transportation and warehousing	.02253	.01583	.02062	.01000	.05913	.03075	.00870	.00971	.01121	.01431	.02673
66	Communications; except radio and TV broadcasting	.00246	.00247			.00120	.00165	.00161	.00082	.00042	.00419	.00368
67	Radio and TV broadcasting											
68	Electric, gas, water and sanitary services	.00316	.00517	.00026	.00082	.02799	.02475	.02172	.01145	.03125	.01312	.00081
69	Wholesale and retail trade	.01349	.05350	.02168	.01052	.01044	.01689	.02144	.01162	.02144	.01567	.08140
70	Finance and insurance	.00839	.01100	.00812	.00090	.00516	.01866	.01015	.00618	.01074	.00806	.00716
71	Real estate and rental	.01551	.07223	.00679	.02673	.07633	.02640	.05050	.16161	.03779	.03923	.00750
72	Hotels; personal and repair services except auto	.00021										
73	Business services	.00249	.01313	.00005	.00004	.03556	.01323	.02564	.01609	.03172	.03018	.05485
74	Automobile repair and services	.00103	.00463	.00278	.00022	.00057	.00140	.00196	.00114	.00722	.00088	.00457
75	Amusements											
76	Medical, educational services and nonprofit organizations	.00597	.00061			.00052	.00067	.00066	.00038	.00017	.00185	.00105
77	Federal Government enterprises	.00008	.00014		.00021	.00073	.00085	.00066	.00042	.00047	.00175	.00035
78	State and local government enterprises	.00005										.00036
79	Gross imports of goods and services	.00593	.01168	.25064	.01550	.30057	.19383	.00063	.07159	.01726	.08751	.00110
80	Business travel, entertainment and gifts	.00009	.00129	.00751	.00194	.00161	.00346	.00348	.00576	.00142	.00613	.00666
81	Office supplies	.00003	.00089	.00026	.00019	.00023	.00037	.00011	.00011	.00012	.00029	.00032
82	Scrap, used and secondhand goods					.00113	.00127	.00575	.00573	.00098	.00010	.00075
V.A.	Value added	.26392	.48889	.42098	.57078	.29024	.37272	.58302	.57287	.56091	.58152	.30875
E.C.	*Employee compensation*	.03958	.07901	.05769	.29895	.14483	.25767	.39108	.05865	.31124	.18067	.51413
I.B.T.	*Indirect business taxes*	.08505	.63583	.06576	.08514	.08827	.05408	.08169	.04898	.01976	.08098	.06604
P.T.I.	*Property-type income*	.13935	.58005	.35755	.27868	.11774	.09097	.17045	.46580	.22997	.57995	.07858
T.	Total	1.00000	1.00000	1.00000	1.00000	1.00000	1.00000	1.00000	1.00000	1.00000	1.00000	1.00000

Table 4.10 (continued)

Maintenance and repair construction	Ordnance and accessories	Food and kindred products	Tobacco manufactures	Broad and narrow fabrics, yarn and thread mills	Miscellaneous textile goods and floor coverings	Apparel	Miscellaneous fabricated textile products	Lumber and wood products, except containers	Wooden containers	Household furniture	Other furniture and fixtures	Paper and allied products, except containers	Paperboard containers and boxes	Printing and publishing	Chemicals and selected chemical products	Plastics and synthetic materials	Industry No.
12	13	14	15	16	17	18	19	20	21	22	23	24	25	26	27	28	
0.00013		0.22109		0.00631	0.03415										0.00156		1
		.07693	0.17924	.07228	.00506			0.00355							.00054		2
.00081		.00472				0.00733		.07760								0.00004	3
															.00203		4
																	5
	0.00023	.00044	.00028	.00085	.00039	.00011	.00030	.00024	0.00018	0.00039	0.00032	0.00416	0.00010	0.00003	.00305	.00355	6
.01114		.00009			.00002			.00012							.00212	.00006	7
		.00005			.00004												8
												.00339			.00260		9
												.01155			.02621	.00001	10
.00016	.00227	.00287	.00092	.00322	.00238	.00110	.00084	.00193	.00221	.00349	.00390	0.00715	.00424		.00695	.00627	11
	.07154							.00004	.00055	.00129	.00312			.00020	.00047	.00017	12
		.16576	.00014	.00201	.00308	.00001		.00003		.00111		.00799	.00013		.00047		13
			.20960							.00002					.00835	.00597	14
.00012	.00069	.00003		.32380	.17563	.25092	.41051	.00084		.01967	.00193	.00905			.00009	.00538	15
.00002	.00053	.00019		.02871	.06307	.00416	.09567	.00053		.01964	.01666	.00314	.00076	.00196	.00028	.00017	16
.00017	.00652	.00051		.00247	.01405	.20625	.01830	.00101	.00111	.00295	.00269	.00057	.00109	.00080	.00023	.00038	17
	.00064	.00086	.00023	.00279	.01204	.01656	.00191	.00051	.00092	.00334	.00588	.00099	.00002	.00024	.00072	.00002	18
.01694	.00723	.00008	.00010	.00028	.00026			.27056	.36535	.13708	.06032	.07069	.00201		.00239	.00052	19
		.00123	.00069				.00154	.00256	.03171	.06729	.06382	.00004		.00007			20
.00036	.00001			.00002	.00107	.00015	.00033	.00154		.01529	.01935	.00004		.00002			21
.00040	.00002			.00001	.00015		.00074	.00058	.00037	.02470		.00004		.00007			22
.00194	.00043	.00975	.00665	.00036	.00623	.00231	.00074	.00519	.00332	.00310	.00248	.16031	.40517	.14985	.00994	.03053	23
	.00651	.01905	.00722	.00502	.00321	.00447	.01527	.00184	.00571	.00156	.02470	.01277	.40809	.03325	.00199	.00995	24
.00001	.00014	.00564	.00451	.00431	.00184	.00044		.00022		.01277	.00071	.02821	.01809	.11003	.00020		25
.00076	.00095	.00093	.00451	.00178	.01388	.00238	.00019	.01240	.03350	.00199	.00071	.00833	.00562	.02341	.00831	.00026	26
			.01068	.09546	.16001	.01966	.00588	.00117		.00254	.00167	.03714	.02341	.01831	.02915	.34750	27
.03710	.00016	.00300	.00205	.00112	.00056	.00023	.00114	.00002		.00008		.01150	.00345	.00194	.01334	.02782	28
.02666	.00244	.00905	.00005	.00163	.00002	.00002	.00447	.00073	.00147	.01503	.01187	.00090	.00071	.00967	.00341	.00576	29
.00462	.00824	.00244		.00131	.00133	.00094	.00041	.00062		.00133	.00138	.00610	.00400	.00182	.07765	.01415	30
		.00769	.00620	.00260	.01647	.00133	.01898	.00469	.00074	.01403	.00420	.01824	.00459	.00442	.00408	.02311	31
	.00005	.00001		.00002	.00013	.00013	.00297	.00002		.00074	.00032	.00003			.00004	.00001	32
.00304	.00140	.00119			.00017	.00088	.00043	.00014		.00008	.00011	.00015	.00017		(*)	.00001	33
.02978	.00140	.00001				.00088	.00003	.00037	.00018	.00023			.00027		.00008		34
.01265	.00015							.00014	.00424	.00576	.00234	.00197	.00527	.00047	.00795	.00046	35
.00863	.04877	.00006			.00034	.00088	(*)	.00657	.00369	.01881	.08867	.00017	.00017	.00023	.01388	.00325	36
	.02780	.02213	.00013					.00332	.00369	.00068	.00057	.00023	.00330	.00023	.00179	.00094	37
.05533	.00050						.00012	.00023		.00033	.00415	.00088			.01037	.00094	38
.00080	.00126	.00217					.00017	.00391	.00147	.00381	.11758		.00017	.00009	.00306	.00095	39
.01643	.01363	.00255	.00207	.00046	.00036	.00108	.00140	.01384	.00003	.05566	.04540	.11127	.00562	.00307	.00347	.00072	40
.00002	.00053							.00012			.00025				.00001		41
											.00156						42
.00079	.00077	(*)					.00001			.00064	.00304		.00002				43
.00554	.00136										.00234			.00002	.00001		44
(*)	.00007	.00011	.00003	.00018	.00004	.00001	.00005	.00067	.00037	.00016		.00097	.00910	.00084	.00002	.00003	45
	.00884	.00072	.00081	.00040	.00048	.00043	.00247	.00114	.00205	.01223	.00369	.00105	.00610	.00990	.00963	.00191	46
.00164	.00007	.00120		.00512	.03800		.00094	.00140	.00184	.00004	.00055	.00157	.00070	.00070	.00383	.00223	47
.00026	.00233	.00060	.00008	.00013	.00009			.00081	.00055	.00092		.00011	.00323	.00002	.00312	.00161	48
	.00988	(*)						.00106			.00177	.00323		.00003	.00001	.00223	49
	.00001							.00002			.00058				.00001		50
.00825	.00130									.00008	.00461	.00023			.00003		51
.00217	.00158				.00031			.00035			.00028				.00013		52
.00759	.00158	.00005					.00021	.00019	.00019	.00028	.00089	.00047	.00015	.00009	.00084		53
.01217	.00010					.00002	.00002	.00035	.00032	.00043	.00012	.00022		.00010	.00022	.00026	54
.00212	.02340						.00001	.01043	.00018	.00012	.00032	.00047	.00015	.00009			55
	.02346							.00018		.00002	.00004	.00365					56
.00032	.00037	.00002		.00004			.00240	.00034		.00023		.00011	.00022	.00001	.00002	.00002	57
.00004	.00042	.00005					.00043	.00036	.00037			.00149		.00001	.00002		58
	.11742						.00023	.00043				.00411			.00067		59
(*)	.00034						.00019	.00043			.00149	.00043		.00035	.00010	.00012	60
.00104	.00871						.00465	.00035			.00411	.00043					61
	.00771	.00012	.00008	.00032	.00019	.00057	.00026	.00009		.00787	.00018	.00094	.00028	.00333	.00016	.00013	62
.00390	.00043	.00002	.00005	.00009	.00002	.00015	.00801	.00119	.00092	.00716	.00323	.00093	.00008	.00803	.00047	.00004	63
.02944	.00056	.00010		.00009	.00379	.01384	.00655	.00119	.00092	.02150	.00023	.00084	.00032	.00164	.00085	.00030	64
.00191	.00963	.02898	.00437	.01587	.02260	.00655	.00691	.03321	.03613	.01400	.01400	.03433	.13767	.01152	.26373	.20097	65
		.00332		.00180	.00244	.00406	.00311	.00248	.00276	.00560	.00560	.00292	.00244	.01132	.03328	.00364	66
																	67
.00040	.00490	.00708	.00150	.01007	.00778	.00431	.00532	.00062	.00885	.00627	.00656	.02083	.00748	.00546	.03013	.01422	68
.07365	.02491	.08673	.00723	.03046	.04449	.02530	.02694	.04416	.04348	.04387	.03147	.03198	.02509	.02486	.02344	.03090	69
.00368	.00273	.00375	.00207	.00304	.00302	.00472	.00432	.00610	.00536	.00936	.00723	.00446	.00282	.00607	.00433	.00418	70
.00433	.00426	.00832	.00627	.00765	.01180	.01380	.00453	.00842	.00055	.01318	.01297	.01307	.01508	.04364	.01972	.01972	71
.02260	.00181	.03465	.00222	.00765	.00086	.00028	.00138	.00055		.00059	.00057	.00148	.00302	.00163	.00072	.00115	72
.00254	.00152	.00215	.00015	.00112	.00536	.01621	.01170	.01524	.01382	.02430	.02261	.02145	.02197	.04163	.02938	.02861	73
								.00068	.00147	.00143	.00152	.00079	.00123		.00093	.00095	74
																	75
.00056	.00146	.00050	.00015	.00030	.00039	.00062	.00047	.00037		.00070	.00082	.00048	.00063	.00198	.00072	.00072	76
.00017	.00120	.00070	.00169	.00078	.00025	.00057	.00057	.00057		.00073	.00131	.00074	.00083	.01259	.00149	.00049	77
.00021	.00008	.00020	.00001	.00011		.00009	.00004	.00016		.00023		.00023	.00005	.00005	.00033	.00012	78
.00057	.00554	.02960	.00326	.02624	.08726	.00264	.00026	.05872	.00424	.00041	.11102	.08162	.00041	.00098	.02924	.11469	79
.00696	.01367	.00405	.00519	.00299	.00251	.00504	.00353	.00264	.00793	.00699	.00478	.00368	.00285	.01178	.00560	.00827	80
.00017	.00119	.00067	.00024	.00047	.00047	.00065	.00053	.00074		.00105	.00117	.00063	.00081	.00248	.00068	.00049	81
.00024		(*)	.00006		.00829		(*)					.01425		.00002	.00141		82
.58652	.45273	.26822	.48611	.30132	.26322	.36999	.29161	.37430	.40313	.44156	.45130	.25429	.37010	.36776	.49694	.34775	V.A.
.05888	.58175	.14757	.07597	.11199	.16973	.50161	.21067	.35900	.48184	.58678	.58769	.22897	.27807	.37181	.18577	.25576	E.C.
.00115	.06680	.04982	.37189	.06411	.05810	.00485	.00595	.00868	.00795	.00784	.00702	.01014	.00795	.00750	.00909	.00858	I.B.T.
.07951	.06418	.07163	.15885	.08892	.08859	.06415	.07708	.16662	.11536	.10754	.11660	.13099	.08777	.11783	.17555	.10561	P.T.I.
1.00000	1.00000	1.00000	1.00000	1.00000	1.00000	1.00000	1.00000	1.00000	1.00000	1.00000	1.00000	1.00000	1.00000	1.00000	1.00000	1.00000	T.

(continued)

Table 4.10 (continued)

Industry No.	For the composition of inputs to an industry, read the column for that industry.	Drugs, cleaning, and toilet preparations 29	Paints and allied products 30	Petroleum refining and related industries 31	Rubber and miscellaneous plastics products 32	Leather tanning and industrial leather products 33	Footwear and other leather products 34	Glass and glass products 35	Stone and clay products 36	Primary iron and steel manufacturing 37	Primary nonferrous metals manufacturing 38	Metal containers 39
1	Livestock and livestock products	0.00095				0.01330						
2	Other agricultural products		0.01994									
3	Forestry and fishery products	.00014	.00034									
4	Agricultural, forestry and fishery services											
5	Iron and ferroalloy ores mining								.00088	.04717	.00022	
6	Nonferrous metal ores mining									.00112	.00180	.05012
7	Coal mining	.00033	.00007	.00037	.00070	.00156	.00009	.00050	.00507	.02030	.00058	.00012
8	Crude petroleum and natural gas			.42840								
9	Stone and clay mining and quarrying	.00026	.00607	.00234	.00052			.01113	.07227	.00209	.00018	
10	Chemical and fertilizer mineral mining	.00098		.00031	.00081			.00108	.00377	.00083	.00013	
11	New Construction											
12	Maintenance and repair construction	.00385	.00405	.01347	.00361	.00202	.00130	.00834	.00896	.00919	.00333	.00069
13	Ordnance and accessories					.00017				.00007	(*)	.00009
14	Food and kindred products	.02428	.02656	.00114	.00014	.23502	.00146		.00055	.00002	.00038	.00030
15	Tobacco manufactures											
16	Broad and narrow fabrics, yarn and thread mills	.00021	.00021			.02375			.00414			.00046
17	Miscellaneous textile goods and floor coverings	.00004	.00017			.03272	.00083		.00220			.00002
18	Apparel	.00033	.00034	.00010	.00199		.01075	.00121	.00083	.00066	.00049	.00048
19	Miscellaneous fabricated textile products	.00014	.00003		.00081		.01064		.00007	.00003	.00006	.00006
20	Lumber and wood products, except containers	.00048	.00007	.00006	.00296	.00037		.01099	.00294	.00233	.00362	.00116
21	Wooden containers							.00005	.00121		.00016	
22	Household furniture	.00002			.00023			.00007	.00158	.00001		
23	Other furniture and fixtures				.00019			.00033	.00011	.00001		.00001
24	Paper and allied products, except containers	.00719	.00199	.00315	.01900	.00450	.00126	.01788	.00929	.00093		.00230
25	Paperboard containers and boxes	.02676	.00769	.00277	.01222	.00193	.01384	.05214	.00507	.00057	.00075	.01344
26	Printing and publishing	.00220	.00034	.00010	.00054	.00009	.00071	.00021	.00031	.00012	.00063	.04078
27	Chemicals and selected chemical products	.10871	.21047	.02311	.03734	.05000	.00132	.02302	.01857	.01236	.00883	.00161
28	Plastics and synthetic materials	.00501	.04163	.00816	.16402	.00101	.00045	.00524	.00001		.00741	
29	Drugs, cleaning and toilet preparations	.05363	.01002	.00341	.00121	.03596	.00149	.00097	.00041		.00010	.00075
30	Paints and allied products	.00289	.00655	.00056	.00164	.00018	.00012	.00508	.00075	.00045	.00052	.02704
31	Petroleum refining and related industries	.00128	.01565	.06787	.00151	.00275	.00085	.00914	.00366	.00231	.00101	
32	Rubber and miscellaneous plastics products	.03121	.00220	.00214	.01608	.00294	.06866	.02415	.00109	.00105	.00282	.00146
33	Leather tanning and industrial leather products				.00002	.00028	.10935		.00027	.00005		(*)
34	Footwear and other leather products	.00001		.00003	.00019	.00181	.00358	.00002	.00003			(*)
35	Glass and glass products	.01535			.00274				.00030			.00004
36	Stone and clay products	.00172	.00343	.00215	.00168	.00165		.02877	.01673	.11165	.00355	.00298
37	Primary iron and steel manufacturing	.00005	.00422	.00031	.00317				.00112	.01133	.18966	.36890
38	Primary nonferrous metal manufacturing	.00016	.01050	.00151	.00114		.00021	.00745	.00233	.02708	.32214	.00642
39	Metal containers	.01561		.00758	.00036				.00112	.00006	.00086	.00516
40	Heating, plumbing and structural metal products			.00014	.00072		.00034		.00097	.00213	.00031	.00054
41	Stampings, screw machine products and bolts	.00362			.00487		.00509	.00018	.00025	.00662	.00213	.01490
42	Other fabricated metal products	.01338	.00645	.00059	.01480	.00101	.01413	.00074	.01036	.00143	.00380	.00393
43	Engines and turbines							.00093		.00019	.00027	
44	Farm machinery and equipment				.00011				.00002	.00105	.00002	
45	Construction, mining and oil field machinery				.00009				.00021	.00055	.00003	
46	Materials handling machinery and equipment	.00006	.00010	.00067	.00012	.00018	.00022	.00018	.00058	.00151	.00067	.00033
47	Metalworking machinery and equipment	.00064	.00055	.00018	.00344	.00291	.00294	.00303	.00234	.00937	.00758	.00814
48	Special industry machinery and equipment				.00125	.00037	.00189		.00096	.00109	.00008	.00107
49	General industrial machinery and equipment	.00015	.00010	.00240	.00096	.00018		.00092	.00279	.01084	.00128	.00015
50	Machine shop products	.00039	.00096			.00083			.00007	.00015	.00093	.00009
51	Office, computing and accounting machines				.00012				.00017	(*)		
52	Service industry machines	.00010	.00007		.00004			.00011	.00038	.00001	.00014	
53	Electric industrial equipment and apparatus	.00004			.00021			.00021	.00129	.00910	.00574	.00005
54	Household appliances	.00037			.00012			.00005	.00010	.00011	.00027	.00212
55	Electric lighting and wiring equipment	.00005			.00057		.00083	.00168	.00299	.00061	.00106	.00033
56	Radio, television and communication equipment	.00010	.00007	.00044	.00024			.00008	.00014	.00011	.00062	
57	Electronic components and accessories				.00037			.00005	.00001		.00105	
58	Miscellaneous electrical machinery, equipment and supplies	.00001	.00007	(*)	.00014			.00011	.00002	.00028	.00195	
59	Motor vehicles and equipment	.00013	.00045	.00010	.00110		.00374		.00383	.00615	.00210	.00009
60	Aircraft and parts				.00366		.00012		.00006	.00003	.00005	.00116
61	Other transportation equipment				.00009		.00012		.00006		.00003	.00018
62	Scientific and controlling instruments	.00124	.00010	.00063	.00071	.00018	.00193	.00176	.00044	.00157	.00021	.00018
63	Optical, ophthalmic and photographic equipment	.00011	.00010	.00003	.00059	.00009	.00137	.00013	.00005	.00008	.00002	.00003
64	Miscellaneous manufacturing	.00096	.00065	.00003	.00073	.00957	.00176	.00372	.00034		.00080	
65	Transportation and warehousing	.01286	.02779	.03149	.01723	.02816	.00635	.02849	.02892	.04477	.00385	.02203
66	Communications; except radio and TV broadcasting	.00412	.00309	.00101	.00448	.00248	.00415	.00345	.00526	.00300	.00211	.00179
67	Radio and TV broadcasting											
68	Electric, gas, water and sanitary services	.00406	.00542	.01711	.01101	.00853	.00488	.03565	.03249	.02592	.02044	.00742
69	Wholesale and retail trade	.02934	.03459	.00121	.03183	.00247	.03377	.03102	.02627	.02943	.03576	.00972
70	Finance and insurance	.00474	.00453	.00927	.00405	.00743	.00608	.00521	.00812	.00372	.00555	.00456
71	Real estate and rental	.03077	.02313	.02334	.01230	.01248	.01420	.01905	.01888	.00252	.00731	.00945
72	Hotels; personal and repair services except auto	.00439	.00477	.00324	.00130	.00009	.00066	.00103	.00062	.00084	.00051	.00048
73	Business services	.16422	.03303	.02883	.03160	.01211	.02743	.02931	.02368	.02652	.01320	.02468
74	Automobile repair and services	.00082	.00141		.00042	.00093	.00064	.00099	.00093	.00093	.00051	.00048
75	Amusements											
76	Medical, educational services and nonprofit organizations	.00168	.00100	.00024	.00068	.00064	.00106	.00071	.00091	.00047	.00053	.00027
77	Federal Government enterprises	.00165	.00151	.00060	.00080	.00063	.00316	.00113	.00093	.00061	.00042	.00027
78	State and local government enterprises	.00008	.00010	.00010	.00010	.00055		.00011	.00071	.00019	.00014	.00003
79	Gross imports of goods and services	.01069	.00896	.02782	.02806	.07082	.00297	.02494	.01603	.04476	.09808	.00170
80	Business travel, entertainment and gifts	.01344	.01534	.00101	.01642	.00229	.00512	.00663	.00662	.00268	.00251	.02605
81	Office supplies	.00077	.00030	.00041	.00060	.00060	.00064	.00065	.00091	.00091	.00060	.00027
82	Scrap, used and secondhand goods	.00001	.01228		.00042	.00117		.00197	.00023	.02651		.04173
83	Value added	.38401	.32363	.25541	.44736	.29566	.43176	.55479	.45570	.39047	.27381	.34874
V.A.	*Employee compensation*	.19556	.21053	.08401	.35010	.21438	.30880	.37808	.30667	.29925	.16846	.22444
E.C.	*Indirect business taxes*	.00677	.00878	.11895	.02131	.05085	.00230	.00863	.01131	.01158	.02002	.00909
I.B.T.	*Property-type income*	.18167	.09432	.05854	.11596	.07805	.07858	.17413	.13772	.08996	.10093	.11581
P.T.I.												
T.	Total	1.00000	1.00000	1.00000	1.00000	1.00000	1.00000	1.00000	1.00000	1.00000	1.00000	1.00000

Table 4.10 (*continued*)

Heating, plumbing and structural metal products	Stampings, screw machine products and bolts	Other fabricated metal products	Engines and turbines	Farm machinery and equipment	Construction, mining and oil field machinery	Materials handling machinery and equipment	Metalworking machinery and equipment	Special industry machinery and equipment	General industrial machinery and equipment	Machine shop products	Office, computing and accounting machines	Service industry machines	Electric industrial equipment and apparatus	Household appliances	Electric lighting and wiring equipment	Radio, television and communication equipment	Industry No.
40	41	42	43	44	45	46	47	48	49	50	51	52	53	54	55	56	
																	1
																	2
																	3
																	4
		0.00006													0.00024		5
																	6
0.00008	0.00031	.00022	0.00050	0.00052	0.00040	0.00028	0.00009	0.00016	0.00019	0.00013	0.00009	0.00021	0.00032	0.00040	.00022	0.00009	7
.00006		.00015															8
		.00054															9
																	10
																	11
.00321	.00392	.00303	.00311	.00267	.00370	.00232	.00324	.00324	.00342	.00261	.00230	.00248	.00321	.00319	.00274	.00265	12
.00099	.00042	.00116	.00622	.00077	.00124	.00035	.00025	.00222	.00055	.00048	.00013	.00027	.00193	.00004	.00134	.00926	13
	.00006							.00090	.00013			.00025					14
																	15
								.00092				.00074	.00019	.00283	.00095		16
.00002		.00188							.00055	.00114		.00023	.00041			.00019	17
.00076	.00082	.00085	.00050	.00060	.00064	.00063	.00081	.00067	.00081	.00107	.00049	.00051	.00075	.00066	.00083	.00066	18
.00020	.00039	.00022	.00005	.00010	.00012	.00047	.00006	.00005	.00005	.00005	.00001			.00004			19
.00241	.00372	.00383		.00199	.00131	.00126	.00089	.00481	.00277	.00016	.00024	.00116	.00132	.00156	.00092	.00050	20
.00075	.00101	.00021		.00033	.00022	.00028	.00010	.00023	.00041	.00010		.00174	.00029	.00272		.00152	21
.00019	.00062	.00097	.00031		.00005		.00005	.00007		.00008		.00013		.00090	.00012	.01559	22
.00251	.00024	.00121		.00087		.00051	.00008	.00004	.00067	.00086	.00141	.00080		.00004	.00005	.00004	23
.00196	.00317	.00500	.00026	.00037	.00032	.00020	.00037	.00046	.00054	.00051	.00489	.00129	.00674	.00033	.00107	.00138	24
.00435	.00659	.01003	.00342	.00137	.00084	.00083	.00096	.00086	.00182	.00391	.00141	.00149	.00403	.01824	.01887	.00240	25
.00012	.00025	.00097	.00008	.00012	.00015	.00016	.00015	.00116	.00014	.00013	.01407	.00009	.00090	.00004	.00010	.00193	26
.00110	.00367	.01098	.00044	.00041	.00008	.00001	.00116	.00062	.00171	.00178	.00022	.00335	.00668	.00554	.00566	.00088	27
	.00180	.00007					.00009	.00035	.00013		.00087		.00115	.00530	.00809	.00264	28
.00068	.00041	.00062					.00001	.00028	.00026	.00023		.00013		.00057			29
.00814	.00228	.00550	.00112	.00245	.00189	.00114	.00150	.00032	.00058	.00063	.00127	.00386	.00274	.00851	.00413	.00047	30
.00269	.00185	.00349	.00103	.00226	.00331	.00205	.00492	.00456	.00382	.01101	.00100	.00210	.00147	.00152	.00129	.00156	31
.00209	.00630	.01679	.00199	.02698	.01639	.01225	.00833	.00783	.00526	.00520	.00904	.01004	.00871	.04512	.02079	.00663	32
	.00019	.00012	.00021		.00602		.00003	.00025	.00051			.00019	.00023	.00024			33
.00002	.00015	.00013		.00002	.00002	.00016	.00009	.00009	.00001	.00003	.00001	.00002	.00002	.00086		.00005	34
.00446	.00041	.00154					.00005	.00062	.00012	.00013		.00021	.00069	.00362	.03038	.00252	35
.00306	.00238	.00455	.00873	.00220	.00700	.00331	.00976	.00503	.01094	.00777	.00093	.00924	.01043	.00787	.00974	.00077	36
.24128	.23758	.17575	.10045	.13568	.15911	.10546	.08015	.08518	.10836	.08499	.01233	.05893	.05095	.07536	.06120	.00550	37
.06990	.05636	.06962	.05101	.01697	.00963	.03250	.02661	.02799	.03953	.03665	.01372	.05020	.06108	.01878	.06309	.01610	38
.00064	.00271	.00031					.00074		.00024								39
.02380	.00241	.00717	.00332	.00299	.00676	.01316	.03341	.01734	.01617	.00193	.00311	.02423	.00115	.00446	.00442	.00042	40
.02224	.01894	.01675	.01929	.02172	.00906	.01288	.03524	.00827	.00719	.01261	.01193	.02019	.01652	.01388	.02715	.01605	41
.02709	.01253	.03530	.01114	.01492	.01212	.02628	.01953	.01308	.02503	.01203	.00925	.03631	.00950	.03476	.01460	.00831	42
.00231	.00105	.03105	.07399	.06094	.02163	.01249	.00074	.00583	.00940	.00195		.00095	.01216				43
.00061	.00083	.00087	.00659	.04720	.00964	.00784	.00091	.00246	.00237	.00058	.00006	.00034	.00002	.00092	.00245	.00001	44
.00338	.00005	.00166	.03749	.01997	.05045	.04211	.00221	.00519	.00746	.00074	.00009	.00199	.00156		.00002		45
.00220	.00046	.00119	.00013	.00054	.01249	.05204	.00097	.00405	.00251	.00033	.00001	.00337	.00121	.00007	.00005	.00005	46
.00511	.01819	.01490	.01271	.00794	.01992	.01513	.07056	.02426	.02004	.02558	.01127	.00769	.01354	.00903	.00631	.00604	47
.00167	.00110	.00246	.00345	.00184	.00167	.00335	.00545	.06825	.01110	.00145	.00057	.00231	.00044	.00002	.00024	.00002	48
.01050	.00150	.00740	.03637	.06698	.06006	.05878	.02532	.01399	.06589	.01477	.00510	.01487	.00704	.00949	.00185	.00090	49
.00954	.01257	.00579	.02601	.00862	.03639	.01950	.00801	.00391	.00828	.06273	.01052	.00085	.00223	.00117	.00452	.00357	50
.00049	.00117	.00011		.00002	.00005		.00613	.00143	.00003	.00003	.13182	.00044	.00024			.00684	51
.01309	.00173	.00293		.00033	.00008	.00437	.00156	.00201	.00628	.00033	.00007	.06200	.00068	.02830	.00051	.00052	52
.01020	.00061	.00186	.02115	.00493	.01237	.03585	.03054	.03568	.03239	.00604	.02169	.07764	.07426	.05267	.03558	.01483	53
.00285	.00158	.00051		.00276			.00058	.00083	.00038	.00005		.10763	.00032	.01367	.00007	.00122	54
.00064	.00256	.00223	.00008	.00017	.00050	.00032	.00038	.00155	.00077	.00200	.02375	.00625	.01646	.01195	.03312	.00855	55
.00020	.00033	.00022			.00017	.00047	.00068	.00764	.00037	.00033	.01217	.00330	.01799	.00028	.00296	.05979	56
.00003	.00026	.00014	.00165	.00004		.00024	.00008	.00013	.00117	.00005	.10779	.00009	.02598	.00006	.00452	.18529	57
	.00004	.00010	.01924	.00833	.00174	.00193	.00018	.00051	.00047	.01261	.00006		.00509	.00297	.02394	.00106	58
.00409	.02453	.00590	.02314	.00640	.01081	.01083	.00894	.00125	.00530	.00673	.00034	.01710	.00387	.00736	.00432		59
.00325	.00074	.00085	.03945	.00017	.00402	.00181	.00246	.00188	.00786	.00051	.00024	.01318	.00137	.00125	.00078	.01220	60
.00452	.00030	.00062	.00923	.00153	.00487	.00071	.00001	.00361	.00224	.00091		.00104	.00846	.00046	.00005		61
.00532	.00218	.00274	.00146	.00292	.00554	.00485	.00161	.00227	.00332	.00058	.00275	.01313	.01143	.02666	.00124	.00317	62
.00012	.00028	.00027	.00005	.00006	.00007		.00013	.00102	.00015	.00010	.00054	.00042	.00057	.00018	.00231	.00069	63
.00025	.00222	.00207		.00085	.00044	.00071	.00116	.00065	.00015	.00020	.00088	.00373	.00046	.00697	.00066	.00177	64
.01604	.01528	.01133	.00829	.01345	.00994	.00780	.00678	.00794	.00913	.00711	.00431	.00915	.00812	.01206	.01035	.00549	65
.00601	.00377	.00460	.00421	.00377	.00499	.00682	.00536	.00674	.00615	.00497	.00635	.00434	.00635	.00373	.00476	.00828	66
																	67
.00759	.00879	.00964	.00497	.00504	.00665	.00414	.00643	.00474	.00663	.01043	.00289	.00449	.00689	.00789	.00891	.00447	68
.03270	.01925	.02396	.03383	.03574	.03366	.03096	.03082	.03618	.03296	.02495	.03683	.03898	.03285	.03292	.02912	.02830	69
.00668	.00439	.00519	.00188	.00767	.00564	.00504	.00437	.00558	.00412	.00469	.00599	.00280	.00441	.00330	.00236	.00314	70
.01382	.01026	.01190	.00735	.00953	.01363	.01548	.01483	.03139	.01287	.02936	.03821	.01159	.01996	.01800	.01974	.01314	71
.00341	.00054	.00093	.00084	.00124	.00079	.00098	.00090	.00060	.00077	.00071	.00034	.00019	.00086	.00059	.00061	.00061	72
.01945	.01581	.02209	.01647	.02953	.01950	.02494	.01893	.01584	.02164	.02086	.02226	.02392	.01867	.06072	.02501	.02756	73
.00127	.00063	.00103	.00105	.00095	.00116	.00126	.00099	.00120	.00124	.00099	.00099	.00091	.00128	.00066	.00109	.00178	75
																	76
.00079	.00059	.00071	.00068	.00062	.00080	.00114	.00090	.00109	.00100	.00084	.00096	.00070	.00090	.00057	.00078	.00125	77
.00087	.00060	.00086	.00078	.00106	.00092	.00106	.00093	.00113	.00113	.00086	.00105	.00083	.00084	.00171	.00087	.00149	78
.00003	.00008	.00007	.00013	.00008	.00005	.00004	.00003	.00004	.00005	.00005	.00004	.00006	.00008	.00011	.00007	.00006	79
.00432	.01226	.02337	.02157	.05551	.01527	.00867	.03233	.04739	.02524	.00041	.02519	.00254	.02203	.00185	.01460	.03907	80
.01062	.00355	.00664	.00886	.00613	.00576	.00662	.00934	.01093	.01099	.01231	.02350	.01013	.01439	.00804	.00971	.00868	81
.00086	.00047	.00077	.00071	.00091	.00077	.00095	.00081	.00100	.00085	.00076	.00103	.00072	.00084	.00055	.00068	.00126	82
.00259		.00131	.00243	.00180	.00042		.00091	.00248	.00129	.00183					.00056	.00001	83
.36778	.45862	.44070	.35758	.34931	.42283	.39426	.50354	.42000	.44409	.55375	.41158	.31695	.45871	.35647	.46731	.45076	V.A.
.27462	*.33137*	*.28964*	*.26236*	*.25882*	*.28913*	*.31098*	*.37934*	*.33304*	*.32947*	*.41508*	*.29936*	*.21798*	*.33647*	*.24685*	*.29130*	*.36435*	*E.C.*
.00690	*.00802*	*.00679*	*.00711*	*.00692*	*.00926*	*.00717*	*.00833*	*.00653*	*.00781*	*.00688*	*.00500*	*.00525*	*.00736*	*.00620*	*.00646*	*.00555*	*I.T.B.*
.08627	*.11923*	*.14427*	*.08811*	*.08357*	*.12444*	*.07611*	*.11586*	*.08043*	*.10681*	*.13179*	*.10722*	*.09372*	*.11488*	*.10342*	*.16956*	*.08086*	*P.T.I.*
1.00000	**1.00000**	**1.00000**	**1.00000**	**1.00000**	**1.00000**	**1.00000**	**1.00000**	**1.00000**	**1.00000**	**1.00000**	**1.00000**	**1.00000**	**1.00000**	**1.00000**	**1.00000**	**1.00000**	**T.**

(*continued*)

Table 4.10 (continued)

Industry No.	For the composition of inputs to an industry, read the column for that industry	Electronic components and accessories 57	Miscellaneous electrical machinery, equipment and supplies 58	Motor vehicles and equipment 59	Aircraft and parts 60	Other transportation equipment 61	Scientific and controlling instruments 62	Optical, ophthalmic and photographic equipment 63	Miscellaneous manufacturing 64	Transportation and warehousing 65
1	Livestock and livestock products									.00008
2	Other agricultural products						0.00137		0.00108	.00078
3	Forestry and fishery products								.00026	.00005
4	Agricultural, forestry and fishery services									
5	Iron and ferroalloy ores mining									
6	Nonferrous metal ores mining		0.00217				.00042			
7	Coal mining	0.00009	.00029	0.00036	0.00010	0.00024	.00006		.00018	.00013
8	Crude petroleum and natural gas									.00048
9	Stone and clay mining and quarrying						.00015		.00046	
10	Chemical and fertilizer mineral mining									.00003
11	New construction									
12	Maintenance and repair construction	.00338	.00265	.00239	.00295	.00282	.00294	.00121	.00249	.02474
13	Ordnance and accessories	.00022	.00006	.00046	.01848	.00358	.00344	.00023	.00057	
14	Food and kindred products						.00202		.00018	.00315
15	Tobacco manufactures								.00020	
16	Broad and narrow fabrics, yarn and thread mills			.00027	.00097	.00003	.01207	.00040	.01503	
17	Miscellaneous textile goods and floor coverings	.00022		.00314	.00021	.00512	.00287		.00736	.00067
18	Apparel	.00101	.00073	.00010	.00062	.0004	.00124		.00254	.00035
19	Miscellaneous fabricated textile products	.00002	.00003	.01364	.00001	.00044	.00103	.00052	.00119	.00174
20	Lumber and wood products, except containers		.00175	.00097		.00051	.03827	.00145	.01581	.00005
21	Wooden containers			.00015	.00015		.00013		.00032	
22	Household furniture	.00103					.00387		.00100	
23	Other furniture and fixtures		.00006	.00098	.00238	.00038	.00156	.00004	.00104	
24	Paper and allied products, except containers	.00072	.00045	.00126	.00046	.00186	.01131	.01762	.01631	.00135
25	Paperboard containers and boxes	.00159	.00075	.03107	.00067	.00010	.00078	.00373	.02844	.00048
26	Printing and publishing	.00015	.00006	.00005	.00022	.00006	.00016	.00075	.00371	.00094
27	Chemicals and selected chemical products	.01343	.02312	.00139	.00064	.00023	.00326	.04355	.00571	.00087
28	Plastics and synthetic materials	.00778	.00899	.00056	.00133	.00273	.00407	.00760	.02338	
29	Drugs, cleaning and toilet preparations						.00861		.00164	.00009
30	Paints and allied products	.00099	.00022	.00350	.00072	.00365	.00066	.00033	.00463	.00120
31	Petroleum refining and related industries	.00141	.00108	.00167	.00409	.00170	.00181	.00082	.00302	.03785
32	Rubber and miscellaneous plastics products	.01966	.01894	.02056	.00384	.01773	.01914	.01325	.03884	.00544
33	Leather tanning and industrial leather products					.00001			.00167	
34	Footwear and other leather products	.00004		.00001	.00005	.00006	.00087	.00002	.00418	
35	Glass and glass products	.02848	.00035	.00807		.00292	.00200	.01000	.00348	.00078
36	Stone and clay products	.00552	.00746	.00224	.00187	.00448	.00200	.00107	.00266	.00021
37	Primary iron and steel manufacturing	.01337	.02188	.07095	.02056	.11390	.02681	.00427	.02630	.00494
38	Primary nonferrous metal manufacturing	.03473	.11107	.01538	.03329	.03723	.03324	.04041	.03968	.00126
39	Metal containers			.00007			.00200		.00025	
40	Heating, plumbing and structural metal products	.00098	.00223	.00067	.00034	.03601	.00155	.00004	.00064	
41	Stampings, screw machine products and bolts	.02030	.00174	.05711	.01800	.00682	.01823	.01155	.00929	.00335
42	Other fabricated metal products	.01475	.02105	.02833	.01606	.01960	.02990	.01580	.01926	.00389
43	Engines and turbines			.00574	.00286	.03637				.00122
44	Farm machinery and equipment			.00046	.00017	.00397	.00126	.00004	.00123	
45	Construction, mining and oil field machinery			.00145	.00003	.00335	.00042			
46	Materials handling machinery and equipment	.00086	.00006	.00050	.00017	.00067	.00082	.00004	.00007	.00004
47	Metalworking machinery and equipment	.00849	.01170	.00935	.01532	.01060	.01111	.00071	.00041	.00012
48	Special industry machinery and equipment	.00035	.00006	.00013	.00029	.00056	.00011	.00057	.00056	
49	General industrial machinery and equipment	.00033	.01199	.00680	.00903	.03642	.00499	.00255	.00044	.00255
50	Machine shop products	.00244	.00089	.01003	.03811	.00458	.00486	.00107	.00075	.00027
51	Office, computing and accounting machines	.00784		.00002	.00027	.00001	.00121	.00002	.00239	
52	Service industry machines			.00010	.01011	.00008	.00128	.00010	.00042	.00007
53	Electric industrial equipment and apparatus	.01928	.00050	.00332	.00030	.01078	.02629	.00766	.00500	.00073
54	Household appliances	.00002	.00134	.00030	.00010	.00439	.00006		.00171	
55	Electric lighting and wiring equipment	.00406	.02459	.00578	.00005	.00307	.00569	.00123	.00213	.00017
56	Radio, television and communication equipment	.03414	.00494	.00310	.02812	.00006	.02308	.00552	.00213	.00001
57	Electronic components and accessories	.14011	.01368	.00080	.06662		.02328	.01710	.00300	.00065
58	Miscellaneous electrical machinery, equipment and supplies	.00191	.05514	.01190	.00307	.00110	.00334	.00094	.00046	.00087
59	Motor vehicles and equipment	.00026	.04471	.27793	.00174	.01827	.00737			.00135
60	Aircraft and parts	.00029	.00070	.00112	.21151		.00753	.00110	.00139	.00593
61	Other transportation equipment			.00007	.00121	.05631	.00094	.00023	.00196	.00764
62	Scientific and controlling instruments	.00136	.00450	.00367	.01578	.00170	.07407	.00165	.00154	.00080
63	Optical, ophthalmic and photographic equipment	.00193	.00271	.00006	.00046	.00008	.01265	.06397	.00015	.00014
64	Miscellaneous manufacturing	.00048	.00029	.00036	.00042	.00280	.00048	.00245	.05296	.00031
65	Transportation and warehousing	.00676	.00012	.01636	.00442	.01359	.00615	.00716	.01445	.09897
66	Communications; except radio and TV broadcasting	.00784	.00430	.00182	.00833	.00376	.00745	.00640	.00486	.00956
67	Radio and TV broadcasting									
68	Electric, gas, water and sanitary services	.00781	.00692	.00447	.00491	.00588	.00509	.00433	.00518	.00648
69	Wholesale and retail trade	.03192	.03218	.02116	.02010	.03053	.03655	.03007	.04498	.03081
70	Finance and insurance	.00479	.00603	.00261	.00229	.00389	.00396	.00488	.00621	.01478
71	Real estate and rental	.01343	.01722	.00440	.01545	.01098	.01610	.01641	.01613	.02575
72	Hotels; personal and repair services except auto	.00120	.00185	.00657	.00291	.00658	.00126	.00109	.00058	.00114
73	Business services	.02664	.02255	.01442	.02525	.01320	.04028	.03009	.03670	.01631
74	Automobile repair and services	.00125	.00089	.01506	.00179	.00079	.00136	.00092	.00097	.01505
75	Amusements					.00009			.00036	
76	Medical, educational services and nonprofit organizations	.00122	.00067	.00027	.00121	.00058	.00121	.00103	.00107	.00086
77	Federal Government enterprises	.00099	.00064	.00098	.00113	.00082	.00163	.00096	.00214	.00199
78	State and local government enterprises	.00010	.00019	.00010	.00013	.00003	.00006	.00002	.00001	.02738
79	Gross imports of goods and services	.02556	.03001	.01453	.00802	.02220	.02302	.03823	.07769	.04277
80	Business travel, entertainment and gifts	.01585	.00835	.00264	.01228	.00781	.01659	.00797	.00510	.00459
81	Office supplies	.00092	.00061	.00043	.00097	.00061	.00150	.00073	.00138	.00147
82	Scrap, used and secondhand goods	.00001		.00185	.00001	.00006				.00012
V.A.	Value added	.44716	.41644	.30630	.43067	.36985	.42393	.56136	.40298	.58677
E.C.	*Employee compensation*	.38889	.31012	.19585	.38990	.31882	.31647	.39684	.39604	.39619
I.B.T.	*Indirect business taxes*	.00570	.00769	.04562	.01050	.00675	.06758	.06488	.00677	.03484
P.T.I.	*Property-type income*	.05858	.09865	.06743	.03027	.04428	.10007	.13964	.10557	.15633
T.	Total	1.00000	1.00000	1.00000	1.00000	1.00000	1.00000	1.00000	1.00000	1.00000

Table 4.10 (continued)

66 Communications; except radio and TV broadcasting	67 Radio and TV broadcasting	68 Electric, gas, water and sanitary services	69 Wholesale and retail trade	70 Finance and insurance	71 Real estate and rental	72 Hotels; personal and repair services except auto	73 Business services	75 Automobile repair and services	76 Amusements	77 Medical, educational services and non-profit organizations	78 Federal Government enterprises [1]	79 State and local government enterprise	80 Gross imports of goods and services	81 Business travel, entertainment and gifts	82 Office supplies	83 Scrap, used and secondhand goods	Industry No.
					0.00995	0.00032				0.00539	0.00036			0.00276			1
			0.00006		.01059					.02108	.00055	0.00025		.01028			2
			.00085		.00001					.00257	(*)			.00447			3
		0.00001	(*)		.00140												4
		.00002	.00002		.00003												5
0.00002	0.00009	.02399	(*)	0.00003	.00009	.00026	0.00001	0.00002	.00002	.00020	0.00930			.00720			6
		.06756			.00032												7
		(*)	.00003		.00145												8
		(*)			.00024												9
					.00006					.00041							10
.02934	.00195	.03047	.00322	.00282	.06321	.00905	.00459	.00224	.01080	.01523	.00785			.17735			11
		.00001	.00023		.00010	.00004											12
		.00004	.00546		.00122	.00010								.00144		.01401	13
		.00001	.00006		.00007					.01036				.26413			14
		.00005	.00012		.00099									.01671		.00502	15
.00027		.00018	.00033		.00019	.00058	.00015	.00001		.00015	.00021					.03008	16
		.00022	.00082		.00019	.00045		.00049		.00001	.00012	.00015					17
			.00049		.00003	.00520	(*)	.00065		.00068	.00045	.00055		.00070		.00467	18
		.00002	.00056		.00025	.00050				.00045	.00185	.00021				.00156	19
			.00065		.00001										.00031	0.00008	20
			.00015		.00006												21
			.00016		.00003												22
.00110	.00013	.00081	.00616	.00525	.00036	.00524	.00178	.00033	.00082	.00195	.00109	.00106		.00061	.20236	.00839	23
.00001	.00006	.00008	.00350		.00003	.00160	.00001	.00001	.00009	.00049	.00023	.00001				.01923	24
.00210	.09031	.00020	.00282	.00932	.00111	.00063	.16565	.00002	.00215	.01388	.00374			.00123	.56980	.03731	25
.00003		.00150	.00132	.00002	.00266	.00302	.00264	.00030	.00402	.00111		.01261		.00019	.00506		26
		.00006	.00015		.00026												27
			.00168		.00089												28
.00005	.00003	.00001	.00031		.00013	.02275	.00178	.00047		.02350	.00217	.00215		.00698			29
.00336	.00016	.00737	.00842	.00192	.00635	.00065	.00030	.00249	.00015	.00002	.00003	.00992					30
.00123	.00016	.00061	.00137	.00028	.00119	.01117	.00232	.01178	.00185	.00437	.00585	.00291		.00039	.00468	.00583	31
		(*)	.00001		.00945	.00717	.01611		.00026	.00309	.00172					.00482	32
			.00024		.00001	.00024				.00001	.00021					.00226	33
			.00079		.00005	.00966			.00062		.00008	.00017		.00345		.00010	34
.00001		.00002	.00097		.00016	.00048	.00739	.00055		.00009	.00007	.00050		.00082	.00019		35
		.00109	.00023		.00033	.00311	.00135	.00634	.00028	.00024	.00003	.00023					36
.00052		.00029	.00026		.00054	.00017				.00001	.00001				.00207	.10330	37
			.00066		.00032	.00013					.00010					.07819	38
			(*)		.00007											.01431	39
			.00110		.00040									.00004		.01984	40
.00003		.00072	.00038		.00011	.00384	.06432		.00019	.00048		.00036		.00023		.05956	41
		.00005	.00094		.00020	.00699	.00452	.01117		.00012	.00008	.00081		.00146		.02914	42
		.00002	.00010		.00003	.00133	.00108	.00100			.00001	.00133				.00608	43
			.00021		.00009							.00010				.00341	44
			.00031		.00033					.00003						.01145	45
			.00020		.00014											.00211	46
.00001			.00041		.00021	.00046	.00051	.00012		.00010		.00001		.00004		.00402	47
			.00049		.00123									.00008		.00291	48
.00001		.00098	.00042		.00019	.00159	.00232		.02158		.00015			.00004		.01537	49
		(*)	.00021		.00042	.00112	.00277					.00038				.00296	50
			.00054		.00218		.00278		.00452		.00030				.00495	.00121	51
.00028		.00106	.00030		.00016	.00042	.00229	.00029	.00010		.00004	.00008				.00457	52
			.00034		.00056	.00140	.00019				.00030	.00004		.00047		.01050	53
.00003	.00097	.00078	.00038	.00013	.00022	.00600	.00277	.00452		.00016	.00010	.00006				.00603	54
.01100	.00311	.00003	.00040		.00025	.00069	.00019	.00407		.00028	.00010	.00010		.00134		.00497	55
.00136	.00905	.00006	.00048		.00069	.00048	.00002	.00017		.00060	.00016	.00003		.00785	.00004	.00889	56
.01673		.00002	.00043	.00004	.00030	.01631	.00033	.01645	.00004	.00116	.00016	.00004				.01120	57
.00009		.00007	.00058		.00009	.00033	.00016	.08533		.07426	.00011	.00046		.00039		.00643	58
.00017			.00103		.00025	.00068						.00075				.04947	59
			.00028		.00028	.00037				.00007	.00001	.00047				.01155	60
			.00025		.00052	.00087	.00049				.00596	.00001		.00145		.00618	61
.00002	.00097		.00076		.00028	.00027	.00031	.01748	.00030	.00864	.00335	.00047		.00354		.00201	62
.00018	.00063	(*)	.00150	.00004	.00031	.00783	.00466	.00924	.00030	.00357	.00374	.00008		.00664	.06744	.00959	63
.00212	.04037	.01507	.00756	.00241	.00968	.00691	.01748	.00587	.00804	.00434	.01196	.00107		.41307	.14140	.02883	64
.00738	.02720	.00267	.01083	.02038	.00187	.00819	.02266	.00601	.00694	.01183	.00259			.00448			65
					.00016	.05409				.00039							66
.00698	.01388	.18456	.01478	.00820	.00385	.01764	.00356	.00890	.03087	.01961	.01718	.11773					67
.00746	.01655	.00542	.02070	.01253	.01423	.03171	.01532	.00956	.02076	.00544	.01136					.00055	68
.00735	.00540	.00586	.01514	.18221	.03155	.01913	.00646	.01373	.01116	.00802	.01794	.01669		.06677		.00251	69
.01673	.04596	.00415	.05269	.04107	.03226	.06926	.03808	.02555		.05574	.02416						70
.01096		.00142	.00280		.00458	.02798	.00612	.00994		.00448	.00038	.00052		.12655			71
.03266	.04266	.00769	.05182	.08286	.02746	.02903	.00501	.01051	.04123	.02602	.02590	.03587				.00316	72
.00520	.00306	.00127	.01080	.00301	.00149	.01618	.00894	.00178	.00316	.00674	.00560	.00310					73
			.00112		.00185	.00007	.00307			.20305	.00064						75
.00098	.00104	.00035	.00140		.00084	.00328	.00209	.00055		.00081	.00231	.00010		.01672			76
.00411	.00110	.01711	.01096	.01177	.01783	.00264	.01053	.00046		.00231	.01371	.00010		.00632			77
	.00099	.13320	.00006		.00267	.00052	.00016	.01048		.00421	.00686	.00031	.00133				78
.00886	.00016	.00389	.00140		.00212	.00065				.00103	.00103	.00020	.00066				79
.00680	.03481	.00344	.01252	.01689	.00092	.01437	.02039	.00468		.00702	.02320	.04441		.03177		.34626	80
.00360	.00101	.00063	.00208	.01277	.00048	.00165	.00326	.00040		.00530	.01607	.00363		.00502	.00158		81
.00001			.00006		.00001	(*)	.00001	.00001		.00001	.00001	.00078				.00001	82
.82931	.49629	.47458	.72393	.56331	.74234	.59960	.51512	.54897	.52056	.69881	.71245	.54338					83
.33621	.33304	.13141	.18273	.18773	.01660	.34006	.28410	.25663	.39814	.18821	.73198	.21456					V.A.
.12746	.01043	.05687	.14011	.04007	.16117	.01346	.00751	.01596	.07630	.00606							E.C.
.56564	.15882	.28660	.15648	.11549	.56457	.24308	.22572	.27854	.14612	.20855	−.05958	.32882					I.T.B.
																	P.T.I.
1.00000	1.00000	1.00000	1.00000	1.00000	1.00000	1.00000	1.00000	1.00000	1.00000	1.00000	1.00000	1.00000	1.00000	1.00000	1.00000	1.00000	T.

Source: Surv. Curr. Bus., February 1974, p. 44.

Table 4.11 Major suppliers of the CPI and related industries

Buyer	Major Suppliers	Input per total dollar output
Crude petroleum and natural gas (8)	Real estate and rental (71)	$0.16161
	Gross imports of goods and services (80)	0.07159
	Maintenance and repair construction (12)	0.03168
	Crude petroleum and natural gas (8)	0.02487
	Business services (73)	0.01619
Chemical and fertilizer mineral mining (10)	Gross imports of goods and services (80)	0.08751
	Chemical and fertilizer mineral mining (10)	0.05948
	Electric, gas, water, and sanitary services (68)	0.04312
	Real estate and rental (71)	0.03923
	Business services (73)	0.03018
Paper and allied products, except containers (24)	Paper and allied products, except containers (24)	0.16031
	Gross imports of goods and services (80)	0.08162
	Lumber and wood products, except containers (20)	0.07089
	Chemicals and selected chemical products (27)	0.03714
	Transportation and warehousing (65)	0.03433
Chemicals and selected chemical products (27)	Chemicals and selected chemical products (27)	0.19999
	Petroleum refining and related industries (31)	0.07765
	Electric, gas, water, and sanitary services (68)	0.03013
	Business services (73)	0.02938
	Gross imports of goods and services (80)	0.02924
Plastics and synthetic materials (28)	Chemicals and selected chemical products (27)	0.34756
	Wholesale and retail trade (69)	0.03090
	Paper and allied products, except containers (24)	0.03053
	Business services (73)	0.02861
	Plastics and synthetic materials (28)	0.02787
Drugs, cleaning and toilet preparations (29)	Business services (73)	0.16422
	Chemicals and selected chemical products (27)	0.10871
	Drugs, cleaning and toilet preparations (29)	0.05365
	Rubber and miscellaneous plastics products (32)	0.03121
	Real estate and rental (71)	0.03077

Table 4.11 (*continued*)

Buyer	Major Suppliers	Input per total dollar output
Paints and allied products (30)	Chemicals and selected chemical products (27)	0.21017
	Plastics and synthetic materials (28)	0.09463
	Metal containers (39)	0.05788
	Business services (73)	0.03503
	Wholesale and retail trade (69)	0.03459
Petroleum refining and related industries (31)	Crude petroleum and natural gas (8)	0.42840
	Petroleum refining and related industries (31)	0.06787
	Transportation and warehousing (65)	0.05149
	Gross imports of goods and services (80)	0.03782
	Business services (73)	0.02853
Rubber and miscellaneous plastics products (32)	Plastics and synthetic materials (28)	0.16182
	Chemicals and selected chemical products (27)	0.03731
	Miscellaneous textile goods and floor coverings (17)	0.03272
	Wholesale and retail trade (69)	0.03183
	Business services (73)	0.03160
Glass and glass products (35)	Stone and clay mining and quarrying (9)	0.01113
	Glass and glass products (35)	0.06377
	Paperboard containers and boxes (25)	0.05244
	Electric, gas, water, and sanitary services (68)	0.03565
	Wholesale and retail trade (69)	0.03102
Primary iron and steel manufacturing (37)	Primary iron and steel manufacturing (37)	0.18966
	Iron and ferroalloy ores mining (5)	0.04717
	Transportation and warehousing (65)	0.04477
	Gross imports of goods and services (80)	0.04476
	Wholesale and retail trade (69)	0.02943
Primary nonferrous metal manufacturing (38)	Primary nonferrous metal manufacturing (38)	0.32214
	Gross imports of goods and services (80)	0.09808
	Nonferrous metal ores mining (6)	0.05042
	Scrap, used, and secondhand goods (83)	0.04173
	Wholesale and retail trade (69)	0.03576

we return to Eq. (4.10), where the set of direct-requirement equations is given in vector form as

$$X = DX + F$$

Rearranging gives

$$X - DX = F$$

$$(I - D)X = F$$

where I is the identity matrix. By inverting the matrix $I - D$ we arrive at

$$X = (I - D)^{-1}F$$

The matrix $(I - D)^{-1}$ is equal to an infinite series and can be approximated by truncation to term n

$$(I - D)^{-1} \approx I + D + D^2 + D^3 + \cdots + D^n \tag{4.12}$$

The output now becomes

$$X = (I + D + D^2 + \cdots)F$$

where IF represents the original final demand and each subsequent term represents a round of buying of the supplying industries to cover production needs. Defining the matrix $(I - D)^{-1}$ as the total coefficient matrix T we have

$$X = TF \tag{4.13}$$

where each element T_{ij} of T is the total input (both direct and indirect) required from industry i for a dollar of output to final demand by industry j. Assuming that the total coefficients remain constant, changes in output from industry i required

Table 4.12 Transaction table (2-sector economy)

Output from	Input to A	Input to B	Intermediate output	Final demand	Total output
A	4	4	8	2	10
B	1	2	3	7	10
Intermediate input	5	6			
Value added	5	4			GNP = 9
Total input	10	10		GNP = 9	

as a result of changes in output by other industries to final demand can be estimated:

$$\Delta X_i = \sum_{j=1}^{n} T_{ij} \, \Delta F_j \tag{4.14}$$

Equation (4.14) can be used to estimate change in output due to a change in final demand.

A simple example will illustrate how the various relationships are applied and indicate some additional uses of input-output analysis.

Example 4.1 To illustrate the basic concepts without algebraic complexity a two-industry economy is considered. We will assume that some central agency such as the federal government has collected statistics on suppliers and supplies needed to develop the transaction table shown in Table 4.12.

Since final demand is known, $F_A = 2$ and $F_B = 7$, a set of two equations can be written to describe the situation:

Industry A: $\qquad\qquad 10 = 4 + 4 + 2$

Industry B: $\qquad\qquad 10 = 1 + 2 + 7$

The direct-coefficient table is obtained by dividing the interindustry transaction by total output [Eq. (4.8)]:

	A	B
A	0.4	0.4
B	0.1	0.2

These equations can be written in symbolic notation, using the direct-coefficient form of Eqs. (4.9):

Industry A: $\qquad\qquad X_A = 0.4X_A + 0.4X_B + 2$

Industry B: $\qquad\qquad X_B = 0.1X_A + 0.2X_B + 7$

$$\mathbf{X} = \mathbf{DX} + \mathbf{F}$$

In vector form

$$\begin{pmatrix} X_A \\ X_B \end{pmatrix} = \begin{pmatrix} 0.4 & 0.4 \\ 0.1 & 0.2 \end{pmatrix} \begin{pmatrix} X_A \\ X_B \end{pmatrix} + \begin{pmatrix} 2 \\ 7 \end{pmatrix}$$

To use the system of equations for predictive purposes, we must convert to the form shown as Eq. (4.13):

$$X = TF$$

$$T = (I - D)^{-1}$$

$$= \left[\begin{pmatrix} 1 & 0 \\ 0 & 1 \end{pmatrix} - \begin{pmatrix} 0.4 & 0.4 \\ 0.1 & 0.2 \end{pmatrix} \right]^{-1}$$

$$= \begin{pmatrix} 0.6 & -0.4 \\ -0.1 & 0.8 \end{pmatrix}^{-1} = \cfrac{1}{\begin{pmatrix} 0.6 & -0.4 \\ -0.1 & 0.8 \end{pmatrix}} \begin{pmatrix} 0.8 & 0.4 \\ 0.1 & 0.6 \end{pmatrix} = \begin{pmatrix} 1.82 & 0.91 \\ 0.23 & 1.36 \end{pmatrix}^{\dagger}$$

The total coefficient equations now appear as

$$\begin{pmatrix} X_A \\ X_B \end{pmatrix} = \begin{pmatrix} 1.82 & 0.91 \\ 0.23 & 1.36 \end{pmatrix} \begin{pmatrix} F_A \\ F_B \end{pmatrix}$$

or $$X_A = 1.82 F_A + 0.91 F_B \qquad X_B = 0.23 F_A + 1.36 F_B$$

In this form we can now easily predict changes in any industry output, given changes in final demand. Suppose final demand for industry B changes by one unit and final demand for industry A remains unchanged. Equation (4.14) applies:

$$\Delta X_A = T_{AB} \, \Delta F_B = 0.91 \, (1) = 0.91$$

$$\Delta X_B = T_{BB} \, \Delta F_B = 1.36 \, (1) = 1.36$$

† NOTE: A 2×2 matrix can be inverted as follows. If

$$M = \begin{pmatrix} a & b \\ c & d \end{pmatrix}$$

then

$$M^{-1} = \frac{1}{ad - cb} \begin{pmatrix} d & -b \\ -c & a \end{pmatrix}$$

A 3×3 matrix can be inverted as follows. If

$$M = \begin{pmatrix} a & b & c \\ d & e & f \\ g & h & i \end{pmatrix}$$

then

$$M^{-1} = \frac{1}{|M|} \begin{pmatrix} ei - hf & hc - bi & bf - ec \\ gf - di & ai - gc & dc - af \\ dh - ge & gb - ah & ae - bd \end{pmatrix}$$

Computer programs are available for inverting matrices of higher rank.

Thus for a change in final demand of 1 unit (or 10 percent) for products from industry B, 0.91 unit of extra output from A are required and 1.36 extra units of output from B are required.

Now suppose there is a change in technology that allows products from B to be made more efficiently with less input required from A. Assume the **D** matrix changes as follows:

$$
\begin{array}{c}
 \\
A \\
B
\end{array}
\begin{array}{cc}
A & B \\
\begin{pmatrix} 0.40 & 0.30 \\ 0.10 & 0.20 \end{pmatrix}
\end{array}
$$

Although it is not necessary for this simple example, it is instructive to use the series approximation [Eq. (4.12)] to estimate $(\mathbf{I} - \mathbf{D})^{-1}$:

$$(\mathbf{I} - \mathbf{D})^{-1} = \mathbf{T} = \mathbf{I} + \mathbf{D} + \mathbf{D}^2 + \mathbf{D}^3 + \cdots$$

Using the first two terms of the series produces

$$
\mathbf{T} \approx \begin{vmatrix} 1 & 0 \\ 0 & 1 \end{vmatrix} + \begin{vmatrix} 0.4 & 0.3 \\ 0.1 & 0.2 \end{vmatrix} = \begin{vmatrix} 1.4 & 0.3 \\ 0.1 & 1.2 \end{vmatrix}
$$

Adding the squared term shows the effect of a second round of purchases to meet final demand:

$$
\mathbf{D}^2 = \begin{vmatrix} 0.19 & 0.18 \\ 0.06 & 0.07 \end{vmatrix} \qquad \mathbf{T} \approx \begin{vmatrix} 1.59 & 0.48 \\ 0.16 & 1.27 \end{vmatrix}
$$

Including the cubic terms takes account of the third round of purchases:

$$
\mathbf{D}^3 = \begin{vmatrix} 0.09 & 0.09 \\ 0.03 & 0.03 \end{vmatrix} \qquad \mathbf{T} \approx \begin{vmatrix} 1.68 & 0.57 \\ 0.19 & 1.30 \end{vmatrix}
$$

Inverting the $\mathbf{I} - \mathbf{D}$ matrix by the same procedure as before gives

$$
\mathbf{T} = \begin{vmatrix} 1.78 & 0.66 \\ 0.22 & 1.33 \end{vmatrix}
$$

The total output is now

$$
\mathbf{X} = \mathbf{TF} = \begin{pmatrix} 1.78 & 0.66 \\ 0.22 & 1.33 \end{pmatrix} \begin{pmatrix} 2 \\ 7 \end{pmatrix} = \begin{pmatrix} 8.2 \\ 9.8 \end{pmatrix}
$$

There is an 18 percent drop in output of A merely because B has learned how to economize on using supplies from A.

NOTE Multiplication of two square matrices $[a_{ij}]$ and $[b_{jk}]$, where a_{ij} and b_{jk} are the elements of each matrix, can be carried out as follows:

$$[a_{ij}][b_{jk}] = \sum_{j=1}^{n} a_{ij} b_{jk}$$

Table 4.13 Transaction table (2-sector economy revised)

Output from	Input to		Inter-mediate output	Final demand	Total output
	A	B			
A	3.28	2.94	6.2	2	8.2
B	0.82	1.96	2.8	7	9.8
Intermediate input	4.1	4.9			
Value added	4.1	4.9			GNP = 9
Total input	8.2	9.8		GNP = 9	

Reconstructing the transactions table gives Table 4.13. By improving its technology, industry B decreased its total output by 27 percent, but its value added has increased by 22.5 percent from $4 to $4.90.

The total-requirements table for the four-sector economy of Table 4.2 is shown in Table 4.14. The elements of Table 4.14 were obtained by inverting the $I - D$ matrix, with D given by Table 4.9. Table 4.15 shows the total requirements for each dollar of delivery to final demand of the industry of the column. For example, the energy sector requires 40.5 cents of input from the service sector to produce $1 of final demand. This is much more than the 18.5 cents shown on the direct-requirement table (Table 4.9).

The total-requirements table for the United States economy for 1967 is given as Table 4.15. The elements of this table are obtained by inverting the $I - D$ matrix, where D is given by Table 4.10. Each column shows the output required both directly and indirectly from the industry named at the left of each row per dollar of delivery to final demand by the industry named at the head of the column. Returning to our automobile example, a $10 million increase in final demand for the products of industry 59 requires an increase of $0.02202 \times$

Table 4.14 Total requirements table for a four-sector economy

	Consumer	Basic	Energy	Service
Consumer	1.334	0.081	0.025	0.081
Basic	0.713	1.783	0.089	0.165
Energy	0.059	0.090	1.576	0.060
Service	0.298	0.305	0.405	1.389

$10,000,000 = $220,200 in total output in both direct and indirect requirements for products of industry 27. This is about 16 times the direct-requirement increase of $13,900 computed by using the direct coefficient.

Table 4.16 shows the total coefficients as taken from Table 4.15 of food and kindred products (14), apparel (18), household furniture (22), drugs, cleaning and toilet preparations (29), new construction (11), household appliances (54), and motor vehicles and equipment (59) for the input requirements of the CPI and related industries.

You are urged to construct your own tables to illustrate features of the input-output tables which are of personal or professional interest.

4.4 APPLYING INPUT-OUTPUT ANALYSIS

Input-output analysis has been described in this chapter and used to identify the role of the CPI in the United States economy. We have also shown how the industrial responses to changes in demand can be measured. Input-output analysis can also be applied in a variety of situations by individual corporations. A survey conducted by Arthur D. Little, Inc., found that about 200 major United States corporations have used input-output analysis in some form for corporate planning at one time or another and that at least 60 major firms use input-output analysis regularly [4]. A. D. Little has classified the use of input-output analysis in corporate planning into the four following major functions.

Forecasting To date the major corporate use of input-output analysis has been in providing forecasts of the United States economy and forecasts of changes in the coefficients of the direct- and total-requirements tables. These forecasts have been used by companies in identifying acquisition and diversification opportunities. Studying the effect of changes in final demand for automobiles on the CPI is one such forecasting input-output-analysis application.

Sensitivity testing Input-output analysis can be used to test the consequences of " what if " questions. For example, the input-output tables can be used in studying the effects on an industry's or company's growth under various alternative scenarios, e.g., different rates of GNP growth or potential changes in technology, as shown by Example 4.1 for a simple two-industry economy.

Flow and structural analysis Input-output analysis can be used effectively to determine patterns by which products move through an economy. This can help illuminate problems like bottlenecks or show how specific markets are coupled. Table 4.7 is one example of tracing input-output flows through intermediate markets to final demand.

Table 4.15 Total transactions table for 1967 (dollars of direct and indirect input per total dollar output to final demand)

Industry No.	Each entry represents the output required, directly and indirectly, from the industry named at the beginning of the row for each dollar of delivery to final demand by the industry named at the head of the column	Livestock and livestock products (1)	Other agricultural products (2)	Forestry and fishery products (3)	Agricultural, forestry and fishery services (4)	Iron and ferroalloy ores mining (5)	Nonferrous metal ores mining (6)	Coal mining (7)	Crude petroleum and natural gas (8)	Stone and clay mining and quarrying (9)	Chemical and fertilizer mineral mining (10)
1	Livestock and livestock products	1.30625	0.07638	0.08008	0.10563	0.00245	0.00203	0.00237	0.00381	0.00238	0.00220
2	Other agricultural products	.39445	1.06771	.08926	.23337	.00263	.00208	.00298	.00393	.00253	.00212
3	Forestry and fishery products	.00130	.00057	1.01823	.00079	.00048	.00108	.00108	.00025	.00036	.00039
4	Agricultural, forestry and fishery services	.04441	.05170	.02929	1.01315	.00037	.00028	.00037	.00058	.00031	.00027
5	Iron and ferroalloy ores mining	.00063	.00078	.00087	.00043	1.05798	.00608	.00224	.00114	.00230	.00308
6	Nonferrous metal ores mining	.00056	.00088	.00046	.00042	.02395	1.15012	.00103	.00050	.00339	.00412
7	Coal mining	.00155	.00162	.00090	.00113	.00288	.00345	1.14708	.00143	.00601	.00338
8	Crude petroleum and natural gas	.01572	.02481	.01332	.00892	.00877	.00976	.01235	1.13133	.02285	.00537
9	Stone and clay mining and quarrying	.00267	.00576	.00092	.00159	.00347	.00424	.00225	.00146	1.03280	.00447
10	Chemical and fertilizer mineral mining	.00172	.00380	.00065	.00137	.00401	.00339	.00095	.00063	.00218	1.06448
11	New construction										
12	Maintenance and repair construction	.02641	.02772	.00742	.01173	.03208	.02133	.01900	.04783	.01964	.01921
13	Ordnance and accessories	.00014	.00018	.00014	.00011	.00016	.00024	.00023	.00019	.00024	.00014
14	Food and kindred products	.19297	.01658	.03170	.03940	.00337	.00425	.00367	.00448	.00463	.00462
15	Tobacco manufactures	.00018	.00018	.00025	.00019	.00014	.00019	.00017	.00022	.00021	.00023
16	Broad and narrow fabrics, yarn and thread mills	.00261	.00362	.01062	.00793	.00220	.00123	.00933	.00095	.00562	.00123
17	Miscellaneous textile goods and floor coverings	.00258	.00313	.03463	.01073	.00166	.00081	.00202	.00080	.00277	.00072
18	Apparel	.00090	.00082	.00074	.00078	.00039	.00043	.00048	.00036	.00062	.00032
19	Miscellaneous fabricated textile products	.00126	.00216	.00104	.00104	.00284	.00040	.00033	.00040	.00019	.00026
20	Lumber and wood products, except containers	.00379	.00484	.00203	.00671	.00519	.01240	.01278	.00214	.00338	.00369
21	Wooden containers	.00206	.00411	.00058	.00597	.00008	.00011	.00014	.00008	.00009	.00007
22	Household furniture	.00010	.00011	.00012	.00013	.00007	.00009	.00010	.00008	.00008	.00005
23	Other furniture and fixtures	.00007	.00008	.00005	.00006	.00007	.00007	.00010	.00009	.00008	.00006
24	Paper and allied products, except containers	.0122k	.00435	.00549	.02822	.00497	.00511	.00524	.00394	.01791	.00574
25	Paperboard containers and boxes	.00794	.00495	.00358	.05024	.00132	.00182	.00166	.00110	.00243	.00181
26	Printing and publishing	.01311	.01576	.00396	.00694	.01188	.00831	.01647	.00772	.01184	.01048
27	Chemicals and selected chemical products	.65220	.11611	.01992	.02736	.02817	.00324	.00404	.00316	.03696	.04079
28	Plastics and synthetic materials	.00461	.00681	.00911	.00704	.00397	.00391	.00505	.00230	.00608	.00396
29	Drugs, cleaning and toilet preparations	.06470	.00266	.00111	.00145	.00095	.00123	.00102	.06088	.00126	.00125
30	Paints and allied products	.00179	.00198	.00268	.00108	.00176	.00148	.00137	.00284	.00143	.00121
31	Petroleum refining and related industries	.03205	.05202	.02884	.01802	.01221	.01459	.02054	.00925	.04339	.01070
32	Rubber and miscellaneous plastics products	.00916	.01069	.00650	.00504	.01247	.00961	.01367	.00492	.01734	.01196
33	Leather tanning and industrial leather products	.00015	.00009	.00007	.00013	.00006	.00006	.00007	.00006	.00012	.00006
34	Footwear and other leather products	.00054	.00016	.00015	.00045	.00009	.00010	.00011	.00010	.00013	.00011
35	Glass and glass products	.00321	.00084	.00081	.00088	.00059	.00053	.00062	.00060	.00060	.00045
36	Stone and clay products	.00267	.00374	.00159	.00166	.00309	.00487	.00701	.00912	.06122	.00218
37	Primary iron and steel manufacturing	.00024	.00029	.01651	.00674	.00412	.00426	.00100	.02169	.04304	.00327
38	Primary nonferrous metal manufacturing	.00526	.00276	.00561	.00401	.00999	.01124	.01310	.00727	.01222	.00816
39	Metal containers	.00628	.00263	.02190	.00216	.00074	.00074	.06098	.00083	.00104	.00085
40	Heating, plumbing and structural metal products	.00195	.00211	.01108	.00098	.00254	.00210	.00235	.00667	.00341	.00382
41	Stampings, screw machine products and bolts	.00370	.00233	.00180	.00135	.00376	.00674	.01830	.00192	.00316	.00197
42	Other fabricated metal products	.00576	.00554	.00760	.00851	.00510	.00695	.00881	.00760	.01039	.00403
43	Engines and turbines	.00079	.00136	.00180	.00158	.00372	.00778	.00684	.00424	.01239	.00217
44	Farm machinery and equipment	.00483	.01195	.00114	.00269	.00041	.00046	.00067	.00026	.00045	.00032
45	Construction, mining and oil field machinery	.00077	.00120	.00046	.00050	.01802	.01841	.03985	.00497	.01174	.01329
46	Materials handling machinery and equipment	.00039	.00049	.00020	.00026	.00065	.00124	.00088	.00055	.00406	.00105
47	Metalworking machinery and equipment	.00119	.00119	.00126	.00133	.00068	.00081	.00293	.00192	.00123	.00205
48	Special industry machinery and equipment	.00113	.00166	.00069	.00095	.00071	.00100	.00090	.00073	.00103	.00076
49	General industrial machinery and equipment	.00186	.00265	.00172	.00127	.00325	.00438	.00628	.00811	.01149	.00282
50	Machine shop products	.00132	.00142	.00080	.00068	.00253	.03975	.00499	.00689	.00399	.00646
51	Office, computing and accounting machines	.00045	.00066	.00019	.00030	.00049	.00031	.00043	.00063	.00040	.00036
52	Service industry machines	.00062	.00069	.00029	.00033	.00069	.00052	.00057	.00082	.00069	.00049
53	Electric industrial equipment and apparatus	.06122	.00160	.00101	.00078	.00243	.00334	.00248	.01366	.00530	.00341
54	Household appliances	.00046	.00049	.00031	.00027	.00046	.00037	.00037	.00063	.00040	.00035
55	Electric lighting and wiring equipment	.00080	.00082	.00054	.00039	.00087	.00098	.00379	.00131	.00102	.06080
56	Radio, television and communication equipment	.00056	.00057	.00034	.00033	.00652	.00052	.00050	.00119	.00050	.00048
57	Electronic components and accessories	.00056	.00060	.00044	.00039	.00057	.00055	.00054	.00117	.00066	.00049
58	Miscellaneous electrical machinery, equipment and supplies	.00164	.00209	.00133	.00065	.00110	.00269	.00097	.00054	.00080	.00042
59	Motor vehicles and equipment	.00285	.00255	.00165	.00121	.00069	.00289	.00793	.00162	.00293	.00148
60	Aircraft and parts	.00076	.00066	.00062	.00064	.00117	.00128	.00107	.00077	.00133	.00064
61	Other transportation equipment	.00075	.00077	.00931	.00071	.00105	.00253	.00076	.00055	.00066	.00093
62	Scientific and controlling instruments	.00059	.00057	.00048	.00037	.00078	.00097	.00077	.00134	.00076	.00051
63	Optical, ophthalmic and photographic equipment	.00075	.00087	.00038	.00045	.00065	.00055	.00063	.00053	.00070	.00060
64	Miscellaneous manufacturing	.00160	.00177	.00334	.00100	.00153	.00162	.00144	.00117	.00181	.00152
65	Transportation and warehousing	.06069	.03935	.04166	.03343	.08365	.06672	.02616	.02472	.03439	.03168
66	Communications; except radio and TV broadcasting	.00968	.00806	.00310	.00379	.00554	.00668	.00576	.00397	.00495	.00799
67	Radio and TV broadcasting	.00272	.00398	.00098	.00142	.00309	.00188	.00262	.00186	.00296	.00468
68	Electric, gas, water and sanitary services	.01998	.02212	.00783	.01090	.04557	.04529	.03935	.04006	.02078	.05201
69	Wholesale and retail trade	.10176	.07972	.04607	.04167	.02754	.03599	.04006	.02895	.04038	.02965
70	Finance and insurance	.02837	.02531	.01698	.01140	.01599	.03324	.02158	.01794	.02164	.01803
71	Real estate and rental	.07273	.10448	.02777	.06192	.09732	.04682	.07365	.18099	.05860	.05565
72	Hotels; personal and repair services except auto	.00314	.00270	.00224	.00225	.00211	.00214	.00212	.00266	.00249	.00244
73	Business services	.04861	.07121	.01751	.02541	.05530	.03370	.04698	.03295	.05314	.04748
75	Automobile repair and services	.01078	.00630	.00536	.00357	.00356	.00418	.00434	.00300	.00988	.00294
76	Amusements	.00158	.00209	.00077	.00096	.00164	.00111	.00142	.00140	.00157	.00144
77	Medical, educational services and nonprofit organizations	.00923	.00216	.00115	.00138	.00136	.00175	.00160	.00118	.00111	.00274
78	Federal Government enterprises	.00368	.00371	.00186	.00195	.00369	.00385	.00352	.00276	.00359	.00479
79	State and local government enterprises	.00564	.00542	.00272	.00315	.00939	.00857	.00687	.00515	.00876	.01018
80	Gross imports of goods and services	.03088	.02947	.27937	.03177	.34469	.23883	.01388	.08124	.05578	.10494
81	Business travel, entertainment and gifts	.00806	.00766	.01143	.00863	.00663	.00866	.00735	.00946	.00963	.01041
82	Office supplies	.00133	.60122	.06092	.00085	.00085	.00113	.00147	.00136	.00114	.00112

Table 4.15 (*continued*)

New construction	Maintenance and repair construction	Ordnance and accessories	Food and kindred products	Tobacco manufactures	Broad and narrow fabrics, yarn and thread mills	Miscellaneous textile goods and floor coverings	Apparel	Miscellaneous fabricated textile products	Lumber and wood products, except containers	Wooden containers	Household furniture	Other furniture and fixtures	Paper and allied products, except containers	Paperboard containers and boxes	Printing and publishing	Chemicals and selected chemical products	Industry No.
11'	12	13	14	15	16	17	18	19	20	21	22	23	24	25	26	27	
0.00384	0.00293	0.00334	0.35807	0.01892	0.02652	0.05585	0.01147	0.01806	0.01133	0.00613	0.00648	0.00425	0.00652	0.00420	0.00429	0.00622	1
.00583	.00378	.00315	.20677	.24390	.12385	.04719	.04301	.05868	.02552	.01151	.01356	.00610	.00754	.00462	.00442	.00685	2
.00675	.00221	.00132	.00671	.00045	.00061	.00081	.00987	.00104	.10884	.04141	.01564	.00754	.00967	.00444	.00195	.00154	3
.00268	.00123	.00034	.01705	.01189	.00648	.00347	.00260	.00326	.00404	.00174	.00126	.00066	.00083	.00053	.00050	.00063	4
.00404	.00270	.00494	.00124	.00036	.00075	.00079	.00048	.00077	.00113	.00106	.00260	.00738	.00083	.00127	.00070	.00416	5
.00435	.00220	.00466	.00070	.00038	.00097	.00106	.00060	.00081	.00071	.00063	.00176	.00268	.00083	.00110	.00074	.00670	6
.00343	.00220	.00365	.00252	.00132	.00419	.00364	.00233	.00328	.00204	.00197	.00308	.00510	.00799	.00456	.00247	.00745	7
.01472	.01747	.00713	.01201	.00770	.01424	.01319	.00823	.00987	.01240	.00883	.00778	.00684	.01313	.01213	.00719	.05708	8
.01614	.01498	.00104	.00204	.00157	.00175	.00156	.00087	.00120	.00173	.00138	.00165	.00151	.00535	.00267	.00136	.00503	9
.00111	.00090	.00139	.00145	.00131	.00400	.00394	.00191	.00245	.00110	.00079	.00126	.00108	.00426	.00283	.00169	.03554	10
1.00000																	11
.01205	1.00857	.04113	.01980	.01080	.01790	.01612	.01202	.01390	.01549	.01348	.01418	.01440	.01967	.01862	.01555	.02459	12
.00044	.00030	1.08395	.00016	.00010	.00020	.00021	.00015	.00020	.00024	.00082	.00169	.00394	.00019	.00017	.00040	.00082	13
.00775	.00746	.00927	1.26514	.00805	.01480	.01655	.00950	.01097	.00785	.00794	.00819	.00645	.01642	.01018	.00987	.01749	14
.00035	.00030	.00050	.00028	1.26746	.00025	.00025	.00030	.00027	.00020	.00032	.00032	.00027	.00025	.00024	.00042	.00030	15
.00499	.00230	.00462	.00396	.00223	1.50769	.30275	.49411	.67435	.00599	.00487	.09034	.02406	.02158	.01070	.00938	.00318	16
.00465	.00106	.00198	.00247	.00136	.04790	1.07989	.02437	.12750	.00555	.00282	.02768	.02271	.00667	.00416	.00428	.00147	17
.00182	.00085	.00160	.00145	.00070	.00615	.02101	1.26344	.02864	.00228	.00263	.00556	.00506	.00171	.00242	.00181	.00091	18
.00068	.00043	.00123	.00193	.00066	.00557	.01503	.02348	1.02747	.00125	.00174	.00469	.00714	.00185	.00107	.00091	.00134	19
.08360	0.2626	.01435	.00671	.00415	.00449	.00551	.00367	.00840	1.37635	.52241	.19575	.09353	.12001	.05415	.02241	.00858	20
.00054	.00032	.00029	.00261	.00195	.00062	.00032	.00027	.00037	.00386	1.03428	.00102	.00081	.00049	.00034	.00016	.00016	21
.00479	.00061	.00075	.00018	.00006	.00019	.00130	.00016	.00189	.00327	.00845	1.01626	.02068	.00041	.00024	.00014	.00009	22
.00331	.00068	.00058	.00009	.00005	.00009	.00026	.00009	.00048	.00092	.00081	.00353	1.02568	.00025	.00024	.00030	.00008	23
.01581	.01024	.01226	.03741	.02268	.01946	.02870	.01859	.03272	.01589	.01659	.01971	.01937	1.21526	.51005	.21367	.02745	24
.00457	.00368	.01027	.02924	.01184	.01289	.01114	.01223	.02454	.00512	.00932	.01846	.01771	.02806	1.03796	.01002	.01002	25
.01915	.01070	.01315	.02705	.02354	.01216	.01459	.01262	.01236	.00996	.01013	.01310	.01348	.02301	.02432	1.14708	.01588	26
.01992	.02245	.04266	.04088	.04031	.13538	.13491	.06420	.08114	.03417	.02373	.03625	.02730	.07719	.06840	.04601	1.26870	27
.00735	.00778	.00788	.00724	.01843	.16339	.21939	.08301	.10324	.00746	.00538	.02943	.01820	.02568	.01802	.01070	.04225	28
.00154	.00162	.00162	.00625	.00413	.00550	.00518	.00324	.00491	.00127	.00119	.00197	.00186	.00317	.00235	.00185	.01893	29
.00858	.03921	.00176	.00242	.00106	.00321	.00478	.00186	.00259	.00777	.01195	.01817	.01485	.00336	.00323	.00246	.00654	30
.02992	.03731	.01250	.02280	.01539	.02562	.02409	.01445	.01708	.02383	.01568	.01354	.01125	.02235	.02171	.01247	.11357	31
.01637	.01046	.01604	.01680	.01296	.01362	.02974	.01000	.03169	.01115	.00758	.05432	.04988	.02819	.01887	.01274	.01158	32
.00018	.00011	.00015	.00013	.00008	.00016	.00044	.00457	.00424	.00016	.00012	.00106	.00060	.00016	.00016	.00012	.00016	33
.00022	.00018	.00031	.00032	.00016	.00019	.00043	.00082	.00070	.00033	.00023	.00039	.00039	.00027	.00040	.00029	.00017	34
.00423	.00561	.00234	.01588	.00051	.00753	.00343	.00291	.00400	.00272	.00166	.00840	.01126	.00111	.00112	.00079	.00170	35
.09176	.03707	.00503	.00267	.00151	.00397	.00624	.00209	.00328	.01209	.01049	.01077	.00678	.00587	.00362	.00218	.00675	36
.07785	.05214	.09667	.02284	.00540	.00886	.00974	.00671	.01167	.02082	.01998	.05000	.14652	.01306	.02228	.01178	.02734	37
.06666	.03218	.07204	.00789	.00344	.00744	.00892	.00573	.00788	.00848	.00793	.02496	.03606	.00816	.01308	.00900	.03392	38
.00177	.00327	.00132	.03013	.00144	.00265	.00284	.00170	.00200	.00356	.00234	.00252	.00206	.00226	.01032	.00969	.01521	39
.10263	.05862	.00242	.00168	.00088	.00162	.00152	.00109	.00148	.00318	.00205	.00246	.00677	.00194	.00173	.00131	.00253	40
.00830	.00600	.02187	.00593	.00149	.00178	.00231	.00182	.01187	.00806	.00601	.00857	.02443	.00268	.00286	.00226	.00280	41
.03160	.02449	.02557	.00821	.00555	.00442	.00492	.00468	.00620	.02390	.02106	.06672	.05834	.01954	.01620	.00913	.00930	42
.00278	.00107	.00199	.00070	.00050	.00058	.00053	.00038	.00048	.00068	.00055	.00064	.00117	.00062	.00056	.00039	.00100	43
.00061	.00041	.00131	.00257	.00283	.00153	.00071	.00063	.00086	.00047	.00031	.00112	.00220	.00027	.00026	.00021	.00034	44
.00438	.00250	.00270	.00093	.00077	.00087	.00085	.00062	.00074	.00078	.00072	.00099	.00139	.00108	.00090	.00076	.00196	45
.00652	.00649	.00070	.00054	.00026	.00079	.00063	.00042	.00059	.00132	.00108	.00081	.00327	.00174	.00105	.00355	.00192	46
.00506	.00321	.01779	.00280	.00190	.00254	00726	.00208	.00551	.00342	.00549	.00609	.00930	.00328	.00986	.00209	.00316	47
.00128	.00090	.00129	.00255	.00074	.01111	.00862	.00462	.00597	.00286	.00349	.00204	.00148	.00364	.00293	.00236	.01397	48
.00781	.00556	.00815	.00292	.00133	.00272	.00278	.00156	.00218	.00317	.00292	.00392	.00468	.03628	.00423	.00207	.00731	49
.00451	.00280	.01962	.00132	.00078	.00128	.00150	.00090	.00131	.00287	.00174	.00220	.00534	.00128	.00130	.00094	.00211	50
.00062	.00042	.00109	.00052	.00043	.00041	.00045	.00042	.00044	.00034	.00034	.00043	.00142	.00068	.00052	.00061	.00068	51
.01045	.01046	.00248	.00066	.00047	.00052	.00091	.00044	.00084	.00091	.00249	.00090	.09600	.00064	.00060	.00054	.00075	52
.01216	.00720	.00632	.00153	.00089	.00168	.00187	.00122	.00171	.00164	.00169	.00219	.06464	.00173	.00186	.00137	.00418	53
.00369	.00932	.00249	.00052	.00031	.00038	.00044	.00062	.00063	.00062	.00367	.00053	.00180	.00100	.00067	.00052	.00053	53
.01756	.01360	.00163	.00077	.00040	.00071	.00071	.00054	.00070	.00125	.00101	.00186	.00212	.00100	.00092	.00068	.00117	55
.00208	.00310	.03463	.00063	.00038	.00060	.00072	.00059	.00075	.00055	.00061	.00103	00530	.00051	.00061	.00128	.00081	56
.00162	.00142	.03972	.00069	.00048	.00070	.00367	.00057	.00118	.00055	.00060	.00048	.00235	.00035	.00077	.00106	.00084	57
.00211	.00134	.00231	.00098	.00060	.00061	.00050	.00041	.00050	.00114	.00070	.00068	.00087	.00045	.00046	.00039	.00063	58
.00457	.00316	.01105	.00258	.00113	.00153	.00223	.00128	.00227	.00316	.00289	.00283	.00526	.00170	.00183	.00154	.00294	59
.00186	.00128	.16317	.00094	.00040	.00076	.00032	.00058	.00099	.00161	.00131	.00141	.00723	.00102	.00103	.00076	.00118	60
.00147	.00093	.00122	.00687	.00037	.00063	.00067	.00056	.00076	.00177	.00119	.00083	.00125	.00081	.00085	.00051	.00080	61
.00574	.00265	.01417	.00084	.00047	.00110	.00102	.00152	.00603	.00113	.00124	.00333	.01021	.00187	.00143	.00111	.00106	62
.00123	.00077	.01022	.00116	.00101	.00098	.00094	.00107	.00127	.00078	.00077	.00113	.00125	.00208	.00153	.01100	.00154	63
.00427	.00590	.00273	.00224	.00164	.00212	.00665	.02061	.01162	.00340	.00329	.00610	.00615	.00297	.00264	.00431	.00294	64
.06495	.04724	.03908	.07348	.02481	.05317	.05941	.03763	.04558	.06895	.07865	.05659	.04696	.06914	.08128	.04312	.06459	65
.01170	.00725	.01731	.01154	.00562	.00855	.00927	.01065	.01005	.00767	.00858	.01073	.01178	.00869	.01108	.01810	.00960	66
.00492	.00263	.00304	.00437	.00467	.00275	.00288	.00271	.00271	.00221	.00226	.00299	.00290	.00276	.00306	.00396	.00368	67
.02093	.01390	.02148	.02574	.01116	.03738	.03205	.02399	.03039	.02558	.02605	.02413	.02536	.04394	.03373	.02146	.06202	68
.11487	.09639	.05499	.09304	.03529	.07779	.07771	.07316	.07801	.06723	.08087	.07730	.06296	.06235	.06190	.05113	.05246	69
.02086	.01297	.01193	.02129	.01197	.01622	.01556	.01689	.01731	.01844	.01819	.01816	.01857	.01535	.01464	.01735	.01744	70
.03645	.02643	.02559	.05394	.04057	.04508	.04494	.04270	.04188	.03086	.03237	.03647	.03419	.03721	.04311	.06974	.06102	71
.00421	.00334	.00649	.00582	.00559	.00358	.00423	.00361	.00488	.00229	.00367	.00405	.00374	.00453	.00666	.00622	.00437	72
.08841	.04718	.05465	.07846	.08393	.04935	.05172	.04860	.04857	.03964	.04053	.05357	.05199	.04960	.05497	.07103	.06608	73
.00945	.00586	.00485	.00887	.00351	.00449	.00440	.00422	.00435	.00938	.00714	.00559	.00502	.00463	.00518	.00582	.00450	75
.00254	.00153	.00186	.00227	.00222	.00156	.00161	.00156	.00155	.00125	.00142	.00169	.00158	.00151	.00164	.00222	.00198	76
.00248	.00154	.00288	.00400	.00118	.00173	.00198	.00192	.00187	.00139	.00147	.00189	.00199	.00157	.00183	.00332	.00205	77
.00448	.00304	.00421	.00469	.00460	.00452	.00457	.00609	.00514	.00342	.00386	.00452	.00445	.00419	.00437	.01729	.00559	78
.00596	.00411	.00464	.00672	.00277	.00746	.00689	.00512	.00627	.00622	.00645	.00560	.00540	.00875	.00764	.00510	.01131	79
.03509	.02172	.03581	.05965	.01647	.06345	.12406	.03485	.04743	.12297	.05863	.04001	.04701	.12373	.06118	.03135	.06712	80
.01605	.01368	.02347	.01279	.01142	.01148	.01134	.01325	.01229	.00909	.01460	.01437	.01209	.01030	.01047	.01926	.01384	81
.00190	.00124	.00252	.00211	.00112	.00211	.00188	.00252	.00226	.00167	.00200	.00237	.00246	.00184	.00219	.00393	.00199	82

(*continued*)

Table 4.15 (*continued*)

Industry No.	Each entry represents the output required, directly and indirectly, from the industry named at the beginning of the row for each dollar of delivery to final demand by the industry named at the head of the column	Plastics and synthetic materials	Drugs, cleaning, and toilet preparations	Paints and allied products	Petroleum refining and related industries	Rubber and miscellaneous plastics products	Leather tanning and industrial leather products	Footwear and other leather products	Glass and glass products	Stone and clay products	Primary iron and steel manufacturing
		28	29	30	31	32	33	34	35	36	37
1	Livestock and livestock products	0.00693	0.01503	0.01624	0.00353	0.00619	0.00277	0.00544	0.00263	0.00310	0.00180
2	Other agricultural products	.00670	.01010	.03176	.00344	.00817	.00236	.00902	.00285	.00344	.00181
3	Forestry and fishery products	.00124	.00114	.00133	.00034	.00105	.00037	.00185	.00175	.00091	.00066
4	Agricultural, forestry and fishery services	.00064	.00097	.00201	.00048	.00065	.00032	.00070	.00035	.00038	.00025
5	Iron and ferroalloy ores mining	.00187	.00153	.00313	.00094	.00134	.00048	.00075	.00061	.00275	.05366
6	Nonferrous metal ores mining	.00296	.00141	.00333	.00078	.00140	.00058	.00069	.00129	.00272	.00782
7	Coal mining	.00819	.00277	.00419	.00239	.00399	.00330	.00216	.00326	.00984	.03160
8	Crude petroleum and natural gas	.03162	.01335	.02698	.47988	.01256	.00835	.00639	.00985	.01572	.01042
9	Stone and clay mining and quarrying	.00254	.00197	.00861	.00403	.00215	.00078	.00076	.01461	.08493	.00402
10	Chemical and fertilizer mineral mining	.01326	.00590	.00927	.00136	.00509	.00241	.00145	.00275	.00594	.00220
11	New construction										
12	Maintenance and repair construction	.02267	.01719	.02026	.04400	.01531	.00987	.01027	.01965	.02360	.02298
13	Ordnance and accessories	.00040	.00028	.00034	.00017	.00053	.00013	.00020	.00015	.00021	.00033
14	Food and kindred products	.01997	.04415	.04825	.00629	.01092	.00738	.00722	.00617	.00710	.00444
15	Tobacco manufactures	.00038	.00055	.00057	.00020	.00037	.00017	.00027	.00027	.00028	.00020
16	Broad and narrow fabrics, yarn and thread mills	.01236	.00486	.00371	.00132	.05296	.00216	.07313	.00433	.01104	.00201
17	Miscellaneous textile goods and floor coverings	.00246	.00246	.00145	.00080	.00834	.00180	.03984	.00200	.00435	.00081
18	Apparel	.00125	.00126	.00122	.00053	.00415	.00136	.01602	.00225	.00180	.00152
19	Miscellaneous fabricated textile products	.00084	.00109	.00083	.00035	.00205	.00041	.01256	.00058	.00101	.00055
20	Lumber and wood products, except containers	.00945	.00705	.00542	.00297	.01001	.00302	.02033	.02039	.00975	.00713
21	Wooden containers	.00016	.00023	.00030	.00009	.00022	.00012	.00025	.00148	.00013	.00036
22	Household furniture	.00010	.00023	.00009	.00068	.00043	.00006	.00031	.00509	.00012	.00012
23	Other furniture and fixtures	.00009	.00012	.00008	.00008	.00064	.00005	.00051	.00042	.00011	.00019
24	Paper and allied products, except containers	.05798	.04106	.02519	.01149	.03630	.01405	.00776	.04443	.03558	.00687
25	Paperboard containers and boxes	.01681	.03500	.01504	.00471	.01907	.00540	.02007	.06005	.00972	.00257
26	Printing and publishing	.01653	.04658	.01211	.01334	.01544	.00957	.01474	.01284	.01315	.01261
27	Chemicals and selected chemical products	.46704	.18485	.32504	.04446	.14411	.08240	.04478	.04607	.04256	.02842
28	Plastics and synthetic materials	1.05204	.02117	.11190	.00378	.19641	.00636	.03444	.00959	.01363	.00346
29	Drugs, cleaning and toilet preparations	.01408	1.06077	.01726	.00481	.00554	.00470	.01147	.00258	.00196	.00106
30	Paints and allied products	.00934	.00574	1.01148	.00324	.00470	.00136	.00178	.00711	.00267	.00224
31	Petroleum refining and related industries	.06190	.02556	.05419	1.08561	.02251	.01506	.01093	.01277	.02579	.01491
32	Rubber and miscellaneous plastics products	.03273	.04211	.01183	.00696	1.05411	.00818	.10020	.03184	.01913	.00648
33	Leather tanning and industrial leather products	.00015	.00019	.00015	.00009	.00088	1.12891	.21132	.00011	.00046	.00019
34	Footwear and other leather products	.00024	.00036	.00032	.00011	.00217	.00426	1.02840	.00020	.00020	.00015
35	Glass and glass products	.00197	.01874	.00165	.00075	.00429	.00121	.00143	1.06894	.00122	.00082
36	Stone and clay products	.00410	.00524	.00780	.00834	.00811	.00349	.00271	.02296	1.13302	.00801
37	Primary iron and steel manufacturing	.01665	.02308	.04806	.01659	.02015	.00581	.01300	.00956	.03186	1.27607
38	Primary nonferrous metal manufacturing	.02045	.01233	.03378	.00917	.01347	.00427	.00813	.01747	.01319	.06292
39	Metal containers	.00778	.02089	.06492	.00473	.00327	.00212	.00150	.00191	.00251	.00102
40	Heating, plumbing and structural metal products	.00212	.00166	.00209	.00468	.00235	.00092	.00123	.00196	.00338	.00512
41	Stampings, screw machine products and bolts	.00258	.00778	.00376	.00199	.00800	.00147	.00918	.00248	.00343	.01291
42	Other fabricated metal products	.00714	.02060	.01296	.00630	.02075	.00404	.02036	.00571	.01724	.02395
43	Engines and turbines	.00072	.00072	.00079	.00233	.00058	.00032	.00039	.00062	.00286	.00180
44	Farm machinery and equipment	.00029	.00049	.00060	.00025	.00043	.00014	.00030	.00019	.00039	.00171
45	Construction, mining and oil field machinery	.00139	.00176	.00134	.00287	.00111	.00059	.00070	.00100	.00977	.00401
46	Materials handling machinery and equipment	.00128	.00064	.00097	.00128	.00103	.00049	.00044	.00064	.00155	.00253
47	Metalworking machinery and equipment	.00432	.00329	.00367	.00177	.00808	.00437	.00592	.00531	.01102	.01581
48	Special industry machinery and equipment	.00803	.00242	.00428	.00092	.00432	.00160	.00383	.00098	.00225	.00241
49	General industrial machinery and equipment	.00571	.00292	.00393	.00752	.00394	.00149	.00184	.00288	.00715	.01791
50	Machine shop products	.00393	.00220	.00303	.00374	.00355	.00163	.00144	.00108	.00299	.01098
51	Office, computing and accounting machines	.00055	.00101	.00058	.00057	.00062	.00032	.00045	.00037	.00041	.00061
52	Service industry machines	.00067	.00120	.00077	.00083	.00083	.00056	.00056	.00071	.00116	.00099
53	Electric industrial equipment and apparatus	.00262	.00237	.00264	.00723	.00219	.00099	.00150	.00181	.00431	.01563
54	Household appliances	.00052	.00106	.00070	.00061	.00058	.00028	.00125	.00049	.00064	.00065
55	Electric lighting and wiring equipment	.00113	.00090	.00094	.00157	.00136	.00039	.00059	.00258	.00328	.00201
56	Radio, television and communication equipment	.00074	.01002	.00084	.00087	.00113	.00040	.00067	.00069	.00087	.00111
57	Electronic components and accessories	.00078	.00124	.00097	.00092	.00144	.00043	.00085	.00073	.00085	.00124
58	Miscellaneous electrical machinery, equipment and supplies	.00054	.00053	.00068	.00052	.00065	.00030	.00058	.00054	.00069	.00150
59	Motor vehicles and equipment	.00208	.00261	.00300	.00180	.00359	.00113	.00186	.00696	.00250	.00974
60	Aircraft and parts	.00119	.00098	.00109	.00106	.00571	.00060	.00121	.00083	.00141	.00135
61	Other transportation equipment	.00072	.00066	.00084	.00090	.00071	.00049	.00050	.00059	.00105	.00157
62	Scientific and controlling instruments	.00096	.00571	.00100	.00168	.00165	.00080	.00298	.00250	.00132	.00307
63	Optical, ophthalmic and photographic equipment	.00125	.00237	.00145	.00081	.00166	.00078	.00253	.00099	.00091	.00089
64	Miscellaneous manufacturing	.00274	.00508	.00328	.00159	.00960	.00223	.01359	.00385	.00624	.00208
65	Transportation and warehousing	.06281	.04491	.07460	.08123	.05030	.04857	.03784	.05544	.09509	.08307
66	Communications; except radio and TV broadcasting	.01071	.01426	.01347	.00663	.01079	.00704	.01016	.00837	.01108	.00888
67	Radio and TV broadcasting	.00386	.01177	.00435	.00327	.00355	.00216	.00306	.00290	.00298	.00309
68	Electric, gas, water and sanitary services	.04747	.02360	.03377	.03792	.03277	.02141	.02044	.05848	.06931	.05359
69	Wholesale and retail trade	.06467	.06138	.07105	.03517	.06294	.01049	.07630	.05254	.05214	.05736
70	Finance and insurance	.01717	.01753	.01860	.02548	.01448	.01701	.01744	.01436	.02098	.01713
71	Real estate and rental	.05654	.05554	.06093	.11961	.03911	.03251	.03756	.03858	.04496	.02707
72	Hotels; personal and repair services except auto	.00551	.01089	.01051	.00324	.00536	.00239	.00386	.00416	.00379	.00297
73	Business services	.06916	.21145	.07802	.05847	.06375	.03875	.05679	.05203	.05539	.05547
75	Automobile repair and services	.00475	.00564	.00581	.00404	.00425	.00358	.00408	.00401	.00738	.00449
76	Amusements	.00213	.00539	.00253	.00183	.00195	.00126	.00171	.00158	.00166	.00158
77	Medical, educational services and nonprofit organizations	.00219	.00348	.00262	.00143	.00192	.00159	.00228	.00165	.00206	.00316
78	Federal Government enterprises	.00474	.00702	.00567	.00389	.00429	.00390	.00652	.00444	.00458	.00406
79	State and local government enterprises	.00919	.00561	.00772	.00858	.00662	.00560	.00464	.01010	.01221	.01025
80	Gross imports of goods and services	.05232	.03519	.04422	.04857	.08654	.05699	.09099	.04045	.04297	.09633
81	Business travel, entertainment and gifts	.01745	.02526	.02614	.00876	.01690	.00761	.01219	.01230	.01287	.00906
82	Office supplies	.00194	.00261	.00281	.00168	.00204	.00165	.00285	.00200	.00218	.00180

Table 4.15 (*continued*)

Industry No.	Primary nonferrous metals manufacturing 38	Metal containers 39	Heating, plumbing and structural metal products 40	Stampings, screw machine products and bolts 41	Other fabricated metal products 42	Engines and turbines 43	Farm machinery and equipment 44	Construction, mining and oil field machinery 45	Materials handling machinery and equipment 46
1	0.00210	0.00486	0.00303	0.00196	0.00255	0.00274	0.00254	0.00238	0.00262
2	.00209	.00455	.00294	.00204	.00259	.00249	.00247	.00231	.00250
3	.00095	.00087	.00089	.00092	.00099	.00053	.00070	.00060	.00062
4	.00028	.00044	.00035	.00026	.00030	.00030	.00030	.00029	.00031
5	.00317	.02459	.01756	.01679	.01302	.00982	.01180	.01290	.01021
6	.08743	.00696	.00928	.00766	.00851	.00764	.00447	.00366	.00576
7	.00403	.01315	.00971	.00954	.00775	.00643	.00732	.00770	.00623
8	.00922	.00846	.00815	.00715	.00829	.00775	.00683	.00722	.00642
9	.00145	.00236	.00204	.00171	.00196	.00201	.00152	.00195	.00154
10	.00135	.00143	.00104	.00101	.00188	.00074	.00083	.00078	.00072
11									
12	.01527	.01568	.01654	.01557	.01443	.01407	.01378	.01487	.01336
13	.00022	.00040	.00160	.00076	.00160	.00894	.00183	.00215	.00116
14	.00526	.01430	.00799	.00474	.00617	.00742	.00644	.00592	.00654
15	.00020	.00073	.00040	.00022	.00029	.00039	.00033	.00030	.00034
16	.00288	.00243	.00269	.00305	.00396	.00272	.00361	.00309	.00328
17	.00086	.00096	.00111	.00123	.00362	.00123	.00199	.00156	.00155
18	.00139	.00161	.00197	.00191	.00199	.00167	.00178	.00176	.00183
19	.00050	.00057	.00080	.00129	.00081	.00100	.00075	.00078	.00118
20	.01073	.00767	.00929	.01045	.01086	.00493	.00729	.00608	.00619
21	.00085	.00027	.00114	.00132	.00049	.00030	.00064	.00049	.00061
22	.00012	.00011	.00048	.00080	.00119	.00058	.00021	.00024	.00022
23	.00012	.00013	.00286	.00044	.00145	.00039	.00119	.00027	.00086
24	.00806	.02518	.01231	.01343	.01864	.00941	.00925	.00786	.00856
25	.00315	.01707	.00792	.00948	.01358	.00686	.00481	.00365	.00407
26	.01047	.06077	.01286	.01078	.01309	.01152	.01438	.01178	.01339
27	.03172	.02876	.01956	.01978	.03159	.01435	.01658	.01414	.01386
28	.01506	.00691	.00538	.00705	.00851	.00497	.00897	.00651	.00636
29	.00130	.00249	.00209	.00143	.00198	.00109	.00118	.00107	.00113
30	.00216	.02930	.01042	.00416	.00742	.00311	.00139	.00375	.00320
31	.01276	.01301	.01285	.01081	.01332	.01327	.01125	.01186	.01057
32	.00885	.00735	.00902	.01258	.02369	.01047	.03624	.02432	.02110
33	.00052	.00017	.00019	.00040	.00033	.00044	.00022	.00021	.00024
34	.00013	.00027	.00025	.00032	.00034	.00020	.00026	.00022	.00039
35	.00075	.00082	.00588	.00153	.00263	.00129	.00099	.00099	.00113
36	.00565	.00778	.00830	.00677	.00912	.01584	.00807	.01327	.00946
37	.05002	.49144	.35037	.33516	.25747	.19514	.23540	.25764	.20336
38	1.50358	.09100	.13926	.11226	.13022	.11866	.06235	.04743	.08674
39	.00223	1.01717	.00230	.00391	.00188	.00109	.00114	.00099	.00103
40	.00220	.00329	1.03131	.00514	.01010	.00760	.00704	.01142	.01845
41	.00697	.02238	.03155	1.04131	.02426	.03247	.03258	.01885	.02390
42	.01816	.01670	.04140	.02469	1.05033	.02609	.02897	.02563	.04155
43	.00173	.00107	.00434	.00241	.00237	1.08778	.07207	.02793	.01849
44	.00032	.00082	.00150	.00156	.00157	.00868	1.05262	.01181	.01007
45	.00232	.00208	.00589	.00187	.00359	.04528	.02724	1.06148	.05017
46	.00151	.00155	.00359	.00142	.00224	.00169	.00195	.01503	1.05845
47	.01476	.01668	.01424	.02719	.02299	.02533	.01843	.03096	.02707
48	.00103	.00264	.00329	.00246	.00410	.00574	.00441	.00403	.00595
49	.00970	.00858	.02002	.00908	.01476	.05343	.08517	.07766	.07786
50	.01230	.00566	.01621	.01881	.01096	.03735	.01668	.01326	.02788
51	.00034	.00051	.00110	.00180	.00059	.00053	.00054	.00053	.00054
52	.00087	.00082	.01556	.00309	.00423	.00162	.00200	.00172	.00671
53	.01208	.00768	.02026	.00780	.00867	.03376	.01601	.02384	.05089
54	.00081	.00283	.00523	.00241	.00146	.00081	.00367	.00072	.00129
55	.00272	.00158	.00248	.00418	.00363	.00266	.00190	.00217	.00256
56	.00178	.00109	.00192	.00147	.00135	.00390	.00149	.00195	.00286
57	.00127	.00103	.00201	.00161	.00138	.00569	.00199	.00214	.00340
58	.00860	.00118	.00185	.00196	.00165	.02488	.01217	.00398	.00458
59	.00724	.00562	.01233	.03980	.01324	.04286	.01805	.02236	.02302
60	.00110	.00264	.00613	.00220	.00256	.05758	.00608	.00891	.00569
61	.00093	.00130	.00609	.00118	.00153	.01207	.00360	.00686	.00259
62	.00133	.00192	.00812	.00400	.00451	.00502	.00550	.00843	.00822
63	.00071	.00143	.00118	.00106	.00119	.00114	.00114	.00103	.00106
64	.00263	.00222	.00255	.00413	.00426	.00203	.00321	.00246	.00297
65	.06248	.08102	.06053	.05259	.04760	.04441	.04853	.04386	.04128
66	.00771	.00909	.01288	.00935	.01045	.01141	.01093	.01159	.01405
67	.00222	.00345	.00297	.00247	.00283	.00269	.00347	.00279	.00316
68	.05012	.03731	.03427	.03298	.03309	.02624	.02570	.02738	.02407
69	.07144	.04839	.06924	.04997	.05473	.07088	.07075	.06635	.06609
70	.01905	.01760	.01974	.01503	.01610	.01278	.01975	.01688	.01673
71	.02981	.03387	.03689	.02899	.03200	.03061	.03197	.03479	.03858
72	.00250	.00673	.00762	.00315	.00414	.00499	.00493	.00418	.00477
73	.03985	.06189	.05332	.04436	.05088	.04837	.06233	.04999	.05677
75	.00381	.00436	.00500	.00407	.00416	.00497	.00460	.00460	.00482
76	.00126	.00225	.00177	.00134	.00156	.00164	.00187	.00158	.00177
77	.00172	.00176	00214	.00164	.00184	.00201	.00195	.00204	.00249
78	.00381	.00421	.00433	.00346	.00391	.00397	.00449	.00408	.00434
79	.00926	.00794	.00707	.00655	.00647	.00559	.00559	.00565	.00516
80	.17839	.05545	.05393	.05669	.06696	.06360	.09521	.05134	.04648
81	.00906	.03422	.01863	.00989	.01338	.01824	.01498	.01381	.01563
82	.00154	.00176	.00226	.00161	.00196	.00204	.00233	.00207	.00233

Industry No.	Metalworking machinery and equipment 47	Special industry machinery and equipment 48	General industrial machinery and equipment 49	Machine shop products 50	Office, computing and accounting machines 51	Service industry machines 52	Electric industrial equipment and apparatus 53	Household appliances 54
1	0.00249	0.00351	0.00293	0.00297	0.00503	0.00355	0.00345	0.00345
2	.00229	.00324	.00265	.00268	.00432	.00348	.00317	.00387
3	.00049	.00102	.00080	.00045	.00061	.00085	.00074	.00094
4	.00028	.00039	.00032	.00032	.00048	.00039	.00036	.00041
5	.00744	.00792	.00943	.00707	.00242	.00761	.00517	.00756
6	.00442	.00478	.00598	.00506	.00308	.00800	.00748	.00700
7	.00461	.00490	.00581	.00159	.00215	.00522	.00406	.00556
8	.00702	.00718	.00724	.01035	.00492	.00739	.00771	.00767
9	.00180	.00151	.00209	.00160	.00095	.00215	.00193	.00205
10	.00063	.00062	.00075	.00062	.00058	.00101	.00097	.00131
11								
12	.01233	.01422	.01380	.01278	.01305	.01445	.01342	.01550
13	.00074	.00321	.00139	.00083	.00079	.00144	.00300	.00071
14	.00649	.00886	.00777	.00727	.01352	.00937	.00915	.00838
15	.00035	.00041	.00041	.00040	.00077	.00047	.00049	.00040
16	.00243	.00383	.00264	.00257	.00277	.00577	.00343	.01028
17	.00109	.00115	.00170	.00219	.00134	.00223	.00176	.00325
18	.00179	.00171	.00191	.00208	.00161	.00188	.00183	.00204
19	.00060	.00047	.00057	.00055	.00042	.00091	.00051	.00081
20	.00461	.01094	.00818	.00386	.00448	.00847	.00709	.00976
21	.00035	.00054	.00072	.00030	.00023	.00261	.00059	.00323
22	.00021	.00040	.00021	.00022	.00067	.00064	.00059	.00127
23	.00027	.00027	.00098	.00107	.00180	.00125	.00016	.00035
24	.00740	.00813	.00879	.00834	.02055	.01560	.01902	.02231
25	.00359	.00366	.00174	.00639	.00598	.01161	.00797	.02454
26	.01033	.01203	.01184	.01035	.03113	.01528	.01219	.02117
27	.01253	.01243	.01456	.01299	.01489	.02365	.02494	.03359
28	.00490	.00502	.00486	.00423	.00829	.00987	.01156	.02142
29	.00097	.00138	.00139	.00120	.00133	.00184	.00142	.00264
30	.00312	.00208	.00243	.00197	.00312	.00764	.00459	.01124
31	.01217	.01259	.01214	.01895	.00822	.01226	.01329	.01231
32	.01441	.01447	.01190	.01042	.01951	.02548	.01670	.05730
33	.00022	.00049	.00078	.00014	.00015	.00052	.00044	.00072
34	.00029	.00030	.00022	.00020	.00032	.00041	.00026	.00127
35	.00094	.00180	.00119	.00094	.00639	.00260	.00345	.00580
36	.01528	.01048	.01734	.01244	.00516	.01737	.01629	.01417
37	.14789	.15758	.18754	.14038	.04726	.15023	.10123	.14888
38	.06684	.07253	.09139	07767	.04929	.12754	.12095	.10957
39	.00176	.00095	.00125	.00090	.00124	.00168	.00133	.00220
40	.00633	.02243	.02073	.00429	.00564	.03025	.00377	.00817
41	.04499	.01665	.01596	.01949	.02261	.03841	.02538	.05536
42	.02996	.02458	.03776	.02078	.01943	.05696	.01947	.04932
43	.00262	.00927	.01305	.00338	.00104	.00402	.01559	.00206
44	.00158	.00355	.00343	.00113	.00048	.00122	.00064	.00166
45	.00414	.00827	.01079	.00228	.00108	.00451	.00368	.00198
46	.00188	.00557	.00386	.00103	.00062	.00487	.00207	.00108
47	1.08331	.03470	.03006	.03403	.01927	.01888	.02138	.01801
48	.00748	1.07613	.01400	.00276	.00161	.00420	.00166	.00166
49	.03420	.05750	1.08312	.02181	.00950	.02546	.01350	01671
50	.01302	.00895	.01428	1.07196	.01573	.00698	.00666	.00615
51	.00061	.00234	.00053	.00045	1.15435	.00125	.00126	.00081
52	.00292	.00374	.00843	.00127	.00087	1.07348	.00167	.03223
53	.04080	.04929	.04483	.01240	.03465	.10401	1.08975	.06724
54	.00140	.00187	.00187	.00063	.00064	.11807	.00108	1.02026
55	.00269	.00368	.00276	.00364	.03057	.01170	.02014	.01549
56	.00257	.01095	.00282	.00150	.02234	.00813	.02373	.00362
57	.00251	.00514	.00421	.00149	.15171	.00660	.03946	.00464
58	.00162	.00214	.00238	.01546	.00218	.00301	.00804	.00538
59	.01810	.00692	.01312	.01452	.00401	.03286	.01085	.01750
60	.00474	.00524	.01283	.00190	.00179	.02034	.00450	.00403
61	.00104	.00547	.00391	.00172	.00083	.00314	.01053	.00194
62	.00360	.00477	.00605	.00188	.00499	.02180	.01471	.03210
63	.00095	.00211	.00113	.00090	.00226	.00192	.00185	.00196
64	.00308	.00264	.00216	.00187	.00332	.00772	.00260	.01083
65	.03469	.03906	.04270	.03566	.03712	.04851	.04051	.04961
66	.01072	.01305	.01247	.00989	.01399	.01266	.01257	.01200
67	.00239	.00242	.00277	.00244	.00297	.00366	.00256	.00543
68	.02281	.02186	.02600	.02750	.01677	.02690	.02505	.03029
69	.05670	.06697	.06414	.04905	.07067	.08160	.06361	.07046
70	.01358	.01683	.01457	.01425	.01798	.01522	.01478	.01544
71	.03312	.05374	.03374	.04835	.06604	.03963	.04135	.04491
72	.00431	.00464	.00478	.00142	.00681	.00500	.00534	.00510
73	.04281	.04327	.04966	.04371	.05314	.06564	.04593	.09751
75	.00382	.00427	.00447	.00365	.00424	.00514	.00439	.00473
76	.00145	.00158	.00167	.00154	.00219	.00212	.00168	.00274
77	.00194	.00235	.00221	.00185	.00253	.00222	.00214	.00202
78	.00356	.00413	.00414	.00350	.00450	.00468	.00380	.00571
79	.00468	.00490	.00540	.00544	.00428	.00584	.00530	.00637
80	.06203	.08216	.06156	.02828	.05391	.04391	.05805	.04186
81	.01605	.01900	.01897	.01843	.03601	.02154	.02265	.01844
82	.00185	.00224	.00206	.00175	.00246	.00226	.00203	.00210

(*continued*)

Table 4.15 (continued)

Industry No.	Each entry represents the output required, directly and indirectly, from the industry named at the beginning of the row for each dollar of delivery to final demand by the industry named at the head of the column.	Electric lighting and wiring equipment	Radio, television and communication equipment	Electronic components and accessories	Miscellaneous electrical machinery, equipment and supplies	Motor vehicles and equipment	Aircraft and parts	Other transportation equipment	Scientific and controlling instruments	Optical, ophthalmic and photographic equipment	Miscellaneous manufacturing
		55	56	57	58	59	60	61	62	63	64
1	Livestock and livestock products	.00294	.00290	.00368	.00288	.00266	.00327	.00342	.00463	.00255	.00499
2	Other agricultural products	.00293	.00273	.00328	.00278	.00350	.00304	.00389	.00694	.00246	.00789
3	Forestry and fishery products	.00067	.00079	.00064	.00072	.00064	.00054	.00497	.00086	.00059	.00290
4	Agricultural, forestry and fishery services	.00033	.00031	.00036	.00033	.00034	.00033	.00049	.00057	.00029	.00066
5	Iron and ferroalloy ores mining	.00599	.00183	.00240	.00367	.00912	.00350	.01041	.00360	.00137	.00291
6	Nonferrous metal ores mining	.00768	.00327	.00481	.01464	.00458	.00523	.00611	.00535	.00477	.00475
7	Coal mining	.00437	.00188	.00256	.00350	.00609	.00269	.00645	.00296	.00177	.00306
8	Crude petroleum and natural gas	.00668	.00495	.00654	.00725	.00705	.00678	.00713	.00624	.00648	.00786
9	Stone and clay mining and quarrying	.00228	.00090	.00180	.00168	.00160	.00094	.00175	.00165	.00105	.00178
10	Chemical and fertilizer mineral mining	.00114	.00062	.00130	.00166	.00096	.00051	.00089	.00095	.00220	.00143
11	New construction										
12	Maintenance and repair construction	.01388	.01108	.01310	.01306	.01372	.01236	.01432	.01291	.01217	.01265
13	Ordnance and accessories	.00189	.01145	.00103	.00056	.00122	.02622	.00492	.00490	.00058	.00296
14	Food and kindred products	.00742	.00761	.01020	.00726	.00542	.00872	.00731	.01124	.00658	.01085
15	Tobacco manufactures	.00037	.00041	.00036	.00036	.00024	.00049	.00036	.00057	.00031	.00064
16	Broad and narrow fabrics, yarn and thread mills	.00493	.00407	.00379	.00408	.01820	.00455	.00663	.02552	.00332	.03375
17	Miscellaneous textile goods and floor coverings	.00174	.00181	.00260	.00197	.00912	.00144	.00795	.00605	.00127	.01252
18	Apparel	.00194	.00185	.00226	.00187	.00227	.00176	.00229	.00276	.00126	.00474
19	Miscellaneous fabricated textile products	.00053	.00042	.00047	.00139	.02009	.00049	.00146	.00191	.00035	.00214
20	Lumber and wood products, except containers	.00655	.00809	.00547	.00709	.00662	.00465	.06105	.00816	.00563	.03074
21	Wooden containers	.00029	.00189	.00031	.00029	.00055	.00045	.00051	.00044	.00018	.00064
22	Household furniture	.00050	.01745	.00223	.00029	.00048	.00088	.00452	.00221	.00030	.00139
23	Other furniture and fixtures	.00021	.00027	.00013	.00029	.00164	.00330	.00101	.00196	.00615	.00130
24	Paper and allied products, except containers	.02042	.01426	.02598	.01378	.01186	.00847	.01085	.02905	.03381	.04769
25	Paperboard containers and boxes	.02324	.00713	.01079	.01241	.00657	.00377	.00431	.01221	.00993	.03593
26	Printing and publishing	.01235	.01560	.01354	.01217	.01146	.01325	.01086	.01741	.01361	.02057
27	Chemicals and selected chemical products	.02597	.01707	.03773	.05045	.02207	.01241	.01904	.02562	.07283	.04178
28	Plastics and synthetic materials	.01814	.01056	.01842	.02001	.01350	.00552	.01227	.01655	.01627	.03452
29	Drugs, cleaning and toilet preparations	.00139	.00113	.00161	.00150	.00131	.00131	.00125	.00137	.00189	.00385
30	Paints and allied products	.00616	.01116	.00462	.00293	.00700	.00232	.00641	.00362	.00184	.00569
31	Petroleum refining and related industries	.01026	.00813	.01048	.01174	.01163	.01204	.01160	.01248	.01139	.01394
32	Rubber and miscellaneous plastics products	.02969	.01799	.03867	.02929	.03785	.01118	.02719	.02997	.03204	.03082
33	Leather tanning and industrial leather products	.00016	.00015	.00016	.00019	.00026	.00016	.00022	.00039	.00012	.00313
34	Footwear and other leather products	.00022	.00027	.00031	.00023	.00025	.00032	.00031	.00128	.00021	.00488
35	Glass and glass products	.03482	.01116	.03693	.00332	.01352	.00153	.00185	.00524	.01281	.00532
36	Stone and clay products	.01555	.00502	.01071	.01289	.00410	.00587	.01062	.00610	.00371	.00609
37	Primary iron and steel manufacturing	.11235	.03531	.04760	.06926	.18138	.06882	.20705	.00723	.03612	.03577
38	Primary nonferrous metal manufacturing	.12369	.03808	.05761	.11932	.09645	.05505	.05242	.07539	.07613	.07584
39	Metal containers	.00157	.00098	.00137	.00153	.00157	.00100	.00126	.00366	.00132	.00227
40	Heating, plumbing and structural metal products	.00967	.00214	.00285	.00462	.00405	.00251	.04266	.00379	.00143	.00240
41	Stampings, screw machine products and bolts	.03489	.02706	.02948	.02305	.09070	.03053	.01763	.02790	.01586	.01416
42	Other fabricated metal products	.02421	.01912	.02429	.03358	.05168	.02918	.03498	.03231	.02228	.02814
43	Engines and turbines	.00150	.00045	.00092	.00165	.00694	.00496	.04413	.00141	.00060	.00083
44	Farm machinery and equipment	.00307	.00032	.00032	.00048	.00139	.00070	.00547	.00199	.00028	.00175
45	Construction, mining and oil field machinery	.00140	.00045	.00103	.00150	.00399	.00137	.00754	.00178	.00091	.00105
46	Materials handling machinery and equipment	.00074	.00065	.00156	.00082	.00160	.00077	.00187	.00101	.00050	.00063
47	Metalworking machinery and equipment	.01301	.00279	.00498	.01982	.01983	.02193	.02892	.00589	.00374	.00425
48	Special industry machinery and equipment	.00137	.00076	.00010	.00152	.00173	.00139	.00262	.00139	.00191	.00207
49	General industrial machinery and equipment	.00688	.00381	.00360	.01848	.01655	.01547	.05023	.00997	.00516	.00362
50	Machine shop products	.08456	.00752	.00579	.00569	.02031	.04449	.01150	.00923	.00310	.00327
51	Office, computing and accounting machines	.00057	.01103	.01143	.00067	.00061	.00135	.00049	.00264	.00069	.00349
52	Service industry machines	.00145	.00129	.00072	.00175	.01627	.00107	.00354	.00383	.00069	.00123
53	Electric industrial equipment and apparatus	.00465	.02531	.00517	.02949	.01256	.01075	.00113	.00635	.01152	.00867
54	Household appliances	.00074	.00188	.00082	.00212	.00275	.00080	.00573	.00106	.00043	.00241
55	Electric lighting and wiring equipment	1.03035	.01195	.00698	.02920	.01043	.00182	.00511	.00851	.00239	.00342
56	Radio, television and communication equipment	.00345	1.07608	.04542	.00820	.00660	.04119	.00178	.03031	.00806	.00362
57	Electronic components and accessories	.00906	.23369	1.17463	.02064	.00443	.02116	.00235	.04103	.02394	.00579
58	Miscellaneous electrical machinery, equipment and supplies	.02707	.00288	.00359	1.06625	.01961	.00395	.00394	.00548	.00193	.00151
59	Motor vehicles and equipment	.01219	.00339	.00404	.00241	1.40019	.00791	.03353	.01527	.00233	.00538
60	Aircraft and parts	.00240	.01918	.00212	.00241	.00428	1.27575	.00704	.01263	.00219	.00303
61	Other transportation equipment	.00105	.00066	.00074	.00088	.00111	.00232	1.06402	.00199	.00075	.00289
62	Scientific and controlling instruments	.00314	.00552	.00311	.00687	.00657	.00321	.00427	1.08428	.00273	.00285
63	Optical, ophthalmic and photographic equipment	.00355	.00239	.00347	.00114	.00108	.00214	.00101	.01598	1.07022	.00133
64	Miscellaneous manufacturing	.00281	.00415	.00287	.00250	.00298	.00273	.00553	.00829	.00456	1.07211
65	Transportation and warehousing	.04266	.02981	.03758	.04119	.05490	.03218	.05408	.03865	.02928	.04629
66	Communications, except radio and TV broadcasting	.01065	.01364	.01483	.01058	.00878	.01632	.01054	.01485	.01149	.01131
67	Radio and TV broadcasting	.00292	.00312	.00311	.00288	.00272	.00310	.00250	.00409	.00311	.00374
68	Electric, gas, water and sanitary services	.02933	.01831	.02574	.02740	.02628	.02909	.02696	.02168	.01813	.02251
69	Wholesale and retail trade	.05884	.03596	.05208	.05613	.06182	.04034	.07696	.06928	.03186	.07621
70	Finance and insurance	.01280	.01225	.01499	.01751	.01416	.01259	.01563	.01451	.01319	.01732
71	Real estate and rental	.00492	.03397	.03563	.03978	.02746	.03826	.03364	.03991	.03444	.03977
72	Hotels, personal and repair services except auto	.00143	.00160	.00623	.00563	.00377	.00820	.00440	.00662	.00430	.00498
73	Business services	.05334	.05597	.05573	.05164	.04883	.05567	.04489	.07350	.05578	.06716
74	Automobile repair services	.00417	.00173	.00135	.00493	.02419	.00503	.00487	.00491	.00334	.00443
76	Amusements	.00170	.00180	.00194	.00167	.00148	.00201	.00154	.00237	.00168	.00204
77	Medical, educational services and nonprofit organizations	.00190	.00259	.00258	.00192	.00149	.00268	.00405	.00263	.00201	.00232
78	Federal Government enterprises	.00385	.00145	.00414	.00381	.00434	.00412	.00408	.00509	.00357	.00509
79	State and local government enterprises	.00590	.00399	.00528	.00557	.00601	.00430	.00597	.00180	.00387	.11444
80	Gross imports of goods and services	.05027	.06646	.05513	.07366	.05435	.03751	.06618	.03612	.06397	
81	Business travel, entertainment and gifts	.01710	.01907	.02548	.01636	.01117	.02278	.01645	.02640	.01408	.01688
82	Office supplies	.00182	.00254	.00221	.00184	.00181	.00233	.00195	.00291	.00171	.00272

Table 4.15 (*continued*)

Transportation and warehousing	Communications; except radio and TV broadcasting	Radio and TV broadcasting	Electric, gas, water and sanitary services	Wholesale and retail trade	Finance and insurance	Real estate and rental	Hotels; personal and repair services except auto	Business services	Automobile repair and services	Amusements	Medical, educational services and nonprofit organizations	Federal Government enterprises	State and local government enterprises	Gross imports of goods and services	Business travel, entertainment and gifts	Office supplies	Industry No.
65	66	67	68	69	70	71	72	73	75	76	77	78	79	80	81	82	
0.00341	0.00147	0.00918	0.00169	0.00502	0.00388	0.01579	0.00431	0.00474	0.00237	0.01636	0.00787	0.00157	0.00215	...	0.10249	0.00474	1
.00368	.00133	.01341	.00170	.00418	.00335	.01734	.00475	.00454	.00238	.03615	.00611	.00164	.00246	...	.07446	.00540	2
.00037	.00020	.00043	.00032	.00043	.00040	.00031	.00054	.00067	.00032	.00040	.00041	.00017	.00058	...	.00670	.00355	3
.00040	.00018	.00184	.00027	.00130	.00038	.00269	.00052	.00053	.00035	.00547	.00061	.00020	.00054	...	.00592	.00057	4
.00086	.00019	.00022	.00055	.00031	.00619	.00042	.00064	.00068	.00244	.00027	.00028	.00024	.00083	...	.00092	.00127	5
.00058	.00023	.00025	.00043	.00028	.00018	.00044	.00066	.00055	.00155	.00030	.00028	.00018	.00067	...	.00069	.00167	6
.00163	.00060	.00120	.03657	.00124	.00117	.00113	.00189	.00134	.00222	.00102	.00195	.01168	.01337	...	.00186	.00372	7
.02414	.00374	.00464	.09534	.00772	.00439	.00797	.01062	.00522	.00993	.00581	.00762	.00802	.02104	...	.01597	.00872	8
.00097	.00059	.00047	.00139	.00055	.00040	.00154	.00097	.00077	.00131	.00076	.00064	.00041	.00313	...	.00130	.00224	9
.00036	.00012	.00024	.00044	.00028	.00022	.00038	.00062	.00061	.00049	.00048	.00039	.00018	.00123	...	.00080	.00239	10
...	...	...	...	...	...	...	...	...	...	...	...	...	...	...	...	...	11
.04070	.03341	.01697	.07628	.01269	.01316	.07094	.02099	.01535	.01304	.02574	.02574	.01692	.19220	...	.02726	.01579	12
.00032	.00018	.00019	.00010	.00037	.00010	.00019	.00023	.00023	.00034	.00013	.00013	.00008	.00014	...	.00191	.00045	13
.00859	.00366	.01744	.00385	.01350	.00978	.00606	.00927	.01173	.00529	.01416	.02188	.00329	.00510	...	.34174	.01116	14
.00021	.00021	.00103	.00021	.00044	.00056	.00020	.00045	.00066	.00024	.00073	.00045	.00015	.00025	...	.02146	.00041	15
.00284	.00079	.00087	.00134	.00223	.00118	.00134	.01057	.00315	.00408	.00113	.00224	.00245	.00171	...	.00491	.01500	16
.00172	.00031	.00045	.00071	.00106	.00053	.00065	.00301	.00167	.00201	.00063	.00073	.00082	.00082	...	.00238	.06585	17
.00091	.00057	.00036	.00070	.00138	.00032	.00082	.00667	.00072	.00141	.00037	.00125	.00028	.00110	...	.00275	.00217	18
.00226	.00018	.00025	.00031	.00080	.00025	.00027	.00608	.00047	.00273	.00032	.00076	.00226	.00050	...	.00242	.00124	19
.00276	.00166	.00151	.00308	.00344	.00284	.00293	.00414	.00568	.00288	.00202	.00230	.00138	.00606	...	.00489	.04204	20
.00010	.00006	.00013	.00006	.00077	.00007	.00015	.00014	.00013	.00028	.00023	.00010	.00004	.00010	...	.00093	.00030	21
.00012	.00023	.00013	.00008	.00023	.00005	.00014	.00016	.00011	.00028	.00006	.00007	.00004	.00014	...	.00030	.00039	22
.00010	.00004	.00004	.00007	.00022	.00004	.00011	.00010	.00012	.00027	.00005	.00006	.00004	.00015	...	.00012	.00043	23
.00717	.00604	.00677	.00544	.01549	.02214	.00492	.01582	.04430	.00745	.00823	.01189	.00564	.00831	...	.01879	.37717	24
.00203	.00074	.00147	.00104	.00517	.00143	.00111	.00540	.00346	.00350	.00180	.00291	.00106	.00164	...	.01079	.01735	25
.01044	.01339	.01786	.00840	.01838	.04696	.01131	.01440	.20604	.00888	.01924	.02822	.01299	.01677	...	.01791	.66245	26
.00892	.00311	.00709	.01132	.00762	.00563	.00052	.01750	.01711	.01161	.01491	.01085	.00493	.02468	...	.02235	.05996	27
.00319	.00122	.00151	.00196	.00270	.00165	.00201	.00678	.00507	.00660	.03198	.00273	.00159	.00351	...	.00577	.01975	28
.00105	.00071	.00120	.00108	.00271	.00133	.00169	.02609	.00334	.00156	.00126	.02625	.00277	.00338	...	.01340	.00250	29
.00334	.00151	.00102	.00325	.00119	.00081	.00310	.00227	.00169	.00427	.00151	.00143	.00102	.00777	...	.00267	.00331	30
.05030	.00655	.00597	.01846	.01343	.00675	.01283	.01887	.00918	.01913	.00958	.01000	.01381	.02323	...	.03191	.01515	31
.00941	.00312	.00314	.00403	.00748	.00352	.00362	.01710	.01311	.02416	.00356	.00699	.00423	.00712	...	.01348	.02665	32
.00007	.00006	.00014	.00035	.00014	.00009	.00007	.00228	.00042	.00012	.00026	.00009	.00010	.00007	...	.00113	.00056	33
.00012	.00019	.00051	.00010	.00042	.00020	.00017	.01050	.00037	.00019	.00106	.00023	.00029	.00012	...	.00512	.00094	34
.00174	.00057	.00103	.00073	.00153	.00052	.00088	.00224	.00140	.00976	.00078	.00132	.00058	.00161	...	.00604	.00256	35
.00288	.00163	.00136	.00412	.00233	.00110	.00346	.00581	.00334	.01011	.00200	.00190	.00117	.00833	...	.00342	.00368	36
.01673	.00356	.00397	.01016	.00582	.00355	.00721	.01185	.01266	.04793	.00454	.00503	.00455	.01514	...	.01729	.02244	37
.00822	.00340	.00334	.00536	.00361	.00231	.00450	.00022	.00749	.02210	.00369	.00358	.00249	.00866	...	.00927	.02349	38
.00087	.00040	.00082	.00062	.00150	.00086	.00074	.00131	.00299	.00108	.00090	.00148	.00044	.00123	...	.00899	.00651	39
.00311	.00204	.00119	.00495	.00213	.00094	.00474	.00172	.00144	.00196	.00172	.00170	.00118	.01144	...	.00229	.00169	40
.00343	.00150	.00167	.00196	.00260	.00170	.00157	.00823	.00861	.07707	.00171	.00211	.00209	.00291	...	.00511	.00538	41
.00787	.00194	.00217	.00457	.00333	.00223	.00311	.01177	.00920	.02064	.00250	.00291	.00211	.00707	...	.00890	.01648	42
.00231	.00020	.00030	.00115	.00047	.00032	.00038	.00192	.00184	.00246	.00034	.00027	.00049	.00205	...	.00149	.00053	43
.00023	.00009	.00028	.00019	.00040	.00021	.00040	.00025	.00135	.00039	.00054	.00018	.00011	.00033	...	.00106	.00045	44
.00076	.00039	.00062	.00226	.00096	.00085	.00093	.00074	.00645	.00104	.00064	.00052	.00079	.00248	...	.00082	.00089	45
.00047	.00026	.00019	.00059	.00040	.00017	.00068	.00033	.00038	.00047	.00026	.00026	.00018	.00135	...	.00045	.00082	46
.00149	.00050	.00063	.00083	.00120	.00052	.00092	.00216	.00222	.00578	.00056	.00079	.00050	.00124	...	.00212	.00298	47
.00042	.00015	.00033	.00033	.00089	.00032	.00162	.00067	.00082	.00076	.00046	.00039	.00021	.00054	...	.00112	.00270	48
.00483	.00054	.00075	.00309	.00141	.00079	.00124	.00147	.00363	.00372	.00088	.00083	.00099	.00228	...	.00335	.00352	49
.00196	.00058	.00065	.00136	.00115	.00073	.00114	.00270	.00378	.02686	.00072	.00074	.00069	.00163	...	.00182	.00162	50
.00033	.00039	.00067	.00025	.00110	.00071	.00284	.00075	.00378	.00053	.00060	.00043	.00060	.00037	...	.00060	.00675	51
.00089	.00055	.00050	.00098	.00086	.00059	.00112	.00132	.00362	.00684	.00060	.00055	.00046	.00233	...	.00099	.00068	52
.00256	.00121	.00124	.00376	.00141	.00088	.00182	.00386	.00434	.00398	.00116	.00110	.00076	.00290	...	.00281	.00339	53
.00060	.00050	.00054	.00083	.00078	.00041	.00103	.00687	.00107	.00124	.00056	.00050	.00043	.00192	...	.00610	.00088	54
.00117	.00074	.00167	.00256	.00089	.00056	.00146	.00146	.00084	.00382	.00096	.00127	.00057	.00434	...	.00120	.00141	55
.00101	.01231	.00513	.00064	.00121	.00086	.00130	.00167	.00151	.00566	.00086	.00088	.00040	.00095	...	.00954	.00208	56
.00157	.00471	.01261	.00063	.00135	.03072	.00134	.02078	.00256	.00203	.00092	.00113	.00049	.00067	...	.00572	.00399	57
.00175	.00037	.00034	.00049	.00107	.00033	.00043	.00114	.00079	.02002	.00045	.00051	.00041	.00106	...	.00133	.00068	58
.00550	.00138	.00104	.00149	.00309	.00134	.00242	.00396	.00375	.12482	.00147	.00171	.00304	.00280	...	.00398	.00225	59
.00891	.00040	.00050	.00053	.00097	.00035	.00073	.00071	.00078	.00122	.00048	.00045	.00109	.00065	...	.00458	.00126	60
.00929	.00017	.00041	.00046	.00053	.00033	.00056	.00102	.00093	.00050	.00053	.00032	.00159	.00048	...	.00435	.00093	61
.00163	.00031	.00044	.00058	.00112	.00046	.00073	.00195	.00132	.00188	.00044	.00702	.00041	.00119	...	.00316	.00165	62
.00085	.00088	.00524	.00055	.00180	.00258	.00091	.00962	.00818	.00077	.01265	.00478	.00064	.00093	...	.00617	.07909	63
.00182	.00188	.00325	.00132	.00338	.00445	.00169	.02140	.01285	.00210	.00673	.00596	.00119	.00249	...	.01184	.15506	64
1.12580	.01147	.03268	.03801	.02469	.02449	.02100	.02887	.03446	.02915	.03550	.02332	.12632	.03436	...	.49336	.04811	65
.01423	1.00989	.04831	.00692	.01493	.03027	.00546	.01342	.03212	.01128	.01324	.01570	.00612	.00937	...	.01269	.01466	66
.00199	.00235	1.03215	.00169	.00380	.00664	.00259	.00311	.05984	.00199	.00398	.00298	.00212	.00327	...	.00304	.00362	67
.02007	.01175	.02680	1.25748	.02437	.01874	.01069	.03094	.01492	.02035	.01997	.04454	.02619	.15461	...	.02270	.02626	68
.04981	.01666	.03933	.02414	1.03371	.02891	.02906	.05307	.04361	.12123	.04357	.03468	.01708	.03864	...	.12633	.05718	69
.02683	.01237	.01894	.01844	.02508	1.22981	.04396	.03293	.01773	.02565	.02604	.01686	.01971	.02983	...	.02433	.01665	70
.04575	.02520	.08782	.03461	.06764	.06716	1.04627	.09106	.06799	.04737	.11245	.07173	.03673	.03542	...	.05535	.05616	71
.00359	.01322	.00828	.00379	.00637	.00523	.00620	1.03341	.01227	.00382	.00676	.00912	.00211	.00331	...	.13477	.00555	72
.03565	.04211	.07505	.03030	.06813	.11915	.04346	.05563	1.07613	.03566	.07116	.04615	.03800	.05866	...	.05451	.06489	73
.01876	.00661	.00373	.00415	.01301	.00642	.00348	.01922	.01230	1.00658	.00668	.00894	.00855	.00602	...	.01395	.00519	75
.00167	.00121	.33210	.00100	.00347	.00347	.00359	.00205	.02420	.00131	1.25739	.00262	.00215	.00167	...	.02300	.00201	76
.00184	.00153	.00300	.00135	.00234	.01548	.00190	.00463	.00366	.00164	.00413	1.01481	.00078	.00243	...	.00922	.00271	77
.00462	.00563	.00552	.02321	.01370	.02507	.00593	.00606	.01589	.00385	.00830	.00985	1.00239	.00632	...	.00540	.01182	78
.03438	.00260	.00629	.16916	.00846	.00726	.01084	.00674	.00412	.01504	.00530	.00852	.00768	1.02288	...	.01788	.00580	79
.05801	.01134	.01065	.01914	.00841	.01069	.00631	.01370	.01485	.01687	.01768	.00844	.05374	.01136	1.00000	.07853	.06462	80
.00942	.00960	.04803	.00890	.01676	.02601	.00495	.02061	.03043	.01089	.03367	.02058	.00675	.01130	...	1.01278	.01677	81
.00257	.00414	.00253	.00199	.00303	.01663	.00149	.00291	.00488	.00160	.00279	.00419	.00156	.00274	...	.00240	1.00315	82

Source: *Surv. Curr. Bus.*, February 1974, p. 50.

Table 4.16 Total coefficients of several industries for CPI and related industries

Output from	Input to						
	Food and kindred products (14)	Apparel (18)	Household furniture (22)	Drugs, cleaning and toilet preparations (29)	New construction (11)	Household appliances (54)	Motor vehicles and equipment (59)
Crude petroleum and natural gas (8)	0.012	0.008	0.008	0.013	0.015	0.008	0.007
Chemical and fertilizer mineral mining (10)	0.00	0.002	0.001	0.006	0.001	0.001	0.002
Paper and allied products, except containers (24)	0.037	0.019	0.020	0.041	0.016	0.022	0.012
Chemicals and selected chemical products (27)	0.014	0.064	0.036	0.165	0.020	0.034	0.022
Plastics and synthetic materials (28)	0.007	0.083	0.029	0.021	0.007	0.021	0.013
Drugs, cleaning and toilet preparations (29)	0.006	0.1003	0.1002	1.061	0.002	0.003	0.001
Paints and allied products (30)	0.002	0.002	0.018	0.006	0.009	0.011	0.007
Petroleum refining and relating industries (31)	0.023	0.014	0.013	0.026	0.030	0.012	0.012
Rubber and miscellaneous plastics products (32)	0.017	0.010	0.054	0.042	0.016	0.057	0.038
Glass and glass products (35)	0.016	0.003	0.008	0.019	0.001	0.006	0.013
Primary iron and steel manufacturing (37)	0.023	0.007	0.050	0.023	.078	0.149	0.181

Sorting and screening Input-output analysis can be used to order markets and industries according to a number of criteria, e.g., size, category, energy intensiveness, etc. For example, Table 4.10 screens all industries to show which are the largest suppliers of the CPI.

A variety of additional uses of input-output analysis have been investigated, including its use in predicting chemical prices [5]. But in spite of its potential, input-output analysis has not yet found widespread use or acceptance as a business tool. The major barriers to such development appear to be:

1. Lack of detailed and current information for constructing the input-output tables; for example, the 1967 input-output tables of the United States economy were not completed until 1974
2. Lack of understanding of those who are in a position to use input-output analysis
3. Lack of published cases of how input-output has been applied by individual companies

In short, although input-output analysis has been in existence for some time, its full potential can be realized only with better-educated managers and better data bases.

4.5 SUGGESTED READINGS

A great deal of information concerning definitions and assumptions made in arriving at the United States input-output tables can be found in the following articles published in the *Survey of Current Business* (Sec. I.1.1):

The Interindustry Structure of the United States, A Report on the 1958 Input-Output Study, November 1964.

The Transactions Table of the 1958 Input-Output Study and Revised Direct and Total Requirements Data, September 1965.

Input-Output Structure of the U.S. Economy: 1963, November 1969.

The Composition of Value Added in the 1963 Input-Output Study, April 1973.

The Input-Output Structure of the U.S. Economy: 1967, February 1974.

Interindustry Transactions in New Structures and Equipment, 1967, September 1975.

Several interesting articles written by Wassily W. Leontief about the mechanics of input-output analysis and its application have appeared in *Scientific American*:

Input-Output Economics, October 1951.

The Economic Effects of Disarmament, April 1961.

The Structure of Development, September 1963.

The Structure of the U.S. Economy, April 1965.

Additional articles on input-output analysis may be of interest:

George A. Gols, The Use of Input-Output in Industrial Planning, *Bus. Econ.*, May 1975.

David Liebeskind, A Marketing Tool: Price Forecasting via Input/Output Techniques, *CHEMTECH*, September 1973.

4.6 REFERENCES

1. "Input-Output Analysis: An Appraisal," pp. 215–252, a report on the National Bureau of Economics Research, Princeton University Press, Princeton, N.J., 1955.
2. *Surv. Curr. Bus.*, February 1974.
3. *Surv. Curr. Bus.*, September 1975, pp. 9–21.
4. *Bus. Econ.*, May 1975, p. 19.
5. David Liebeskind, A Marketing Tool: Price Forecasting via Input/Output Techniques, *CHEMTECH*, September 1973, (pp. 543–547).

4.7 PROBLEMS

4.1 (*a*) Referring to the 1967 United States input-output tables, calculate the fraction of total output that is value added for the following industries:

Input-output number	Industry
8	Crude petroleum and natural gas
10	Chemical and fertilizer mineral mining
27	Chemicals and selected chemical products
28	Plastics and synthetic materials
29	Drugs, cleaning and toilet preparations
30	Paints and allied products
31	Petroleum refining and related industries
32	Rubber and miscellaneous plastics products

(*b*) Most international oil companies are involved in industries 8, 27, and 31. Can you tell by the value-added figures where these oil companies make most of their money?

4.2 Does a high value added necessarily mean a high return on investment? Why? Does a low value added necessarily mean a low profit margin of sale?

4.3 (*a*) List some of the industries having the highest value added as measured by fraction of total output. What do these industries have in common?

(*b*) List some of the industries having the lowest value added as measured by fraction of total output.

(*c*) For industries 8, 10, and 27 to 32 what percent of value added goes to employee compensation? How does this compare with the industries given in your answers to part (*a*)?

4.4 Table 4.4 breaks the total output to final demand into the following categories:

1. Personal-consumption expenditures
2. Gross private fixed capital formation
3. Net inventory change
4. Net exports
5. Federal government purchases
   a. Defense
   b. Nondefense
6. State and local government purchases
   a. Education
   b. Other

Find the percentages of total final demand (1967) going to each of these categories for industries 27 to 30 and 32. Can you explain the variations in the fraction amounts going to the different categories from these industries?

4.5 Expand Table 4.7 to include the eighth and ninth largest buyers of chemical and selected chemical products (27). Determine the six industries buying the most from these two sectors and show the dollar amounts.

4.6 Determine the *direct* effect on output for sector 27 if all the buyers in Table 4.7 increase their final output by $10 million.

4.7 Are the CPI export-intensive? Compare the percentage of total final demand going to net exports for the components of the CPI to that of the total economy and to other sectors such as agricultural products (2), motor vehicles and equipment (59), scientific instruments (62), and finance and insurance (70).

4.8 Compare the ratio of property-type income to employee compensation for the various CPI segments. Compared with industries such as finance (70), apparel (18), motor vehicles (59), primary metals (37, 38), and food (14), are the CPI more capital- or labor-intensive?

4.9 New housing starts and new auto sales are two of the most important indicators of business climate. Calculate the impact on the various CPI segments for a 10 percent increase in each of these. List at least 10 different CPI products important in each of these industries.

4.10 Consider all of crude petroleum and natural gas (8), electric services (68), and coal mining (7), as energy. What percent of GNP is devoted to energy? Which industries are most energy-intensive as measured by percentage input by energy per total output? Which industries would be highly affected by an increase in energy costs and which would not? How do the CPI compare?

4.11 If electric services (68) were to switch half the present supply of oil into supply from coal, how would the total output of coal mining and oil production be changed? Use Table 4.3 and the following values: a 42-gal barrel of oil = 5.8 million Btu heating value; 1 ton of coal = 25 million Btu heating value; 1968 energy costs for oil fuel are 35 cents per million Btu and for coal 33 cents per million Btu (National Coal Association figures for the "as-consumed" fuel costs for 1968 for steam electric plants located in New Jersey).

4.12 If motor vehicles (59) reduced the use of steel by 30 percent but increased plastics use to make up for the decline in steel use, how would the production of steel and plastics be affected? *Hint:* Use the following perturbation calculations. Let $\mathbf{T} \to \mathbf{T} + \mathbf{e}$ be the result of $\mathbf{D} \to \mathbf{D} + \Delta$. To estimate $\mathbf{e}$

$$(\mathbf{I} - \mathbf{D})\mathbf{T} = \mathbf{I} \quad \text{and} \quad (\mathbf{I} - \mathbf{D} - \Delta)(\mathbf{T} + \mathbf{e}) = \mathbf{I}$$

so that

$$\mathbf{e} - \mathbf{D}\mathbf{e} - \Delta\mathbf{T} - \Delta\mathbf{e} = \mathbf{0}$$

Assume $\Delta\mathbf{e}$ is small. Then

$$(\mathbf{I} - \mathbf{D})\mathbf{e} = \Delta\mathbf{T} \quad \text{and} \quad \mathbf{e} = \mathbf{T}\,\Delta\mathbf{T}$$

4.13 An earth reconnaissance satellite reports drought in the U.S.S.R. Government experts estimate that Soviet wheat production will probably be down by 50 million bushels. What could the U.S.S.R. do to cover this shortage? In which CPI sectors would it have an impact? Can you estimate the potential impact on the CPI by using the input-output tables?

4.14 After completing his last assignment and being bored of his consulting duties with Universal Motor Company, Professor Sharppencil moved to a small Middle Eastern country, where he was promptly hired as Head Government Economist by the ruler, Sheik Gushofoil. The country has only three industries, A, O (as in oil), and EI (as in export-import). Having recently read about input-output analysis, Sharppencil decides to impress Gushofoil by constructing input-output tables. Using a recently installed computerized information retrieval system Sharppencil finds the following:

1. Industry A has total sales of $100 million annually. In 1 year industry A buys $10 million worth of goods from A itself, $5 million worth of goods from O, and $50 million of goods from EI.

2. Industry O has total sales of $100 million annually. In 1 year industry O buys $20 million worth of goods from A, $5 million worth of goods from O itself, and $50 million worth of goods from EI.
3. Industry EI has total annual sales of $200 million. In 1 year EI buys $50 million worth of goods from A, $80 million worth from O, and none itself.

Help Sharppencil construct the transactions table, direct-requirements table, and total-requirements table.

4.15 Suppose you were asked to determine the input required to produce 10 billion pounds of polyethylene. How would you estimate the dollar value of needed raw materials, energy, and other inputs?

4.16 Changes in technology can often be incorporated into a input-output analysis by estimating new direct coefficients for a specific industry or industries. Once a new **D** matrix has been estimated, the new **T** matrix can be found by inverting **I** − **D**. However, often it is either inconvenient or too expensive to perform the inversion. This problem considers two ways in which changes in the **T** matrix can be estimated with a new **D** matrix.

(a) If the new **D** matrix is written as **D** + Δ and the new **T** matrix is written as **T** + **e**, the perturbation calculations shown in Prob. 6.12 yield **e** = **T** Δ**T** providing Δ**e** is small. Using this method, estimate the new **T** matrix for the change in technology given in solution 2 of Example 4.1. How does the estimation compare with the exact answer?

(b) It is also possible to estimate a new **D** by a series expansion [Eq. (4.12)]:

$$(I - D)^{-1} = I + D^2 + D^3 + D + \cdots + D^n$$

or

$$T \approx I + D + \cdots + D^n$$

Estimate the maximum error in **T** that would result from expanding through the D^n term.

PRODUCTS AND COMPANIES OF THE CPI

The CPI require, as input, virtually every basic raw material available from the primary farming and mining industries and a vast array of intermediates from secondary manufacturing industries. Within the CPI the inputs are transformed into chemical products by chemical and physical processes.

The important raw materials for the manufacture of some of the intermediates and a partial list of products of the chemical industry are shown in Fig. 5.1. A similar diagram showing some of the chemical transformations for the petrochemical segment of the CPI is given in Fig. 5.2. A simplified flow diagram for the petroleum refining industry is shown in Fig. 5.3. The processing units which effect the needed chemical and physical transformation are built and operated by some 11,000 individual companies, all attempting to make a profit by upgrading raw materials and intermediates.

The chemical professional needs to know which products and intermediates are of particular importance to the CPI, including the interrelationships between raw materials, intermediates, and products going to final demand, and which companies play an important role in the CPI.

In this chapter we examine the CPI by discussing their products and the companies manufacturing these products. The discussion concentrates on SIC 281, 286, and 29.[1]

---

[1] Most of the statistics are from the Facts and Figures issues of *Chemical and Engineering News*, *Statistical Abstract of the United States*, and the Fortune 500 issues of *Fortune* magazine. The reader can conveniently update the data by consulting the most recent issues of these readily available publications.

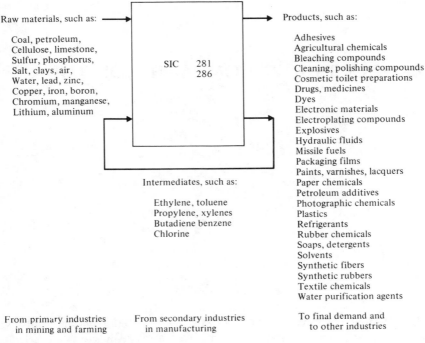

Raw materials, such as: →

Coal, petroleum,
Cellulose, limestone,
Sulfur, phosphorus,
Salt, clays, air,
Water, lead, zinc,
Copper, iron, boron,
Chromium, manganese,
Lithium, aluminum

SIC   281
       286

Products, such as:

Adhesives
Agricultural chemicals
Bleaching compounds
Cleaning, polishing compounds
Cosmetic toilet preparations
Drugs, medicines
Dyes
Electronic materials
Electroplating compounds
Explosives
Hydraulic fluids
Missile fuels
Packaging films
Paints, varnishes, lacquers
Paper chemicals
Petroleum additives
Photographic chemicals
Plastics
Refrigerants
Rubber chemicals
Soaps, detergents
Solvents
Synthetic fibers
Synthetic rubbers
Textile chemicals
Water purification agents

Intermediates, such as:

Ethylene, toluene
Propylene, xylenes
Butadiene benzene
Chlorine

From primary industries
in mining and farming

From secondary industries
in manufacturing

To final demand and
to other industries

Figure 5.1 The chemical industry.

5.1 PRODUCTS OF THE CPI

5.1.1 SIC 28 Chemicals and Allied Products

To bring some order into any discussion of the immense number of CPI products, some means of classification must be used. The products of the CPI can be classified in several ways.

Product end use Typical end-use groups are shown in Table 5.1. It is evident from our discussion in Chaps. 2 and 4 that any reasonable analysis of a CPI operation should include a study of the end use of the product ultimately produced even though the operation under analysis may not produce the end-use product itself. End-use classifications are generally based upon the industry served by the chemical after it leaves the CPI, e.g., automotive chemicals.

Differentiated and undifferentiated products An undifferentiated chemical product is one which has a specific chemical formula and particular physical specifications regardless of who produces it. An example is propylene oxide, defined by the

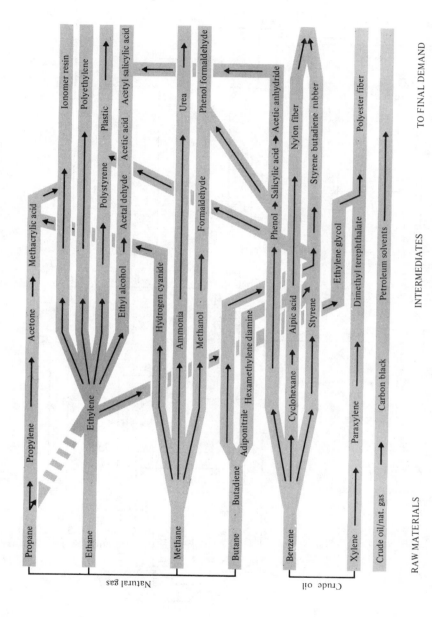

Figure 5.2 Raw materials, intermediates, and products of the petrochemical industry.

RAW MATERIALS   INTERMEDIATES   TO FINAL DEMAND

153

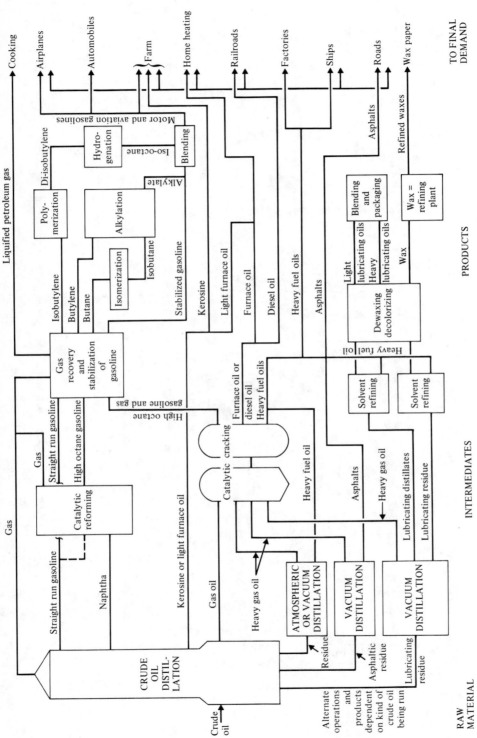

Figure 5.3 The petroleum refining industry. (*American Petroleum Institute.*)

154

Table 5.1 Some chemical end-use groups

Automotive chemicals	Paper additives
Diagnostic aids	Paint additives
Drilling-mud additives	Petroleum additives
Flavor and fragrances	Photographic chemicals
Flotation reagents	Plastic additives
Food additives	Printing chemicals
Foundry additives	Rubber-processing chemicals
Industrial cleaning products	Textile chemicals
Laboratory chemicals	Water-treatment chemicals
Metal-finishing chemicals	

specifications shown in Table 5.2. Most of the high-volume chemicals produced by the chemical industry, such as H_2SO_4, O_2, N_2, ethylene, NH_3, benzene, etc., can be classified as undifferentiated.

A product is classified as differentiated when its producer claims that it has a real or imputed difference compared with a similar product made by a competitor. It is usually sold on the basis of performance in use. Differentiation can be accomplished by various means.

1. A polymer such as polyethylene or polypropylene can be given different properties by changing molecular-weight distribution or crystallinity, or by modifying the physical processing steps.
2. A basic chemical such as ethylene glycol may be sold as a differentiated product (antifreeze) by adding compounds which inhibit rust and provide " puncture proofing" to the consumer's radiator.
3. Some products which have essentially the same chemical formulation may be classified as differentiated because their method of delivery is unique. Air Products (Chap. 7) did this with industrial gases by providing on-site plants and eliminating rail-car delivery. Technical service in the form of providing formulations, process design for the customer's operations, and subsequent trouble-shooting have been used by companies like Du Pont to make their pigments business unique.

Table 5.2 Specifications for propylene oxide

Distillation range at 760 mmHg (initial boiling point to dew point), °C	33.0–37.0
Specific gravity at 25/25°C	0.825–0.827
Acidity (as acetic acid), maximum, %	0.005
Water, maximum, %	0.05
Total chlorides (as Cl), maximum, %	0.01
Color (APHA), maximum	10
Aldehydes (as acetaldehyde), maximum %	0.03

Annual production volume This is a common means of ordering and is used by *Chemical and Engineering News* in publishing the top 50 chemicals. A classification into high, intermediate, low and, very low volume can be made as follows:

Volume	United States annual production, 10^6 lb/yr
High	> 1,000
Intermediate	100–1,000
Low	10–100
Very low	< 10

Product price A somewhat arbitrary classification of chemicals into high, intermediate, and low price is as follows:

Price	United States price, dollars per pound, 1976 dollars, f.o.b.
High	> $0.80
Intermediate	$0.20–$0.80
Low	< $0.20

An ordering by gross sales is given in Table 5.3. Figure 5.4, a log-log plot which considers both price and production, was prepared using 1972 data for a range of CPI products. The equation for the line drawn through the points is

$$p = 5,000Q^{-0.5} \quad \text{or} \quad Q = (25 \times 10^6)p^{-2}$$

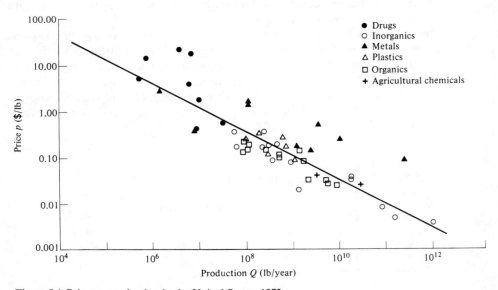

Figure 5.4 Price vs. production in the United States, 1972.

Table 5.3 The most significant organic chemicals

Chemical	Sales volume (millions)	Chemical	Sales volume (millions)
Tetra (methyl-ethyl) lead	$292	Bisphenol A	$34.4
Ethylene oxide	271	Methylene chloride	
Styrene	260	(dichloromethane)	32.2
Ethylene dichloride	224	Chlorobenzene	29.1
Ethylene glycol	213	Carbon disulfide	28.8
Dimethyl terephthalate	203	Glycerol tri(polyoxypropylene) ether	28.2
Vinyl chloride	202	Sodium carboxymethylcellulose	27.9
Ethylbenzene	193	Etheylene glycol	25.6
Urea	187	Methyl chloride	25.4
Adipic acid	173	o-Xylene	24.0
Tetraethyllead	172	Diethylene glycol	23.9
Acetaldehyde	145	Methyl isobutyl ketone	23.9
Acetic anhydride	143	Acrylic acid	22.1
Methanol, synthetic	132	Nonyl phenol, ethoxylated	21.2
Phenol	123	Sorbitol	21.0
Ethanol, synthetic	118	Pentaerythritol	19.6
Acetic acid, synthetic	116	Etheylene glycol monoethyl ether	17.7
Isopropanol	115	Tridecylbenzene sulfonic	
Acrylonitrile	114	acid, sodium salt	16.6
Propylene oxide	106	Ethylene glycol monobutyl ether	16.0
Toluene 2,4- and 2,6-diisocyanate		n-Butyl acrylate	15.2
(80 : 20 mixture)	97.6	Cresylic acid, refined	14.8
Dichlorodifluoromethane	97.6	Diisodecyl phthalate	14.8
p-Xylene	95.4	Chloroform	14.4
Formaldehyde	88.5	Decyl alcohols	14.2
Cumene	79.3	Ethyl acetate	12.9
Cyclohexanone	78.6	Ethylenediamine	12.4
Vinyl acetate	72.3	α- and β-pinenes	11.6
Tallow acids, sodium salt	70.7	Triethylene glycol	11.6
Phthalic anyhydride	66.0	Polypropylene glycol	11.6
Acetone	64.6	Hexamethylenetetramine	11.5
Alkyl benzenes	55.3	Triethanolamine	10.9
Cyclohexane	55.2	Ethylene glycol monomethyl ether	10.7
Ethylene dibromide	53.4	Fumaric acid	10.6
Dodecyl benzene sulfonic acid,		Benzyl chloride	10.5
sodium salt	52.1	Diisooctyl phthalate	10.2
Carbon tetrachloride	50.6	Monoethanolamine	9.6
Perchloroethylene	49.5	DDT	9.5
Coconut oil acids, sodium and		Diethanolamine	9.3
potassium salts	47.9	Lignin sulfonic acid, calcium salt	9.2
Trichlorofluoromethane	46.4	Isooctyl alcohols	9.0
Aniline	43.8	Nonyl phenol	8.6
Methyl ethyl ketone	43.2	n-Octyl-n-decyl phthalate	8.3
Trichloroethylene	42.9	n-Butyl acetate	8.2
Ethyl chloride	40.7	Dimethylamine	7.8
Di(2-ethylhexyl) phthalate	38.5	Lignin sulfonic acid, sodium salt	6.6
Propylene glycol	38.5	o-Dichlorobenzene	6.6
n-Butanol	37.4	n-Propanol	6.6
2-Ethyl-1-hexanol	36.6	p-Dichlorobenzene	6.3
Glycerol, synthetic	36.2	Isobutanol	4.0
Ethyl acrylate	35.2	Dicyclopentadiene	2.0
Maleic anhydride	34.4		

Source: Chem. Eng., Aug. 5, 1975, p. 98.

Table 5.4 Classification of chemicals by composition

1. Inorganics	Benzene	Polyester
a. Acids	1,3-Butadiene	Urea
Hydrochloric	Carbon tetrachloride	*b.* Thermoplastic resins
Nitric	Cyclohexane	Polyamide
Phosphoric	Ethanol, synthetic	Polyethylene
Sulfuric	Ethanolamines	Polypropylene
b. Chlorine and alkalies	Ethylene	Polystyrene
Chlorine gas	Ethylene oxide	Polyvinyl alcohol
Sodium carbonate	Formaldehyde	Polyvinyl chloride
Sodium hydroxide	Maleic anhydride	
c. Industrial gases	Methanol, synthetic	4. Elastomers
Carbon dioxide	Perchloroethylene	Natural rubber
Hydrogen	Phenol, synthetic	Styrene-butadiene
Nitrogen	Phthalic anhydride	Polybutadiene
Oxygen	Propylene	Butyl rubber
d. Fertilizer chemicals	Propylene oxide	Polyisoprene
Ammonia	Styrene	Neoprene
Ammonium nitrate	Toluene	Silicone
Ammonium sulfate	Urea	Nitrile
e. Other	Vinyl acetate	Ethylene-propylene—
Aluminum sulfate	Vinyl chloride	
Phosphorus	Xylenes	5. Fibers
Sodium phosphate	*o*-Xylene	*a.* Cellulosic fibers
Sodium silicate	*p*-Xylene	Acetate
Sodium sulfate		Rayon
Titanium dioxide	3. Plastics	*b.* Noncellulosic fibers
2. Organics	*a.* Thermosetting resins	Acrylic
Acetone	Epoxy	Nylon
Acrylonitrile	Melamine	Olefins
Aniline	Phenolic	Polyester
		Textile glass

As might be expected, some of the high-volume inorganics, e.g., chlorine and sodium hydroxide, have the lowest prices and low-volume drugs, e.g., tetracycline and penicillin, have the highest prices ($22 and $19 per pound).

Chemical composition Chemicals are often separated into two major groups, inorganics and organics. In the past few decades three additional major groups, plastics, fibers, and elastomers, have been designated. Within each of these major groups are subgroups classified by further chemical similarities. They are listed in Table 5.4 along with some of the major products (as classified by production volume) in each. This classification scheme is widely used by *Chemical and Engineering News* in their articles on CPI performance.

Product function Chemicals are often classified by the function they perform. Examples of such functions are given in Table 5.5.

Table 5.5 Some functional chemical product groups

Antioxidants	Flame retardants
Biocides	Pigments
Catalysts	Solvents
Chelates	Thickeners
Corrosion inhibitors	Ultraviolet absorbers

There are of course other methods of classifying the products of the CPI. Combinations of classifications are also used to give insights into various aspects of the industry. One of the more useful of these is a classification obtained by combining production volume and differentiation to yield the four product classifications shown in Table 5.6. This separation into commodity, pseudo commodity, fine chemical, and specialty chemical [1] is particularly useful in examining differences in research and development, manufacturing methods, and marketing and finance for different chemicals; it is used in Chap. 8.

Several of the classifications are interrelated. For example, price is closely associated with product differentiation and product volume. Commodity chemicals tend to be low-priced, while specialty chemicals tend to be high-priced. Classification interrelationships often change the magnitude or meaning of a group within a classification. For example, a high-priced specialty connotes a different price range from a high-priced commodity. Differentiated chemicals are most often those which have particular functions.

Classification and ranking by annual production volume is used by *Chemical and Engineering News* to identify the top 50 chemicals annually. This list ranks the 50 largest inorganic and organic chemicals by their annual United States production volumes. It specifically excludes fibers and plastics. Data for 1975 to 1976 are shown in Table 5.7. Some initial comments can be made about these top 50 chemicals:

1. The chemicals are all high-volume, having annual production rates ranging from 1.4 to 64.7 billion pounds per year.
2. Nearly all of the top 50 chemicals are undifferentiated. The notable exception is carbon black, which is sold largely on physical and performance characteristics.

Table 5.6 Chemical product classification by a combination of volume and differentiation

Annual production volume	Undifferentiated	Differentiated
High	True commodities, e.g., sulfuric acid, benzene, oxygen	Pseudo commodities, e.g., carbon black, polyethylene, antifreeze
Low	Fine chemicals, e.g., aspirin, vitamin C, food colorings	Specialty chemicals, e.g., pharmaceuticals, formulated pesticides

Table 5.7 The top 50 chemicals produced in the United States ranked by production volume

Rank 1976	Rank 1975^a		Production Billions of lb 1976	1975	Production Common units^b 1976	1975	Average annual change 1975–76	1974–75	1971–76	1966–76
1	1	Sulfuric acid	66.02	64.30	33,012 tt	32,151 tt	2.7%	−5.3%	2.6%	1.5%
2	2	Lime^c	38.10	36.27	19,050 tt	18,135 tt	5.1	−11.0	0.3	1.8
3	3	Ammonia, anhydrous	32.85	32.79	16,423 tt	16,393 tt	0.2	4.2	2.5	4.5
4	4	Oxygen, high and low purity	32.20	29.22	389 bcf	353 bcf	10.2	−9.5	4.0	6.2
5	5	Ethylene	22.03	20.50	22,027 mp	20,499 mp	7.5	−14.2	3.6	7.0
6	7	Nitrogen, high and low purity	21.23	18.33	293 bcf	253 bcf	15.8	0.4	11.7	12.5
7	6	Sodium hydroxide	20.29	19.17	10,144 tt	9,583 tt	5.9	−14.4	1.0	2.9
8	8	Chlorine, gas	20.12	18.21	10,060 tt	9,103 tt	10.5	−15.3	1.5	3.4
9	9	Phosphoric acid, total	15.09	15.34	7,547 tt	7,671 tt	−1.6	6.4	4.8	5.1
10	10	Nitric acid	15.02	15.05	7,510 tt	7,527 tt	−0.2	−7.3	−0.3	3.2
11	11	Sodium carbonate^d	24.91	14.31	7,459 tt	7,155 tt	4.2	−5.3	0.8	0.9
12	12	Ammonium nitrate^e	14.37	14.18	7,187 tt	7,088 tt	1.4	−6.0	1.6	3.5
13	16	Benzene	10.61	7.51	1,448 mg	1,024 mg	41.4	−31.2	6.1	4.3
14	13	Propylene	9.76	8.71	9,758 mp	8,709 mp	12.1	−16.9	7.2	7.6
15	18	Toluene, all grades	8.22	5.10	1,136 mg	705 mg	61.1	−23.5	5.4	6.9
16	14	Ethylene dichloride	7.92	7.98	7,923 mp	7,977 mp	−0.7	−13.0	0.9	8.2
17	15	Urea, primary solution	7.72	7.60	7,721 mp	7,600 mp	1.6	0.2	4.0	8.1
18	21	Xylene, all grades	7.28	4.61	1,010 mg	639 mg	58.1	−20.3	10.6	11.9
19	20	Styrene	6.30	4.67	6,301 mp	4,673 mp	34.8	−21.5	6.1	7.1
20	17	Methanol, synthetic	6.24	5.18	6,241 mp	5,176 mp	20.6	−24.8	4.8	6.7
21	19	Ethylbenzene	6.13	4.82	6,127 mp	4,822 mp	27.1	−20.3	4.2	6.6
22	26	Vinyl chloride	5.74	4.20	5,736 mp	4,196 mp	36.7	−25.4	5.8	8.7
23	23	Formaldehyde, 37% by weight	5.62	4.56	5,621 mp	4,558 mp	23.3	−20.9	4.4	4.2
24	21	Terephthalic acid^f	5.05	4.61	5,051 mp	4,614 mp	9.5	8.3	16.7	19.2
25	27	Hydrochloric acid	4.86	3.98	2,428 tt	1,989 tt	22.1	−18.9	3.0	4.8
26	24	Ethylene oxide	4.18	4.47	4,184 mp	4,467 mp	−6.3	6.4	3.1	6.1
27	29	Carbon dioxide, all forms	4.02	3.70	2,011 tt	1,851 tt	8.8	2.6	8.4	6.4
28	25	Ammonium sulfate	3.50	4.21	1,750 tt	2,106 tt	−16.9	−0.7	−0.8	−1.8
29	28	Ethylene glycol	3.36	3.81	3,357 mp	3,809 mp	−11.9	14.0	1.8	4.9
30	31	Butadiene (1,3-), rubber grade	3.25	2.60	3,254 mp	2,597 mp	25.3	−29.5	−0.5	1.1
31	32	p-Xylene	3.20	2.48	3,199 mp	2,484 mp	28.8	−8.2	14.0	19.9
32	30	Carbon black	3.02	2.76	3,023 mp	2,756 mp	9.7	−17.7	−0.1	1.6
33	37	Cumene	2.69	2.00	2,690 mp	2,003 mp	34.3	−31.1	4.7	11.6
34	33	Sodium sulfate^g	2.52	2.45	1,258 tt	1,227 tt	2.5	−9.0	−1.4	−1.4
35	36	Acetic acid, synthetic	2.43	2.20	2,430 mp	2,197 mp	10.6	−15.0	4.4	5.6
36	34	Calcium chloride^h	2.40	2.34	1,200 tt	1,171 tt	2.5	−5.8	−0.2	0.1
37	38	Phenol, synthetic	2.18	1.75	2,183 mp	1,746 mp	25.0	−24.0	4.6	5.4
37	35	Aluminum sulfate, commercial	2.18	2.33	1,090 tt	1,163 tt	−6.3	−9.0	−0.7	−0.3
37	39	Cyclohexane	2.18	1.73	2,177 mp	1,734 mp	25.6	−26.3	4.5	1.4
40	40	Acetone	1.92	1.64	1,922 mp	1,640 mp	17.2	−17.2	4.5	3.8
41	42	Propylene oxide	1.80	1.52	1,795 mp	1,524 mp	17.8	−13.2	8.5	9.7
42	42	Isopropyl alcohol	1.72	1.52	1,720 mp	1,521 mp	13.1	−21.6	0	0.1
43	44	Acetic anhydride	1.60	1.46	1,600 mp	1,458 mp	9.7	−10.7	1.1	0.1
44	45	Sodium silicate (water glass)	1.57	1.45	786 tt	724 tt	8.6	−6.0	4.3	2.4
45	49	Acrylonitrile	1.52	1.22	1,518 mp	1,215 mp	24.9	−14.0	3.2	7.8
45	47	Adipic acid	1.52	1.34	1,515 mp	1,344 mp	12.7	−9.1	3.0	4.6
47	48	Vinyl acetate	1.48	1.29	1,481 mp	1,290 mp	14.8	−8.1	9.8	9.4
48	41	Sodium tripolyphosphate	1.46	1.54	730 tt	770 tt	−5.2	−14.7	−6.8	−3.2
49	50	Titanium dioxide	1.43	1.21	716 tt	604 tt	18.5	−23.3	1.1	1.9
50	46	Ethanol, synthetic	1.18	1.43	1,181 mp	1,429 mp	−17.4	−11.7	−6.2	−4.6

a Revised. b tt = thousand tons, bcf = billion cubic feet, mp = million pounds, mg = million gallons. c Except refractory dolomite. d Synthetic and natural. e Original solution. f Includes both the acid and the ester without double counting. g High and low purity. h Solid and liquid. **Sources:** Bureau of the Census, Bureau of Mines, International Trade Commission, and C&EN estimates

Source: Chem Eng. News, Facts and Figures issue, June 6, 1977, p. 42, with permission.

3. The chemicals listed as the top 50 are consumed almost exclusively as intermediates in making other chemicals and chemical products. Several of the chemicals are intermediates for making other chemicals on the list; e.g., ethy-

lene and oxygen are consumed in making ethylene oxide, which in turn is consumed in making ethylene glycol.
4. The top 50 are split almost equally between inorganics and organics, although inorganics dominate the top of the list.

5.1.2 SIC 29 Petroleum Refining and Related Industries

The petroleum refining industry is far more homogeneous and coherent in raw-material needs and market served than chemical and allied products (SIC 28). The major raw-material supply is natural gas and crude oil from wells. Initially, the main producers in the United States were in the western Pennsylvania oil fields following Drake's development of the drilled oil well in 1859. The chief petroleum product sold was kerosene for illumination. The unwanted by-product, gasoline, was poured into creeks, to the consternation of the Pennsylvania public. When Henry Ford began mass-producing automobiles at the turn of the century, gasoline became a desirable product and was no longer dumped. Hydrocarbon oil was developed to replace sperm whale oil as a lubricant. As the Pennsylvania fields were depleted, crude oil was obtained from Texas, Oklahoma, California, and other parts of the United States and Canada. Today, the bulk of the world's reserve in petroleum is in the Persian Gulf, and the United States imports up to 50 percent of its needs in crude oil and petroleum products from abroad. To reduce its dependence on foreign petroleum products, the United States is currently engaged in a national effort to search for domestic substitutes, by converting its vast resources in coal, oil shale, and tar sand into desirable forms of energy.

The modern refinery produces a large slate of products which find use in heating, lighting, shipping, lubricating, paving roads, and many other areas. The values of refinery shipments of the major products, unit costs, value of products consumed, and volume produced are shown in Table 5.8. The costs are considerably lower than the retail value of the products because taxes, transportation, and marketing costs are not included here. In addition to crude petroleum, the United States also imports considerable quantities of refined products from refineries overseas, particularly residual fuel oil from the Caribbean.

Most of the products from the petroleum refinery are true commodities, specified by their chemical compositions and physical characteristics rather than by their special effectiveness in use. They are mostly undifferentiated products sold at high volume and low price. Innovations take place more often in refining processes than in introduction of new products.

Liquefied petroleum gas (LPG, also called *bottled gas*) consists principally of propane and butane. It is obtained from condensates in natural gas and in refinery streams. LPG is used mainly as a source of heat in homes and farms and as a petrochemical feedstock. LPG is also used as fuel in commercial, industrial, and utility heating, and in taxies and tractors. It is clean and convenient but must be stored in pressurized containers.

Motor gasoline is the most valuable refinery product, consisting of hydrocarbons with 5 to 12 carbons and with a boiling point of 120 to 400°F. It is obtained from distillation of crude oil, from synthesis of smaller molecules by alkylation

Table 5.8 United States petroleum products

Value of shipments, 1972

	Manufacturers' shipment value (millions)
Petroleum refining	$25,415
Liquefied refinery gas	1,153
Gasoline	13,030
Jet fuel	1,372
Kerosene	372
Distillate fuel oil	4,408
Residual fuel oil	1,107
Lubricating oil and grease	1,537
Unfinished oil and grease	734
Asphalt	672
Other	1,031
Paving and roofing materials	1,795
Other	139

Volume, 10^6 bbl

Product	1965	1970	1972
Liquefied gases	107	116	121
Gasoline	1,694	2,100	2,316
Jet fuel	191	302	310
Kerosene	93	95	79
Distillate fuel oil	765	896	962
Residual fuel oil	269	258	293
Lubricants	63	66	65
Asphalt	124	147	155

Source: U.S. Bureau of the Census, *Statistical Abstract of the United States: 1975*, 96th ed., tables 1286 and 1166.

and polymerization, from breaking larger molecules by catalytic cracking and hydrocracking, and by molecular rearrangement to increase octane number by reforming. It is cheaper and has a higher heat value Btu per pound than any other competitive product, e.g., methanol.

Diesel fuel has a boiling point of 375 to 725°F and is used as a fuel for railroads, trucks, buses and a few cars. It is atomized and burned in high-pressure cylinders without spark ignition; consequently, it must have the proper viscosity to prevent leakage and to economize on pumping power. The cetane index and diesel index are designed to specify ease of ignition start and reduction of odor and fume.

Distillate fuel oil, particularly important for home heating, has a boiling-point range similar to that of diesel fuel. It is obtained by distillation of crude oil.

Residual fuel oil, the bottom fraction in the distillation column, contains most of the undesirable sulfur, metals, and carbon deposits from the crude oil. It has a very high viscosity and can solidify in cold weather. Its use requires high-pressure nozzles and heated containers, making it unsuited for home use. It is primarily used in industrial and utility boilers and as marine bunker fuel.

Lubricating oil is a highly refined product used to reduce friction and wear in motors and machinery. It must have a viscosity sufficient to prevent its being squeezed out between moving parts but not so high that it consumes excessive power. It must perform in a wide range of temperatures, to ensure easy starting in cold weather and sufficient lubrication in hot conditions. Stability to rust and formation of gum and sludge are other important qualities.

Asphalt is a thermoplastic material recovered from distillation bottoms. It may have been used by Noah to seal the ark. Nowadays, the major uses are in paving highways and roads and for roofing. Petroleum coke is obtained by subjecting the distillation bottoms to pyrolitic polymerization and thermal decomposition in a delayed or fluid coker. It is used in the manufacture of calcium and silicon carbides, electrodes for aluminum manufacturing, and graphite. It also finds use as a utility fuel and as a construction material in foundry and blast furnaces.

The specification of petroleum products is controlled by the American Society of Testing Materials (ASTM). Some of the important physical specifications are:

API gravity. This is equal to (141.5/specific gravity) − 131.5. Larger numbers indicate lighter products. Products having API gravity less than 10 sink in water.

Vapor pressure. Reid vapor pressure is measured at 100°F (37.8°C) and gives an indication of a tendency for a fuel to vapor-lock.

ASTM distillation. This is the boiling-point–vs.–percentage-remaining curve, including the initial boiling point, the points at each 10 percent incremental distillate, and the endpoint.

From the consumer's point of view, the important performance specifications for petroleum products are:

Flash and fire points. These should be sufficiently high to assure safety in handling.

Viscosity and viscosity index. These tests should be sufficiently low to prevent excessive loss and sufficiently high to withstand squeezing out within the operating- and testing-temperature ranges.

Cloud and pour point. These tests measure cold-temperature handling characteristics.

Octane numbers. The research method at an engine speed of 600 rpm simulates city driving, and the motor method at 900 rpm simulates highway performance of motor fuels.

Tests to determine sulfur, water, gum, sludge, carbon, and metal content are also important parts of the specification for certain petroleum products.

5.1.3 Other CPI Sectors

Most chemical professionals in industry are employed in the chemical and petroleum industries, especially in SIC 281, 286, and 29, but other industries in the CPI also employ chemists and chemical engineers and are important customers of the chemical and petroleum industries. Chemical professionals should familiarize themselves with the size and function of the other CPI sectors and be informed about their prosperity and changing needs. *Chemical Week* regularly lists other CPI sectors and the companies involved in these sectors in their feature Chemical Week 300.[1]

The most important sectors of the CPI are

Pharmaceuticals (SIC 283)
Detergents, toiletries, cosmetics (284)
Paint, ink, carbon black (285 to 289)
Stone, clay, glass (32)
Pulp and paper (26)
Ferrous metal (331 to 332)
Nonferrous metal (333 to 336)
Rubber (30)
Food processing (2)

5.2 COMPANIES OF THE CPI

5.2.1 The United States

Chemical and Engineering News has ranked the top 50 United States firms by annual chemical sales for every year since 1968. Listed in Table 5.9 are the top 50 ranked by 1976 chemical sales. This list can be used to illustrate certain features of the chemical industry.

1. The companies include a varied group. Only 40 percent are classified as basic chemical makers (ESIC 28.1). About 30 percent are classified as petroleum companies (ESIC 29.1). The remaining 30 percent are scattered among 11 other ESIC groupings. For 60 percent of the top 50 chemical producers, chemicals make up less than 50 percent of net sales.

---

[1] There is not enough space here to do justice to the diversity and interest of these industries. For further information, you should consult a text such as Shreve's "Chemical Process Industries" or a reference like the "Kirk-Othmer Encyclopedia of Chemical Technology" (Sec. 0.1.2).

Table 5.9 Top 50 United States chemical producers ranked by chemical sales

Rank 1976	Rank 1975	Company	Chemical sales 1976 ($ millions)	Change from 1975	Total sales 1976 ($ millions)	Chemical sales as % of total sales	Enterprise SIC code number[a]	Net income[b] ($ millions)	Profit margin[c] Per cent 1976	Profit margin Rank 1976	Profit margin Rank 1975	Return on stockholders' equity[d] Per cent 1976	Return on equity Rank 1976	Return on equity Rank 1975
1	1	Du Pont	$6400	16%	$8,361	77%	281	$459.3	5.5%	23	35	11.4%	34	42
2	2	Dow Chemical	3900	16	5,652	69	281	612.8	10.8	3	2	21.4	2	2
3	3	Union Carbide[e]	3800	17	6,346	60	281	441.2	7.0	12	14	14.4	19	22
4	4	Monsanto	3577	17	4,270	84	281	366.3	8.6	7	8	16.3	9	14
5	5	Exxon	3238	25	48,631	7	291	2641.0	5.4	24	19	14.3	21	15
6	6	W. R. Grace[e]	1961	9	3,615	54	281	131.9	3.6	36	26	11.4	33	12
7	7	Celanese	1926	12	2,123	91	281	69	3.3	41	43	8.7	43	43
8	8	Allied Chemical	1738	14	2,630	66	281	126.3	4.8	28	23	11.3	35	31
9	10	Shell Oil	1574	31	9,230	17	291	705.8	7.6	10	16	15.4	11	23
10	9	Occidental Petroleum	1401	-3	5,534	25	509	183.7	3.3	39	39	14.1	22	16
11	11	Hercules	1325	16	1,596	83	281	106.8	6.7	16	44	14.4	20	45
12	13	Eastman Kodak	1247	18	5,438	23	383	650.6	12.0	1	4	16.2	10	8
13	12	American Cyanamid	1190	8	2,094	57	281	135.8	6.5	17	11	12.2	27	18
14	15	Borden[e]	1115	13	3,381	33	202	112.8	3.3	38	41	12.0	30	35
15	14	Rohm & Haas	1096	10	1,153	95	281	(11.8)[f]		48	45		48	46
16	18	Standard Oil (Ind.)	1080	22	11,532	9	291	893.0	7.7	9	9	14.5	16	20
17	23	Gulf Oil	1062	31	16,451	6	291	816	5.0	26	24	11.8	31	34
18	17	Mobil Oil[e]	1027	13	26,063	4	291	942.5	3.6	37	33	12.3	26	29
19	21	Ethyl Corp.	1009	21	1,135	89	281	69.1	6.1	19	18	14.5	17	21
20	19	Stauffer Chemical	1000	15	1,100	91	281	113.0	10.3	6	6	18.9	5	6
21	22	Phillips Petroleum	990	19	5,698	17	291	411.7	7.2	11	15	15.1	13	19
22	24	Texaco	950	19	26,452	4	291	869.7	3.3	40	37	9.7	39	37
23	25	PPG Industries	804	15	2,255	36	321	151.5	6.7	15	27	14.8	14	36
24	26	Diamond Shamrock[e]	802	15	1,357	59	281	140.0	10.3	5	7	20.8	3	3
25	16	FMC[g]	801	10	2,145	37	352	80.2	3.7	34	20	9.2	40	24
26	27	Air Products[e,h]	793	17	818	97	281	63.5	7.8	8	10	17.5	6	7
27	20	International Minerals[i]	780	-8	1,260	62	287	135.4	10.7	4	3	23.3	1	1
28	29	Ashland Oil[h]	743	16	4,087	18	291	136.0	3.1	42	38	16.8	8	9
29	36	B. F. Goodrich[e]	695	34	1,996	35	301	15.8	0.8	46	47	2.1	46	47
30	33	Ciba-Geigy	690	21	975	71								
31	30	Standard Oil of California	685	8	19,434	4	291	880.1	4.5	31	29	12.6	25	27
32	32	NL Industries[e]	680	10	1,286	53	281	58.8	4.6	30	36	10.6	38	41
33	34	BASF Wyandotte	675	21	710	95		34.9	4.9	27	21	15.2	12	11
34	31	Olin	657	5	1,377	48	281	72.6	5.3	25	28	12.2	29	32
35	28	U.S. Steel	648	-1	8,604	8	331	410.3	4.8	29	13	8.0	44	30
36	37	American Hoechst	600	28	745	80								
37	43	Reichhold Chemicals	585	43	585	100	281	16.1	2.7	43	34	10.8	37	26
38	41	Mobay Chemical	545	30	545	100		20.1	3.7	35	32	8.7	42	39
39	38	Atlantic Richfield	534	20	8,463	6	291	575.2	6.8	14	25	14.1	23	38
40	45	National Distillers	507	33	1,504	34	208	90.3	6.0	20	22	13.4	24	33
41	35	Williams Cos.	481	-7	1,003	48	287	61.2	6.1	18	1	9.0	41	5
42	44	Esmark[e,j]	453	2	5,268	9	201	82.6	1.6	45	46	11.6	32	25
43	40	Lubrizol	451	8	451	100	289	51.0	11.3	2	5	19.5	4	4
44	42	Ker:-McGee[e]	437	5	1,955	22	291	134.1	6.9	13	12	14.7	15	10
44	48	Tenneco	437	25	6,423	7	291	383.5	6.0	21	17	14.5	18	17
46	47	Goodyear Tire	425	21	5,791	7	301	122.0	2.1	44	40	6.6	45	40
47	39	Akzona	423	-1	729	58	221	5.6	0.8	47	48	1.8	47	48
48	46	Pennwalt	419	15	777	54	281	34.9	4.5	32	31	12.2	28	28
49		Borg-Warner	399	43	1,862	21	371	81.7	4.4	33	42	11.0	36	44
50		Continental Oil	385	31	7,958	5	291	460.0	5.8	22	30	17.5	7	13

a Enterprise Standard Industrial Classification according to the "Directory of Companies Filing Annual Reports with the Securities & Exchange Commission." b Excludes extraordinary or nonrecurring income or losses. c Net income as a percentage of net sales. d Net income as a percentage of net worth. e Chemical sales include significant amounts of nonchemical products, such as welding equipment, fabricated plastics, coatings, metals, minerals, adhesives, and the like. f Deficit. g Data for continuing operations. h For year ended Sept. 30. i For year ended June 30. j For year ended Oct. 30. **Enterprise Standard Industrial Classifications used above are as follows:** 201 Meat products; 202 Dairy products; 208 Alcoholic and malt beverages; 221 Weaving and finishing mills, yarn and thread mills, miscellaneous textile mill products; 281 Basic chemicals, plastics materials, and synthetics; 287 Agricultural chemicals; 289 Chemical products not elsewhere classified; 291 Petroleum refining; 301 Tires and inner tubes; 321 Glass products; 331 Iron and steel; 352 Farm machinery, construction, mining, and materials handling machinery; 371 Motor vehicles and equipment; 383 Optical and ophthalmic goods, photographic equipment and supplies; 509 Wholesale trade, miscellaneous wholesalers.

Source: *Chem. Eng. News.* Facts and Figures issue, June 6, 1977, p. 50, with permission.

Table 5.10 Top 50 companies in the United States ranked by sales, 1976

RANK '76	'75	COMPANY	SALES ($000)	ASSETS ($000)	RANK	NET INCOME ($000)	RANK	STOCKHOLDERS' EQUITY ($000)	RANK
1	1	Exxon (New York)	48,630,817*	36,331,346	1	2,640,964	2	18,470,352	1
2	2	General Motors (Detroit)	47,181,000	24,442,400	2	2,902,800	1	14,385,200	2
3	4	Ford Motor (Dearborn, Mich.)	28,839,600	15,768,100	6	983,100	4	7,107,000	6
4	3	Texaco (New York)	26,451,851	18,193,818	4	869,731	9	9,002,077	4
5	5	Mobil (New York)¹	26,062,570*	18,767,450	3	942,523	5	7,651,811	5
6	6	Standard Oil of California (San Francisco)	19,434,133	13,765,397	7	880,127	8	7,007,013	7
7	8	Gulf Oil (Pittsburgh)	16,451,000*	13,449,000	8	816,000	10	6,942,000	8
8	7	International Business Machines (Armonk, N.Y.)	16,304,333	17,723,326	5	2,398,093	3	12,749,287	3
9	9	General Electric (Fairfield, Conn.)²	15,697,300	12,049,700	9	930,600	6	5,252,900	10
10	10	Chrysler (Highland Park, Mich.)	15,537,788	7,074,365	16	422,631**	19	2,815,326	20
11	11	International Tel. & Tel. (New York)	11,764,106	11,070,078	11	494,467	15	4,574,256	13
12	12	Standard Oil (Indiana) (Chicago)	11,532,048*	11,213,198	10	892,968	7	6,146,705	9
13	14	Shell Oil (Houston)	9,229,950*	7,836,516	14	705,838	11	4,591,182	12
14	13	U.S. Steel (Pittsburgh)	8,604,200	9,167,900	12	410,300	21	5,129,000	11
15	15	Atlantic Richfield (Los Angeles)	8,462,524*	8,853,334	13	575,178	14	4,091,133	14
16	17	E. I. du Pont de Nemours (Wilmington, Del.)	8,361,000	7,027,100	17	459,300	17	4,039,200	15
17	16	Continental Oil (Stamford, Conn.)	7,957,620	6,041,516	21	459,994	16	2,635,444	24
18	18	Western Electric (New York)	6,930,942	5,178,460	24	217,383	40	3,261,615	17
19	19	Procter & Gamble (Cincinnati)³	6,512,728	4,102,996	32	401,098	22	2,357,470	26
20	22	Tenneco (Houston)	6,389,236	7,177,100	15	383,500	23	2,651,000	23
21	21	Union Carbide (New York)	6,345,700	6,621,600	19	441,200	18	3,055,100	18
22	20	Westinghouse Electric (Pittsburgh)	6,145,152	5,318,342	23	223,217	39	2,138,435	30
23	23	Goodyear Tire & Rubber (Akron, Ohio)	5,791,494	4,336,125	29	121,967	88	1,861,911	36
24	26	Phillips Petroleum (Bartlesville, Okla.)	5,697,516	5,068,463	25	411,656	20	2,720,341	21
25	32	Dow Chemical (Midland, Mich.)	5,652,070	6,848,664	18	612,767	13	2,865,010	19
26	25	Occidental Petroleum (Los Angeles)	5,525,451	3,904,995	34	183,721	48	1,305,276	52
27	24	International Harvester (Chicago)⁴	5,488,123	3,574,832	42	174,088	51	1,580,781	40
28	30	Eastman Kodak (Rochester, N.Y.)	5,438,170	5,524,416	22	650,618	12	4,026,299	16
29	36	Sun (Radnor, Pa.)⁵	5,387,064	4,835,573	27	356,182	27	2,555,069	25
30	27	Union Oil of California (Los Angeles)	5,350,693*	4,226,825	31	268,815	33	2,103,815	32
31	34	RCA (New York)	5,328,500	3,837,700	36	177,400	50	1,277,700	54
32	35	Esmark (Chicago)⁴	5,300,566	1,757,480	98	82,550	138	710,588	126
33	28	Bethlehem Steel (Bethlehem, Pa.)	5,248,000	4,939,100	26	168,000	53	2,692,600	22
34	31	Rockwell International (Pittsburgh)⁶	5,220,100	2,888,600	49	123,400	85	1,178,900	59
35	40	United Technologies (Hartford)	5,166,264	2,626,405	55	157,403	58	1,244,633	56
36	29	Caterpillar Tractor (Peoria, Ill.)	5,042,300	3,893,900	35	383,200	24	2,027,300	34
37	33	Kraft (Glenview, Ill.)	4,976,643	1,821,854	91	135,650	76	1,015,906	75
38	38	Beatrice Foods (Chicago)⁶	4,690,569	1,844,434	89	153,107	62	997,934	77
39	37	LTV (Dallas)	4,496,893	2,134,874	72	30,700	300	413,242	207
40	39	Xerox (Stamford, Conn.)	4,403,897	4,612,382	28	358,906	26	2,178,960	28
41	48	R. J. Reynolds Industries (Winston-Salem, N.C.)	4,291,149*	4,276,761	30	353,893	28	2,112,817	31
42	46	Monsanto (St. Louis)	4,270,200	3,959,100	33	366,300	25	2,252,500	27
43	45	Ashland Oil (Russell, Ky.)⁶	4,086,845*	2,104,863	74	135,983	74	808,973	106
44	44	General Foods (White Plains, N.Y.)⁹	3,978,294	2,012,932	78	150,428	65	983,172	79
45	53	Cities Service (Tulsa)	3,964,600	3,614,900	40	217,000	41	1,798,200	38
46	42	Firestone Tire & Rubber (Akron, Ohio)⁴	3,939,107	3,260,593	46	96,003	120	1,567,950	41
47	43	Boeing (Seattle)	3,918,535	1,918,598	84	102,895	110	1,084,826	71
48	54	Amerada Hess (New York)	3,914,595	2,777,271	53	152,637	63	1,161,843	62
49	41	Greyhound (Phoenix)	3,727,306	1,472,554	123	77,081	146	652,327	143
50	47	W.R. Grace (New York)	3,615,153	2,755,862	54	131,882	81	1,155,342	63

THE DEFINITIONS AND CONCEPTS UNDERLYING THE FIGURES IN THIS DIRECTORY ARE EXPLAINED ON PAGE 386.

N.A. Not available.

*Does not include excise taxes; see the explanation of "sales" on page 386.

**Reflects an extraordinary credit of at least 10 percent; see the explanations of "net income" and "earnings per share" on page 386.

†Average for the year; see the reference to "employees" on page 386.

¹A holding company created in 1976 as a successor to Mobil Oil, now a wholly owned subsidiary.

²Figures for 1976 include Utah International (1975 rank: 273), merged in December, 1976.

³Figures are for fiscal year ending June 30, 1976.

⁴Figures are for fiscal year ending October 31, 1976.

Source: *Fortune,* May 1977, p. 366, with permission.

2. The companies include many of the largest companies in the nation. Looking at the top 50 United States industrial companies ranked by 1976 annual sales (Table 5.10), one finds that 20 of the top 50 chemical producers are also among the top 50 United States companies.

3. Chemical operations are big business, ranging from $385 million to $6,400 million in annual sales for the 50 companies listed. The combined 1976 chemi-

EMPLOYEES		NET INCOME AS PERCENT OF				EARNINGS PER SHARE					TOTAL RETURN TO INVESTORS				INDUSTRY CODE
		SALES		STOCKHOLDERS' EQUITY					GROWTH RATE 1966-76		1976		1966-76 AVERAGE		
NUMBER	RANK	%	RANK	%	RANK	'76($)	'75($)	'66($)	%	RANK	%	RANK	%	RANK	
126,000†	15	5.4	196	14.3	204	5.90	5.60	2.53	8.84	201	26.98	286	11.08	140	29
748,000†	1	6.2	146	20.2	37	10.08	4.32	6.24	4.91	305	45.85	181	8.24	215	40
443,917†	2	3.4	344	13.8	224	10.45	3.46	5.63	6.38	269	46.15	1/5	10.44	155	40
72 766	33	3.3	352	9.7	377	3.20	3.06	2.62	2.02	363	27.28	283	3.05	368	29
199,500	7	3.6	322	12.3	286	9.08	7.95	3.51	9.97	163	44.96	188	8.70	202	29
38,397	102	4.5	262	12.6	272	5.18	4.55	2.52	7.47	239	46.89	171	9.56	177	29
53,300	57	5.0	227	11.8	316	4.19	3.60	2.44	5.56	284	49.27	159	5.26	298	29
291,977	5	14.7	8	18.8	57	15.94	13.35	3.83	15.33	52	28.04	277	8.67	203	44
380,000†	3	5.9	157	17.7	74	4.12	3.17	1.88	8.16	215	23.64	312	5.25	302	36
244,865†	6	2.7	388	15.0	164	7.02**	(4.33)	4.16	5.37	290	104.17	27	0.50	401	40
375,000	4	4.2	280	10.8	343	4.00	3.20	2.04	6.97	253	57.66	128	2.89	370	36
45,399	83	7.7	8(	14.5	193	6.09	5.36	1.81	12.90	94	45.28	187	13.51	90	29
32,227	128	7.6	84	15.4	153	10.11	7.59	4.19	9.21	186	56.70	101	7.40	240	29
166,645†	8	4.8	240	8.0	409	5.03	6.89	3.07	5.06	300	19.70	337	13.35	94	33
26,972	150	6.8	119	14.1	213	5.04	3.08	1.99	9.74	165	30.96	263	12.98	100	29
132,737	13	5.5	192	11.4	333	9.30	5.43	8.23	1.23	379	10.96	389	3.23	366	28
43,899	85	5.8	164	17.5	81	4.38	3.25	1.27	13.18	87	26.98	285	12.17	118	29
151,052	11	3.1	364	6.7	429	N.A.	N.A.	N.A.							36
52,200	63	6.2	144	17.0	89	4.86	4.05	1.74	10.82	143	7.61	400	12.26	115	43
82,074	28	6.0	152	14.5	196	4.33	4.1	1.88	8.70	204	44.18	198	11.38	135	29
113,118	17	7.0	110	14.4	197	7.15	6.23	3.82	6.47	267	5.32	408	7.55	234	28
160,945†	9	3.6	320	10.4	357	2.54	1.89	1.59	4.80	313	39.04	217	1.06	394	36
151,263†	10	2.1	419	6.6	431	1.69	2.24	1.66	0.18	389	14.25	374	5.38	297	30
27,797	144	7.2	99	15.1	162	5.39	4.50	2.26	9.08	190	25.12	302	14.12	81	29
53,033	58	10.8	28	21.4	29	3.30	3.33	0.68	17.11	38	(3.36)	435	18.26	35	28
33,600	117	3.3	348	14.1	212	2.77	2.64	0.64	15.78	50	78.58	64	9.33	188	10
97,550†	22	3.2	360	11.0	340	6.02	2.77	3.86	4.54	318	55.10	138	5.46	294	45
127,000	14	12.0	15	16.2	121	4.03	3.80	1.97	7.42	241	(17.02)	467	4.78	318	38
32,499	126	6.6	126	13.9	218	7.33	4.20	2.50	11.36	126	82.97	56	7.26	247	29
15,725	249	5.0	221	12.8	263	7.42	6.81	4.74	4.58	317	49.12	163	5.31	299	29
110,000	20	3.3	346	13.9	222	2.30	1.40	2.20	0.45	387	45.74	182	(0.58)	409	36
47,000†	75	1.6	440	11.6	322	4.49	5.05	1.30	13.20	85	18.03	349	10.35	159	20
105,000†	21	3.2	359	6.2	438	3.85	5.54	3.72	0.34	388	28.90	271	9.44	179	33
119,517	16	2.4	410	10.5	356	3.62	2.96	4.11⁷	(1.26)	410	40.10	212	5.44	295	41
133,383	12	3.0	371	12.6	269	5.05	3.89	2.02	9.60	172	72.78	79	4.04	340	41
77,793	31	7.6	87	18.9	56	4.45	4.64	1.76	9.72	168	27.88	278	12.48	109	45
46,790	78	2.7	387	13.4	244	4.86	5.01	2.54	6.70	262	14.40	371	7.55	235	20
67,000†	38	3.3	355	15.3	155	1.86	1.71	0.79	8.94	195	24.15	310	11.44	132	20
56,800	50	0.7	476	7.4	423	2.34	1.02	4.02	(5.27)	435	32.09	255	(11.36)	454	20
97,336	23	8.1	69	16.5	108	4.51	3.07	1.25	13.69	77	17.05	359	(0.17)	406	38
37,296	105	8.2	65	16.7	99	7.48	7.39	3.44	8.08	221	15.05	366	12.31	113	21
61,903	43	8.6	54	16.3	117	10.05	8.63	3.41	11.41	125	18.98	338	12.37	112	28
30,000	137	3.3	347	16.8	97	5.03	4.42	2.43	7.55	233	85.87	49	5.60	290	29
47,000	74	3.8	309	15.3	158	3.02	2.00	1.87	4.91	307	14.93	368	2.74	374	20
17,600	228	5.5	194	12.1	300	7.98	5.12	4.82**	5.17	298	60.25	116	7.36	244	29
113,000	18	2.4	407	6.1	443	1.68	2.36	1.76	(0.46)	400	11.69	386	4.48	328	30
65,400†	41	2.6	391	9.5	382	4.85	3.60	4.13	1.62	372	88.70	45	(0.96)	416	41
6,634†	425	3.9	296	13.1	252	3.90	3.26	1.39¹⁰	10.87	141	96.60	34	6.13	274	29
51,976†	64	2.1	421	11.8	311	1.76	1.87	1.50	1.61	373	22.60	318	5.73	284	20
59,700	44	3.6	318	11.4	331	3.55	5.31	3.95**	(1.06)	405	26.30	292	(0.09)	403	28

⁵Name changed from Sun Oil in April, 1976.
⁶Figures are for fiscal year ending September 30, 1976.
⁷Figure is for North American Aviation.
⁸Figures are for fiscal year ending February 29, 1976.
⁹Figures are for fiscal year ending March 31, 1976.
¹⁰Figure is for Hess Oil & Chemical.

cal sales of the *Chemical and Engineering News* top 50 total $59.1 billion. For 13 of the top 50, chemicals account for over 75 percent of total company net sales.

The *Chemical and Engineering News* top 50 companies list clearly shows the important role of the major oil companies in producing chemicals in the United States. A study of the top 50 companies for 1968 to 1974 shows that the percentage

Table 5.11 Percentage of total chemical sales of the top 50 United States chemical producers accounted for by oil companies, 1968–1975

Year	Total chemical sales of top 50 (billions)	Percentage of total chemical sales accounted for by major oil companies†
1968	$25.03	16
1969	26.4	18.4
1970	26.4	17.8
1971	27.8	18
1972	30.8	17.2
1973	36.5	17.8
1974	51.9	22.6

† Major oil companies as classified by SIC 291 and ESIC 29.1.

Source: Compiled from *Chem. Eng. News* over a period of years.

of chemical sales accounted for by ESIC 29.1 companies ranges from 16 percent (1968) to 22.6 percent (1974), as seen in Table 5.11. Many of the chemical products provided by the oil companies are based on petrochemical feedstocks obtained during the petroleum refining process (Figs. 5.2 and 5.3).

By looking at previous top 50 chemical companies lists it is obvious that in recent years there has been little movement at the top (Table 5.12). However, ranked by total assets, the companies at the top of the chemical industry have changed a great deal over the last 70 years (Table 5.13).

Another useful listing of chemical companies appearing on a regular basis is the chemical week 300 published in *Chemical Week*. This list presents quarterly and yearly financial data not only for the basic chemical companies but for other CPI-related companies as well. Table 5.14 presents the top five companies ranked by 1976 first quarter sales of the various industrial groupings listed in the Chemical Week 300.

The top 50 United States Chemical producers are the most visible in the industry. They usually receive the most attention in chemical-industry news publications and financial publications and from graduating chemists and chemical engineers. However, in 1972 there were a total of 11,799 firms involved in industry SIC 28.[1] Most of these firms have total sales substantially less than those of the top 50.

Fifteen of the more profitable small chemical companies with annual sales in the $25 million to $99 million range are listed in Table 5.15. These small firms tend to manufacture specialty chemicals, as contrasted with the top 50, which tend to produce commodities and pseudo-commodity chemicals.

[1] U.S. Bureau of the Census, *Statistical Abstract of the United States: 1975*, 96th ed., table 1266.

Table 5.12 The top 20 United States chemical producers ranked by chemical sales, 1968–1974

1968	1969	1970	1971	1972	1973	1974
Du Pont	Du Pont	Du Pont	Du Pont	Du Pont	Du Pont	Du Pont
Monsanto	Union Carbide	Union Carbide	Union Carbide	Union Carbide	Union Carbide	Dow Chemical
Union Carbide	Monsanto	Monsanto	Monsanto	Dow Chemical	Monsanto	Union Carbide
Dow Chemical	Dow Chemical	Dow	Dow Chemical	Monsanto	Dow Chemical	Monsanto
W. R. Grace	Celanese	Standard Oil (N.I.)	Celanese	Celanese	Exxon	Exxon
Standard Oil (N.J.)	W. R. Grace	Celanese	Standard Oil (N.J.)	Exxon	Celanese	Celanese
Celanese	Standard Oil (N.J.)	W. R. Grace	W. R. Grace	W. R. Grace	W. R. Grace	W. R. Grace
Allied Chemical	Allied Chemical	Allied Chemical	Allied Chemical	Allied Chemical	Allied Chemical	Occidental Petroleum
Hercules	Hercules	Occidental Petroleum	Occidental Petroleum	Occidental Petroleum	Occidental Petroleum	Allied Chemical
FMC	Occidental Petroleum	Hercules	Hercules	Hercules	Hercules	Hercules
Occidental Petroleum	FMC	American Cyanamid	FMC	Eastman Kodak	Eastman Kodak	Shell Oil
American Cyanamid	American Cyanamid	FMC	Eastman Kodak	FMC	Rohm & Haas	Phillips Petroleum
Shell Oil	Shell Oil	Eastman Kodak	American Cyanamid	Shell Oil	Shell Oil	American Cyanamid
Eastman Kodak	Eastman Kodak	Shell Oil	Shell Oil	American Cyanamid	FMC	Eastman Kodak
Stauffer Chemical	Uniroyal	Stauffer Chemical	Rohm & Haas	Rohm & Haas	American Cyanamid	Rohm & Haas
Uniroyal	Stauffer Chemical	Rohm & Haas	Stauffer Chemical	Stauffer Chemical	Phillips Petroleum	FMC
Phillips Petroleum	Phillips Petroleum	Mobil Oil	Mobil Oil	Phillips Petroleum	Borden	Borden
Rohm & Haas	Rohm & Haas	Ethyl Corp.	Ethyl Corp.	Bordon	Stauffer Chemical	Gulf Oil
Mobil Oil	Mobil Oil	Gulf Oil	Phillips Petroleum	Mobil Oil	Mobil Oil	Mobil Oil
Cities Service	Borden	Standard Oil (Ind.)	Borden	Ethyl Corp.	Standard Oil (Ind.)	Texaco

Source: Compiled from *Chem. Eng. News* data for the years shown.

Table 5.13 Top United States chemical companies ranked by total assets, 1909–1974

1909†	1948†	1960†	1968†	1974‡
Du Pont	Du Pont	Du Pont	Du Pont	Du Pont
Virginia Carolina	Union Carbide	Union Carbide	Union Carbide	Dow Chemical
Chemical	Allied Chemical	Monsanto	Dow Chemical	Union Carbide
International Salt	Dow Chemical	Dow Chemical	Monsanto	Monsanto
General Chemical	Celanese	Olin Mathieson	W. R. Grace	W. R. Grace
(predecessor of	American Viscose	Allied Chemical	Celanese	Allied Chemical
Allied Chemical)	American Cyanamid	American Cyanamid	Allied Chemical	Celanese
	Monsanto	W. R. Grace	Olin Mathieson	FMC

† From J. Backman, "The Economics of the Chemical Industry," pp. 43–44, Manufacturing Chemists Association, Washington, 1970.

‡ *Chem. Eng. News*, Facts and Figures issue, June 2, 1975.

Table 5.14 The top five companies of the various industrial groupings listed in the *Chemical Week* 300

Company	Annual sales, 1976 (millions)	Company	Annual sales, 1976 (millions)
Chemicals:		Pharmaceuticals:	
Du Pont	8,361	Johnson & Johnson	2,472
Union Carbide	6.346	American Home Products	2,523
Dow Chemical	5.652	Warner-Lambert	2,349
Monsanto	4.270	Bristol-Myers	1,986
W. R. Grace	3,615	Pfizer	1,888
Petroleum, natural gas, chemicals:		Pulp, paper, and packaging products:	
Exxon	48,631	International Paper	3,541
Texaco	26,452	Continental Group	3,458
Mobil Oil	26,063	American Can	3,143
Standard Oil (California)	19,434	Georgia-Pacific	2,911
Gulf Oil	16,451	Champion International	3,038
Multi-industry companies with chemical process operations:		Products of stone, clay and glass:	
General Electric	15,697	Owens-Illinois	2,572
Eastman Kodak	5,438	Johns-Manville	1,309
Minnesota Mining & Mfg.	3,514	Owens-Corning	1,079
Gulf & Western	3,396	Corning Glass	1,026
Textron	2,627	U.S. Gypsum	872
Tires, other rubber and plastic products:		Detergents, sanitation products, toiletries, and cosmetics:	
Goodyear Tire	5,792	Procter & Gamble	6,513
Firestone Tire	3,939	Colgate-Palmolive	3,512
Uniroyal	2,315	Gillette	1,492
General Tire	1,996	Avon Products	1,434
B. F. Goodrich	2,023	Revlon	956

Table 5.14 (*continued*)

Company	Annual sales, 1976 (millions)	Company	Annual sales, 1976 (millions)
Food and dairy companies with chemical operations:		Paints, printing inks and related products:	
Esmark	5,268	Sherwin-Williams	952
Kraft Inc.	4,977	Inmont	534
Beatrice Foods	4,691	Sun Chemical	292
Borden	3,381	Desoto	290
Consolidated Foods	2,755	H. B. Fuller	168
Nonferrous metals:		Steel, coke, chemicals:	
Engelhard Mining & Chemicals	6,464	U.S. Steel	8,604
Aluminum Company of America	2,925	Bethlehem Steel	5,248
Reynolds Metals	2,084	Armco Steel	3,151
Kaiser Aluminum & Chem.	1,852	National Steel	2,841
Anaconda	1,481	Republic Steel	2,546

Source: Chem. Week, April 27, 1977.

The small chemical company usually requires less capital but more people per pound of product than a large company. Processes are often batch and flexible enough to be used for several different products. Research and development tends to be product-application-oriented, compared with the process-oriented research and development of commodity producers. Marketing and product innovation are vital to the success of many small chemical firms. This text does not deal in

Table 5.15 Sales and profitability of 15 most profitable chemical companies with sales of $25 million to $99 million, 1973

Rank	Company	Sales (millions)	Profits (millions)	Return on equity, %
1	Beker Industries	$74	$12.4	47.8
2	Polymer Materials	38	1.7	37.4
3	Loctite	34	5.6	30.4
4	First Mississippi	26	3.2	26.1
5	Lea-Ronal	84	2.2	22.5
6	Quaker Chemical	38	3.2	22.0
7	A. Schulman	92	3.1	20.6
8	Sigma International	24	3.1	20.5
9	Philip A. Hunt Chemical	52	6.1	18.9
10	MacDermid	28	2.4	18.2
11	Corenco	44	2.5	16.8
12	Oakite	34	2.4	16.5
13	Betz Laboratories	70	5.8	16.1
14	Filtrol	41	4.4	15.7
15	Burdox	26	0.9	15.6

Source: Charles Kline, Maximizing Profits in Chemicals, *CHEMTECH*, February 1976, p. 115.

Table 5.16 Top 50 chemical producers in the world, 1974

All dollar values in millions

Ranking 1974	Ranking 1973	Company	Country	Sales	Pretax profits	Capital employed	R & D spending	Capital expenditure	Number of employees
1	4	BASF	W. Germany	$8,541.6	$ 515.9	$3,657.3	$231.5	$ 537.7	110,989
2	2	Hoechst	W. Germany	7,795.2	694.6	5,509	308.7	649.1	178,710
3	5	ICI	U.K.	7,331	1,088	5,475	208	476	132,000
4	3	Bayer	W. Germany	7,180	330.4	2,117.4	182.9	339.6	65,658
5	1	Du Pont	U.S.	6,910	682	4,903.6	344	1,038	136,866
6	6	Montedison	Italy	6,178	141[a]	2,710	6.4	465	103,000
7	7	Union Carbide	U.S.	5,320	907.4	3,776	94	517	
8	11	Dow	U.S.	4,938	1,120	3,502	148	870	53,300
9	10	Rhône-Poulenc	France	4,426.3	396.5	1,206.9	171	454.9	119,263
10	9	Akzo	Netherlands	4,063	236.1	2,482	136	301.7	105,400
11		Royal Dutch Shell[b]	Netherlands	3,567.2	.....	1,127[b]	.....	366[b]	
12	15	Monsanto	U.S.	3,498	574	2,356	105	313	60,926
13	13	W. R. Grace	U.S.	3,472	254.7	1,672.1	31.4	276.6	74,800
14	16	Exxon Chemical	U.S.	3,300	900	1,930	.....	121	
15	55	Borden	U.S.	3,264	158.8	1,176.7			
16	14	Ciba-Geigy[c]	Switzerland	3,108	291	1,260	232.8		
17	18	DSM	Netherlands	2,644.7	391.3	1,100	.....	147	29,500
18	17	Allied Chemical	U.S.	2,216	232.9	1,273.3	30.8	305.8	32,167
19	19	Solvay & Cie	Belgium	2,124	194	1,610	51.8	178.3	44,467
20	33	Veba-Chemie	W. Germany	2,006.8[b]	8.4[b]	719.3	.....	90.3	8,284
21	21	Celanese Corp.	U.S.	1,928	198	1,391	58	220	26,000
22	17	Warner-Lambert	U.S.	1,911	270.8	1,243.4	68.9	97.1	58,500
23	20	Mitsubishi Chemical	Japan	1,889	64.7	2,282	.....	.....	10,777
24	22	Hoffmann–La Roche	Switzerland	1,881	24.8[d]	212.9[e]	.....	.....	34,900[e]
25	26	Sumimoto Chemical	Japan	1,842	62.2	1,674	35.8	171	14,682

26	23	Henkel & Cie	W. Germany	1,791	70.3	416	49	103.4	34,094
27	20	American Cyanamid	U.S.	1,780	233	1,251	58.8	138.7	38,024
28	86	PPG Industries[f]	U.S.	1,744	143.1	1,233.8	21.5	198.8	......
29	25	Asahi Chemical	Japan	1,711.8	109.5	1,144	......	182.8	......
30	32	Occidental[b]	U.S.	1,688[b]	168.4[b]	947[b]	12.8[b]	119.3[b]	19,000[b]
31	131	NL Industries	U.S.	1,597	125.7	809	22	54.8	25,800
32	101	Bristol-Myers[f]	U.S.	1,591	215	689.5	55	31.2	29,700
33	31	Toray Industries	Japan	1,567	189	1,108	......	135	......
34	34	Degussa	W. Germany	1,551.7	37	430.8	......	......	13,616
35	24	Pfizer	U.S.	1,542	135.3	1,232	67.7	136.8	39,500
36	28	Hercules, Inc.	U.S.	1,525	146.6	1,086	......	......	33,646[e]
37	29	Sandoz AG	Switzerland	1,330.7	22.6	1,204.4[e]	......	......	27,000
38	30	Merck	U.S.	1,330	362	1,369	103	159	......
39	79	Union Explosives Rio Tinto	Spain	1,266.8	40.1	760.4	......	......	......
40	95	Olin	U.S.	1,249	84.1	701	......	......	19,335
41	76	Showa Denko	Japan	1,218.9	38.1	1,327	......	67	23,000
42	41	Phillips Petroleum[b]	U.S.	1,184[b]	309.3[b]	3,043	......	618	9,015
43	52	UBE Industries	Japan	1,161.1	49.8	1,252	21.5	112.3	30,802
44	27	Mitsui Toatsu Chemicals	Japan	1,159.3	40	1,043	28.9	127.5	11,049
45	35	Eli Lilly	U.S.	1,148	302.6	1,001	......	......	9,270
46	50	Chemische Werke Huls	W. Germany	1,119.1	......	......	......	60.6	......
47	48	Anic SpA	Italy	1,108	16.3[g]	828.5[e]	......	......	......
48	73	Standard Oil Indiana[b]	U.S.	1,088[b]	175.1[b]	6,556.3	......	151.3	47,217
49	40	Teijin	Japan	1,076	118	829.4	25.6	111	13,500
50	108	Beecham	U.K.	1,044.1	148	600.7	......	54.3	30,000

[a] Tax estimated at 12.5%; Montedison has losses to carry forward.
[b] Chemical operations only.
[c] Sales for group; other figures for parent.
[d] Profits are after tax.
[e] Previous year's figure.
[f] Fully included for first time; chemical operations only previously.
[g] Tax charge estimated on basis of previous years.
Source: *Chem. Age*, July 25, 1975, p. 517.

Table 5.17 The 50 largest companies outside the United States ranked by 1976 sales

RANK '76	'75	COMPANY	COUNTRY	INDUSTRY	SALES[1] ($000)	ASSETS[2] ($000)	NET INCOME[3] ($000)	STOCK-HOLDERS' EQUITY[4] ($000)	EMPLOYEES
1	1	Royal Dutch/Shell Group	Neth.-Britain	Petroleum	36,087,130	29,645,758	2,347,766	11,186,285	153,000
2	2	National Iranian Oil[5]	Iran	Petroleum	19,671,064	6,544,991	17,175,182	4,261,182	57,331
3	3	British Petroleum	Britain	Petroleum	19,103,330	14,925,935	324,615	4,862,138	78,000
4	4	Unilever	Britain-Neth.	Food products, detergents	15,762,219	7,793,812	517,614	2,949,024	317,000
5	5	Philips' Glŏeilampenfabrieken	Netherlands	Electronics, appliances	11,521,549[6]	12,245,086	212,940	4,142,039	391,500[6]
6	10	ENI[5]	Italy	Petroleum	9,983,105*,6	12,803,525*,6	(37,026)*,6	1,561,125*,6	100,747*,6
7	6	Française des Pétroles	France	Petroleum	9,927,775[7]	8,946,164[7]	34,731[7]	1,662,038[7]	44,000[7]
8	13	Renault[5]	France	Motor vehicles	9,352,884	N.A.	N.A.	N.A.	241,259
9	9	Hoechst	Germany	Chemicals	9,332,979[6]	8,753,727	188,010	1,891,270	182,980[6]
10	12	BASF	Germany	Chemicals	9,202,592[6]	6,579,049	241,176	2,330,841	112,686[6]
11	•	Petróleos de Venezuela[5]	Venezuela	Petroleum	9,083,587	4,962,648	876,153	3,357,774	23,000
12	11	Daimler-Benz	Germany	Motor vehicles	8,938,321[6]	3,566,418	164,182	977,264	160,863[6]
13	15	Volkswagenwerk	Germany	Motor vehicles	8,513,304	6,144,450	399,164	1,611,331	183,238
14	16	Bayer[8]	Germany	Chemicals	8,297,808[6]	8,516,779[6]	181,364[6]	1,980,957[6]	171,200[6]
15	7	Nippon Steel[9]	Japan	Metal refining—steel	8,089,530	11,624,997	38,572	1,466,814	98,746
16	14	Siemens[10]	Germany	Electronics, appliances	8,060,411	8,229,723	221,969	2,360,882	304,000
17	8	Thyssen[10,11]	Germany	Metal refining—steel, machinery	7,947,640	5,647,055	105,499	1,269,672	139,440
18	17	Toyota Motor[12]	Japan	Motor vehicles	7,695,997[6]	4,834,692[6]	345,433[6]	1,802,237[6]	59,479[6]
19	19	Nestlé	Switzerland	Food products	7,627,869	5,706,916	348,922	3,007,705	137,329
20	18	ELF-Aquitaine[5]	France	Petroleum	7,536,225	9,770,720	340,108	2,410,557	34,000
21	20	Imperial Chemical Industries[13]	Britain	Chemicals	7,465,412	7,773,570	442,328	3,116,232	192,000
22	49	Peugeot-Citroën[14]	France	Motor vehicles	7,346,998[6]	4,823,651[6]	287,426[6]	1,269,079[6]	185,875[6]
23	21	Petrobrás (Petróleo Brasileiro)[5]	Brazil	Petroleum	7,252,110	8,259,491	934,579	3,779,641	49,435
24	23	Hitachi[10]	Japan	Electronics, appliances	6,680,423	8,389,765	200,377	1,990,350	143,014
25	22	BAT Industries[10,15]	Britain	Tobacco, paper products	6,668,743	5,182,520	323,541	2,314,040	148,000
26	25	Nissan Motor[10]	Japan	Motor vehicles	6,583,517	5,233,182	273,005	1,588,756	76,089
27	24	Mitsubishi Heavy Industries[10]	Japan	Industrial equipment, motor vehicles	6,137,230	8,917,191	47,711	705,741	109,300
28	30	Saint-Gobain-Pont-à-Mousson	France	Building materials	5,979,469	5,685,223	98,775	1,413,289	160,075
29	26	Montedison	Italy	Chemicals,	5,826,432[6]	7,221,152[6]	(195,019)[6]	842,090[6]	144,595[6]
30	32	Matsushita Electric Industrial[16]	Japan	Electronics, appliances	5,736,562	5,101,767	220,641	2,146,643	83,081
31	29	AEG-Telefunken	Germany	Electronics, appliances	5,351,388	3,693,985	164,134	653,607	161,900
32	38	General Motors of Canada	Canada	Motor vehicles	5,264,237	1,284,673	162,101	569,358	31,639
33	27	British Steel[5,9]	Britain	Metal refining—steel	5,003,793	6,247,750	(541,209)	1,805,927	219,000
34	36	Ruhrkohle	Germany	Mining—coal	4,904,094	4,992,769	14,668	253,162	147,505
35	35	Ford Motor of Canada	Canada	Motor vehicles	4,837,382	1,651,434	128,010	889,273	36,700
36	28	Mannesmann	Germany	Metal manufacturing	4,688,566	3,778,677	109,372	883,848	108,684
37	33	Pechiney Ugine Kuhlmann	France	Metal refining—aluminum, copper, steel	4,662,784	5,478,604	31,994	1,306,059	96,500
38	31	Fiat	Italy	Motor vehicles	4,658,028[17]	6,159,348[17]	80,412[17]	817,711[17]	143,223[17]
39	42	Rhône-Poulenc	France	Chemicals,	4,554,127	4,938,731	(76,265)	1,378,784	113,500
40	40	Tokyo Shibaura Electric[10]	Japan	Electronics, appliances	4,459,929	5,723,384	13,879	606,412	105,000
41	34	Idemitsu Kosan[9]	Japan	Petroleum	4,425,749	4,208,787	(3,859)	41,162	11,040
42	46	Imperial Oil	Canada	Petroleum	4,365,762	3,109,807	267,788	1,719,855	14,753
43	44	Gutehoffnungshütte[12]	Germany	Industrial equipment	4,306,991[6]	3,317,777	31,241	358,774	84,508[6]
44	52	National Coal Board[5,9]	Britain	Mining—coal	4,208,618	2,439,458	11,382	57,669	312,000
45	37	British Leyland[5]	Britain	Motor vehicles	4,177,512*	2,747,819	61,205*	641,490	183,384
46	45	Dunlop Pirelli Union	Britain-Italy	Rubber products, cables	4,172,326	N.A.	N.A.	N.A.	164,200
47	•	Denain Nord-Est Longwy	France	Metal refining—steel	4,122,641	6,686,268	(516,843)	610,563	80,000
48	47	Petrofina	Belgium	Petroleum	4,081,955	4,697,841	156,247	1,383,113	21,000
49	39	Sumitomo Metal Industries[10]	Japan	Metal refining—steel	4,075,256	6,905,397	23,678	527,408	44,867
50	48	Akzo Group	Netherlands	Chemicals, synthetic fibers	4,069,438	3,564,574	(57,831)	1,069,378	91,100

• Not on last year's list.
N.A. Not available.
*FORTUNE estimate.
[1]All companies on the list must have derived more than 50 percent of their sales from manufacturing and/or min′g. Sales do not include excise taxes or customs duties levied according to either volume or value of ..les, and so the figures for some corporations—most of them sell gasoline, liquor, or tobacco—may be lower than those published by the corporations themselves. Unless otherwise noted, figures exclude intracompany transactions and include subsidiaries more than 50 percent owned, either on a fully consolidated or prorata basis. Sales and net income have been converted to

dollars, using an exchange rate that consists of the average rate in the official exchange market during the company's fiscal year; total assets and stockholders' equity have been converted at the market rate prevailing at the company's year-end (December 31, 1976, unless otherwise noted).
[2]As shown at the company's year-end.
[3]After taxes and minority interest. Figures in parentheses are losses.
[4]Sum of capital stock, surplus, and retained earnings at the end of the fiscal year. Figures in parentheses are losses.
[5]Government owned.
[6]Also includes certain subsidiaries owned 50 percent or less, either fully or on a prorated basis.

Source: The Fortune Directory of the 300 Largest Industrial Corporations outside the United States, *Fortune,* August 1977, p. 226, with permission.

detail with small companies, but when studying the CPI and making employment decisions, chemical professionals should keep in mind what a small company offers in terms of both contribution to the CPI and professional opportunity. The small company can offer the autonomous individual and entrepreneur many opportunities that may not be available in the large firm, e.g., being placed in a responsible position at an early stage in one's career. The risks involved in working for a small firm may be great, but the rewards for contributing to its growth and prosperity may be correspondingly great.

Small companies in the CPI with sales in the $500,000 to $20 million range have developed their own organization. The Chemical and Specialties. Management Council (CSMC). This group provides opportunities for executives of small companies to meet with their peers and discuss problems of common interest. Membership in the organization is limited to the top one or two officers of a company which must have at least 75 percent of its sales based on chemical processing operations.

5.2.2 International

Table 5.16 lists the top 50 chemical producers in the world in 1974, as given by *Chemical Age*. This table is discussed in more detail in Chap. 9. Note that United States companies account for only 22 of the top 50 chemical companies and that the top 4 are all foreign companies. Table 5.17 lists the top manufacturing companies outside the United States ranked by 1976 sales. Of the top 10 companies, 8 produce chemicals, petroleum products, or allied products (such as pharmaceuticals, synthetic fibers, detergents, cosmetics, toiletries, and rubber products). Over 40 percent of the top 50 produce chemicals, petroleum products, or allied products.

5.3 REFERENCES

1. C. H. Kline, Maximizing Profits in Chemicals, *CHEMTECH*, February 1976.

Chemical and Engineering News has published the Facts and Figures issue annually since 1956 and has also published annually since 1969 the top 50 United States companies ranked by chemical sales and the top 50 chemicals ranked by production volume. Beginning in 1972, the Facts and Figures issue has included the top 50 companies and the top 50 chemicals, which can be found in the following issues:

Year	Issue
1968	June 16, 1969, p. 23
1969	Apr. 27, 1970, p. 21
1970	Apr. 26, 1971, p. 13
1971	Apr. 24, 1972, p. 10
1972	Apr. 30, 1973, p. 11
1973	June 3, 1974, p. 31
1974	June 2, 1975, p. 36
1975	June 7, 1976, p. 47
1976	June 6, 1977, p. 42

The top 50 United States companies are taken from The Fortune Directory of the 500 Largest Industrial Corporations, *Fortune*, May 1977, p. 366. This is an annual *Fortune* issue. The top 50 foreign companies are taken from The Fortune Directory of the 300 Largest Industrial Corporations outside the U.S., *Fortune*, August 1977, p. 226. The top chemical companies in the world are from the *Chemical Age*, July 1975. This list is published annually.

5.4 QUESTIONS FOR DISCUSSION

These questions were developed to enliven classroom discussion or self-directed study. They are intended to help you see the significance of the tabular data. It is suggested that some of them be done as an in-class exercise and some be done as an assignment for outside work. All these questions can be answered using data in the chapter; no additional library research is required.

1 List the top 15 organic chemicals in Table 5.7. What is their ranking in Table 5.3. Why are the rankings different? Is the word "chemical" used in the same sense in these two tables?

2 Rank the fibers listed in Chap. 6 in both Tables 5.3 and 5.7.

3 List the top 20 of the top 50 chemicals (Table 5.7) in terms of average annual change in sales volume (1964 to 1974). Classify as organic and inorganic. Which of your top 20 are listed in Table 5.3?

4 Prepare a top 10 list of United States chemical producers (Table 5.9) ranked by (a) profit margin and (b) return on stockholders equity.

5 Prepare a list of companies from Table 5.9 whose chemical sales are all less than 10 percent. What do these companies have in common if anything?

6 List all the chemical companies in Table 5.9 which also appear in Table 5.10.

7 Rank the top 15 of companies listed in Table 5.10 with respect to growth rate 1964 to 1974. Which chemical firms are among the top 15?

8 Compute sales per employee for the top 20 companies listed in Table 5.10 and prepare a list ranking them.

9 Which of the companies listed in Table 5.14 also appear in Table 5.10?

10 Compute sales per employee for the top 20 companies listed in Table 5.16 and prepare a list which is ranked on this basis. Can you draw any conclusions?

11 Find the top 20 from Table 5.16 in terms of research and development funds spent. Compute the ratio of research and development funds spent to total sales and rerank. Can you make any general statements?

12 Prepare a list of the top 10 from Table 5.17 ranked on the basis of sales per employee.

5.5 PROBLEMS

5.1 Consider the top 10 inorganic chemicals in Table 5.7. Find their 1975 prices and determine where they would rank in Table 5.3 (Some of the data are in Chap. 6.)

5.2 Take the top 10 in the list you have prepared for Prob. 5.1 and determine which important consumer products are made from these chemicals.

5.3 Prepare from Table 5.13 a list of the 10 chemicals whose growth rate is the lowest over the period from 1964 to 1974. Which firms manufacture these chemicals? List the three most important for each of the 10 chemicals.

5.4 (a) In what general areas of the p-vs.-Q chart (Fig. 5.4) do the chemical products listed in Table 5.4 fit? Using the price production data from Chap. 6, check five or six specific chemicals.

(b) How does Fig. 5.4 differ from the p-vs.-Q curves presented in Chap. 2? Compute an elasticity for the p-Q relationship in Fig. 5.4. How would you interpret this number?

(c) If you were a corporate planner charged with investigating new business possibilities, how would you use Fig. 5.4?

5.5 Compare Table 5.7 with the latest Facts and Figures issue of *Chemical and Engineering News*. Are there major changes? If so, can you account for them?

5.6 Only a few chemical industry products have been identified in the text. There are thousands of others. A perusal of the advertisements in *Chemical and Engineering News* and *Chemical Week* is an easy way to develop a list of 20 less known chemical products and their manufacturers. How would you classify the products you found with respect to the categories listed in this section? In your readings did you find much advertising for chemicals in the top 50?

5.7 The *Buyer's Guide* published by *Chemical Week* lists about 6,000 of the chemical products produced in the United States and the companies that manufacture them. This publication is well worth some of your time. You can quickly find, for example, the companies that produce the same products as the company for which you work or for which you may wish to work. Why is it important to know something of the competition?

5.8 In view of the uniform specifications for gasoline and all the advertising claims you have heard, would you classify gasoline as a true commodity or a pseudo commodity?

5.9 Find the latest "refinery gate" prices for the products listed in Table 5.8 (see *Oil and Gas Journal*, listed in Sec. I.1.1). For which products should a refinery try to maximize production?

5.10 What vehicles of transportation do not need a fuel derived from oil? How important are they in terms of number of people or tons of goods they can carry? Approximately what percentage of the United States energy requirement is needed for transportation?

5.11 Is there any nonpetroleum substitute for gasoline and fuel oil which has suitable properties and convenience and which is available in large quantities at a low price?

5.12 Where do gasoline and residual fuel oil fit in Fig. 5.4?

5.13 In Prob. 5.6 you developed a list of less known chemical products and their manufacturers. Pick five of these products and using the Buyers' Guide of *Chemical Week* or some other source, find which other companies manufacture the products. How many of them are in the top 50?

5.14 Find the total sales for each firm which produces one of your products. Are the firms listed on the New York, American, or on an over-the-counter exchange (*The New York Times, The Wall Street Journal*)? If not, where would you look for information?

5.15 Large chemical companies recruit chemical professionals by making trips and interviewing at universities. If you were looking for your first job or a different job from the one you now have, how would you develop a list of small companies which have promising opportunities? Develop a list of at least three with the statistics which you feel are important.

5.16 Study Table 5.12 and list foreign companies which have United States operations. List five products these firms make which compete with those made by United States firms.

5.17 Find a chemical company with annual sales of $25 million to $99 million and carry out an analysis of its operations. Discuss the products made, the customers served, the manufacturing process used, the dollars of sales, the net income, the profit margin, and the return on investment. Several of these companies are listed as over-the-counter stocks, and information on them is readily available in the standard references.

6

SPECIFIC CHEMICAL PRODUCTS

The CPI produce an array of products with widely varying properties and uses, but most CPI products, from industrial gases to fibers and plastics, follow a life cycle, identifiable with the seasons of the year (Fig. 6.1).

In a traditional society, products like tallow soap and beeswax candles may be continuously in use for centuries without significant change. In our modern dynamic society, most products in the CPI go through complete life cycles in a few decades, from youthful newcomers to tired oldsters requiring replacement.

In the spring the product is new. There is uncertainty about acceptance in the marketplace. It may be a new artificial sweetner for soft drinks. Will the public find that it has a bitter aftertaste? Will it compare favorably with a new extract

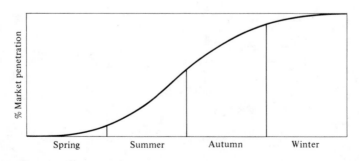

Figure 6.1 Product life cycle.

from grapefruit peels? Will it induce cancer of the bladder when fed in massive doses to rats? Will 1 consumer out of 1,000 develop a rash after a drink? In the spring, the chemistry is rudimentary and the technology of manufacturing is crude. There is only one manufacturer, who is struggling to finance costly investments in marketing, advertising, manufacturing facilities, inventory buildup, and government certification. The hope of profit lies in the distant future. Many products fail at this phase, leaving the innovative entrepreneur sadder and poorer.

In the summer the product that survives is gaining acceptance in the marketplace. Being the first in the market means a good margin of profit, but it also means that the company is even more cash-hungry than in the spring. The rapid expansion of sales requires even more capital to design and build new plants and to penetrate new markets. The sweet smell of success also draws many imitators and competitors, who try to enter the market despite any previously and cautiously laid out barriers to entry. Research on product improvements continues to be very important since it enables the product to penetrate more markets and to compete favorably with new products from competitors.

When autumn arrives, the heady growth period is over, and market saturation is being felt. The profit margin declines from what it was in the summer, and competition between the numerous manufacturers leads to the disappearance of the less efficient producers. Manufacturing costs must be reduced by superior engineering, and larger-scale, low-cost manufacturing units need to be designed if a firm is to survive in this period. A less creative but more hard-headed management is needed to optimize the manufacturing process. In the autumn the product provides for the first time a large quantity of discretionary cash.

The product is mature and may even turn overripe in winter. Market growth depends strictly on growth in the GNP. There are few new users. The product is now an undifferentiated commodity, produced at a very low profit margin. Manufacturing costs and quantities produced are stable. In fact, the product is in danger of being phased out by more vigorous newcomers that are in the springtime of their cycle. No new chemistry or technology has been developed in many years. The management may be thought of as caretakers. Occasionally, the sparkle of a new idea may occur in deep winter and lead to a new product cycle. But many products in winter are managed by undertakers, waiting for the funeral to begin.

Chemical professionals in industry usually deal with only a limited number of products at any one time during their careers. To study any product in depth they must answer the types of questions posed in Sec. 0.2.2. This chapter serves two purposes: it illustrates a detailed analysis of one chemical and presents some basic facts for several important organic and inorganic chemicals, plastics, and fibers.

Methanol has been chosen for the detailed analysis in Sec. 6.1. The facts and written discussion presented for methanol should help readers in preparing their own analyses and should show them how to examine the analyses of others critically.

Section 6.2 gives an overall perspective on a variety of important chemical products. Given this foundation, you should be able to expand these data and contrast them with those for other products. The information presented in Sec. 6.2 will be referred to again in Chaps. 8 to 10. All the products discussed in Sec. 6.2 are in the autumn or winter phase of their cycles. This is the only time in the life cycle when sufficient data have been accumulated to define methods of manufacture, to allow production and price histories to be established, to identify end-use patterns, and to identify major producers.

6.1 A PRODUCT REPORT: METHANOL

6.1.1 Method of Manufacture

Methanol (CH_3OH) is a toxic, colorless liquid at room temperatures. Its properties are summarized in Table 6.1. Methanol's identity was established in 1834, and it was synthesized in 1857 by Berthelot by the saponification of methyl chloride. Initially, methanol was commercially produced by wood distillation (hence the common name of wood alcohol). In the early 1920s, BASF, of Germany, began commercial production by reacting carbon monoxide and hydrogen at approximately 400°C and 200 atm over a metal oxide catalyst.

In the United States both Du Pont and Commercial Solvents Corporation began experimental work on methanol synthesis in 1926. By the end of 1927 both companies had commercial production units operating. Commercial Solvents used a high-pressure reaction in which carbon dioxide and hydrogen react to yield methanol and water:

$$CO_2 + 3H_2 \longrightarrow CH_3OH + H_2O$$

This route requires considerable separation equipment to remove the water and by-product higher alcohols formed during the reaction; nonetheless, it is still in

Table 6.1 Summary of properties of methanol

Molecular weight	32.04
Specific gravity	0.792 at 20°C
Melting point, °C	−97.6
Boiling point, °C	+64.6
Flash point (closed-cup), °C	12
Ignition temperature, °C	470
Vapor density (air = 1)	1.11
Explosive limits (% by volume in air), lower	6
upper	36.5
Threshold limit value, ppm	200
Latent heat of vaporization at boiling point, Btu/lb	502
Heat of combustion (liquid fuel–liquid H_2O), Btu/lb	9,776
Octane number, research	106
Motor	92

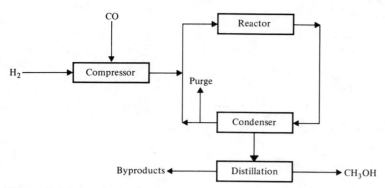

Figure 6.2 Methanol manufacture.

use in some plants. Du Pont's first methanol plant was based on a by-product carbon monoxide stream from an existing ammonia synthesis plant:

$$2H_2 + CO \longrightarrow CH_3OH$$

Today, practically all methanol is made by this method, utilizing a catalyst and operating at 50 to 350 atm and temperatures of 250 to 300°C (Fig. 6.2). The reactants are fed to the reactor in the stoichiometric ratio of 2 : 1. Per pass methanol yield is greater than 60 percent. Product purities of 99 percent are common after distillation. The catalyst is usually a mixture of metal oxides, although a copper-based catalyst process allowing operation at a lower pressure and temperature is becoming important. This copper catalyst makes methanol synthesis possible at 50 to 100 atm and 250 to 270°C, compared with the 200 to 350 atm and 300°C operating conditions of high-pressure processes. The process (developed by ICI) saves money thanks to lower energy costs, lower by-product formation, and lower investment and maintenance costs. Over 85 percent of recent world methanol expansion is based on the new low-pressure process. Plant sizes vary from about 80 to 800 million pounds per year.

About 99 percent of the methanol raw materials are currently obtained by reforming natural gas and refinery light-gas streams. From natural gas

$$3CH_4 + 2H_2O + CO_2 \xrightarrow[800°C]{Ni\ cat} 4CO + 8H_2$$

However, other raw-material sources have been used, and potentially large sources may be tapped in coming years (see Sec. 6.1.6).

6.1.2 Production and Pricing

In 1975, methanol ranked eighteenth among the list of biggest-volume chemicals in the United States. The United States production history of synthetic methanol is shown graphically in Fig. 6.3. Summarized in Table 6.2 are production and annual growth rates for 1972 to 1975. From 1963 to 1973 average annual growth

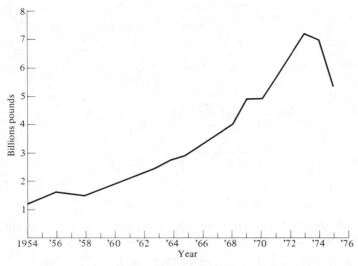

Figure 6.3 Annual United States production history for methanol.

of United States production was 11.8 percent. The recent down trend can be attributed to softness in markets during the economic recession of 1974 to 1975. In particular, the drastic decline in new construction during this period reduced the need for many methanol derivatives ultimately consumed by the building industries.

The United States price history in cents per gallon for synthetic methanol is shown in Fig. 6.4. The price dropped from a high in 1951 of about 27.9 cents per gallon to a low of about 9.6 cents per gallon in 1972. The drastic drop in price in 1970 to 1971 was caused by a severe oversupply situation. By mid-1972 supply and demand were more in balance, allowing prices to stabilize. By 1973 a tight supply situation developed due to a number of factors, including a shortage of natural gas to make the methanol raw materials. Recently, increased feedstock prices and capital costs have forced methanol prices to a list price of 40 to 50 cents per gallon in spite of the downturn in demand in 1974 to 1975.

The experience curve for methanol is shown by Fig. 6.5 using the data in Table 6.3. Industry total accumulated volume is plotted vs. the price in constant

Table 6.2 Methanol production history

Year	Production, 10^9 lb	Change from previous year, %
1975	5.18	−24.7
1974	6.88	−3.4
1973	7.12	17.5
1972	6.06	22.4

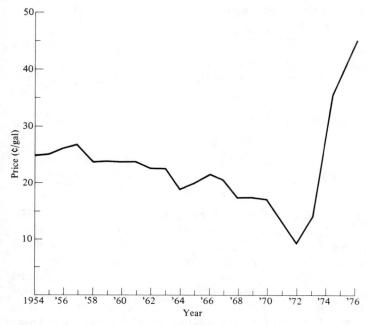

Figure 6.4 United States price history for synthetic methanol.

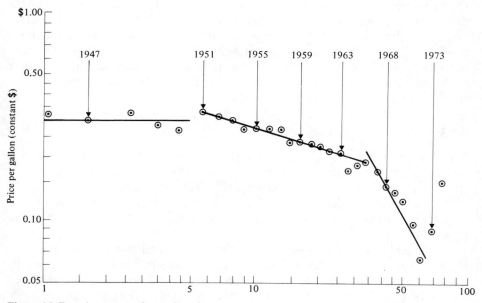

Figure 6.5 Experience curve for methanol.

Table 6.3 Industry total accumulated volume for methanol from 1947 (see Fig. 6.3)

Year	Accumulated U.S. production volume, 10^9 lb	Price per gallon (constant 1958 dollars)
1947	1.6	$0.30
1951	5.6	0.33
1959	16.7	0.24
1963	25.3	0.21
1968	41.3	0.14
1973	69.0	0.09

dollars on log-log paper. Four distinct trend periods emerge. From 1946 to 1951, the constant-dollar price remained fairly stable at about 30 cents per gallon. From 1951 to about 1966 the constant-dollar price decreased at a rate of about 19 percent for every doubling in accumulated volume. From 1966 to 1972 constant-dollar price decreased at a rate of 70 percent for every doubling in accumulated volume. The "knee" in the curve starting at about 1966 is a typical unstable pattern. It indicates a large enough differential between price and cost to attract new production facilities. Both old and new producers find it attractive to build. Each company does its own evaluation and to achieve economy of scale may decide to build a large processing plant. It is not unusual to find a number of plants coming on stream at the same time. When this happens, price drops. Had price decreased at a higher rate, this instability might have been avoided and the drastic price decline between 1967 and 1971 might not have occurred. Any situation in which price does not decline in accordance with cost will eventually show this instability. Methanol is a classic example. The trend since 1972 has been one of rising price. If one were to subtract raw-material costs from the price, the curve might be more similar to typical experience curves, showing continued down trend vs. accumulated volume.

6.1.3 End-Use Consumption Patterns

Methanol is one of the cheapest industrial chemicals, which makes it a very competitive intermediate building block. United States methanol consumption by end use is shown for several recent years in Table 6.4. Major end uses can be categorized into chemical intermediates, exports, solvents, and other direct uses. Exports are discussed in Sec. 6.1.5, and each of the other subcategories is discussed below.

Chemical intermediates account for the bulk of methanol consumption. The more important intermediates and their end uses are summarized in Table 6.5. By far the largest single end use for methanol is the production of formaldehyde, which accounts for 45 percent of methanol consumption. The thermosetting urea-formaldehyde and phenol-formaldehyde resins account for over half of formal-

Table 6.4 United States synthetic methanol consumption by end use (10^6 lb)

End use	1960	1965	1970	1973
Formaldehyde and inhibitor	825	990	1,320	2,844
Exports	191	396	132	824
Solvents	132	165	185	565
Dimethyl terephthalate (DMT)	66	112	145	435
Methyl halides	46	73	85	435
Methyl methacrylate	86	125	172	265
Methyl amines	59	112	165	232
Acetic acid	...	...	...	240
Miscellaneous	555	700	766	1,288
Total	1,960	2,673	2,970	7,128

dehyde consumption. These resins are used mostly as adhesives in plywood and particleboard manufacture, which is tied to the fortunes of the housing industry.

Dimethyl terephthalate (DMT) is used almost exclusively as an intermediate in the production of polyester fibers and films. This use of methanol is dependent upon the fortunes of the textile industry. Moreover, there is a recent trend toward substituting terephthalic acid (TPA) for DMT in polyester manufacturing, which could seriously limit this need for methanol.

Tetramethyllead is used entirely as an additive to automotive gasoline and is in danger of being phased out.

Table 6.5 Major derivatives of methanol

Derivative and process	End uses of derivative	U.S. consumption %	Major final demand
Formaldehyde $CH_3OH \longrightarrow HCHO + H_2$ or $CH_3OH + \frac{1}{2}O_2 \longrightarrow HCHO + H_2O$	Urea-formaldehyde resins Phenol-formaldehyde resins Acetal resins Pentaerythritol Hexamethylenetetramine Melamine-formaldehyde resins Miscellaneous and export	30 24 9 6 6 4 21	Adhesives in plywood and particleboard manufacture
Dimethyl terephthalate (DMT) Esterification of terephthalic acid or Hercules-Witten Process	Polyester fibers Polyester film Export	88 7 5	Textiles
Methyl chloride $CH_3OH + HCl \longrightarrow CH_3Cl + H_2O$	Silicones Tetramethyllead Miscellaneous	38 38 24	Gasoline additive
Methyl methacrylate Acetone cyanohydrin process	Acrylic sheet Surface-coating resins Molding and extrusion powders Oil additives Miscellaneous and export	45 23 21 5 6	Lucite, Plexiglas, and automotive paints

Methyl methacrylate, known commercially as Lucite and Plexiglas, has outstanding optical properties as blocks or sheets. Its use as an important automobile paint is declining.

Acetic acid is used mostly in making cellulose acetate and vinyl acetate. Cellulose acetate is static in growth because of competition from the wholly synthetic fibers.

Industrial solvent use of methanol includes extracting, drying, washing, and crystallizing operations, in which methanol has had the advantage of being available at low cost and high purities. In addition to its industrial uses, methanol is used as a solvent in inks, dyes, shellac, metal finishes, coated fabrics, and many other products.

Several direct uses of methanol have been significant in the past, e.g., use as an automotive antifreeze and as an aircraft-fuel additive, but both these uses claim only small amounts of present methanol consumption. Many direct uses have been suggested as potentially large markets for methanol in the future and will be discussed in Sec. 6.1.6.

6.1.4 Producers

There are presently 10 synthetic methanol producers in the United States. Most of these companies also produce methanol derivatives (Table 6.6). Nine produce formaldehyde. Du Pont, the largest methanol producer in the United States, produces most of the major methanol derivatives. Major plant-expansion plans currently under way include a new plant for Du Pont and a large (about 1.5 billion pounds per year) plant for Celanese.

Table 6.6 United States synthetic-methanol producers

Company	Total capacity, 10^6 methanol lb/yr	Formal-dehyde	DMT	Methyl chloride	Methyl amines	Methyl methacrylate	Acetic acid
Air Products and Chemicals	332				x		
Borden Chemical	1,061	x					x
Celanese	1,923	x					
Commercial Solvents	332	x			x		
Du Pont	2,088	x	x	x	x	x	
Georgia-Pacific	663	x					
Hercules	663	x	x				
Monsanto	663	x					x
Rohm & Haas	146	x				x	
Tenneco	530	x					

Source: "Chemical Economics Handbook," SRI International, Menlo Park, Calif.

6.1.5 International Aspects

The United States is the world's largest methanol producer:

Area	Methanol production, 1973, 10^9 lb
United States	7.1
Western Europe	5.7
Japan	2.6

United States exports of methanol often exceed the volume of other uses, as shown by Table 6.4. Foreign markets for methanol have been particularly important for United States producers during domestic oversupply periods such as 1971 to 1973. The largest customers for United States methanol have been Canada, western Europe, and Latin America. Imports have been large enough to merit attention only in times of extreme domestic undersupply, mostly because of high United States import tariffs on methanol (15.3 cents per gallon before 1968; 7.6 cents per gallon in 1976).

Japan is the world's second largest methanol-producing country. Before 1969 most of Japan's methanol capacity was in small uncompetitive plants, but they have now been phased out and replaced by large complexes for methanol production. In fact, Japanese firms have been extremely aggressive in investigating joint-venture possibilities in the Middle East to build megaton methanol plants. These plants would use the readily available Middle East natural gas to feed methanol plants of capacities as high as 40 to 70 million pounds per day.

Other world areas having major methanol capacities include Canada, western Europe, Latin America, and the U.S.S.R.

6.1.6 Future Prospects

To evaluate the future prospects for methanol it is necessary to examine potentially large new markets for methanol, growth of, and threats to, traditional methanol markets, and potential process innovations for methanol production.

Potentially large new markets for methanol There are several possibilities of large new methanol markets including:

1. Use as direct fuel or as fuel feedstock
2. Use in sewage-treatment applications
3. Use as a substrate for fermentation production of animal-feed protein
4. Use in the reduction of iron ore in the production of steel

The most promising of these are use as fuel or fuel feedstock and in steel production.

Table 6.7 Methanol versus gasoline as a fuel

	Btu/gal	Cents/gal†	Dollars per 10^9 Btu (approximate)
Methanol	64,500	45	$7.03
Gasoline	124,800	35	2.80
Ratio of methanol to gasoline (use as auto fuel)	0.52	1.3	2.50

† Before tax, transportation, and marketing.

The greatest fuel potential appears to be as an automobile fuel. Recent studies have indicated that conventional engines could operate on methanol with only slight modifications. Several important factors to be considered when studying this possibility are summarized in Table 6.7. Methanol permits higher compression ratios and lesser than stoichiometric fuel-air operation compared with gasoline, and thus has been reported to be as high as 45 percent more efficient on an energy basis.[1] On a cost basis, methanol is currently 45 cents per gallon compared with gasoline at about 35 cents per gallon at the refinery (before taxes, transportation, and marketing). The big disadvantage of methanol as auto fuel is that it contains about half the energy of gasoline on a volume basis. Thus, even though methanol allows more efficient operation, a car would have to carry 60 to 70 percent more fuel than with gasoline to travel the same distance. Methanol currently costs about twice as much as gasoline for traveling the same distance and is not now competitive. Since the major raw material for methanol is natural gas and refinery off-gas, any increase in the price for oil and gas will bring increases in the price of methanol.

Methanol has two additional disadvantages with respect to gasoline. It causes corrosion problems in metals and ruins plastics now used in fuel distribution and car fuel systems. Methanol and water are soluble, and the water always present in today's fuel-distribution system can extract the methanol from methanol-gasoline blends, producing an unusable two-phase mixture. In an attempt to overcome these two problems, Mobil Corporation has built and successfully operated a pilot plant producing a good grade gasoline from methanol. The process consumes about 2.4 gal of methanol to make 1 gal of gasoline. The company is considering commercial operation of a methanol-to-gasoline plant in New Zealand. At a projected capital cost of $200 million, the plant would have a capacity of 110 million gallons per year of motor fuel.

Production of methane from methanol has also been given consideration. Such a process could be used to recover natural gas that has been converted into methanol on site in the Middle East or the north slopes of Alaska. Of course, the conversion energy losses and necessary capital investment in going from natural

[1] *Fortune*, September 1975, p. 153.

gas to methanol to methane would have to be economically justified by savings in transport or handling costs. Methanol (CH_3OH) is "half water" compared with hydrocarbons $[(CH_2)_n]$ like liquefied natural gas, and hauling water can be expensive.

Methanol-driven gas turbines at electric power plants have been receiving considerable attention. Tests using such turbines have shown that methanol lowers nitrogen oxide emissions, compared with conventional fuels, and also lowers maintenance costs. Turbine fuel use of methanol as a "chemical flywheel" may become particularly attractive if electric companies begin using gasified coal for fuel. The methanol would be produced during off-peak hours, when demand for the coal gas for generating electricity is low. The methanol would then be stored and used to power the turbines during peak loads. This would allow steady operation and efficient utilization of the coal-gasification plant.

Growth of, and threats to, traditional methanol markets As the United States economy rebounds from the recession of 1974 to 1975, methanol production should recover from its depressed production level of 1975. Methanol output in the United States has been forecast to grow at the rate of 6 to 10 percent per year through 1978. Fastest growing of the methanol markets may be its use in acetic acid production by the newly developed Monsanto process. However, the declining cellulose acetate market is a serious concern. Formaldehyde is tied to the phenolic and urea thermosetting-resins market, a very static market tied to the housing industry. DMT is tied to the rapidly growing polyester market but is in danger of being phased out by TPA. Polymethyl methacrylate is an expensive plastic for premium use for its optical properties. Some of these end uses are slated for above-average growth. Solvent use and methyl halide production should show moderate rates of growth. Markets for methanol derivatives, such as methyl chloride, used in tetramethyllead production, will probably decline.

Potential process innovations for methanol production Future process innovations for making methanol will focus mostly on new sources of raw materials. Several potentially large sources of hydrogen and carbon monoxide for methanol production have been suggested:

1. Coal gasification
2. Agricultural, wood, and municipal-waste gasification
3. Carbon monoxide from the off-gas of basic oxygen furnaces in steel mills
4. Partial oxidation of heavy petroleum feedstocks

6.2 SELECTED CHEMICALS, PLASTICS, AND FIBERS: BASIC DATA

This section provides basic information concerning methods of manufacture, production history, price history, consumption patterns (Table 6.10), and major producers (Table 6.11) for ten organic chemicals, three inorganic chemicals, two plastics, and three types of fibers. Ethylene, propylene, butadiene, toluene, benzene, and xylenes were chosen because they are the basic building blocks of most of the organic chemical industry. Ethylene oxide, ethylene dichloride, ethylbenzene, and ethanol were chosen for discussion to show how one basic building block, ethylene, is connected to intermediates and final demand. Polypropylene is included as a contrast to polyethylene. The remaining chemicals in the inorganics, plastics, and fibers groups were chosen on the basis of their prominence within their group. The annual United States production is given in Figs. 6.6 to 6.12. Prices (Figs. 6.13 to 6.17) are average unit sales price unless otherwise stated.

6.2.1 Methods of Manufacture: Organics

Only processes which dominate the industry are discussed.

Ethylene *Reaction* Steam cracking of natural gas or petroleum fractions. Most ethylene in the United States is made from ethane and propane recovered from refinery gases or from natural gases:

$$C_2H_6 \longrightarrow C_2H_4 + H_2$$

$$2C_3H_8 \longrightarrow C_2H_4 + H_2 + C_3H_6 + CH_4$$

About 15 percent of ethylene (1970, United States) is made from cracking gas oils or naphtha. Product distribution depends on the raw material used and the severity of reaction conditions. Typical for various feeds are the figures shown in Table 6.8.

Ethylene oxide *Reaction* Oxidation of ethylene

$$CH_2{=}CH_2 + \tfrac{1}{2}O_2 \xrightarrow{\text{Ag}} CH_2{-}CH_2$$
$$\underset{O}{\diagdown\diagup}$$

Reaction is accomplished at pressures of about 10 to 30 atm and 270 to 290°C over a silver catalyst using either air or oxygen. In addition to ethylene oxide, carbon dioxide is formed by the competing reaction

$$C_2H_4 + 3O_2 \longrightarrow 2CO_2 + 2H_2O$$

Table 6.8 Ethylene feed stocks

Product	Ethane, %	Propane, %	Naphthas, %	Heavy gas oil, %
Ethylene	76.3	42.0	31.2	23.4
Propylene	2.9	16.2	16.1	14.3
Butadiene	1.3	3.2	4.5	4.0
Butylene, butane	0.6	1.4	4.5	4.4
C_5 and greater	2.8	7.2	26.5	43.9
Off-gas	16.1	30.0	17.2	10.0

Per pass conversion of ethylene is typically 30 percent. Selectivity, defined as (ethylene converted to ethylene oxide)/(ethylene reacted), is between 70 and 80 percent. A variety of reactor systems are used.

Ethylene dichloride *Reaction* Vapor or liquid-phase catalytic reaction of ethylene and chlorine:

$$CH_2 = CH_2 + Cl_2 \longrightarrow ClCH_2CH_2Cl$$

A common catalyst is ethylene dibromide, although a variety of catalysts have been used.

Ethylbenzene *Reaction* Over 90 percent produced by the alkylation of benzene with ethylene:

$$C_6H_6 + CH_2 = CH_2 \longrightarrow C_6H_5CH_2CH_3$$

Overall yields of over 99 percent are achieved. Reaction is either in the liquid phase, using aluminum chloride catalyst, or in the vapor phase, using a boron trifluoride catalyst. Ethylbenzene can also be recovered by fractionation of some gasoline or naphtha fractions. Large distillation columns are required, with as many as 300 plates. Less than 10 percent of current ethylbenzene production is by this method.

Synthetic ethanol *Reaction* Over 80 percent is produced by catalytic hydration of ethylene:

$$CH_2 = CH_2 + H_2O \longrightarrow C_2H_5OH$$

Reaction takes place over a phosphoric acid catalyst. Per pass conversion in the reactor is low. Reaction conditions are typically 330°C and 60 atm. Extensive separation and purification operations are needed. Overall system yield of ethanol is commonly 95 percent.

Propylene *Reaction* Steam cracking of natural gas or petroleum fractions; usually it is a by-product of ethylene production (see ethylene, above).

Butadiene *Reaction* Dehydrogenation of *n*-butane obtained from natural gas or oil refineries:

$$C_4H_{10} \longrightarrow C_4H_8 + H_2$$
$$C_4H_8 \longrightarrow CH_2 = CHCH = CH_2 + H_2$$

Reaction takes place over a chromia-alumina catalyst at 600 to 620°C and 150 mmHg. Increasingly important is butadiene, recovered as a by-product of ethylene production. This route is expected to increase in importance as heavier petroleum feedstocks are used to make ethylene.

Toluene *Reaction* Catalytic reforming of selected petroleum fractions rich in naphthenes. A typical reaction is

$$C_6H_{11}CH_3 \longrightarrow C_6H_5CH_3 + 3H_2$$

Dimethylcyclopentane, methylcyclohexane, and ethylcyclopentane are converted into toluene. Other naphthenes, such as cyclohexane and dimethylcyclohexane, are converted into benzene and xylene, respectively. Average distribution of these aromatics might be benzene, 10 percent; toluene 40 percent; and xylene 50 percent. Several processes, varying in design, catalyst, and operating conditions, are used. Typical is a 10 percent molybdenum oxide on alumina catalyst and reaction conditions of 535 to 575°C and 10 to 20 atm.

Benzene *Reaction* Coproduct of catalytic re-forming of selected petroleum streams rich in naphthenes (see toluene, above). Also important is hydro-dealkylation of toluene:

$$C_6H_5CH_3 + H_2 \longrightarrow C_6H_6 + CH_4$$

Both catalytic and thermal dealkylation processes are used.

Xylenes *Reaction* Coproduct of catalytic re-forming of selected petroleum streams rich in naphthenes (see toluene, above). Separation of the xylene stream into para, meta, and ortho isomers can be accomplished by several methods, e.g., fractional crystallization.

6.2.2 Methods of Manufacture: Inorganics

Only methods which dominate the industry are discussed.

Sulfuric acid *Reaction* Oxidation of sulfur dioxide by air to sulfur trioxide and adsorption of the SO_3 in water (*contact process*):

$$2SO_2 + O_2 \longrightarrow 2SO_3$$
$$SO_3 + H_2O \longrightarrow H_2SO_4$$

Oxidation takes place over a vanadium pentoxide catalyst at temperatures ranging from 400 to 600°C (temperature varies along the length of the reactor) and atmospheric pressure. Overall sulfur trioxide yield is approximately 97 percent. The sulfur trioxide is then sent to an oleum tower, and the remaining gas from this tower is sent to a second tower for scrubbing by 97% H_2SO_4. Sulfuric acid plants typically yield from 100 to 5,000 tons/day. The sulfur dioxide for reaction is usually obtained by burning elemental sulfur or by roasting iron pyrites. However, waste-gas streams from metallurgical plants, oil refineries, and other sources can also provide feed sulfur dioxide.

Ammonia *Reaction* Catalytic reaction of nitrogen and hydrogen:

$$N_2 + 3H_2 \longrightarrow 2NH_3$$

Reaction takes place over an iron oxide promoted catalyst at high temperatures and pressures (400 to 600°C; 130 to 650 atm). Nitrogen is obtained by air liquefaction, the *producer-gas reaction*, or by removing oxygen from air by burning with hydrogen to leave nitrogen behind. Hydrogen is obtained by cracking natural gas or refinery gases in ways similar to those used to obtain hydrogen for methanol manufacture. Typical new plants have capacities in the neighborhood of 1,000 short tons per day.

Chlorine *Reaction* About 95 percent of all chlorine is produced by the electrolysis of salt:

$$2NaCl + 2H_2O \xrightarrow[\text{current}]{\text{direct}} Cl_2 + 2NaOH + H_2$$

Direct current flows through a cell of salt solution to give the chlorine at the anode. Two different kinds of cells, the mercury-cathode and the diaphragm, are used. This process also provides the major method of producing sodium hydroxide. The hydrogen by-product may be reacted with the chlorine to make hydrochloric acid, used on site for making other chemicals, or burned.

6.2.3 Methods of Manufacture: Plastics

Only methods which dominate the industry are discussed.

Polyethylene *Reaction* Addition polymerization of ethylene:

$$nCH_2 {=} CH_2 \longrightarrow (-CH_2-CH_2-)_n$$

Low-density polyethylene (LDPE; $\rho = 0.92$ g/cm^3) is made continuously by a high-pressure (1,200-atm) process at temperatures of about 200°C. Yield per pass through the reactor is about 25 percent. Unreacted ethylene is recycled to the reactor. Overall yield is approximately 95 percent. High-density polyethylene (HDPE; $\rho = 0.97$ g/cm^3) is produced by a low-pressure–low-temperature suspension polymerization (Ziegler-Natta process), using a triethylaluminum–titanium tetrachloride catalyst.

Polypropylene *Reaction* Addition polymerization of propylene:

$$nCH_2 {=} CH_2 {-} CH_3 \longrightarrow \left[-CH_2 - \overset{\overset{\textstyle CH_3}{|}}{CH_2} - \right]_n$$

The Ziegler process is used. Reaction takes place in the presence of a triakyl-aluminum–titanium tetrachloride catalyst at approximately 3 atm pressure and 70°C.

6.2.4 Methods of Manufacture: Fibers

Only methods which dominate the industry are discussed.

Polyester fibers *Reaction* Ester interchange of ethylene glycol with dimethyl terephthalate followed by condensation polymerization of the intermediate:

$$\underset{\text{COOCH}_3}{\overset{\text{COOCH}_3}{\bigcirc}} + 2\,\text{HOCH}_2\text{CH}_2\text{OH} \longrightarrow$$

$$\underset{\text{COOCH}_2\text{CH}_2\text{OH}}{\overset{\text{COOCH}_2\text{CH}_2\text{OH}}{\bigcirc}} + 2\,\text{CH}_3\text{OH} \longrightarrow \left[-\text{OOC}\bigcirc\text{COOCH}_2\text{CH}_2- \right]_n$$

This route accounts for most polyester manufacture. However, the direct polyesterification of ethylene glycol with terephthalic acid is becoming important:

$$\underset{\text{COOH}}{\overset{\text{COOH}}{\bigcirc}} + \text{HOCH}_2\text{CH}_2\text{OH} \longrightarrow$$

$$\left[-\text{OOC}\bigcirc\text{COOCH}_2\text{CH}_2- \right]_n + 2\,\text{H}_2\text{O}$$

Melt spinning transforms the bulk polyester into fiber.

Nylon fibers *Reaction* Industrial routes to nylon are complex, involving several intermediate steps. Nylon 6 and nylon 66, the two types made in the United States, start from phenol, cyclohexane, and toluene. The reaction sequences used for both are shown in Table 6.9. Molten nylon is transformed into fiber by melt-spinning and stretching operations.

Acrylic fibers *Reaction* Free-radical or anionic polymerization of acrylonitrile:

$$n\text{CH}_2=\text{CH}-\text{CN} \longrightarrow \left[-\text{CH}_2-\overset{|}{\text{CH}}-\text{CN} \right]_n$$

Reaction is usually a suspension or solution-polymerization process. The polymer can be either dry- or wet-spun and subjected to stretching processes to produce fiber.

Table 6.9 Industrial routes to nylon

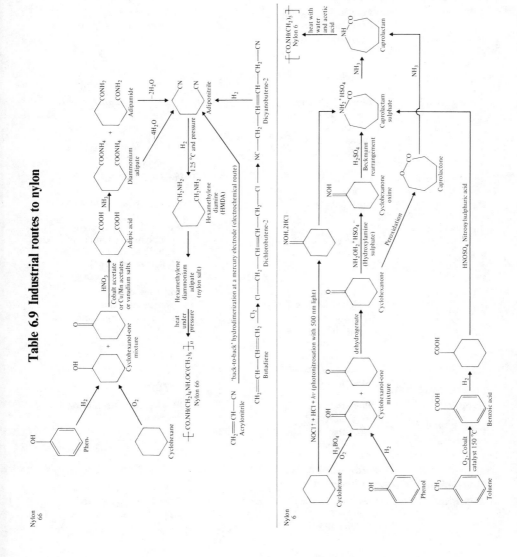

195

Table 6.10 Consumption patterns, 1975

Chemical	Consumption pattern, %		Final demand
Ethylene	Polyethylene	40	Plastics, fibers,
	Ethylene oxide	20	antifreeze, tires
	Ethylene dichloride	14	
	Ethylbenzene	8	
	Ethanol	6	
	Miscellaneous	12	
Ethylene oxide	Ethylene glycol	60	Polyesters, antifreeze,
	Surface-active		
	agents	13	detergents
	Ethanolamines	9	
	Miscellaneous	18	
Ethylene dichloride	Vinyl chloride	77	Polyvinyl chloride
	Exports	8	
	Miscellaneous	15	
Ethylbenzene	Styrene	95.5	Polystyrene, polystyrene
	Solvent	2	copolymers (styrene-butadiene
	Export	2.5	rubber and acrylonitrile-butadiene-styrene)
Ethanol	Chemical manufacture	26	Toiletries, cosmetics,
	Toiletries and cosmetics	20	pharmaceuticals,
	Acetaldehyde	14	surface coatings, adhesives
	Industrial solvents and thinners	12	
	Detergents, flavors, and disinfectants	10	
	Miscellaneous	18	
Propylene	Polypropylene	23	Plastics, solvents, fabrics,
	Acrylonitrile	16	adhesives
	Isopropanol	14	
	Propylene oxide	13	
	Cumene	11	
	Oxo chemicals	8	
	Miscellaneous	15	
Butadiene	Styrene-butadiene rubber	47	Tires, other rubber and plastics products
	Polybutadiene rubber	17	
	Adiponitrile	8	
	Neoprene	8	
	Acrylonitrilebutadiene-styrene resins	6	
	Nitrile rubber	3	
	Miscellaneous	11	

Table 6.10 (*continued*)

Chemical	Consumption pattern, %		Final demand
Toluene	Benzene	51	Plastics, fabrics, tires,
	Solvents	10	rubber products,
	Explosives	9	explosives
	Isocyanates	5	
	Phenol	1	
	Gasoline and miscellaneous	24	
Benzene	Styrene	48	Plastics, fibers, tires,
	Phenol	20	rubber products
	Cyclohexane	17	
	Nitrobenzene	5	
	Maleic anhydride	3	
	Miscellaneous and export	7	
o-Xylene	Phthalic hydride	33	Fabrics, plastics
	Exports and miscellaneous	67	
p-Xylene	DMT	61	Fabrics, plastics
	TPA	18	
	Exports	21	
Sulfuric acid	Phosphate fertilizers	38	Used mostly by industry
	Petroleum refining	8	in producing a wide
	Ammonium sulfate	7	variety of products
	Alcohols	7	
	Titanium dioxide	5	
	Iron and steel pickling	3	
	Explosives	2.5	
	Aluminum sulfate	2	
	Other chemicals	8	
	Batteries	0.5	
	Miscellaneous	19	
Ammonia	Fertilizers and feeds	76	Fertilizers, fibers, plastics,
	Fiber and plastics		coating resins,
	intermediates	9	explosives
	Explosives	4	
	Other	11	
Chlorine	Chlorinated hydrocarbons	59	Plastics, solvents, aerosols,
	Pulp and paper	18	water and sewage treatment,
	Inorganic chemicals	11	paper production
	Water and sewage	6	
	Miscellaneous	6	

(*continued*)

Table 6.10 (*continued*)

Chemical	Consumption pattern, %		Final demand
Polyethylene:			
LDPE	Film	55	Trash bags, industrial liners,
	Extrusion coating	9	shipping bags,
	Wire and cable coating	8	food packaging,
	Exports	7	paper, paperboard, foil
	Other	21	coatings,
			wire and cable coatings
HDPE	Pipe and conduit	12	Milk containers, pipe and
	Wire and cable coating	3	conduit, housewares
	Housewares	10	
	Containers	40	
	Toys	4	
	Exports	8	
	Other	23	
Polypropylene	Filament and fiber	32	Appliances, electrical wire
	Housewares	5	and cable,
	Appliances	5	luggage, housewares,
	Transportation uses, e.g.,		blow-molded bottles,
	battery cases	13	closures, food packaging,
	Packaging	15	toys and novelties,
	Exports	10	transportation uses
	Other	20	
Polyester fibers	Apparel	64	
	Carpets and rugs	6	
	Tire cord	8	
	Fiber fill	6	
	Sheets and pillowcases	6	
	Other	10	
Nylon fibers	Carpets and rugs	43	
	Apparel	24	
	Tire cord	16	
	Exports	5	
	Other	12	
Acrylic fibers	Apparel	58	
	Carpets and rugs	19	
	Blankets	5	
	Exports	14	
	Miscellaneous	4	

Source: Data from *Chem. Eng. News;* "Chemical Economics Handbook," SRI International, Menlo Park, Calif.; U.S. Bureau of the Census, *Statistical Abstract of the United States;* and other sources.

Table 6.11 Major producers in the United States

Chemical	Top four†	Approximate concentration ratio (top four), %‡
Ethylene	Dow Chemical Gulf Oil Shell Chemical Union Carbide	50–60
Ethylene oxide	Dow Chemical Jefferson Chemical PPG Industries Union Carbide	60–70
Ethylene dichloride	Continental Oil Dow Chemical B. F. Goodrich Shell Chemical	50–60
Ethylbenzene	Amoco Chemicals Dow Chemical Foster Grant Monsanto	50–60
Synthetic ethanol	Exxon Publicker Industries Shell Chemical Union Carbide	70–80
Propylene	Exxon Dow Chemical Shell Chemical Union Carbide	40–50
Butadiene	Exxon Neches Butane Petro-Tex Chemical Union Carbide	50–60
Toluene	Amoco Exxon Phillips Petroleum Sun Oil	35–45
Benzene	Amoco Exxon Commonwealth Petrochemical Phillips Petroleum	30–40
Xylenes	Amoco Exxon Sun Oil Chevron Chemical	40–50
Sulfuric acid	Allied Chemical CF Industries (Coop) Du Pont Stauffer Chemical	25–35

(*continued*)

Table 6.11 (*continued*)

Chemical	Top four†	Approximate concentration ratio (top four), %‡
Ammonia	Allied Chemical CF Industries (Coop) Farmland Industries (Coop) Standard Oil of California	20–30
Chlorine	Dow Chemical Diamond Shamrock PPG Industries Occidental Petroleum	50–60
Polyethylene	Union Carbide Dow Du Pont Gulf Oil	40–50
Polypropylene	Hercules Amoco Exxon Shell	70–80
Polyester fibers	Du Pont Eastman Kodak Fiber Industries Hoechst Fibers	70–80
Nylon fibers	Du Pont Fiber Industries§ Fibers International Monsanto	85–95
Acrylic fibers	American Cyanamid Dow Badische Du Pont Monsanto	90–95

† Subject to change as the market shifts.
‡ Included in these figures are production capacities in Puerto Rico of United States subsidiaries.
§ Subsidiary of Celanese.

6.2.5 Production histories

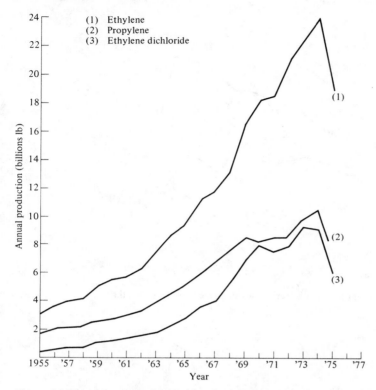

Figure 6.6 United States production histories for ethylene, propylene, and ethylene dichloride.

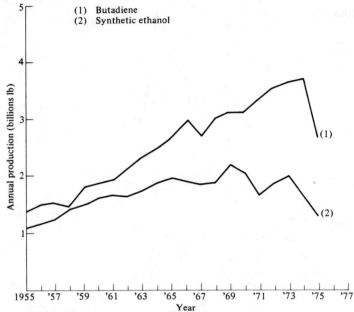

Figure 6.7 United States production histories for butadiene and synthetic ethanol.

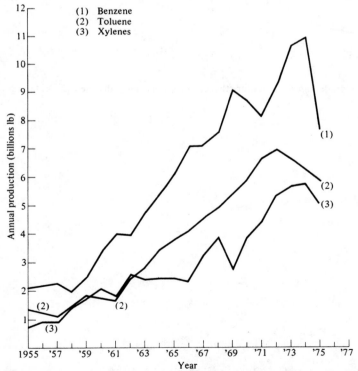

Figure 6.8 United States production histories for benzene, toluene, and xylenes.

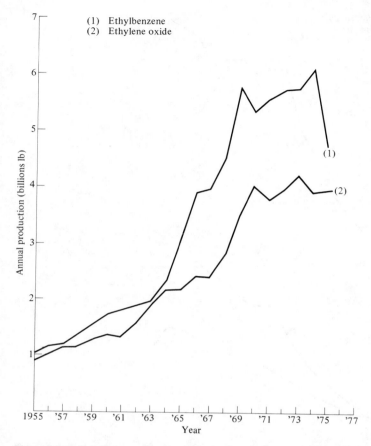

Figure 6.9 United States production histories for ethylbenzene and ethylene oxide.

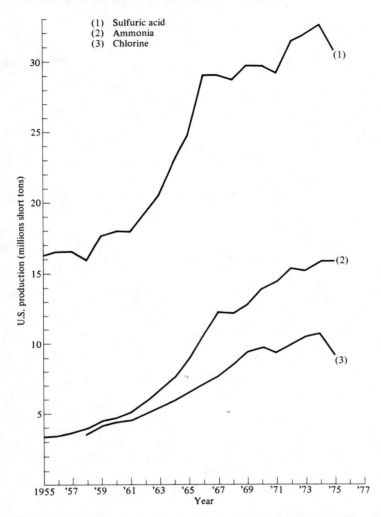

Figure 6.10 United States production histories for sulfuric acid, ammonia, and chlorine.

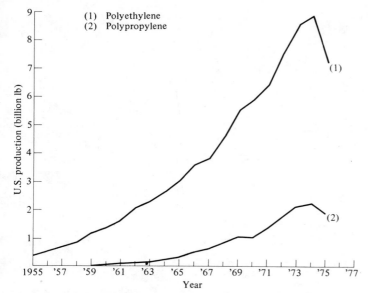

Figure 6.11 United States production histories for polyethylene and polypropylene.

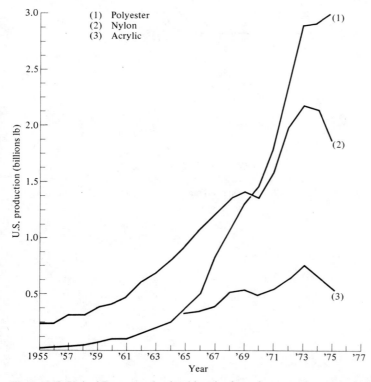

Figure 6.12 United States production histories for polyester, nylon, and acrylic fibers.

6.2.6 Price histories

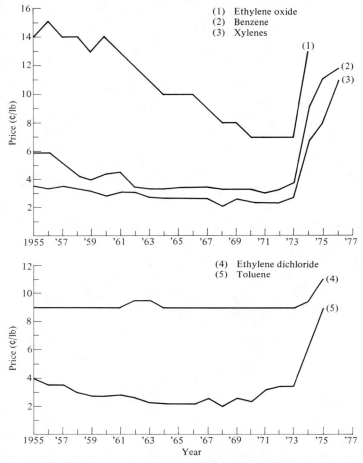

Figure 6.13 Price histories for ethylene oxide, benzene, xylenes, ethylene dichloride, and toluene.

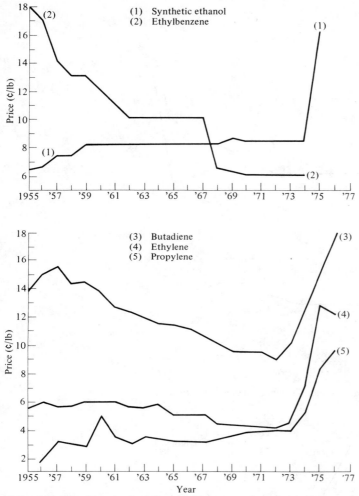

Figure 6.14 Price histories for ethanol, ethylbenzene, butadiene, ethylene, and propylene.

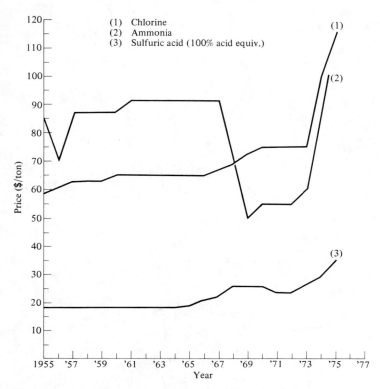

Figure 6.15 Price histories for chlorine, ammonia, and sulfuric acid.

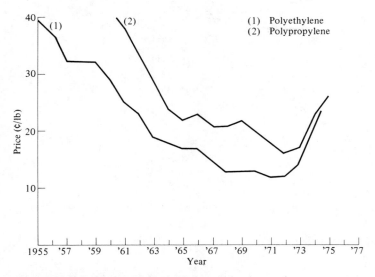

Figure 6.16 Price histories for polyethylene and polypropylene.

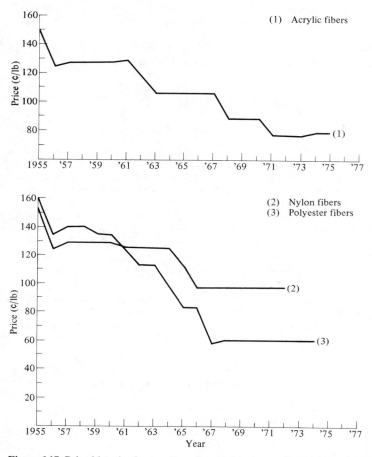

Figure 6.17 Price histories for acrylic, nylon, and polyester fibers, apparel staple, 3.0 denier.

6.3 QUESTIONS FOR DISCUSSION

1 Compare the growth rate in methanol production between 1950 and 1968 with the growth rate over the same period for (*a*) sulfuric acid, (*b*) benzene, and (*c*) synthetic ethanol.

2 Which of the sectors in Table 4.4 would have the greatest effect on methanol production if their final demand changed by 10 percent?

3 List four reasons why it is better to make gasoline from methanol than to develop a system permitting methanol to be used directly as a fuel.

4 What general pattern do all the production histories presented in this chapter show? Which chemical products seem to show different trends? Suggest reasons for the different behavior.

5 Which four of all the chemical products shown have the highest growth rate from 1957 to 1971? Suggest reasons for this in terms of final consumer demand.

6 What general pattern do the price histories show? Which ones seem to show unusual trends? Suggest reasons for their behavior.

7 Which five chemicals have the highest concentration ratios? What are the reasons for this? Which chemical products can you identify which would have a concentration ratio of 100 percent and only one company?

8 Why did most chemicals suffer a drop in production after 1973, together with a price increase? Would the firms manufacturing these chemicals experience an increase or decrease in revenue and profit?

6.4 PROBLEMS

6.1 The Key Chemicals section of *Chem. Eng. News*, Jan. 31, 1977, devotes a page to methanol which is worth reading, as are The Clean Synthetic Fuel That's Already Here (*Fortune*, September 1975), Methanol (*Chem. Week*, September 1975), and Methanol the "New" Fuel from Coal (*CHEMTECH*, January 1974). Read at least two of these articles and summarize their conclusions in one or two paragraphs.

6.2 Compare the latent heat, heat of combustion, and octane number of ethanol with the values for methanol in Table 6.1. What is the price of ethanol in dollars per million Btu (compare with methanol at $7 per million Btu)? What are the important methods of manufacture for ethanol? Who are the five leading producers? How many of these also produce methanol?

6.3 Prepare an experience curve for ethanol using the same format as Fig. 6.5. Compare the behavior of these two chemicals and write a paragraph of discussion.

6.4 Did a number of new producers enter the methanol business in 1966, or did old producers expand capacity? What size plants were built? How could the drastic price decline have been prevented?

6.5 A study presented at the Engineering Foundation Conference, 1974, estimated methanol's worldwide potential in 1980 as follows (t stands for metric tons):

	Worldwide methanol consumption, t/day	
Use	1970	1980
Chemical use	25,000	50,000
Feedstock for substitute natural gas	0	57,600
Gas turbines	0	53,000
Animal protein production	0	33,000
Boiler fuel	0	42,900
Gasoline substitute	0	13,000
Gasoline additive	0	762
Total (maximum)	25,000	250,262

Source: J. Tourtellotte, S. Bangiorno, D. Shah, *Eng. Found. Conf., New England College, Henniker, N.H., 1974.*

Does this predicted *consumption* seem reasonable? How long does it take to build a processing unit to make SNG or protein from methanol? Where would these plants be built? Who would supply that capital? How much time is needed to convert a substantial number of cars from gasoline to methanol? To ethanol? How many cars would consume 13,000 t of methanol? How could the table be made more realistic? Do not do any research; base your changes on what you already know.

6.6 Another estimate of world methanol demand is shown below. If you had an opportunity to interview the people who prepared this estimate, what questions would you ask?

Use	1985 world methanol demand, t/day	
	Low estimate	High estimate
Steel industry	223,500	287,000
Motor fuel	30,000	241,600
Fuel (turbines, etc.)	15,100	45,300
Ammonia synthesis	12,100	15,100
Protein production	7,500	15,100
Total	288,200	604,100

Source: Bureau d'Études Industrielles et de Coopération, Paris, 1975.

6.7 Coal gasification to produce methanol has been a subject of considerable debate. As currently envisioned, fuel-grade methanol containing small amounts of higher alcohols and other impurities would be produced. A coal-based methanol plant to produce 10 million pounds per day of methanol is estimated to cost $575 million (1975 dollars). Depending on the cost of coal, the project is projected to sell methanol in the neighborhood of 41 to 63 cents per gallon (1975 figures, U.S. Bureau of Mines). Is this selling price reasonable, given today's fuel costs? Compare dollar costs per million Btu to obtain your answer.

6.8 Examine the production and price histories of the chemical products discussed in Sec. 6.2 and identify the part of the life cycle that each product was in during 1963 to 1965.

6.9 Divide the experience curve for methanol into spring, summer, fall, and winter periods.

6.10 Identify five chemical products that are clearly in the spring of their life cycles. Identify 10 products that are in the winter of their life cycles. How many of these are likely to be replaced within the next decade?

6.11 Plot production histories for rayon, cellophane, and DDT. What is the general pattern? Contrast and compare with the production histories in this chapter and give reasons for the difference.

6.12 Plot the production history of natural ethanol since about 1930 and compare with the synthetic ethanol history.

6.13 Using the data in this chapter, prepare an experience curve using the format of Fig. 6.5 for (*a*) ethylene oxide, (*b*) nylon, and (*c*) polyester fibers.

6.14 A product with price–quantity-produced characteristics putting it in the lower left-hand part of Fig. 5.4 (to the left of the straight line) can be classified as having *unfulfilled potential.* (At that selling price there should be a greater quantity produced.) Try to identify two such products by searching the appropriate sources for *p* and *Q*. What markets must these products penetrate to fulfill their potential?

6.15 There are a number of products to the upper right-hand side of the line in Fig. 5.4. Such products can be termed *vulnerable* since they seem to be selling at a higher price than might be warranted. Identify five such products and explain why they are selling at this higher price. What would happen if a suitable substitute product were found?

6.16 Fairly detailed histories of the development of processes for the manufacture of various chemicals are presented in " Chemistry in the Economy " (see Sec. I.1.2). Read three histories and summarize in a short report.

Before answering Probs. 6.17 to 6.22 reread Sec. 2.1 to refresh your concept of the consumer's role. Reexamine the tables in Chap. 4 to refresh your memory about industrial sectors which play a key role in the CPI.

6.17 Suppose both the automobile industry and the housing industry increased sales by 20 percent.

Which of the products listed in this chapter would you expect to be affected in each case? Make a rough estimate of the percentage change in each.

6.18 Suppose food production had to be increased by 10 percent. Which of the products discussed would be affected? Estimate the quantitative change. Which other chemical products would be affected?

6.19 How would a 10 percent drop in final demand for clothing affect the chemical products in this chapter?

6.20 Calculate the concentration ratio (top four) for (a) computers, (b) automobiles, (c) tobacco, and (d) aluminum.

6.21 Compare the concentration ratios reported in this chapter with those reported for the following years and products:

Product	Year	Percent
Ethylene	1959	69
Butadiene	1960	50
Sulfuric acid	1961	40

Is there a trend?

6.22 Compute the approximate concentration ratio for the chemical industry as a whole. How does it compare with the numbers obtained in Prob. 6.20?

7

SPECIFIC COMPANIES

A company is reviewed by various groups according to different criteria.

Criterion 1 *Investors* ask three sets of questions. The first set is concerned with present performance. Is the company making money and paying a dividend? Is the price of the stock rising? Does the company have a good net income as measured by profit per dollar of sales, profit per dollar of owners' equity, and by profit per dollar of owners' equity plus long-term debt?

The second set of questions asked by investors concerns the security of the company against unexpected occurrences. Is the company heavily in debt, so that a business downturn will cause it grief? Could it run out of cash? Is it in trouble with the Security and Exchange Commission, the Justice Department Antitrust Division, the Environmental Protection Agency, the Occupational Safety and Health Agency, the Food and Drug Administration? Are its overseas properties about to be confiscated by foreign governments? Is Congress about to pass a law to curtail its activities or profitability?

The final set of questions concerns future performance. Are the gross sales and net income increasing smoothly and outpacing or at least keeping pace with the growth rates of population and GNP? Is there sufficient spending on research and development and on new plants and equipment, so that the company and its technology will not become obsolete? Is the company innovating, so that it will lead the rest of the industry and the economy? Does the firm have the proper portfolio of products to assure that its innovative products are supported by its mature, well-established products?

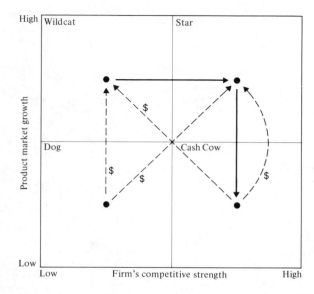

Figure 7.1 Classification of products.

Each product of the firm may be characterized by two parameters: the market growth potential of the product and competitive strength of the firm for that product. Each product occupies a point in Fig. 7.1, which is divided into four quadrants. A "wildcat" product is characterized by high growth potential but low competitive strength. This is a springlike time in the life cycle and requires that management put a great deal of cash into the project and pay considerable attention to it. If the wildcat product is supported generously enough, it will develop greater competitive strength and turn into a star. The star product is characterized by high growth and high competitive strength. Its rapid expansion into the marketplace and the need to build manufacturing facilities demands a heavy flow of capital to sustain its growth. Eventually, the growth of the star slows down to that of the "cash cow" product, characterized by a low growth and high competitive strength. This is a period when there is a large surplus of cash available which can be used to support other projects in the firm. The "dog" product is characterized by low growth and low competitive strength. It is sometimes a contributor of cash and may be kept; but more often it is a candidate for elimination from the portfolio so that funds can be released to finance other products.

A well-managed company, concerned about the future, should have a suitable mix of products in the various sectors. A company with too many wildcats and stars will have no source of cash to finance the many worthwhile projects that need support and growth. A company with too many cash cows and dogs will have plenty of cash on hand but an unexciting future. Very often, a large and stable company specializes in projects in the cash cow and dog positions and has cash available to acquire smaller venturesome companies that have good ideas but no cash.

Criterion 2 *Lenders* ask the same questions as the investors. In addition, lenders are particularly concerned about the company's ability to repay its debt on time—with interest. Lenders are most concerned with short-term cash positions, or liquidity, as measured by the ratio of current liabilities to current assets. They are also concerned with the ratio of cash flow (net income plus depreciation charges plus income tax) to interest on debts.

Criterion 3 *Employees* are concerned with some of the same questions as the investors and lenders. They also have special interest in salaries, occupational health, employment stability, and career opportunities. With less mobility than management, they may be opposed to plant relocations and new plant investment abroad. They may be more interested in salary increases than dividend payout.

Criterion 4 *Customers* are interested in a steady supply of the company's products along with increasing quality and decreasing price. They are also interested in new products, with superior " performance in use " to satisfy new needs and to replace older products.

Criterion 5 The *government* is concerned with taxes. In addition, the government is interested in making sure that the company conforms to regulations relating to pollution, occupational safety, and employee welfare. The government is also concerned with the general economic welfare of the nation—balance of trade with other nations, inflation, unemployment, and safety of the public. When reviewing an industry or a specific company, all these factors affect decisions of the government.

Criterion 6 The *public* is, in general, ambivalent to the needs of a large company. The public fears concentrated power that is self-serving and harmful to the general welfare. It is particularly concerned about product availability and price, encroachment on the rights of individuals, pollution of the environment, and depletion of nonrenewable resources.

In order to deal with the above concerns adequately, much data must be analyzed. This chapter is designed to give the reader basic data for several companies and an idea of how company data can be analyzed. Its format is similar to that of Chap. 6. Section 7.1 gives a detailed analysis of a specific company; Sec. 7.2 gives some basic facts for 10 additional CPI companies.

Air Products and Chemicals, Inc., is analyzed in detail in Sec. 7.1. The analysis answers many of the questions above as well as those posed in Sec. 0.2.2 in the discussion of company term papers. Air Products and Chemicals has been chosen for detailed analysis because it is a relatively new chemical firm whose history of high growth and future prospects are both excellent.

The companies chosen for background material in Sec. 7.3 include the top five United States chemical companies, two oil companies that have significant chemical operations and three medium-sized chemical companies. The section should provide the reader with a basis for understanding some of the similarities and differences of CPI companies. The information presented here will be referred to in future chapters. The short summaries presented in Sec. 7.2 provide a limited amount of information chosen to illustrate important characteristics of the companies. You are encouraged to broaden your knowledge of these and other CPI firms by analyzing pertinent information from numerous sources, including annual reports and form 10-K's. A listing of all chemical companies on the New York, American, and over-the-counter exchanges is provided in Appendix B.

7.1 A COMPANY REPORT: AIR PRODUCTS AND CHEMICALS, INC.

7.1.1 Summary

Air Products and Chemicals, Inc.,[1] was founded in 1940 by Leonard P. Pool to manufacture and sell oxygen generators. Today the company is a major producer of industrial, medical, and specialty gases and related equipment. The company also produces chemicals and provides engineering, construction, and maintenance services. The company's major products and operations can be summarized as follows:

Gas products. Oxygen, nitrogen, acetylene, argon, hydrogen, helium, carbon dioxide, and carbon monoxide
Chemicals. Polyvinyl chloride (PVC) resins, vinyl acetate emulsions, ammonia, alkyl amines, dinitrotoluene (DNT), toluenediamine (TDA), polyvinyl alcohols, methanol, nonenes, heptenes, catalysts, and acetylenic chemicals
Diversified technology and services. A wide variety of engineering, construction, contract maintenance, and related services for CPI and government agencies

Air Products and Chemicals has performed well in terms of sales and profitability in recent years (Table 7.1). Large new uses for gas products, a novel means of providing a commodity product to a customer via the on-site-production concept, rapid diversification of its product mix, and an aggressive use of financial leverage are among the factors contributing to the rapid growth of Air Products and Chemicals. From 1966 to 1975, the company's annual sales have grown at an average compounded rate of 17.3 percent to $699 million in fiscal 1975 (Table 7.2). Net income and earnings per share have grown equally fast. Profitability as measured by return on sales and return on shareholders' equity has been consistently higher than the chemical industry average.

---

[1] For the annual report and form 10-K write Manager of Investor Relations, Air Products and Chemicals, Inc., Allentown, Pa, 18105.

Table 7.1 Air Products and Chemicals: performance in recent years

Year	Net sales (millions)	Operating profit	Return on average shareholders' equity, %
1971	$307.7	$ 38.7	10.1
1972	351.2	42.8	10.3
1973	398.9	53.6	12.1
1974	562.6	87.9	17.3
1975	699.0	119.2	19.7

Source: 1975 company report.

Air Products and Chemicals has a stated policy of continued diversification and rapid growth. Management expects annual sales to surpass $1 billion by the late 1970s. Addition of qualified personnel, accelerated research and development spending, aggressive capital expenditure, continued expansion abroad, and a high percentage of net income retained for reinvestment are all indications that the company will probably continue to grow and prosper.

Table 7.2 Air Products and Chemicals: information summary

Income and balance-sheet statistics (Millions)

Year	Net sales	Net income	Long-term debt	Percentage net income of net sales
1966	$165.9	$10.6	$100.0	6.4
1970	261.4	15.0	130.1	5.7
1975	699.0	54.2	184.1	7.8

Additional statistics, 1975

Millions

Total assets	$776.3	Current ratio	1.29
Shareholders' equity	302.1	Long-term debt-to-equity ratio	0.61
Total liabilities	479.0	Return on equity, %	19.7
R & D spending	16.0	Number of employees	13,000

Major product group	Percentage of 1975 sales
Gases and equipment group, USA,	42
Europe	18
Chemicals group	37
Catalytic group	3

7.1.2 History

Air Products and Chemicals, Inc., was built on the success of a novel means of providing a commodity chemical. Before the Second World War, oxygen was produced at large-volume air-separation plants and shipped to customers as a compressed gas by rail, tube trailers, or in cylinders. The shipping costs contributed greatly to the product price. The founder of the company envisioned building on-site air-separation plants to provide oxygen at the customer's plant, thus eliminating the expensive shipping. Air Products was founded in 1940 to manufacture and lease or sell oxygen generators.

The military needs of the Second World War contributed to Air Products' early success by providing a market for some 240 of the company's oxygen- and nitrogen-generating plants. The company's annual sales grew from $8,295 in 1941 to about $5.25 million in 1945. However, upon termination of the war, the military market evaporated, leaving Air Products with essentially no customers.

In late 1945, the Weirton Steel Company contracted Air Products to build small on-site oxygen generators. In 1947 Weirton again enlisted Air Products to construct a 400 ton/day oxygen plant to provide low-purity oxygen for blast-furnace use. This oxygen plant was about 50 times larger than any oxygen plant previously built by Air Products, and when completed it provided about one-third of all the oxygen made in the United States. This feat established the company and its on-site concept firmly in the industrial-gas market, and substantial growth ensued.

During this initial period Air Products developed another unique way of doing business in the commodity industrial gas market. In addition to building the on-site gas plants, Air Products decided to retain ownership and operate some of the plants. The products were sold to the customer on a long-term (about 15 years) contractual basis, on a take-or-pay arrangement, in which a minimum payment to Air Products was guaranteed regardless of the amount of product actually taken by the customer. This provided a guaranteed minimum return on investment to Air Products over the life of the plant. Moreover, it allowed Air Products to use this guaranteed income as security to attract the needed outside financing for additional on-site plants.

During the 1950s several factors spurred the company's growth. The Korean War created military needs for gas generators. The United States Missile and Space Program provided a large market for liquid oxygen and hydrogen, and Air Products was successful in capturing most of this market. Chemical companies purchased several generators to provide oxygen and hydrogen for processing plants. The basic oxygen furnace process in steelmaking grew rapidly, and by the late 1950s Air Products had several steel-industry customers for its on-site oxygen plants, including Bethlehem, U.S. Steel, Acme, Jones and Laughlin and Weirton.

Diversification By 1960 the Company had annual sales of $48.561 million and annual earnings of $1.914 million. Beginning in the 1960s, Air Products began diversifying into chemicals by acquiring other companies already involved in promising businesses. In 1961 the Company started a joint venture with the Tidewater Oil Company to produce oxo alcohols, which were used for plasticizers. In 1962 Air Products acquired the Houdry Process Company and its subsidiary, the Catalytic Construction Company. The Houdry Process Company licensed processes and produced catalysts for the petroleum and petrochemical industries.

Air Products acquired Escambia Chemical Corporation in 1969. The Company retained Escambia's polyvinyl chloride, industrial chemicals, and ammonia-base fertilizer business but sold its unprofitable chain of retail fertilizer outlets. For a net cost of $10 million, Air Products obtained a $32-million-a-year business yielding more than $1 million annually in after-tax profits. Continuing its move into chemicals, Air Products acquired the chemical business of Airco, Inc., in 1971. This provided the company with facilities for making acetylenic chemicals, polyvinyl chloride resins, polyvinyl acetate emulsions, and fabricated plastics.

The purchase of Catalytic Construction Company provided the basis for Air Products' present catalytic group, and the other chemical acquisitions provided the basis for the chemicals group. The chemicals group accounted for 37 percent of the total sales and 34 percent of pretax profit for the company in 1975. The catalytic group accounted for 2.9 percent of 1975 sales and 9 percent of pretax profits.

Air Products initiated its expansion abroad in Great Britain, where it acquired companies to manufacture oxygen generators and related equipment in the late 1950s. In 1963 the British subsidiary of Air Products built two major on-site plants in the United Kingdom and sold three large oxygen plants to the Italian

Table 7.3 Air Products and Chemicals: historical financial data

Year	Sales (millions)	Net income (millions)	Fully diluted[†] earnings per share	Return on sales, %	Return on average shareholders' equity, %
1966	$165.9	$10.6	$0.88	6.4	11.8
1968	207.2	12.1	0.93	5.8	10
1970	261.4	15.0	1.14	5.7	10.3
1972	351.2	18.3	1.37	5.2	10.3
1974	562.6	39.7	2.95	7.1	17.3
1975	699.0	54.2	4.02	7.8	19.7

† Dilution is "the reduction in earnings per share that would take place if convertible securities were converted or options or warrants were exercised. Potential dilution of less than 3 percent may be ignored in computing earnings per share" (W. B. Meigs, C. E. Johnson, T. F. Keller, and A. N. Mosich, "Study Guide to Accompany 'Intermediate Accounting,'" 3d ed., p. 97, McGraw-Hill, New York, 1974). Fully diluted earnings per share "takes into account the maximum potential dilutive effect of convertible securities, stock options, and warrants outstanding" (W. B. Meigs, C. E. Johnson, T. F. Keller, and A. N. Mosich, "Intermediate Accounting," 3d ed., p. 652, McGraw-Hill, New York, 1974).

steel industry. In the mid-1960s additional subsidiaries were formed to provide large quantities of gases to the steel and other industries throughout Europe. In 1975 the company's European gas and equipment group accounted for about 18 percent of total sales.

Other important foreign activities include operation of gas plants in Puerto Rico and South Africa; chemical exports; and engineering design, construction, and plant-maintenance services. These additional activities contributed 9 percent of total company sales in fiscal 1975. Financial data for 1966 to 1975 are given in Table 7.3.

7.1.3 Present Organization, Products, and Services

Air Products is organized into three main groups, gases and equipment, chemicals, and catalytic. Financial data for these groups are presented in Table 7.4. Notice that both sales and profits for all groups grow smoothly without major down trends. Clearly the company has a "growth," rather than cyclic, operation.

Gases and equipment group This group produces and sells industrial, medical, and specialty gases and related equipment. Table 7.4 shows that in 1975 the gases and equipment group accounted for 60 percent of the total sales for Air Products. In terms of profit, in 1975 the gases and equipment group accounted for 57 percent of

Table 7.4 Air Products and Chemicals

Group	1971	1972	1973	1974	1975
	Sales (millions)				
Gases and equipment group:					
United States	$157.3	$172.0	$180.5	$218.4	$293.5
Europe	52.3	67.1	78.5	113.0	125.3
Chemicals group	86.9	102.6	128.8	216.5	260.2
Catalytic group†	11.2	9.5	11.1	14.7	20.0
Total	$307.7	$351.2	$398.9	$562.6	$699.0
	Profit before interest expense and income taxes (millions) (operating profit)				
Gases and equipment group:					
United States	$19.5	$24.4	$26.3	$28.5	$ 51.3
Europe	9.1	8.2	9.8	11.9	16.3
Chemicals group	5.8	7.0	12.1	39.3	40.8
Catalytic group	4.3	3.2	5.4	8.2	10.8
Total	$38.7	$42.8	$53.6	$87.9	$119.2

† Net of direct costs of construction and maintenance contracts.
Source: Air Products and Chemicals, Inc., form 10-K, for the fiscal year ended Sept. 30, 1975, p. 1.

Table 7.5 Major United States producers of industrial gases, 1972

Company	Industrial gas revenues (millions)	Percentage of market
Union Carbide	$175	29.2
Airco	110	18.3
Air Products and Chemicals	95	16
Chemetron	60	10
Houston Natural Gas (Liquid Carbonic)	50	8
Big Three Industries	30	5
Liquid Air	15	2.5
Burdett Oxygen	15	2.5
Cities Service	10	1.6
Puritan-Bennett	10	1.6
Other	30	5
Total	600	100

Source: Air Products and Chemicals, Inc., p. 4, Harvard Business School, Intercollegiate Case Clearing House, Soldiers Field, Boston.

company profit. A major reason for the strong contribution by the gases and equipment group is the fact that Air Products has a large share of the United States market for industrial gases (Table 7.5). In addition, the European Common Market operation of Air Products has contributed greatly to the profitability of the firm.

In 1972 Air Products was the third largest producer of industrial gases in the United States. It was outranked only by the much larger Union Carbide and a firm of comparable size, Airco. Some pertinent financial data for these three firms

Table 7.6 Comparative financial data (dollar values in millions)

	Air Products and Chemicals		Airco		Union Carbide	
	1970	1975	1970	1975	1970	1975
Net sales	$261.4	$699.0	$405.6	$765.6	$3,026	$5,665
Net income	$15.0	$54.2	$16.7	$42.7	$157.3	$381.7
Stockholders' equity	$153.0	$301.2	$255.7	$322.1	$1,804.6	$2,748
Long-term debt	$130.1	$184.1	$190.5	$187.7	$911.8	$1,277.5
Profit margin, %	5.7	7.8	4.1	5.6	5.2	6.7
Return on stockholders' equity, %	10.3	19.7	6.5	13.2	8.7	13.9
Long-term debt to equity ratio	0.85	0.61	0.74	0.58	0.50	0.46
Compound average annual growth rate of sales 1970–1975, %	28		17.5		17	

Source: Union Carbide, Airco, and Air Products company reports.

are presented in Table 7.6. The leader in industrial gas production is Union Carbide, with 29.2 percent of the market. Note that in 1975, Union Carbide had about 8 times the total net sales of Air Products. Airco had only about 10 percent more than Air Products in net sales, and held about 2.3 percent more of the industrial gas market. Air Products had 27 percent more net income than Airco for 1975. The growth rate of net sales (1970 to 1975) for both Airco and Union Carbide was around 17 percent, while Air Products had a growth rate of 28 percent for the same period. A portion of Air Products' growth is due to the acquisition of other companies during this period; in 1971, they purchased the chemical business of Airco, Inc. These comparative data indicate that Air Products is an aggressive company with an above-average growth rate and competitive profitability.

Gases and equipment This group has five major product and services lines.

Merchant industrial gases Major products include acetylene, argon, carbon dioxide, carbon monoxide, helium, hydrogen, krypton, neon, nitrogen, xenon, mixtures of gases for research, welding, and underwater breathing, and liquid-nitrogen systems for freezing foods, deflashing molded parts, and grinding materials. A major portion of this product division's revenue is from sales of liquid oxygen, nitrogen, and argon.

Pipeline industrial gases Major products are oxygen and nitrogen provided to customers by on-site plants on long-term take-or-pay contracts.

Cryogenic plants and equipment Major products include air-separation plants (gas separation, purification, and liquefaction systems), nuclear vent-gas recovery systems, and waste-water treatment systems.

Metallurgical systems Major products and services include welding and cutting equipment, metal gouging and removal equipment, heat-treating systems, and metal refining and recovery.

Medical products Major products include anesthesia gases, equipment, and supplies; medical oxygen; respiratory-therapy equipment; pulmonary-function products; hospital medical-gas piping systems; and disposable health-care products.

Chemicals group The chemicals group is relatively new, and much of the business has been obtained through acquisition and subsequent aggressive expansion of other firms. Air Products produces a limited number of chemicals, which can be divided into eight major product lines.

Industrial chemicals Major products include dimethylformamide, dinitrotoluene, methanol, methyl amines and higher alkyl amines, nitriles, and toluenediamine.

Ammonia products Major products include ammonium nitrate prills, anhydrous ammonia, nitric acid, nitrogen solutions, and urea solutions.

Polymers Major products include polyvinyl acetate emulsions and copolymers, polyvinyl alcohol, vinyl chloride–vinyl acetate–ethylene terpolymer emulsions.

Processes and catalysts Major products are catalysts for petroleum refining, petrochemical processes, and automobile emission control. The chemicals group offers process engineering services and licenses petroleum and petrochemical process technology.

Chemical additives Major products include polyester promotors, polyvinyl chloride–foam stabilizers, urethane-foam catalysts, and urethane-foam stabilizers.

Acetylenic chemicals Major products include chemical intermediates, corrosion inhibitors, flavor and fragrance chemicals, and surfactants.

Plastics Major products include propylene–vinyl chloride copolymer resins and compounds, vinyl chloride–vinyl acetate copolymers, and polyvinyl chloride homopolymers.

Fabricated plastics Major products include custom molding, hoses for industrial, vacuum-cleaning, and recreational use, and bicycle grips and seat covers.

The attitude toward the market position of the chemicals group has been stated by Edward Donley, President of Air Products. " We basically want to be the leader in the specific business segments in which we compete. We are content to have the lowest costs, not necessarily the largest market share."[1] To evaluate the market position held by Air Products, it is necessary to note how the company stands in relation to its competitors with respect to manufacturing capacity. Capacity comparisons for the production of three important products are shown in Tables 7.7 to 7.9.

Air Products has the second largest capacity for producing polyvinyl acetate emulsions and resins and outranks other firms which are much larger. These data support Donley's statement that Air Products seeks to be a leader in the specific business segments in which it competes.

The data in Table 7.8 permit one to conclude that in capacity for production of methyl amines, a methanol derivative, Air Products is second only to Du Pont (again, the company is a leader in the selected business segment) and that in the methanol market, Air Products has a much lower standing in terms of capacity. It shares sixth place, along with Commercial Solvents. In short, the data from Tables 7.7 to 7.9 indicate that Air Products is a leader in the business of polyvinyl acetate

[1] Air Products and Chemicals, Inc., p. 22, Harvard Business School, Intercollegiate Case, Clearing House, Soldiers Field, Boston.

Table 7.7 Top producers of polyvinyl acetate emulsions and resins for multiple use, ranked by capacity, 1975

Rank	Name	Rank	Name
1	Union Carbide	6	Monsanto
2	Air Products and Chemicals	7	National Starch
3	Borden	8	Celanese
4	Du Pont	9	W. R. Grace
5	Reichhold		

Source: "Chemical Economics Handbook," SRI International, Menlo Park, Calif.

Table 7.8 Companies ranked according to capacity for producing methanol and methanol derivatives

Company	Methanol capacity, 10^6 lb/yr	Methanol derivatives, methyl amines, 10^6 lb/yr
Du Pont	2,088	191
Celanese	1,923	
Borden	1,061	
Georgia-Pacific	663	
Hercules	663	
Monsanto	663	
Tenneco	530	
Air Products and Chemicals	332	50
Commercial Solvents	332	18
Rohm & Haas	142	

Source: "Chemical Economics Handbook," SRI International, Menlo Park, Calif.

Table 7.9 Companies manufacturing polyvinyl chloride resins ranked by capacity, March 1976

Company	Capacity, 10^6 lb/yr	Company	Capacity, 10^6 lb/yr
B. F. Goodrich	1,010	Georgia-Pacific	220
Diamond Shamrock	570	Shintech	200
Borden	545	Air Products and Chemicals	200
Continental Oil	490	Occidental Petroleum	195
Tenneco	475	General Tire & Rubber	185
Firestone Tire & Rubber	450	Ethyl	180
Union Carbide	350	Pentasote of N.Y.	120
Stauffer Chemical	305	Great American Chemical	70
Certain-Teed Products	300	Atlantic Tubing & Rubber	50
Goodyear Tire & Rubber	250	Keysor-Century	35
Robintech	250		

Source: "Chemical Economics Handbook," SRI International, Menlo Park, Calif.

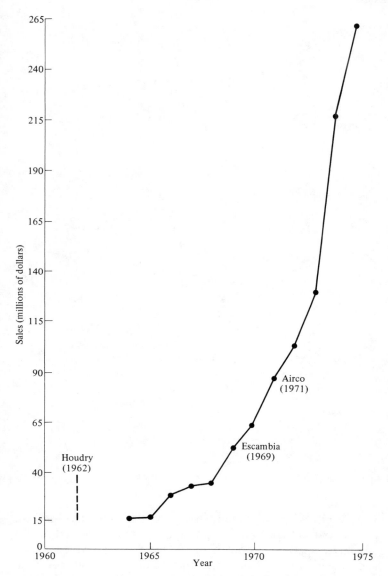

Figure 7.2 Chemicals group: growth of sales from 1964 to 1975; acquisitions indicated.

emulsions and resins and methyl amines but not in that of methanol and PVC resins.

In the 1960s Air Products began diversifying into chemicals by acquiring other companies already involved in promising business ventures. Figures 7.2 and 7.3 dramatize the relationship between sales growth and acquisition of other companies. A remarkable increase in sales following the acquisition of other firms is evident.

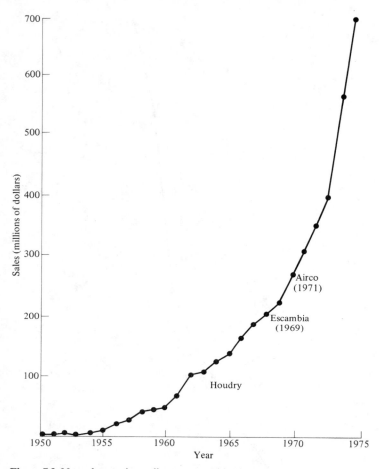

Figure 7.3 Net sales vs. time, all groups combined; acquisitions indicated.

Catalytic group This group is small in comparison to the other two groups, providing only 3 percent of total sales, but it is profitable and has provided 9 to 10 percent of the company's operating profit in recent years. The group's major activities are in the engineering, design, and construction of process plants for the chemical, petrochemical, fiber, plastics, food, drug, and metallurgical industries, mostly in the United States, Canada, and Europe. The group also performs other engineering-related services under contract, including management services, environmental and energy studies, and technical and economic analyses.

7.1.4 Overall Company Performance

In addition to the data already presented, Tables 7.10 to 7.14 are provided for critical evaluation of Air Products. Table 7.10 gives pertinent financial data for Air

Products and Chemicals for selected years 1966 to 1975. Growth and financial ratios are compiled in Tables 7.11, 7.12, 7.13. Some observations are of note:

1. Fully diluted earnings per share have grown 457 percent from 1966 to 1975.
2. Net sales have increased 421 percent from 1966 to 1975.
3. The relationship

$$\frac{\text{Payment of dividends (\$)}}{\text{Net income}}$$

for the period is

1966	1968	1970	1972	1974	1975
0.094	0.099	0.073	0.065	0.065	0.05

In 1968, about 9.9 percent of net income went into common stock dividends. In 1975, the percentage was reduced to about 5 percent, almost half. As the company made more money, it lowered the percentage of income paid out in dividends.
4. Another informative relationship is the ratio of debt to sales:

Year	1966	1968	1970	1972	1974	1975
Ratio, %	60.3	48.4	49.7	37.5	28.9	26

It would appear that although the company was heavily in debt in 1966, its sales have since rapidly outdistanced its debt.
5. The time series on all items change smoothly without alarming sudden increases in debts and costs or sudden decreases in sales and profits.

Several outstanding features of Air Products' performance may be mentioned. It has sustained a record of high growth: net sales have expanded much faster than the chemical industry as a whole. Air Products has grown approximately at an average annual rate of 28 percent from 1970 to 1975 compared with 17.5 percent for Airco and 17 percent for Union Carbide. It has been a relatively profitable company as measured by return on stockholders' equity and profit margin (Table 7.12). Moreover, the company's profit margin has been steadily increasing. Air Products outperformed both Union Carbide and Airco in both years considered. Yield to shareholders on the company's stock has been low. Dividends have been less than 1 percent of the stock's selling price during 1966 to 1975. However, earnings per share have been relatively high and have grown continuously. The company has chosen to reinvest most of the earnings in its effort to grow. Moreover, while the stock may not earn much, it has appreciated significantly, going from a price range of $9 to $18 per share in 1966 to $40 to $79 in 1975.

Table 7.10 Selected financial data for Air Products and Chemicals†

	1966	1968	1970	1972	1974	1975
Operating results						
Sales, net of direct costs of construction and maintenance contracts	$165.9	$207.2	$261.4	$351.2	$562.6	$699.0
Costs and expenses	142.4	179.1	226.8	308.8	480.6	585.2
Operating profit	25.0	30.7	35.7	42.8	87.9	119.2
Interest expense	5.5	7.1	9.0	10.5	14.5	18.2
Provision for income taxes	8.9	11.5	11.7	14.0	33.7	46.8
Net income	10.6	12.1	15.0	18.3	39.7	54.2
Fully diluted earnings per share (dollars)	0.88	0.93	1.14	1.37	2.95	4.02
Summary of changes in financial position						
Source of funds:						
Internal funds generated	$ 29.5	$ 38.9	$ 46.3	$ 62.8	$ 96.7	$121.7
Additional long-term debt	16.5	0.7	25.0	13.8	62.2	49.7
Stock issued	20.1	0.3	0.5	2.5	0.5	1.2
Disposition of funds:						
Additions to plant and equipment	45.0	37.4	45.7	41.7	109.8	149.2
Reduction of long-term debt	10.9	11.1	7.5	30.4	22.3	25.5
Working capital increase (decrease)	2.4	1.4	12.8	3.2	22.9	(6.0)
Investments and other	6.7	(12.3)	3.6	2.5	1.8	1.2
Payment of dividends, common	1.0	1.2	1.1	1.2	2.6	2.7
Preferred	0.1	1.1	1.1	0.1		
Year-end financial position						
Plant and equipment, net of accumulated depreciation	$182.4	$220.5	$266.7	$319.3	$415.6	$506.4
Total assets	286.6	315.4	409.0	466.4	659.1	776.3
Working capital	29.8	32.4	50.0	47.9	61.3	55.3
Long-term debt	100.0	100.4	130.1	131.9	162.6	184.1
Shareholders' equity	105.0	127.2	153.0	187.2	248.5	301.2

† All values in millions except where otherwise noted.
Source: Air Products and Chemicals, Inc., annual report, 1975.

Table 7.11 Growth of Air Products and Chemicals

	Annual compound growth† rate, 1966–1975, %
Total annual sales	17.3
Operating annual profit	19.0
Net annual income	19.9
Total assets	11.7
Long-term debt	7.0
Shareholders' equity	12.4

† Computed from the expression
$$[(1975\ \text{data})/(1966\ \text{data})]^{1/9} - 1.$$

Table 7.12 Pertinent ratios for Air Products

Year	After-tax profit margin, %	Return on shareholders' equity, %	Current ratio	Ratio of long-term debt to shareholders' equity
1966	6.4	11.8	...	0.95
1968	5.8	10.0	1.59	0.79
1970	5.7	10.3	1.65	0.85
1974	7.1	17.3	1.38	0.65
1975	7.8	19.7	1.29	0.61

Air Products has carried on a highly leveraged operation. Although declining significantly since 1966, the long-term debt-to-equity ratio has been much higher than the industry average (Table 7.13). While Air Products is unquestionably highly leveraged, so are several other well known chemical producers. Table 7.14 lists several prominent chemical producers and their debt-to-equity ratios.

Table 7.13 Debt-to-equity ratio

Year	Air Products and Chemicals	Chemicals and allied products†
1966	0.95	0.30
1968	0.79	0.35
1970	0.85	0.38
1974	0.65	0.36
1975	0.61	0.44

† "Standard and Poor's Industry Surveys," vol. 1, January 1976, p. C40.

Table 7.14 Debt-to-equity ratios for several major chemical producers

Company	Debt-to-equity ratio	Company	Debt-to-equity ratio
Air Products and Chemicals	0.6	Thiokol	0.2
		Airco	0.5
Lubrizol	0.0	Pennwalt	0.5
International Minerals and Chemicals	0.6	Sun Chemicals	0.7
Nalco Chemical	0.0	Dow Chemicals	0.6
Ethyl	0.6	Diamond Shamrock	0.6
National Starch and Chemicals	0.3	Monsanto	0.4
		Reichhold Chemicals	0.3
Williams Companies	0.9	Du Pont	0.2
Kewanee Industries	0.5	W. R. Grace	0.6
		Rohm & Hass	0.6

Source: *Forbes*, Jan. 1, 1977. Reprinted by permission of *Forbes* Magazine.

Having looked at the financial background of Air Products, we will find it instructive to consider how the six interest groups mentioned at the beginning of this chapter might react after having studied the data.

1. Investors, lenders, and employees
   a. The company is making money and is paying a dividend.
   b. The price of the stock is rising.
   c. The company has a fair growth in net income as measured by profit per dollar of sale.
   d. The company has been reducing its debt and is not alone in the industry with regard to its debt structure.
2. Customers
   a. The company's policy is to break into specific markets and to excel at producing particular products. Efficient and innovative production means lower prices than those of competitors.
   b. The company has a record of innovation leading to lower prices, e.g., oxygen.
   c. The company is doing well and ought to be reliable for the future.
3. The government
   a. The company has paid increasing amounts in taxes over the years.
   b. The company is providing jobs, and continued growth points towards more employment.
4. The public
   a. The average citizen probably has little direct contact with Air Products. Industrial gases are not front-page items to the average consumer. The general public would be indirectly affected by a failure of Air Products. Moreover, it is an important source of payroll and prosperity at Allentown, Pennsylvania. There have been no pollution or health-hazard problems.

7.1.5 Future Prospects

If Air Products and Chemicals is to continue its rapid growth, it must (1) seek out new uses for its existing products, especially its gases and related technology; (2) diversify into new products and technology; and (3) continue to expand its international efforts. Some of the more significant activities being pursued by the company and possible problems or threats are as follows:

1. Maintenance and expansion of established business
   a. On-site plants for liquid nitrogen to supply the frozen food industry. *Threat:* nitrogen must compete against carbon dioxide and mechanical freezing.
   b. Expansion of its long-term contractual on-site concept to include major petrochemicals. *Threat:* possible problems with feedstock and difficulty in finding customers.

c. Supply of liquid fuels for space exploration. In June 1975 the Company was awarded a 12½-year, $287 million contract to supply liquid hydrogen for the Space Shuttle program. *Threat:* unless there is a major change in national priorities, expansion in space will be only modest.

d. Processes for the liquefaction of natural gas. The company is already quite active in producing large heat exchangers for liquefied-natural-gas plants being built in the Middle East and North Africa. *Threat:* this is an expensive way to supplement temporary and local shortages of natural gas.

e. Waste-water treatment systems. The company has already sold several such systems, which include oxygen generators, to several municipalities. Research is continuing to show the advantages of Air Products' systems in treating specific industrial wastes. *Threat:* these systems are in competition with the well-publicized UNOX system made by Union Carbide.

f. Expansion of commodity chemical production. The Company in 1975 had major shares of total United States capacity for three chemicals, including methyl amines (23 percent of United States capacity), polyvinyl alcohol (18 percent), and polyvinyl acetate (16 percent). An example of expansion into the commodity chemical market is Air Products' new alkyl amines plant at St. Gabriel, Louisiana. This plant is the largest of its kind in the world and will be used to supply amines to the adjacent plants of two of the nations major producers of herbicides. The herbicides produced at St. Gabriel are primarily for use on corn and are essential to the economy of the food industry. In addition, the company is building a toluenediamine plant, which will provide about 35 percent of total United States capacity. Toluenediamine (TDA) is an important ingredient in the production of toluene diisocyanate (TDI), which in turn is essential to the production of polyurethane foams, elastomers, and protective coatings, demand for all of which has been rapidly growing. *Threat:* The major threat to expansion of the company into commodity chemicals may be the lack of secure feedstocks. The company must buy all the basic petrochemicals used in making the above chemicals.

g. Expansion of the service organization. The company's catalytic group already provides a wide variety of engineering, construction, and maintenance services to process industries throughout the world, to the nuclear and power industries, and for various types of government projects. These activities are expanding rapidly, particularly in the energy and environmental areas. In 1975, a special division was organized to provide services to the electric utility industry. Air Products specializes in engineering associated with nuclear power plants. In 1976 the catalytic group's power division was awarded a new assignment in engineering, construction, and nuclear-plant maintenance. The power industry has become quite receptive to the notion of contract maintenance, and the catalytic group plans to move into this opportunity. In addition to providing services to the power industry, the catalytic environmental system has designed and installed water-pollution-abatement facilities for customers in a wide range of industries.

2. Inventing new business
   a. Barge-mounted nitrogen plants for providing nitrogen to repressurize off-shore oil wells.
   b. Processes for coal gasification which would include the use of on-site oxygen plants. *Threat:* this potentially high-growth area is being delayed by the lack of a viable energy policy for the United States.
   c. Equipment for stack-gas desulfurization. *Threat:* this is a tremendous opportunity, but the technology is of unproved reliability and may not be economically feasible.

7.2 SELECTED CPI COMPANIES: BASIC DATA

7.2.1 Diamond Shamrock Corporation

Diamond Shamrock[1] is a composite of two companies, Diamond Alkali Co. and Shamrock Oil & Gas Corp., which merged in 1967. As their names imply, Diamond Alkali was involved in the manufacture of alkali chemicals, and Shamrock Oil & Gas was an oil company. These activities are still very much a part of Diamond Shamrock today. The company's major products and operations can be summarized as follows:

Chemicals. Industrial chemicals (such as chlorine, caustic soda, and chlorinated solvents), polymers, biologicals
Oil and gas. Oil and natural-gas exploration; gasoline, fuel, ammonia, and natural-gas production and sales; crude-oil and natural-gas sales
Diversified technology and services. Leasing and selling electrodes for making caustic soda and chlorine

Table 7.15 Diamond Shamrock

Year	Net sales (millions)	Profit margin		Return on stockholders' equity	
		%	Rank†	%	Rank†
1975	$1,129	10.1	8	21.4	3
1974	965	9.8	9	19.5	7
1973	651	7.8	15	...	22
1972	617	5.4			
1971	573	4.3			

† Rank among the 50 top United States chemical producers.

[1] For annual report and form 10-K write Director, Investor Relations, Diamond Shamrock Corporation, 1100 Superior Avenue, Cleveland, OH 44114.

Table 7.16 Diamond Shamrock: information summary

Income and balance-sheet statistics
(millions)

Year	Net sales	Net income	Capital expen- ditures	Long- term debt	Percentage net income of net sales
1975	$1,129.3	$114.3	$169.7	$354.3	10.1
1970	556.8	30.1	56.6	144.0	5.4
1965	441.4	35.4	51.6	106.7	8.0

Additional statistics, 1975

Millions

	Millions		
Total assets	$1,181.6	Current ratio	2.08
Stockholders' equity	535.1	Long-term debt-to-equity ratio	0.66
Total liabilities	646.5	Return on equity, %	21.4
R & D spending	19.6	Number of employees	10,300

Major product groups (percentage of 1975 sales)

Chemicals	62
Oil and gas	35
Diversified technology and services	3

Diamond Shamrock's performance in terms of sales and profitability have been extremely good in recent years, as shown in Table 7.15. Aggressive management efforts to increase market share of its major products, increase the use of its basic chemicals to make new proprietary products, secure feedstocks for petrochemicals from its internal oil and gas operations, double its research and development effort in 5 years, and expand operations internationally point to continued rapid growth and sustained profitability (Table 7.16). Diamond Shamrock has made good use of borrowed money, and its debt-to-equity ratio is higher than the chemical-industry average.

7.2.2 The Dow Chemical Company

Dow[1] was formed in 1897 by Herbert H. Dow to extract chemicals from native brine deposits of central Michigan. It is now the third largest chemical company in the United States. It has since diversified, and its many activities can be classified

[1] For annual report and form 10-K write Secretary of the Company, 2030 Dow Center, Midland, MI 48640.

into three major groups: chemicals and metals, plastics and packaging, and bioproducts and consumer products. These can be further divided into 10 product
and service groups. The 10 groups and some of the major products and services
offered by each are as follows:

1. Chemicals and metals
    a. Inorganic chemicals: bromine, caustic soda, chlorinated solvents, chlorine,
       ethylene dibromide
    b. Organic chemicals: acetone, ethylene glycol, glycerine, phenol, propylene
       glycols, polyglycols
    c. Metals: magnesium sheet, plate, extrusions, and ingot
    d. Functional products, oil and gas division, and miscellaneous: calcium chlor-
       ide, industrial-equipment-cleaning services, petroleum production, trading
       and marketing of petroleum products
2. Plastics and packaging
    a. Molding compounds: acrylonitrile-butadiene-styrene, polyethylene, poly-
       styrene
    b. Coatings and monomers: epoxy resins, styrene-butadiene latexes, styrene
       and vinyl chloride monomers
    c. Plastic products: polyethylene film, polystyrene film and sheet, Styrofoam
       polystyrene foam, Saran film
3. Bioproducts and consumer products
    a. Health-care products and services: diagnostic products and services, cough
       and cold preparations, antibiotics
    b. Agricultural chemicals: coccidiostats (for treating poultry disease), insecti-
       cides, herbicides
    c. Consumer products: Dow Bathroom Cleaner, Handi-Wrap, and Ziploc
       food bags.

Dow is very active internationally and has major production and sales operations in Canada, Europe, Latin America, and the Pacific area. Percentage of total
1975 Dow sales by world area are United States (55.7 percent); Europe and Africa

Table 7.17 Dow Chemical Company

Year	Profit margin %	Rank†	Return on equity %	Rank†
1975	12.6	2	25.1	2
1974	11.9	3	29.8	1
1973	8.8	11	17.7	4

† Rank among 50 top United States chemical
producers.

Table 7.18 Dow Chemical Company: information summary

Income and balance sheet statistics
(millions)

Year	Net sales	Net income	Capital expen-ditures	Long-term debt	Percentage net income of net sales
1975	4,888.1	615.7	921.5	1,563.2	12.6
1970	1,911.1	132.3	348.1	969.8	6.9
1965	1,176.2	108.1	248.3	454.6	9.2

Additional statistics, 1975

Millions

Total assets	$5,846.7	Current ratio	1.51
Stockholders' equity	2,450.2	Long-term debt-to-equity ratio	0.64
Total liabilities	1,913.3	Return on equity, %	25.1
R & D spending	167.4	Number of employees	53,100

Major product groups percentage of 1975 sales

Chemicals-metals group	56.2
Plastics-packaging group	29.2
Bioproducts-consumer products group	14.6

(26.0 percent); Latin America (7.9 percent); Canada (6.6 percent); and Pacific (3.7 percent).

Dow is noted for its aggressive use of debt to finance capital needs. The company's ratio of long-term debt-to-stockholders' equity (1975) is 0.64, well above the industry average of about 0.44, but Dow's use of this leverage appears to be well justified by its recent performance. Compared with other companies in the chemical industry, Dow ranks high in both profit margin and return on equity, as shown in Table 7.17; see also Table 7.18.

7.2.3 E. I. Du Pont de Nemours & Company

Founded in 1802 by Éleuthère I. Du Pont, this is the world's oldest chemical company.[1] It is the largest chemical company in the United States. Originally a gunpowder manufacturer, Du Pont expanded into nitrocellulose plastics and lacquers, dyes, and phenolic resins in the early 1900s. In the 1920s the company

[1] For annual report and form 10-K write Treasurer's Department, E. I. Du Pont de Nemours & Company, 1007 Market Street, Wilmington, DE 19898.

Table 7.19 Du Pont

	Profit margin		Return on equity	
Year	%	Rank†	%	Rank†
1975	3.8	34	7.1	41
1974	5.8	30	10.8	39
1973	11.4	5	16.2	5

† Rank among 50 top United States chemical producers.

began making ammonia and fibers. Extensive company research and development led to the discovery of nylon and chloroprene in the 1930s. Du Pont has established a reputation as a leader in innovation in the chemical industry, and the emphasis placed by management on technology is reflected by research and development spending ($336 million in 1975, 4.6 percent of sales).

Du Pont's four major product groups and products are as follows:

Fibers. Acetate, nylon, aramid, polyester, fluorocarbon, and spandex yarns; polyester fiber fill; acrylic, nylon, and polyester staple for textile, carpet, and industrial uses; polyethylene, polyester, and polypropylene fibrous spunbonded sheet structures

Plastic materials and synthetics. Nylon, acetal, polyvinyl alcohol, polyolefin, acrylic, and fluorocarbon resins; polyester and polyimide film; cellophane; ethylene copolymers

Industrial chemicals. Sulfuric acid, methanol, methyl amines, dimethylformamide, formaldehyde, tetrahydrofuran, aniline, dyes, pigments, fluorocarbons, and antiknock gasoline additives

Photo products, finishes, agrichemicals, and other products. Laboratory instruments, biomedical equipment, x-ray films, photopolymers, fungicides, weed killer, insecticides, herbicides, pharmaceuticals, automotive finishes, industrial coatings, explosives

Table 7.20 Du Pont net income by product group

	1975, %	1974, %	1973, %	1972, %	1971, %
Fibers	2	31	42	44	44
Plastic materials and synthetics	9	27	21	15	13
Industrial chemicals	38	19	18	22	24
Photo products, finishes, agrichemicals, and other products	51	23	19	19	19

Table 7.21 E. I. Du Pont de Nemours & Company: information summary

Income and balance sheet statistics
(millions)

Year	Net sales	Net income	Capital expenditures	Long-term debt	Percentage net income of net sales
1975	$7,222	$272	$1,066	$889	3.8
1970	4,118	334	499	162	8.1
1965	3,021	407	327	33.5	13.5

Additional statistics, 1975

Millions

Total assets	$6,425	Current ratio	1.98
Stockholders' equity	3,835	Long-term debt-to-equity ratio	0.23
Total liabilities	2,590	Return on equity, %	7.1
R & D spending	336	Number of employees	132,200

Major product groups percentage of 1975 sales

Fibers	36
Plastic materials and synthetics	19
Industrial chemicals	19
Photo products, finishes, agrichemicals, and other products	26

Historically, Du Pont has been an extremely profitable chemical company; lately, however, the company's financial performance has fallen in relation to that of other companies in the CPI (Table 7.19). The drastic decrease in profitability can be attributed to extraordinary weakness in the demand for fibers during the recession of 1974 to 1975. This is vividly shown by Table 7.20, comparing percent of net income by product groups for 1971 to 1975. See also Table 7.21. An increase in Du Pont's profitability will strongly depend on strengthening its fiber markets.

7.2.4 Ethyl Corporation

Ethyl Corporation's[1] major products have always been lead antiknock compounds used as additives in gasoline, and before the early 1960s these were the only products made. However, shortly after Ethyl merged with Albemarle Paper

[1] For annual report and form 10-K write Ethyl Corporation, 330 South Fourth St., Richmond, VA 23219.

Mfg. Co. in 1962, the company acquired several diverse businesses. Today, Ethyl has five major product groups:

Chemicals. Antiknock compounds for gasoline, gasoline ignition-control compounds, gasoline detergent–deicer–corrosion inhibitors, lubricating-oil additives, linear primary alcohols, aluminum alkyl compounds, chlorinated solvents, vinyl chloride, methyl chloride, caustic soda, sodium, and bromine chemicals

Plastics. Polyethylene films and tape, polyvinyl chloride packaging, films, resins, compounds, and containers

Paper products. Coated and uncoated paper and film (the company is selling its paper products operations)

Aluminum. Aluminum structure for windows, doors, curtain walls, boats, trailers, and tub enclosures; residential lawn buildings; aluminum billets; decorative aluminum products

Coal. Mining and leasing of company-owned coal properties

Table 7.22 Ethyl Coporation: information summary

Income and balance-sheet statistics (millions)					
Year	Net sales	Net income	Capital expenditures	Long-term debt	Percentage net income of net sales
1975	$1,029.2	$61.0	$108.86	$272.71	5.9
1970	556.9	35.58	64.19	254.16	6.4
1965	305.0	24.29	52.05	181.8	8.0

Additional statistics, 1975

	Millions		
Total assets	$875.8	Current ratio	3.53
Stockholders' equity	436.0	Long-term debt-to-equity ratio	0.62
Total liabilities	439.8	Return on equity, %	14
R & D spending	28.0	Number of employees	17,000

Major product groups percentage of 1975 sales

Chemicals	54
Plastics	27
Paper	10
Aluminum	8
Coal	1

Federal policies aimed at reducing the lead content of gasoline and prohibition of the use of lead compounds in automobiles with catalytic converters has stifled growth of Ethyl's major product. Although the company has actively diversified, an estimated 27 percent of 1974 sales were still accounted for by lead antiknock compounds. The company thus is still very much at the mercy of environmental control imposed by the government.

From 1963 to 1971 Ethyl's annual sales grew at an average rate of 9 percent annually. From 1971 to 1975 sales grew at 15 percent annually. Profitability of the company as measured by profit margin and return on stockholders' equity has followed the average of the chemical industry (see Table 7.22).

7.2.5 Exxon Corporation

In terms of its sales of $48.8 billion Exxon[1] is the world's largest company. Its origins date back to the dissolution of the Standard Oil Trust in 1911. In 1975 about $2.6 billion (5.3 percent of Exxon's total sales) were attributed to chemicals, making the company the fifth largest United States producer of chemicals. Exxon's chemical products include olefins, aromatics, plastics such as polyethylene and polypropylene, solvents, fuel and lubricant additives, and elastomers. In 1974 about 33 percent of Exxon's chemical sales were in the United States while Europe accounted for 40 percent. Chemical sales grew at a compound annual rate of 24 percent from 1971 to 1975.

Although chemicals accounted for only 5 percent of Exxon's sales, they accounted for 7.3 percent of the company's net income in 1975 and 15 percent in 1974. Chemicals appear to be one of the company's more profitable ventures (Tables 7.23 and 7.24).

In recent years Exxon has been actively diversifying into other industries such as coal and nuclear energy in an attempt to be less dependent on oil and gas. It seems likely that in its desire to diversify Exxon will also concentrate on continued expansion of its already profitable chemical operations.

Table 7.23 Exxon Corp.

Year	Profit margin, %		Return on total assets, %	
	Chemical products	Overall	Chemical products	Overall
1975	7.1	5.6	9.3	7.8
1974	16.3	6.7	23.6	10.8
1973	12.9	8.7	13.9	10.5

[1] For annual report and form 10-K write Secretary, Exxon Corporation, 1251 Avenue of the Americas, New York, NY 10020.

Table 7.24 Exxon Corporation: information summary

Income and balance-sheet statistics
(millions)

Year	Net sales	Net income	Capital expenditures	Long-term debt	Percentage net income of net sales
1975	$48,761.0	$2,503.0	$3,558	$3,451	5.6
1970	16,554.2	1,309.5	1,794	2,443	7.9
1965	11,471.5	1,021.4	971	932	8.9

Additional statistics, 1975

	Millions		
Total assets	$32,839	Current ratio	1.50
Stockholders' equity	17,024	Long-term debt-to-equity ratio	0.20
Total liabilities	15,815	Return on equity, %	14.7
R & D spending	187	Number of employees	137,000

Major product groups percentage of 1975 sales

Petroleum and natural gas	92
Chemical products	5
Other	3

7.2.6 W. R. Grace & Company

Incorporated in 1899, W. R. Grace & Company[1] was originally a trading firm doing business between South America and the United States. Through acquisition and merger Grace became active in the production of chemicals in the early 1950s. In 1954 Grace started a chemical operation, an ammonia plant. By 1975 the company ranked sixth among United States producers in chemical sales. The company presently derives 82 percent of its earnings from chemicals and chemical processes. The company's activities and major products and services are as follows:

Chemicals group. Adsorbents, catalysts, battery separators, chelating agents, construction products, medical products, plasticizers, polyester resins, sealing compounds, synthetic lubricants, nitrogen and phosphate fertilizers, animal

[1] For annual report and form 10-K write Secretary, W. R. Grace & Company, Grace Plaza, 1114 Avenue of the Americas, New York, NY 10036.

Table 7.25 W. R. Grace: information summary

Income and balance-sheet statistics
(millions)

Year	Net sales	Net income	Capital expenditures	Long-term debt	Percentage net income of net sales
1975	$3,529.2	$166.7	$282.3	$572.7	4.7
1970	2,014.8	54.2	112.2	406.0	2.7
1965	1,097.4	48.6	154.8	388.9	4.4

Additional statistics, 1975

Millions

Total assets	$2,523.8	Current ratio	1.93
Stockholders' equity	1,075.0	Long-term debt-to-equity ratio	0.53
Total liabilities	1,448.8	Return on equity, %	15.5
R & D spending	27.9	Number of employees	60,200

Major product groups percentage of 1975 sales

Chemical-based products and services	51
Natural resources	4
Consumer products	45

breeding products, flexible plastic packaging, rigid plastic containers, pollution-control processes, converted vinyls

Natural resources. Coal, natural gas, petroleum

Consumer products. Fashion and leisure products, book distribution, audio-visual software, land developing and housing, restaurants, packaged convenience foods

For a chemical company Grace has unusually heavy investment in consumer products and services. Grace owns Herman's sporting goods, Pix footwear specialty merchandising chains, and Baker & Taylor, a leading distributor of books and educational software to libraries. In 1975 Grace obtained about 45 percent of its sales and 13 percent of its after-tax operating income from consumer products.

Presently, the company's overall goals appear to be growth of its specialty chemicals business, including industrial chemicals, packaging, and plastics, and expansion of its agricultural-chemicals production and distribution operations (see also Table 7.25).

7.2.7 Mobil Oil Corporation

Like Exxon, Mobil Oil[1] was founded upon the dissolution of the Standard Oil Trust in 1911. Today Mobil obtains over 94 percent of its sales from petroleum products, natural gas, and crude oil. However, in the early 1960s the company began an aggressive move to expand into chemicals, and it presently ranks eighteenth in chemical sales among United States chemical producers. Its major chemical products include olefins, aromatics, terephthalic acid, polyethylene resin, polyethylene products (including Hefty bags), polypropylene packaging material, polystyrene foam products (including egg cartons, meat trays, and institutional dinnerware), chemical coatings, fuel and lubricant additives, synthetic catalysts, phosphorus-based industrial chemicals, and some agricultural chemicals, e.g., Modown herbicide.

In terms of Mobil's total sales, chemical products accounted for 4 percent in

Table 7.26 Mobil Oil Corporation: information summary

			Income and balance-sheet statistics (millions)		
Year	Net sales	Net income	Capital expen- ditures	Long- term debt	Percentage net income of net sales
1975	$20,620.0	$809.9	$1,206.2	$1,834.4	3.9
1970	8,206.1	482.7	879.5	974.9	5.9
1965	4,907.5	320.1	462.5	448.4	6.5

Additional statistics, 1975			
	Millions		
Total assets	$15,050.3	Current ratio	1.18
Stockholders' equity	6,841.0	Long-term debt-to-equity ratio	0.27
Total liabilities	8,209.3	Return on equity, %	11.8
R & D spending	115.7	Number of employees	71,300

Major product groups percentage of 1975 sales	
Refined petroleum products	72
Crude oil	17
Natural gas	3
Chemicals	4
Services	2
Other	2

[1] For annual report and form 10-K write Secretary, Room 545, Mobil Oil Corp., 150 East 42 St., New York, NY 10017.

Table 7.27 Mobil Oil

Year	Capital spending (millions)		Profit margin, %		Return on net plant, property, and equipment, %	
	Chemicals	Overall	Chemicals	Overall	Chemicals	Overall
1975	$77	$1,450	9.9	3.9	27.9	12.3
1974	80	1,206	12.2	5.5	36.4	16.6

1975. Other comparative data of interest are given in Table 7.27; see also Table 7.26.

In its move to diversify Mobil has entered a variety of businesses. Perhaps the most publicized of these has been its purchase of controlling interest in Marcor, Inc. Among other interests, Marcor owns Montgomery Ward and Container Corporation of America. Mobil has also invested in real estate including a giant condominium apartment complex (13,000 units) in Hong Kong and suburban community developments in the United States. In view of the comparative profitability of its chemical operations, it seems likely that Mobil will continue to expand its chemical operations.

7.2.8 Monsanto Company

Monsanto[1] was founded in 1902 to produce saccharin and other specialty chemicals. Today the company is the fourth largest chemical company in the United States. It has five major lines of business. These and the major products of each are summarized as follows:

Agricultural products. Herbicides, insecticides, nitrogenous fertilizer materials, plant-growth regulators, animal breeding stock, nitric acid

Commercial products. Process controls and electronics; plastic products, including bottles, meat trays, molded products, coated fabrics, low-density polyethylene film, and oriented polystyrene sheet; pollution-abatement systems; engineering construction services; AstroTurf surfaces; Cycle-Safe containers

Industrial chemicals. Rubber-processing chemicals, instruments and specialized equipment for the rubber-processing industry, flavors and fragrances, aspirin and other pharmaceuticals, animal-feed supplements, functional fluids, dielectric fluids and heat- and pressure-transfer media, bleaching compounds, detergent intermediates, plasticizers, phthalic anhydride, maleic anhydride, adipic acid, defoamers, sulfuric acid, hydrochloric acid, caustic potash, sodium sulfite

Polymers and petrochemicals. Styrene, acrylonitrile, phenol, acetic acid, benzene, naphthalene, o-xylene, methanol, butadiene, ethylene, propylene, polystyrene

---

[1] For annual report and form 10-K write Public Relations Dept., Monsanto Company, 800 N. Lindbergh Blvd., St. Louis, MO 63166.

Table 7.28 Monsanto

	Profit margin		Return on equity	
Year	%	Rank†	%	Rank†
1975	8.5	9	15.5	12
1974	9.2	8	18.4	14
1973	9.0	10	17.2	7

† Rank among the 50 top United States chemical producers.

and styrene copolymers, nylon thermoplastic, polyvinyl butyral sheet; specialty resins
Textiles. Nylon 66, acrylic, monoacrylic, and polyester fibers

After a period of slow growth throughout the late 1960s and early 1970s, Monsanto grew rapidly from 1972 to 1975, when net sales increased at an average compounded annual rate of about 15 percent. During the 6 years before 1972 sales

Table 7.29 Monsanto Company: information summary

			Income and balance-sheet statistics (millions)		
Year	Net sales	Net income	Capital expenditures	Long-term debt	Percentage net income of net sales
1975	$3,624.7	$306.3	$527.7	$845.3	8.5
1970	1,971.6	77.9	300.8	589.3	4.0
1965	1,468.1	123.0	295.2	467.6	8.4

Additional statistics, 1975

Millions

Total assets	$3,450.9	Current ratio	3.39
Stockholders' equity	1,976.7	Long-term debt-to-equity ratio	0.43
Total liabilities	1,474.2	Return on equity, %	15.5
R & D spending	115.7	Number of employees	59,200

Major product groups percentage of 1975 sales

Agricultural products	15
Commercial products	14
Industrial chemicals	28
Polymers and petrochemicals	22
Textiles	21

increased by an average of only 5 percent annually. Profit margin and return on stockholders' equity have both remained about the same during 1973 to 1975 although in comparative terms Monsanto's return on stockholders' equity has lost rank (Table 7.28). See also Table 7.29.

7.2.9 Reichhold Chemicals, Inc.

Reichhold Chemicals (RCI)[1] was founded in 1925 by Henry H. Reichhold to produce surface-coating resins for the automobile industry. The company has been actively buying and merging with several smaller companies since the late 1960s. Presently RCI has a diverse product mix of over 5,500 different chemicals and resins. Practically all of RCI's sales are to industrial customers. The company's major product groups and major products and services offered by each are summarized as follows:

Synthetic resins. Polyester, polyurethane, epoxy, melamine, phenol-formaldehyde and urea-formaldehyde resins; phenolic and polyester molding compounds; alkyds, rosin esters, epoxies, melamines and urethanes used to make paints, varnishes, and inks
Plastic compounds. Cross-linked polyethylene and polyvinyl chloride compounds
Industrial chemicals. Phenol, sodium sulfite, formaldehyde, urea, ammonia, maleic anhydride, pentachlorophenol, *o*-phenylphenol and peroxides
Other products. Fiber-glass panels, rubber latex tubing, glass fiber, color pigments, wood rosin, tall oil rosin, tall oil fatty acids, pine and gloss oils, turpentine, rubber emulsifiers, and specialty rubber chemicals

In terms of sales, Reichhold's growth through the 1960s was slow, increasing a total of 45 percent from 1965 to 1970. However, RCI managed to grow at an

Table 7.30 Reichhold Chemicals

	Profit margin		Return on stockholders' equity	
Year	%	Rank†	%	Rank†
1975	3.9	32	12.3	25
1974	5.1	34	20.9	5
1973	3.8	39	11.6	26
1972	3.6	...	9.0	
1971	1.9	...	4.5	

† Rank among 50 top United States chemical producers.

[1] For annual report and form 10-K with Reichhold Chemicals, Inc., RCI Building, White Plains, NY 10603.

Table 7.31 Reichhold Chemicals: information summary

Income and balance-sheet statistics
(millions)

Year	Net sales	Net income	Capital expenditures	Long-term debt	Percentage net income of net sales
1975	$407.9	$15.95	$23.0	$45.1	3.9
1970	177.9	3.26	22.6	33.6	1.8
1965	122.9	3.54	3.6	17.2	2.9

Additional statistics, 1975

Millions

Total assets	$237.1	Current ratio	2.24
Stockholders' equity	129.6	Long-term debt-to-equity ratio	0.35
Total liabilities	107.5	Return on equity, %	12.3
R & D spending	1.6	Number of employees	4,305

Major product groups percentage of 1975 sales

Synthetic resins	55
Plastic compounds	20
Industrial chemicals	13
Other products	12

average annual rate of 20 percent in 1971 to 1975. Profitability over the same period was unimpressive compared with that of the overall chemical industry (Table 7.30); see also Table 7.31.

Reichhold Chemicals is continuing its acquisition strategy of growth. It recently bought Standard Brands Chemical Industries, Inc., which is a $50 million per year specialty latex business. The company has also recently acquired a glass-fiber company and emulsion-manufacturing facilities. In addition to acquisitions, the company is actively expanding several production facilities.

In 1974 approximately 12 percent of RCI's total sales were outside the United States. The company is also following an active pattern of acquisition overseas.

7.2.10 Union Carbide Corporation

Union Carbide[1] was formed in 1898 to produce calcium carbide and from it acetylene. It now ranks second after Du Pont in United States chemicals. The foundation of today's company was built in 1917, when Union Carbide Company

---

[1] For annual report and form 10-K write Secretary, Union Carbide Corp., 270 Park Avenue, New York, NY 10017.

merged with three other companies, Prest-O-Lite, Linde Air Products Company, and National Carbon Company, to form Union Carbide and Carbon Corporation. These original companies produced batteries, ferroalloys, calcium carbide, and acetylene; the influence of these products on the present company's product mix is evident. The company can be divided into five basic product classes:

Chemicals. Ethylene, ethylene oxide, ethylene glycol, oxo alcohols, ethanol, styrene, isopropanol

Plastics. Polyethylene, polypropylene, phenolics

Gases and related products. Oxygen, nitrogen, argon, acetylene, specialty gases, welding equipment and materials, molecular sieves, waste-treatment systems, steel-processing equipment, cryogenic equipment and processes

Metals and carbons. Ferroalloys, vanadium, tungsten, uranium, carbon and graphite electrodes, electrical brushes, industrial refractories, carbon fibers

Consumer and related products. Automotive products, e.g., Prestone antifreeze; the Glad line of household products; Eveready batteries, flashlights, and lamps; food casings, electronic materials

Union Carbide is the world's leading producer of ethylene oxide, low-density polyethylene, ethanol, urethane intermediates, oxygen, graphite electrodes, ferroalloys, tungsten, vanadium dry-cell batteries, casings for processed foods, plastic wrap and bags for home use, and automotive antifreeze.

In recent years Union Carbide has fluctuated in terms of profitability. In 1973 both the profit margin and return on stockholder's equity were only average compared with those of the overall chemical industry, while in 1974 both these measures reflected outstanding performance. However, in 1975 both measures were again only average for the industry (Table 7.32); see also Table 7.33. The company's basic strategies to increase future profitability can be summarized as follows:

1. It is strengthening its position in businesses in which it already excels.
2. It is actively withdrawing from businesses showing little potential.
3. It is shifting its product mix to include a greater number of "performance products" having special characteristics offering superior value and performance to the customer.

Table 7.32 Union Carbide

Year	Profit margin		Return on stockholders' equity	
	%	Rank†	%	Rank†
1975	6.9	14	13.9	21
1974	10.0	5	21.2	4
1973	7.4	21	13.9	17

† Rank among top 50 United States Chemical producers.

Table 7.33 Union Carbide: information summary

Income and balance-sheet statistics
(millions)

Year	Net sales	Net income	Capital expen-ditures	Long-term debt	Percentage net income of net sales
1975	$5,665.0	381.7	882.0	$1,277.5	6.7
1970	3,026.3	157.3	393.7	911.8	5.2
1965	2,063.9	226.9	242.2	578.5	11.0

Additional statistics, 1975

	Millions		
Total assets	$5,740.8	Current ratio	2.55
Stockholders' equity	2,748.0	Long-term debt-to-equity ratio	0.46
Total liabilities	2,992.8	Return on equity, %	13.9
R & D spending	120.0	Number of employees	106,500

Major product groups percentage of 1975 sales

Chemicals and plastics	42
Gases and related products	16
Metals and carbons	19
Consumer and related products	23

Union Carbide operates in over 30 countries outside the United States, and in 1975 the company derived 34 percent of its sales outside this country.

7.3 QUESTIONS FOR DISCUSSION

1 Compare return on equity and return on sales for Air Products and each firm in Sec. 7.2. Prepare two ordered lists.

2 Which of the industrial input-output sectors (Chap. 4) would have the greatest impact on Air Products sales if the sector's final demand changed by 10 percent?

3 Sketch a new curve for Figs. 7.3 and 7.4 postulating how the sales would have looked if Airco's chemical business had not been acquired.

4 Which firms in Sec. 7.2 have higher debt-to-equity ratios than Air Products?

5 Compare the firms in this chapter with respect to sales per employee and long-term debt to sales. Which firms stand out as having unusual values of both these ratios?

6 Compute the percentage change in sales and profits in Europe and in the United States for the gases and equipment groups of Air Products from 1971 to 1975.

7 Compute the percentage change in sales and net income for the three top producers of industrial gases.

8 What percentage of Mobil's and Exxon's 1975 sales were due to chemicals? Compare with the other firms listed in Sec. 7.2 and prepare an ordered list.

9 Prepare an ordered list of all the firms in this chapter with respect to (a) capital expenditures, 1975; (b) total assets, 1975; and (c) research and development spending per net sales, 1975.

7.4 PROBLEMS

7.1 (a) At the beginning of this chapter it is stated that a company is reviewed by various groups according to different criteria. Consult "Moody's Handbook of Common Stock" or "Standard and Poor's Stock Market Encyclopedia" and get a financial profile on Dow, Du Pont, Air Products, and Reichhold.

(b) How might the six groups outlined on the first pages of this chapter evaluate these companies? Support your conclusions with data.

7.2 Consult "Value Line Investment Survey" and find how this publication rates the 11 companies in this chapter with respect to investment safety and stock performance. Find two firms with higher performance ratings than those in this chapter and discuss the reasons for their high rating. Identify two firms with low performance ratings and explain, using data.

7.3 Consult "Dun & Bradstreet Million Dollar Directory" and "Who's Who in Finance and Industry" and find the name of the president or chief executive officer of Air Products and Chemicals, Ethyl Corporation, W. R. Grace, Monsanto, and Reichhold. Give a brief profile of these people.

7.4 Air Products purchased the chemicals business of Airco in 1971. Which products did Air Products add to their portfolio by this purchase? How would you classify the products with respect to their market growth and cooperative strength characteristics? Find the contribution these operations made to Airco in 1970 and comment upon the wisdom of their selling the business.

7.5 One of the groups interested in the operation of a firm is the public. Generally, the public is ambivalent about the operations of a chemical firm unless it is directly affected. Consult the 1976 annual report and form 10-K for Allied Chemical and outline the financial costs incurred by the company as a result of lawsuits related to the Kepone cases. Who filed suits against the company? What amounts of money were involved? What additional expenditures were made in a public relations effort? What percentage of 1976 sales were paid out in fines or lawsuits?

7.6 Air Products' gases and equipment group has major European operations. Consult the latest company report and determine the location of these operations and what is being produced. What are the possible threats to this European operation? Identify some further opportunities.

7.7 A great deal of Air Products' growth is attributed to the aggressive expansion of acquired businesses, e.g., Houdry, Escambia, and Airco (Chemicals). Diamond Shamrock is a composite of two firms, which merged in 1967. Consult a source such as "Moody's" or "Value Line" and determine what effect, if any, the 1967 merger had on Diamond Shamrock's earnings per share and net income. Do these data combined with the Air Products' data in this chapter indicate that acquisition is a good way to achieve financial stability? How do Air Products and Diamond Shamrock agree or differ in financial status following acquisitions?

7.8 Examine the companies traded on the over-the-counter and American exchanges (Appendix B). Are any of these companies listed in the top 50 (Chap. 5)? What are the criteria for being listed on each exchange?

7.9 Examine the *Chemical Week* 300 list and find 10 companies on this list which are not in the tables of Appendix B. What do these companies have in common?

8

GENERAL CHARACTERISTICS OF THE CPI

In this chapter we discuss the prevailing and unique characteristics of the CPI and subject them to economic and accounting analyses. The emphasis will be on industrial chemicals and petroleum refining, where the predominant economic structure is that of an *oligopoly;* i.e., the manufacturing and marketing of a product is shared by a handful of large firms. The large-scale production of chemicals requires sophisticated technologies and heavy capital investments. The industry must have firms that are sufficiently large and stable to carry on these functions. Under these circumstances an oligopoly is inevitable. Whether it is composed of a group of profit-making firms or government entities, e.g., the Tennessee Valley Authority, it is the only alternative to monopoly.

Firms in the oligopolistic environment are motivated and influenced by a set of outside forces that represent carrots and sticks—technological, economic, and sociopolitical. To succeed in this environment, firms must develop patterns of behavior for both short- and long-term survival. We discuss and analyze these forces and the resulting patterns of behavior in this chapter.

8.1 MARKETING

Many important industries, such as automobile and steel, concentrate on producing essentially one product. In contrast, the CPI produces an astounding variety of products by a myriad of processes in many different and widely scattered plants. Most chemical companies produce hundreds of separate products. Moreover, the

Table 8.1 Concentration ratios for selected industries, 1972

SIC code	Industry	Percent of total shipments accounted for by largest companies	
		Four largest	Eight largest
2851	Paints and allied products	22	34
2834	Pharmaceutical preparations	26	44
2821	Plastic materials and resins	27	41
2911	Petroleum refining	31	56
2819	Industrial inorganic chemicals not elsewhere classified	34	52
3651	Radio and TV receiving sets	49	71
2082	Malt beverages	52	70
2841	Soap and other detergents	62	74
3721	Aircraft	66	86
3011	Tires and inner tubes	73	90
2824	Organic fibers, noncellulosic	74	91
3861	Photographic equipment and supplies	74	85
3724	Aircraft engines and engine parts	77	87
3711	Motor vehicles and car bodies	93	99

Source: U.S. Bureau of the Census, *Statistical Abstract of the United States: 1975*, 96th ed., table 1262.

industry consists of hundreds of separate chemical companies, so that even the largest companies account for a smaller share of the chemical industry output than the large companies in other industries, particularly automobile and aircraft. Table 8.1 shows concentration ratios for some sectors of the CPI and various other industries. The concentration ratio measures the percentage of an industry's economic activity which is accounted for by the four or eight largest companies in that industry. Table 8.1 is based on the value of shipments, but one could develop concentration ratios on the basis of value added, employment, net income, or total assets. Paints and allied products has the lowest concentration ratio of the industries shown, a fact evident if one shops at a hardware store for paint. Equally obvious to the consumer is the fact that there are only four companies in the United States who will supply him with a domestic automobile, hence the ratio of 93 percent for SIC 3711.

Although not very concentrated in terms of total industry shipments, the CPI do tend to be more concentrated for specific products. Some examples are shown in Table 8.2. The number of companies engaged in an SIC classification such as plastic material and resins (2821) is large, so that the class concentration ratio is low. But the number of companies engaged in a specific product is generally below 10, so that product concentration ratio tends to be higher, e.g., titanium pigments 80 percent, carbon dioxide 75 percent, and explosives 69 percent. Most chemical product markets can be classified as oligopolies.

Table 8.2 Concentration ratios for specific products, 1972

SIC code	Product	Percent of value of shipments accounted for by largest producers	
		Four largest	Eight largest
2812	Alkalies and chlorine	54	79
28133	Carbon dioxide	75	86
28161	Titanium pigments	80	99+
28193	Sulfuric acid	55	73
28241	Polyamide fibers, nylon	80	95
28412	Household detergents	84	90
28732	Urea	45	64
28741	Phosphoric acid	53	80
28921	Explosives	69	84
29111	Gasoline	31	55
29112	Jet fuel	52	74
29113	Kerosine	43	64
29115	Residual fuel oil	41	60

Source: U.S. Bureau of the Census, Concentration Ratios in Manufacturing, 1972 Census of Manufacturers.

The product classification of Chap. 5 designating products as commodities, pseudo commodities, fine chemicals and specialty chemicals provides a useful structure for discussing characteristics of the market. Based on dollars of sales, the four categories account for the following approximate percentage of total chemical sales [1]:

Commodities, 41%
Pseudo-commodities, 30%
Fine chemicals, 7%
Specialty chemicals, 22%

8.1.1 Commodities

A commodity chemical is produced in large volume to meet a reasonably uniform set of specifications. By definition it is undifferentiated; i.e., a commodity chemical produced by Dow is essentially the same as one produced by Diamond Shamrock or Union Carbide. Typical commodity chemicals are sulfuric acid, ethylene, chlorine, lime, carbon dioxide, methanol, ethylene oxide, urea, and gasoline.

A company's share of a commodity market is based mainly on price and partly on reliable delivery and convenience. Relatively little product technical service is required, although this depends somewhat upon the product and the company's customers. A typical commodity customer is another industrial

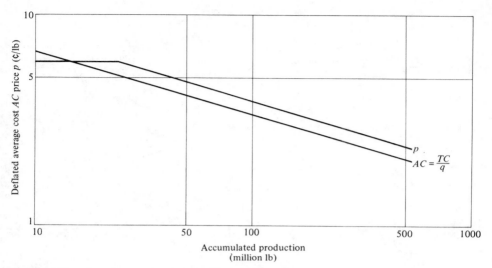

Figure 8.1 Experience curves showing a stable cost-price pattern.

concern. Steel companies buy oxygen for steelmaking and sulfuric and hydrochloric acid for pickling. A chemical company will buy ethylene from a major producer to make ethylene derivatives. Commodity chemical prices tend to be low and hence are not able to "carry much freight." Markets tend to be local. For example, oxygen plants are built adjacent to their steel-plant customers (Chap. 7).

Almost no commodity chemicals are sold directly to the consumer. They satisfy derived demands and provide no pleasure of acquisition from the customer's point of view. Even those few chemicals sold directly to the consumer are adjuncts to the more glamorous products. A person may become quite ecstatic over his purchase of a new car, but he buys gasoline, antifreeze, lubricating oil, and brake fluid only because it would not move without them. Market research is usually not product-innovation-oriented but is directed toward prediction of trends in the economy and the economic health of major users.

Commodity prices show distinct patterns with time. Figure 8.1 shows typical curves, the logarithm of deflated cost and price vs. the logarithm of accumulated production. The situation shown in Fig. 8.1 is typical of a stable cost-price pattern for a commodity chemical. Price starts out below cost, and losses are encountered by the processing firms in the early stages of operation, when the product is being introduced into the market. As experience in production is gained, cost decreases. As a corporate strategy prices could be lowered with accumulated volume in the same functional manner as cost, keeping the profit margin low enough to discourage the entry of new competition and to keep the market share high. Firms which cannot keep their production costs decreasing with time (directly related to accumulated production) must accept lower profits and perhaps eventually lose money and go out of business. Firms which innovate or expand in size can reduce costs faster than the average producer, make greater profits, and attain larger market

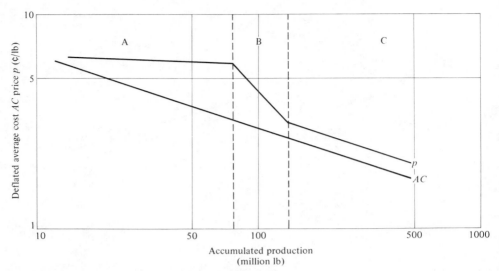

Figure 8.2 Experience curves showing unstable cost-price pattern.

shares. However, there is an upper limit to the market share, set by government antimonopoly regulations. When product concentration ratios become too high, the government will sometimes attempt to break up the dominating firms. There are some famous examples in the CPI, e.g., the breakup of Standard Oil Trust in 1911 and the breakup of the Du Pont's black-powder business, with the formation of Atlas and Hercules.

An unstable cost-price pattern is shown in Fig. 8.2. In this case, the producers of the chemical did not lower prices corresponding to decreasing costs (phase A). The high profit margins encourage building of new processing units by both existing and new producers. Eventually price cutting must take place (phase B). This may be followed by a stable phase, enjoyed by the surviving firms after marginal producers have been forced out of business (phase C). The original producers end up with a lower market share if many new firms enter the business. Had a different pricing policy been followed, a more stable market situation might have been maintained, with a larger market share for the original producers. This unstable pattern is unfortunately quite typical of many commodity chemicals and is indicative of the intense competition in the CPI. Methanol (Fig. 6.5) is a typical example and shows the end result of plant expansion by firms already producing methanol and of new units put on stream by others attracted to the business by potentially high profits. The resultant overcapacity necessitates price cutting. In the petrochemical industry this has happened so frequently that financial analysts have referred to it as the "death wish of the petrochemical industry." One reason leading to this chain of events is that the only barrier to entry in many commodity chemical businesses is the large amount of capital required. The technology for manufacturing is generally well established, and many engineering firms offer "turnkey" plants for commodity chemicals. Any firm with enough capital can buy the technology and enter the commodity chemical market. Of course the firm must do so with a plant large enough to achieve the economy of scale necessary to keep costs at a profitable level. In today's market, when most producers are designing for plants capable of producing 1 billion pounds per year, one cannot make a profit by building a comparatively small ethylene plant with a capacity of 100 million pound per year. Technical expertise is also essential, and it is not possible to remain in the chemical business without a competent staff of chemical professionals. For some commodity chemicals, a lack of inexpensive raw materials forms a barrier to entry. This is obviously true in petroleum refining, where crude-oil supplies must be available. A lack of a local market of sufficient size is another barrier to entry for low-priced commodity chemicals. One must have local customers with sufficient needs to justify the necessary economy of scale in the processing unit. The more mature commodity chemicals have what could be termed a low-profit barrier to entry. A new firm cannot justify a comparatively high-cost processing unit when an older and more experienced firm is operating a similar unit at a much lower cost.

There can be situations where price is set by other factors. Firms can attempt to fix price by setting up a cartel. A very successful one is the OPEC cartel, which has tripled and maintained the price of oil since 1973. Market share and exclusive territory are sometimes agreed upon. Two companies may engage in an illegal agreement to divide the market for certain chemicals. Such cartels, unless backed by government forces, eventually collapse, usually due to cheating by members. Market share can sometimes be legislated by government agencies which regulate the amount of resources that may be produced. The Texas Railroad Commission and Alberta Gas Conservation Board regulate the amount of crude oil which can be produced in their geographical jurisdictions of North America.

Research and development efforts by commodity-chemical manufacturers are directed toward improvement of existing processes and development of new processes (often using new raw materials). Since the manufacturing units need to be large continuous processes producing large volumes of product, a small change in efficiency can often have a marked effect on plant cost. Experienced process engineers capable of innovative design and clever process modifications are essential to the economic health of the producer of commodity chemicals.

8.1.2 Pseudo-Commodities

Pseudo-commodities are differentiated products produced in large quantities. They are not simply characterized by composition specification, as each manufacturer promises to meet an in-use performance specification of his customer. Synthetic fibers, resins and pastics, elastomers, and carbon blacks are good examples of pseudo-commodities.

Market share in a pseudo-commodity business is not solely influenced by price, as in a commodity business. The producer of a pseudo-commodity can influence market share by stressing differences in product performance, by providing technical service, and by advertising. The firm that provides superior technical service with the product sold can charge higher prices and may also increase its market share. The successful pseudo-commodity firm needs chemical professionals who understand the customer's business better than the customer does and who have the skill to solve the customer's problems. The functions of product development, market testing, and customer relations are crucial to success. Such chemical professionals should know about the performance of materials under use (octane number, viscosity index, mechanical strength, thermal conductivity, stability to oxidation, etc.). They should also know the theoretical and empirical relations of these properties to the chemical structure and physical aggregation of the material. They need the ability to design and manufacture these materials by synthesis, use of additives, compounding and formulation, and modification to mechanical operations.

Much research and development effort is directed toward the customer and his needs. It is not uncommon for a single processing unit's output to be custom-made to satisfy a few large customers. This also means that some research and development effort must be directed toward process changes to satisfy changing customer requirements. Pseudo-commodities are produced in large continuously operating plants, and process-improvement research is needed to increase operating efficiencies. Companies selling thermoplastic resins can greatly impress the customer by supplying sound engineering solutions to problems in his molding and extrusion operations. The Chestnut Run Laboratory of Du Pont is dedicated to the proposition that Du Pont should know more about its customers' needs than the customers themselves know.

Advertising in a monopoly market, like that of the telephone company and utilities, is intended to increase total sales of the product. Small firms in an atomistic market, e.g., the milk and egg producer's cooperatives, cannot afford advertising unless they band together to advertise cooperatively in an effort to increase total demand. Advertising pays the best dividend in an oligopolistic differentiated product market, where one needs to entice customers from one producer to another. Many CPI firms manufacturing similar products attempt to differentiate by using trade names and extensive advertising. For example, in the transparent plastics market Du Pont manufactures its methyl methacrylate under the trade name Lucite, while Rohm & Haas sells its product as Plexiglas. Union Carbide markets polyethylene Glad bags, and Mobil markets bags of similar composition under the name Hefty. Laundry bleaches which are identical in composition are sold under a host of trade names for a wide variety of prices.

Barriers to entry into the pseudo-commodity business include all those for commodities plus the all-important customer-service know-how. A lack of technical expertise and patent protection can be formidable barriers to potential producers of the pseudo-commodity. Du Pont was the sole producer of nylon from 1939 to 1951. Barriers to entry were removed under threat of government antitrust action in 1951 with the licensing of Chemstrand (now Monsanto). Since then a number of companies have entered the nylon business, and now there are over 10 major producers. Technical know-how and patent protection played a major role in both high- and low-pressure polyethylene manufacture in the years after the

Second World War. Britain's ICI developed polyethylene, but Union Carbide had a superior tubular high-pressure process. Ziegler, Du Pont, and Phillips all developed low-pressure processes in parallel, which they eventually licensed to other manufacturers. Many pseudo-commodities eventually become commodities by the diffusion of technology, standardization of the product, and the entry of many firms into the business.

8.1.3 Fine Chemicals

These are undifferentiated products made in lower volume than commodity chemicals. At the very low volume end of this classification (under 10 million pounds per year), small and flexible batch-processing operations are common. Some typical fine chemicals are tartaric acid, citric acid, camphor, quinine, vitamin C, aspirin, morphine, and strychnine. Many products in SIC 283 and 285 can be classified as fine chemicals. The fine chemical is produced to some defined property specification, which is generally more stringent than most commodity-chemical specifications and the product does not vary much from firm to firm.

Market share depends on pricing policy, quality of the product, and advertising to remind buyers of the existence of the suppliers. Research and development efforts are directed toward improved product purity. A common process improvement is the conversion from a batch to a continuous processing unit, which can be justified when sales volume is sufficiently high.

Barriers to entry include proprietary manufacturing technology, patent protection, marketing ability, and limited market size.

8.1.4 Specialty Chemicals

These are differentiated end products that are formulated or synthesized in low volume and designed to solve specific customer problems. The categories into which the specialty chemicals in Table 8.3 are divided were developed by Kline [1]. Many of these chemicals are highly proprietary items protected by trade secrets as well as by patents and are the end result of expensive research and development.

These specialty chemicals are often much superior in performance to the next best alternative, so that the pricing of such items is determined more by customer's cost savings than by the producer's costs. For instance, zeolite-based cracking catalysts enable oil refiners to increase gasoline yield and octane number without changing their plants. Because of its excellent performance in use, this catalyst can be sold at more than twice the price per pound of the conventional amorphous alumina-silica catalyst. Flavors and fragrances are priced not according to raw-material and processing costs but according to the pleasurable responses of the consumers. Pesticides are selected according to their potency and their discrimination between kinds of insects. Their prices reflect the cost of research and testing,

Table 8.3 Estimated United States sales of specialty chemicals 1973

	(Millions)	
Low-volume types of pseudo-commodities.		
Adhesives	$ 200	
Elastomers	185	
Plastics and resins	800	
Plasticizers	130	
Surfactants	195	
Total		$ 1,510
Multipurpose functional compounds:		
Antioxidants	$ 180	
Biocides	160	
Catalysts	200	
Chelates	25	
Corrosion inhibitors	100	
Dyes	550	
Enzymes	55	
Flame retardants	100	
Pigments, organic	235	
Thickeners	240	
Ultraviolet absorbers	15	
Total		$ 1,860
End-use chemicals:		
Automotive chemicals	$ 510	
Cosmetic specialties	100	
Diagnostic aids	300	
Drilling-mud additives	90	
Flavors and fragrances, compounded	225	
Flotation reagents	70	
Food additives	275	
Foundry additives	75	
Industrial and institutional cleaning products	1,200	
Laboratory chemicals	130	
Metal finishing and plating chemicals	340	
Paint additives	95	
Paper additives	115	
Pesticides, formulated	1,375	
Petroleum additives	500	
Photographic chemicals	250	
Plastics additives	255	
Printing chemicals	50	
Rubber-processing chemicals	220	
Textile chemicals	105	
Water-treatment chemicals	360	
Total		$ 6,640
Grand total		$10,010

Source: C. H. Kline, Maximizing Profits in Chemicals, *CHEM-TECH*, February 1976.

to satisfy the regulations of the Food and Drug Administration and the Environmental Protection Agency. Many specialty products sell at a premium and hence lie to the upper right-hand side of the price–vs.–production-volume line in Fig. 5.4. They sell at higher prices than average products because of their unique characteristics.

Since unique technologies are incorporated in these specialty chemicals, chemical professionals who are innovative in research and development are needed to search for new compounds, new synthesis methods, and new ways to satisfy customers. The total operation is more chemical-professional-intensive and less capital- and raw-material-intensive. The profit margin of specialty chemicals can be very wide and serves as a fitting reward for being different and for being first in the field.

8.1.5 Oligopoly Marketing and the Theory of Games

With few exceptions, all major chemical products are sold in an oligopolistic market. As we saw in Chap. 2, development of a successful marketing strategy in an oligopoly requires that the firm develop some insights into the effect of price changes on its market share, dp/dq. There is an extensive literature [2, 3] devoted to the analysis of oligopoly marketing using the theory of games. Some of the more interesting results will be discussed to help illustrate some principles of pricing strategy useful to the firm.

Consider a chemical product manufactured by two firms, X and Y (a duopoly). These two firms are scheduled to announce the product price for the next quarter. There is some product loyalty, and there are some long-term contracts, so that if the two announced prices are not identical, the lower-priced product will sell more but not necessarily force the other product completely off the market. Let us assume that the price per unit sold can be set only at three discrete levels and that the two firms announce the new prices on the same day without previous knowledge of the other firm's intentions. Let the resulting market share captured by firm X be displayed in the Table 8.4. The market share captured by Y is simply what is left over by subtraction from 100. The table assumes that when the two prices are equal, the two firms share the market evenly; when prices are unequal, the low-priced seller gains market share at the expense of the high-priced seller. If

Table 8.4 Market-share payoff matrix, market share of firm X

Firm X price	Firm Y price		
	$0.80	$0.90	$1
$0.80	50	80	100
$0.90	20	50	80
$1.00	0	20	50

firm X wishes to maximize its share of the market, it is apparent that the strategy of an 80-cent price is better than any other strategy and constitutes the *dominant strategy*. No matter what the price strategy of firm Y, a firm X price of 80 cents will capture more market share than any other firm X price. Similarly, firm Y will come to the same conclusion and choose 80 cents. The two firms will share the market equally. This is an example of a *zero-sum game*, where the two firms compete and the gain of one firm is the loss of the other. The solution of this game results in a *pure strategy* dominated by price of 80 cents for both firms. This is a stable-equilibrium situation where neither firm can improve its position by making unilateral moves.

However, if we also consider the profits of these firms, we have to consider that any higher price might lower total sales but improve the profit margin. Since the sum of the profits of the two firms need not add to a constant, the profit payoff matrix (Table 8.5) has two numbers in each square; the first is the profit to X, and the second is the profit to Y. When the prices are equal and high, both firms enjoy good profits. At some fixed firm X price, say $1, a low firm Y price will mean large sales and profit for Y and deficits for X. As the firm Y price increases at a constant firm X price of $1, X will capture more market and improve profits. Firm Y will lose market but increase profits at a Y price of 90 cents because of improved profit margins. When the price is equal at $1, firm Y's profit is equal to firm X's profit. It is apparent that if the two firms want to maximize their joint profits cooperatively, they should agree on the highest price of $1. A formally agreed price cartel normally carries the risk of the corporate officials' being sent to break rocks at a federal penitentiary; however, it is the prevailing mode of operation for the oil-exporting nations and for the bauxite-exporting nations. Having jointly settled on the price of $1, firm Y may cheat by making secret price concessions to lower the price to 90 cents, which would increase its sales volume and its profits to $30 million. Firm X will inevitably notice the erosion of its sales orders and profit and will have to follow suit by lowering its price (perhaps all the way to 80 cents) to improve on its profit. In the face of this move by firm X, firm Y has no alternative but to lower its price to 80 cents also. Notice that at the final equilibrium, there is a standoff in market share but the profits of both firms have shrunk from $25 to $5

Table 8.5 Profit payoff matrix (millions of dollars)

(X profit, Y profit)			
	Firm Y price		
Firm X price	$0.80	$0.90	$1
$0.80	(5, 5)	(20, 0)	(25, −20)
$0.90	(0, 20)	(15, 15)	(30, 10)
$1.00	(−20, 25)	(5, 30)	(25, 25)

million. A price of $1 for both firms will not be stable, since either firm can improve its own situation by making unilateral moves. This example combines the elements of both competition and cooperation. If both firms are dominated by the philosophy of profit maximization, both should be reluctant to make any price cuts, since the end result will eventually lower profits (from $25 million to $5 million in the example). Some critics claim that such price cartels indeed exist in the United States, if not by formal agreements, then by undeclared informal understandings. International cartels have a history of instability and price concessions by new entries and by firms with "weaker hands."

Consider next a marketing game with no dominant strategy, so that the best strategy is a *mixed strategy*. We can develop a profit payoff matrix (Table 8.6) to illustrate this case by considering a detergent market dominated by firm A. Firm B must decide whether to enter into the production and marketing of a similar detergent. Firm A can announce the price of the detergent and expect that firm B, a new venture with limited production and higher cost, will follow the price leadership. Firm A may set the price high to enjoy a good profit, but that would allow firm B to penetrate the market. Firm A may set the price low enough to force firm B into a discouraging loss position, but this will cause its own profit to be low. Firm B needs to decide whether there is a reasonable chance of some profit if it enters the market or whether the risk is too great. If firm B stays out, firm A has a monopoly and its profit will increase with price. If firm B enters, firm A will lose market share. To compensate for lost market share, firm A will have to advertise heavily in order to increase total market volume. The sales of both firms are assumed to increase as a result of such advertising. Lower prices benefit the low-cost producer, firm A, more than firm B since lower profit margins hurt the high-cost producer, firm B. There is no dominant strategy for A, since a price of 80 cents maximizes A's profits if B enters but a price of $1 is best if B stays out. Likewise, there is no dominant strategy for B, as entry is best if the price is $1 but staying out is best if the price is 80 cents. There is no stable solution, since in any given situation, each firm can improve its own profit by making a unilateral move. Since no single strategy is best for either firm, the best course of action is to adopt the mixed strategy. This is analogous to the childhood game of paper-stone-scissors, where no single move is the best and a random choice between the three

Table 8.6 Profit payoff matrix (millions of dollars)

(A profit, B profit)		
	Firm B strategy	
Firm A strategy, set price at	Enter	Stay out
$1.00	(10, 6)	(40, 0)
$0.90	(12, 2)	(30, 0)
$0.80	(15, −5)	(20, 0)

options (plus psyching the opponent) becomes the best strategy. It is impossible to predict the outcome of this game.

In the CPI of the United States there are over 1,000 duopolys manufacturing mostly specialty chemicals, whose operations can be analyzed with game theory. Most chemicals, however, are made by more than two firms in competition, and the number of strategies each firm can adopt is usually higher than three. The most difficult part of the game-theory analysis is the estimation and assignment of numbers in the payoff matrix. The matrix can be established for a particular situation only by chemical professionals who have had a great deal of experience and who possess the necessary intuition. The principles of game theory remain the same, but the analysis becomes more complicated.

8.2 MANUFACTURING

The manufacturing of chemical and petroleum products often involves high temperatures and pressures and corrosive substances and requires special and expensive equipment. While small batches of specialty chemicals can be made in multiple-purpose equipment, large-volume chemicals are made in special dedicated equipment in continuous and highly instrumented processes. When the capital cost becomes a significant item in the total cost of the product, the plant operates continuously, except for repair and unexpected difficulties, requiring three shifts of labor over a 24-h day. Many chemical plants are highly automated with monitoring instruments and controlled with computers.

The CPI are among the nation's heaviest investors in capital equipment. Several of the major chemical companies make annual capital expenditures in the $200 million to $1,000 million range. Many oil companies have annual capital expenditures in excess of $1 billion. In terms of capital invested per production worker, the petroleum industry far outranks all others (Table 8.7) with $299,100 of capital invested per production worker in 1971, compared with the industrial average of $41,500 for all manufacturing industries. The chemical industry ranks third after petroleum and tobacco, with $81,800 per production worker.

Heavy capital investment in the chemical and petroleum industries is necessary in order to produce large volumes of products efficiently at low prices. If a company produces a commodity or pseudo-commodity chemical, it must operate a very large-scale plant in order to remain competitive in price. For example, ethylene is now produced in plants with capacities of 1 billion pounds annually. The current investment needed for such a plant ranges from $100 million to $200 million. Also, the complex nature of chemical processing and the high rate of wear due to high temperatures, high pressures, corrosion, and continuous operation dictate the use of special materials and intricate equipment. These factors contribute to the capital-intensive nature of the chemical and petroleum industries, as does the increasing need for pollution-abatement and energy-conservation equipment. Lastly, the high rate of innovation contributes to the high rate of capital investment in the CPI.

Table 8.7 Capital investment per production worker, 1971

Industry	Capital invested per production worker (thousands)
Food	$42.0
Tobacco	93.7
Textiles	17.0
Apparel	9.3
Lumber	29.3
Furniture	11.0
Paper	36.1
Printing	28.5
Chemicals	81.8
Petroleum, including refining, transportation, and extraction	299.1
Rubber	26.6
Leather	12.8
Stone, clay, glass	28.5
Primary metals	47.5
Fabricated metals	24.5
Nonelectrical machinery	45.6
Electrical machinery	39.1
Motor vehicles	73.8
Other transportation	48.7
Instruments	37.1
Miscellaneous	21.3
Total manufacturing	41.5

Source: U.S. Bureau of the Census, *Statistical Abstract of the United States: 1975,* 96th ed., table 1258.

For many processes, the average cost AC of producing a chemical can be approximated by[1]

$$AC = \text{constant} \times size^n \qquad (8.1)$$

where n is usually less than 1. There is a good economy of scale in most chemical processing units, and large plants are much more efficient than small ones. There are also processes where capacity expansion is achieved only by duplicating process units of a fixed size. The production of penicillin in several thousand shake flasks ($n = 1$) is one example where there is no economy of scale.

The construction of a plant with a new processing technology carries a significant risk but can lead to significant improvements in efficiency and to the demise of older processes. A heavy rate of plant investment also means that the firm has newer and more efficient processing equipment and is better able to compete by manufacturing at a lower cost.

---

[1] Notation for this chapter is summarized in Sec. 8.8.

8.2.1 Production Functions

CPI firms are engaged in the transformation of various supplies and factors of production into products. The rate of production can be represented in functional form

$$q = f(K, L, S) \tag{8.2}$$

where q = quantity of product produced, mass/year
  K = cost of fixed and working capital per year, consisting of depreciation (dollars per year), return on capital (opportunity cost), and maintenance and repair
  S = cost of supplies, dollars per year
  L = cost of labor, dollars per year

$$L = \sum w_i x_i \tag{8.3}$$

where w_i is wage and x_i is the number of employees of type i needed to produce the product.

To begin any operation, a firm must design and construct a new plant. In this long-run situation, all the above variables are under the control of the chemical professional, who wishes to design an optimum plant. He may have a target production capacity q_0 suggested by the marketing people, and he may also be required to investigate the profitability of various plant sizes. The cost of supplies is usually proportional to the quantity produced

$$S = p_S q_0 \tag{8.4}$$

where p_S is the unit cost of supply per pound of product.

In any design consideration, there is some trade-off between capital and labor. A batch processing plant is more labor-intensive than a continuous processing unit for the same amount of chemical product. A continuous processing unit which is highly instrumented and computer-controlled is more capital-intensive than one designed with minimum instrumentation. A plant designed for minimum maintenance costs more to build but uses less labor than a plant utilizing processing equipment which must be replaced or repaired frequently. Although it appears impractical to a process designer used to conditions in the United States today, it may be feasible to replace a water pump with a bucket brigade when

Table 8.8 Values of q, 10^6 lb/yr

K, \$/yr	L, \$/yr		
	100,000	200,000	400,000
200,000	0.44	0.57	0.76
400,000	0.76	1.00	1.32
800,000	1.32	1.74	2.30

capital is unattainable and labor is very cheap. A more extreme case but still feasible in very unusual circumstances would be the replacement of a distillation column with large numbers of technicians boiling material in glass flasks.

An economy of scale can be achieved in many chemical-plant designs. The experience curves presented in Figs. 2.9, 6.5, and 8.1 have the slope shown partly due to economy of scale. In functional form the scale-up process can be approximated by

$$q(\alpha K, \alpha L, \alpha S) = \alpha^n q(K, L, S) \tag{8.5}$$

where α is the scale-up factor and $n \geq 1$.

An economic constitutive relationship which has a functional form postulated to take account of capital, labor, and their relationship to process plant size is the Cobb-Douglas function:

$$q(K, L) = cK^a L^b \tag{8.6}$$

where c is a constant and a and b are constants with values between 0 and 1 such that $a + b \geq 1$.

An alternate way of presenting the equation shows the scale-up aspect more clearly:

$$\frac{q}{q_0} = \left(\frac{K}{K_0}\right)^a \left(\frac{L}{L_0}\right)^b \tag{8.7}$$

where q_0, K_0, and L_0 are the values for a reference plant at a given time and state of technology. The behavior of this equation can be best illustrated with a numerical example

$$q = 0.25 K^{0.8} L^{0.4} \tag{8.8}$$

Substituting some values for K and L into Eq. (8.8) yields Table 8.8.

A production quota of $q = 0.76$ million pounds can be attained by two different combinations of K and L, one plant being more capital-intensive and the other being more labor-intensive. In fact, any combination of K and L (isoquant) which satisfies the relation

$$K^{0.8} L^{0.4} = 4(0.76 \times 10^6)$$

will produce $q = 0.76$ million pounds.

The table clearly shows the effect of diminishing returns. At a fixed value of K, each doubling of L brings much less than a doubling of production q. As more and more labor is hired, a point is eventually reached where

$$\frac{\partial^2 q}{\partial L^2} < 0 \tag{8.9}$$

The same diminished-return effect is shown for K when L is constant. Doubling K shows less than a doubling of production. If the labor force is fixed and more capital is put into the process, eventually at some point

$$\frac{\partial^2 q}{\partial K^2} < 0 \tag{8.10}$$

Doubling both K and L brings more than a doubling of production. This economy of scale is illustrated by the diagonal elements in the table from upper left to lower right (note that $a + b = 1.2$ for our example).

The optimum ratio of capital to labor must also be a concern of the cost-minimizing chemical professional. This is attained for a given q when the marginal productivity of capital equals the marginal productivity of labor

$$\frac{\partial q}{\partial K} = \frac{\partial q}{\partial L} \tag{8.11}$$

If the marginal productivity of capital were greater than the marginal productivity of labor, a dollar added to capital would bring more production than a dollar added to labor. In such a situation, one should withdraw dollars from labor and add to capital, since this would increase productivity. One should keep on doing this till the two marginal productivities are equal, at which point there would be no incentive for transferring funds from capital to labor or vice versa. For the Cobb-Douglas function [Eq. (8.6)]

$$\frac{\partial q}{\partial k} = caK^{a-1}L^b = \frac{aq}{K}$$

$$\frac{\partial q}{\partial L} = cbL^{b-1}K^a = \frac{bq}{L}$$

At the point where the marginal productivity of labor and capital are equal

$$\frac{K}{L} = \frac{a}{b} \tag{8.12}$$

In our numerical example the optimum capital-labor ratio is $a/b = 2$.

At a given production rate q_0 an expression for the optimal capital and labor costs can be developed in terms of the three parameters a, b, and c:

$$q_0 = c(K_0)^a(L_0)^b = c(K_0)^a \frac{(bK_0)^b}{a}$$

$$K_0 = \left[\frac{q_0}{c}\left(\frac{a}{b}\right)^b\right]^{1/(a+b)} \tag{8.13}$$

A similar development yields

$$L_0 = \left[\frac{q_0}{c}\left(\frac{b}{a}\right)^a\right]^{1/(a+b)} \tag{8.14}$$

For our numerical example

$$K_0 = 4.0q_0^{0.833}$$

Chemical engineers familiar with process economics are used to the "0.6 rule." The cost of process equipment is assumed to follow the relation

$$\text{Cost} = \text{constant} \times \text{size}^{0.6}$$

The exponent is not always 0.6. Typical values range from 0.8 for process vessels to 0.5 for special items such as crystallizers [4]. The purchase equipment cost is often only one-fourth to one-fifth of the total capital cost, and the total capital cost for which K_0 is derived includes many items where the scale-up power is closer to 1 and some items where n should be closer to 0. The power of $1/(a + b) = 0.833$ used in the numerical example may be considered reasonably close to experience.

8.2.2 Long- and Short-Range Average Costs

The average cost of production AC can be computed using the Cobb-Douglas function for both the long-range average cost (LRAC) and the short-range average cost (SRAC). The long-range average cost is

$$\text{LRAC} = \frac{\text{TC}}{q}$$

The total cost is made up of three components, K, the capital cost; L, the yearly labor cost; and S, the cost of supplies:

$$\text{TC} = K + L + S \tag{8.15}$$

For a unit designed to produce q_0 the long-range cost is

$$\text{LRAC} = \frac{K_0 + L_0 + S}{q_0} \tag{8.16}$$

Equations (8.4), (8.13), and (8.14) can be used to yield an expression for LRAC in terms of the Cobb-Douglas parameters and plant size q_0:

$$\text{LRAC} = p_S + \left(1 + \frac{b}{a}\right)(q_0)^{(1-a-b)/(a+b)}\left[\frac{1}{c}\left(\frac{a}{b}\right)^b\right]^{1/(a+b)} \tag{8.17}$$

For the numerical example

$$\text{LRAC} = p_s + 6.0q^{-0.167} \tag{8.18}$$

The long-run average cost is an important planning function for capital investment and is shown in Fig. 8.3 for $p_s = 20$ cents per pound. In this example, the LRAC continues to decline as plant size increases; a larger plant is more efficient. There are cases where the LRAC becomes essentially independent of plant size after it has reached some critical value (Fig. 8.4, curve A); then it is proper to speak of the *minimum efficient size*. An inefficient smaller plant can survive only under special circumstances, e.g., a market sheltered by geographic location or protective tariff, a favorable raw-material supply, or product differentiation. Eventually, many small plants may be closed before they are physically worn out.

There are also cases where the LRAC increases with plant size beyond some *carrying capacity* or infrastructure of the community (Fig. 8.4, curve B), e.g., limited water supply, well-trained labor, and waste disposal, which are beyond the control of the corporate planner. For instance, unless there is a national consensus, a

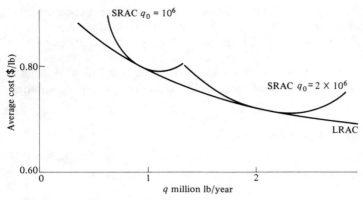

Figure 8.3 Long- and short-range average costs.

company cannot strip-mine coal and bring irrigation water to the arid Southwest for large-scale coal gasification. In the model, p_s becomes a rapidly increasing function of q_0. The prevailing condition in the industrial-chemicals industry is that of declining LRAC, so that larger plants are more efficient. It has led to the construction of larger and larger plants to lower cost, in the hope of capturing the expanding market. When several firms try to capture the same market, the result is often overcapacity and low plant utilization. This can be very costly, as in the case of methanol (Chap. 6). Such overcapacity is less likely in Japan, where all plant-capacity expansions are coordinated and controlled by the Ministry of International Trade and Industry.

After the plant is designed and built, the operating manager takes over and is concerned with short-run optimization, where capital investment is fixed. When

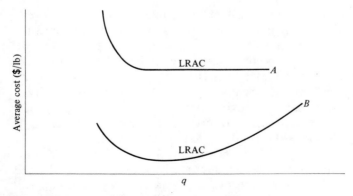

Figure 8.4 Long- and short-range average costs.

the production level changes, the cost of supplies is generally proportional to production when there are no material inefficiencies:

$$S = p_s q$$

S may depend upon q to some power if raw-material efficiency decreases with production rate. A function of the following form was implicitly assumed in Chap. 2:

$$S = p_s q^n$$

where n is usually greater than 1. To simplify the algebra, let us assume that $n = 1$. Then the labor needed to meet production requirement is given by

$$q = C K_0^a L^b \qquad L = \left(\frac{q}{C} \frac{1}{K_0^a} \right)^{1/b} \tag{8.19}$$

If we assume an existing plant with the yearly capital cost K_0 equal to \$400,000 and use the numerical example, we obtain

$$L = (2 \times 10^{-10}) q^{2.5} \tag{8.20}$$

q is a production rate which can vary over a limited range about q_0, the design capacity.

The SRAC is computed as follows:

$$\mathrm{SRAC} = \frac{K_0 + L + p_s q}{q} = p_s + \frac{K_0}{q} + \left(\frac{1}{c K_0^a} \right)^{1/b} q^{(1-b)/b} \tag{8.21}$$

For our example

$$\mathrm{SRAC} = \$0.20 + \frac{400{,}000}{q} + 2 \times 10^{-10} q^{1.5} \tag{8.22}$$

This is similar to the average cost expression derived for the Delos production unit [Eq. (2.20)]:

$$\mathrm{TC} = \frac{\mathrm{AC}}{q} = \frac{45L}{q} + \frac{2}{1 - q/B} \tag{8.23}$$

Equation (2.20) can be rearranged into

$$\mathrm{AC} = \frac{45L}{q} + 2 + 2\frac{q}{B} + \frac{2q^2}{B^2} \tag{8.24}$$

The capital-cost terms are easily identified in Eqs. (8.22) and (8.24). The constant terms 2 and \$0.20 arise partly from the cost of raw materials. The term containing $q^{1.5}$ appears in Eq. (8.22) as a result of labor costs. The terms containing powers of q in Eq. (8.24) appear partly as a result of labor costs and partly as a result of increased raw-material costs due to poorer conversion at higher throughputs.

The curves of SRAC for two design capacities, $q_0 = 1$ million pounds and $q_0 = 2$ million pounds, are also given in Fig. 8.3. When the production volume q is below the designed capacity q_0, SRAC increases since the fixed cost K_0 is spread over a smaller volume of product; when production is above the designed capacity, the decrease in material efficiency and the need for overtime and possibly inexperienced labor also increase the SRAC. A plant of the wrong size is expensive, but if the plant has a lifetime of 20 years, it is seldom of the right size for the entire period. Sometimes the plant capacity can be expanded to suit changing market demand by improvements and "debottlenecking." For example, an oil pipeline can have its flow capacity increased by installing more pumping stations, from a station every 50 mi to a station every 25 mi. Computer control can be installed in an older process to gain better material efficiencies. The LRAC forms the envelope of all the SRAC curves, representing the minimum average cost for plants of all conceivable sizes. Since the production volume q is tied to market demands and can never be predicted with certainty, it is important that the designed capacity q_0 generate a SRAC curve that is the lowest possible within the range of anticipated production requirements. In the design of a plant, there is often a choice between a design that is flexible in regard to changing production volume and raw-material supply and capable of incorporating new processing improvements and another design that is dedicated and narrowly designed to a specialized set of conditions. A firm with several plants may elect to have a mix of flexible and dedicated plants (Fig. 8.5). The design of a flexible plant is more

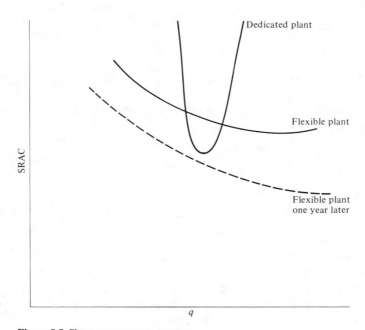

Figure 8.5 Short-range average costs.

tentative, and the equipment employed may have multiple purposes. The operation of a flexible plant requires many more imaginative and resourceful engineers. There is a significant possibility of the lowering of SRAC due to experience gained. The dedicated plant, often a turnkey identical to many existing plants, is rigidly specified with only specialized equipment. It requires fewer engineers and operators, and there is much less potential of process improvement and cost cutting.

All the above discussion is concerned with a given process technology. A new technology should increase the value of c, and it may alter the values of a and b as well. If in the new technology the value of a/b is increased, it is necessary to increase the design value of K_0/L_0. This is an innovation that substitutes capital for labor and is common in the CPI.

Various industries differ greatly in the relative use of capital and labor, from the very labor-intensive garment industry to the very capital-intensive petroleum industry. If we assume that the reported values of capital investment per production worker for the various industries are indeed the optimal ones (Table 8.7), the ratio a/b can be estimated by

$$\frac{K}{L} = \frac{a}{b} = \frac{\text{capital invested}}{\text{production worker}} \times \frac{\text{cost of capital}}{\text{capital invested}} \times \frac{\text{production worker}}{\text{labor wage/year}}$$

$$= \frac{\text{cost of capital}}{\text{cost of labor}}$$

Table 8.9 shows the figures used to obtain the estimate for a/b. Depreciation was assumed to be the same for all industries at 10 percent of capital investment per year. Maintenance is assumed to be the same for all industries at 5 percent of capital investment per year. The return on capital and average wage is available in *Statistical Abstracts*.

The a/b ratio is highest for the petroleum sector. This sector should be spending between \$8 and \$9 for capital per year for every dollar it spends on labor per year. In the rubber sector the ratio is close to 1 and suggests the need of this sector for an even distribution of resources between capital and labor.

Table 8.9 Computation of K/L

$$\frac{K}{L} = \frac{\text{capital invested}}{\text{production worker}} \times \frac{\text{cost of capital}}{\text{capital invested}} \times \frac{\text{production worker}}{\text{labor wage/year}} = \frac{\text{cost of capital}}{\text{cost of labor}}$$

Sector	Capital invested per production worker (Table 8.7)	Return on capital invested	Cost of capital per capital invested†	Average weekly wage	Yearly wage/per production worker	$a/b = k/L$
Petroleum	\$299,100	\$0.109	\$0.259	\$138.4	\$8,997	8.61
Chemical	81,800	0.146	0.296	138.08	8,975	2.70
Paper	36,100	0.120	0.270	111.00	7,150	1.36
Rubber	26,600	0.080	0.230	109.62	7,125	0.86

† Includes return on capital, depreciation, and maintenance.

8.3 EMPLOYMENT

8.3.1 Size of Labor Force and Unemployment

The CPI has created many new jobs through its growth and rapid innovation. In the chemicals and allied products sector alone, total employment has increased by almost 900,000 since the turn of the century (Table 8.10). A breakdown of total employment in all major sectors of the CPI is shown in Table 8.11. Total employment in the CPI sector (3.454 million in 1975) is about 19 percent of all manufacturing and about 5 percent of the total number of persons employed in the United States. The percentage of chemical engineers and chemists for selected CPI sectors was shown in Table 1.8. In the petroleum and coal products sectors, chemical engineers account for 2.18 percent of the total number of employees, whereas chemists account for 1.68 percent.

In a sophisticated manufacturing industry, a high proportion of workers is in the creative functions of research and development engineering and technical service. These are classified as nonproduction workers in any statistical collection. For all manufacturing the ratio of nonproduction to production workers is about 0.4. In the chemical and petroleum sectors this ratio is about 0.6 to 0.8.

United States employment in all manufacturing during the recession of 1975 was some 1.7 million lower than in 1974. The CPI employment decline of 238,000 is only 14 percent of the total, which means that they have suffered less. There were even some sectors in the CPI where there was essentially no change or even an increase in employment (industrial chemicals, drugs, agricultural chemicals, and petroleum). The total unemployment situation is shown in Table 8.12. Unemployment among professional and technical workers is much lower than among all civilian workers. The unemployment rate for all civilian workers increased from 5.6 to 8.5 percent between 1974 and 1975, the worst increase in a decade. Unemployment among professional and technical workers increased more modestly from 2.3 to 3.2 percent.

Table 8.10 Total employment, chemical and allied products

1899	134,000
1939	371,000
1949	618,000
1959	809,000
1975	1,013,000

Source: U.S. Dep. Labor Bull. 1312-6, 1968; *Chem. Eng. News* Facts and Figures issue, June 2, 1975.

Table 8.11 Employment in the CPI

	All employees† (thousands)				Production workers† (thousands)			
	1975	1974	1973	1965	1975	1974	1973	1965
All manufacturing	18,347	20,046	20,068	18,062	13,070	14,613	14,760	13,434
Chemicals and allied products	1,013	1,057	1,033	908	570	612	600	546
Industrial chemicals	324	322	311	290	171	173	169	167
Plastics materials and synthetics	203	230	225	194	133	157	154	131
Drugs	164	165	157	118	81	82	79	67
Soap, cleaners, and toilet goods	119	124	125	106	68	71	71	65
Paints and allied products	65	71	71	66	34	39	40	37
Agricultural chemicals	55	53	50	53	34	32	30	35
Other chemical products	83	93	95	81	49	57	58	51
Petroleum and coal products	197	199	193	183	125	126	122	113
Rubber and plastics products, not elsewhere classified	588	676	677	471	450	530	534	366
Paper and allied products	643	702	701	639	483	540	544	498

† Domestic employment.
Source: Chem. Eng. News, Facts and Figures issue, June 7, 1976.

8.3.2 Wages and Working Conditions

The trend since 1947 for average hourly earnings (constant dollars) in chemical and allied products and in all manufacturing is shown in Table 8.13. The chemical worker has experienced greater increases in earnings than the average industrial worker.

Table 8.12 Unemployed (thousands), 1965–1975

Year	Professional and technical workers %	No.	Managers and administrators, except farm %	No.	All white-collar workers %	No.	All civilian workers %	No.
1975	3.2	425	3.0	276	4.7	2,100	8.5	7,830
1974	2.3	285	1.8	168	3.3	1,418	5.6	5,076
1973	2.2	260	1.4	123	2.9	1,218	4.9	4,304
1972	2.4	282	1.8	145	3.4	1,369	5.6	4,840
1971	2.9	333	1.6	145	3.5	1,387	5.9	4,993
1970	2.0	227	1.3	112	2.8	1,113	4.9	4,088
1969	1.3	144	0.9	76	2.1	780	3.5	2,832
1968	1.2	126	1.0	76	2.0	725	3.6	2,817
1967	1.3	133	0.9	70	2.2	754	3.8	2,975
1966	1.3	125	1.0	76		679	3.8	2,875
1965	1.5	133	1.1	84	2.3	752	4.5	3,366

Source: Chem. Eng. News, Facts and Figures issue, June 7, 1976.

Table 8.13 Hourly earnings in 1958 dollars

Year	Chemical and allied products	All manufacturing
1947	$1.57	$1.57
1957	2.24	2.09
1967	2.82	2.43
1972	6.03	5.51
1976	8.42	7.38

Source: Employment and Earnings. U.S. Dept. of Labor, Bureau of Labor, Statistics (1947–1976).

Table 8.14 shows the trend in wages for production workers in the various sectors of the CPI since 1965. There is a significant difference between the best-paid petroleum workers and the less well paid rubber and agricultural chemical workers.

Table 8.15 shows earnings comparisons with other industry sectors. The highest average hourly wage is $6.76 per hour in the construction industry, followed closely by $5.63 in petroleum, $5.60 in primary metals, and $5.20 in mining. The chemical sector's average wage is $4.88.

The chemical industry has many potential hazards for its workers but also boasts an excellent safety record. The manufacturing sector has the lowest number of injuries per 1,000 employees per year. Primary metals, mining, construction, and forest have the highest number of injuries per 1,000 employees per year.

Unionization is an indication of worker alienation from management. Of the manufacturing sectors, chemicals has the second lowest percentage of unionized

Table 8.14 Wages in the CPI (not corrected for inflation)

	Hourly earnings				Weekly earnings			
	1975	1974	1973	1965	1975	1974	1973	1965
All manufacturing	$4.81	$4.41	$4.08	$2.61	$189.51	$176.40	$166.06	$107.53
Chemicals and allied products	5.37	4.85	4.48	2.89	219.63	201.76	187.71	121.09
Industrial chemicals	5.93	5.38	4.97	3.24	254.50	229.19	212.22	136.08
Plastics materials and synthetics	5.25	4.69	4.34	2.84	214.20	193.70	182.28	120.70
Drugs	5.13	4.64	4.26	2.63	208.79	192.10	177.22	107.04
Soap, cleaners, and toilet goods	5.21	4.81	4.47	2.78	210.48	195.29	182.38	113.15
Paints and allied products	4.94	4.49	4.19	2.72	197.60	180.95	172.63	113.15
Agricultural chemicals	4.73	4.24	3.85	2.32	201.50	180.62	164.01	100.69
Other chemical products	5.05	4.60	4.25	2.78	204.02	189.52	177.23	116.48
Petroleum and coal products	6.42	5.61	5.21	3.28	267.07	238.43	220.38	138.42
Rubber and plastics products, not elsewhere classified	4.35	4.03	3.80	2.61	172.70	162.81	156.18	109.62
Paper and allied products	4.99	4.51	4.19	2.65	207.58	189.87	178.91	114.22

Source: Chem. Eng. News, Facts and Figures issue, June 7, 1976.

Table 8.15 Employment conditions in various sectors

	Number employed in nonagricultural industry, 1974	Workers' injuries per 100 employees per year	1972 union members, %	Average hourly wage
Total	78,334			
Private industry	64,050	...	...	$4.22
Mining	672	19.1	49.3	5.20
Construction	3,985	19.8	69.1	6.76
Manufacturing	20,016	15.3	44.6	4.40
Stone, clay, glass	689	18.2	46.0	4.52
Primary metals	1,335	20.8	59.5	5.00
Forest	8,179	19.2	11.4	3.98
Paper	707	15.8	66.4	4.50
Chemical	1,060	9.7	26.8	4.85
Petroleum	195	9.7	39.5	5.63
Rubber	681	17.8	39.6	4.03
Leather	285	12.4	46.0	3.01
Transportation utility	4,699	10.3	55.4	5.40
Trade	17,011	8.6	7.5	3.47
Finance, insurance, real estate	4,161	2.4	0.8	3.81
Services	13,506	6.2	12.2	3.74
Government	14,285			

Source: U.S. Bureau of the Census, *Statistical Abstract of the United States: 1975.*

workers, 26.8 percent. Only forest products is lower, at 11.4 percent. Clearly there has been no disadvantage to chemical workers in not being unionized; their wages are better than the manufacturing average, and their safety record is the best by almost a factor of 2.

The salaries of chemists are surveyed annually by the American Chemical Society (ACS) and published in *Chemical and Engineering News.* The 1977 survey (Table 8.16) showed a continued gap between the salaries of chemists and chemical engineers. Part of the difference in salary is due to the fact that the chemical engineers in the sample had had longer experience than the chemists. It also is believed that the chemical engineer's closer identification with industrial needs played a crucial role in this gap. Another factor is the larger percentage of chemists working in the lower-paid professions of education and teaching. An advanced degree beyond the bachelor's does seem to yield a long-term financial advantage. The salaries of women chemists continue to trail behind those of men, partly due to their relative lack of seniority. As the chemists' age and experience increase, their salaries gradually increase but appear to reach a maximum at about 25 years of experience. In Table 8.17, the salary spread between the lowest and the highest 10 percentile has also increased. It is interesting to note that as age increases, job dissatisfaction drops, as shown in Fig. 8.6.

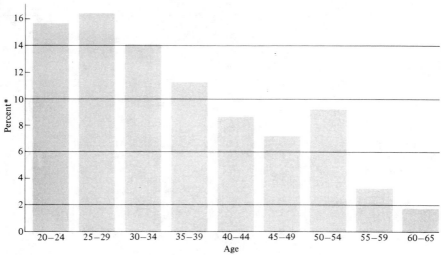

*Percentage of respondents to ACS survey that are employed full-time who are seeking other employment.

Figure 8.6 Steady drop of job dissatisfaction with age. (*Chem. Eng. News, June, 1977.*)

The salaries of chemical engineers are surveyed annually by the American Institute of Chemical Engineers. The 1976 median-salary survey of chemical engineers is given in Table 8.18. It appears that the economic advantages of obtaining a postbachelor's degree are only modest, although surveys by the ACS and the Engineers' Joint Council indicate that the time and effort spent to obtain a degree beyond the bachelor's is worthwhile (Fig. 8.7). Large companies pay somewhat more than small companies. There is a much wider range of income for the

Table 8.16 Comparison of median salaries of chemical professionals (thousands)

	1974	1975	1976	1977	Change 1976–1977, %
Chemists:					
B.S.	$17.5	$19.0	$19.8	$21.0	6
M.S.	18.4	19.8	20.5	22.0	7
Ph.D.	21.7	23.0	24.7	26.0	5
Weighted average					6
Chemical engineers					
B.S.	$21.3	$24.0	$26.0	$28.0	8
M.S.	22.4	25.0	27.0	30.0	11
Ph.D.	24.8	26.0	29.0	30.0	3
Weighted average					7

Table 8.16 (*continued*)

Salaries as of March 1977 (thousands)

	B.S.				M.S.				Ph.D.			
	All chemists	Men	Women	Women's as % of men's	All chemists	Men	Women	Women's as % of men's	All chemists	Men	Women	Women's as % of men's
By employer:												
Industry	$22.0	$22.5	$15.9	71	$24.0	$24.0	$19.1	80	$29.5	$29.6	$23.0	78
Education	13.0	13.7	11.5	84	16.0	16.5	15.0	91	20.0	20.0	16.5	83
Government	21.0	22.0	18.1	82	23.2	24.0	19.0	79	28.0	28.0	23.8	85
Self-employed	26.0	26.0	†	†	26.0	26.0	†	†	30.0	30.0	†	†
Nonprofit	15.0	17.2	13.2	77	18.5	21.0	14.6	70	25.0	26.0	20.0	77
By work activity:												
R & D	19.9	20.5	15.8	77	21.0	22.0	18.4	84	26.0	26.0	21.0	81
Management	27.0	27.5	17.3	63	29.0	29.6	20.0	68	35.0	35.0	28.3	81
Teaching	12.0	12.0	12.8	107	16.3	17.2	14.8	86	19.8	20.0	16.5	83
Marketing, production	20.7	21.0	15.0	71	22.2	22.5	14.5	64	28.0	28.0	25.0	89
By specialty:												
Analytical	19.5	20.0	15.3	77	20.0	21.0	17.2	82	24.0	24.0	19.0	79
Organic	22.0	23.0	16.2	70	24.0	24.7	18.0	73	25.0	25.0	20.0	80
Polymer	23.0	23.4	17.6	75	24.5	25.0	19.0	76	29.5	29.6	27.8	94
Biochemistry	18.2	20.0	15.8	79	20.4	21.6	16.4	76	26.0	27.0	20.0	74
Physical	22.5	23.0	15.0	65	24.0	24.0	†	†	23.0	23.5	19.6	83
Inorganic	24.0	24.0	16.5	69	24.0	25.7	18.0	70	22.0	22.0	15.1	69

† Sample too small for meaningful data.
Source: Chem. Eng. News, June 20, 1977.

277

Table 8.17 Chemists' median annual salary as of March 1977

(Thousands)

Years of experience

Percentile (rank)	1		2–4		5–9		10–14		15–19		20–24		25–29		30–34		35–39		40+		Overall	
	All	Indus-trial	All	Indus-trial	All	Indus-trial	All	Indus-trial	All	Indus-trial	All	Indus-trial	All	Indus-trial	All	Indus-trial	All	Indus-trial	All	Indus-trial	All	Indus-trial
Lower 10%:																						
Bachelors	$8.0	$9.1	$10.0	$11.3	$12.0	$13.0	$14.5	$15.0	$16.1	$16.6	$17.0	$18.0	$18.0	$18.3	$18.0	$19.2	$17.1	$18.0	$20.0	$20.0	$12.9	$13.5
Masters	10.0	13.0	11.0	13.2	12.3	14.5	14.2	16.5	15.0	18.7	17.4	20.0	18.1	20.0	18.0	20.0	16.5	19.0	19.0	18.0	14.0	15.6
Doctors	9.3	18.3	12.4	19.0	14.5	20.4	16.5	23.0	18.5	24.4	20.5	25.0	21.7	25.0	21.2	26.0	23.4	25.0	25.0	30.0	16.0	21.0
Lower 25%:																						
Bachelors	9.7	11.3	12.0	12.5	14.2	15.0	17.5	17.7	19.0	20.0	20.0	20.9	22.0	22.0	22.6	23.0	21.0	21.6	24.0	23.5	16.0	16.9
Masters	11.4	13.3	13.0	14.9	15.0	16.3	17.5	19.9	19.0	21.0	21.8	23.8	22.0	24.0	22.3	24.0	21.5	22.0	21.0	21.0	17.1	19.0
Doctors	11.5	19.0	14.8	20.0	17.5	22.0	19.8	26.0	22.5	28.0	25.0	28.8	26.4	30.0	26.0	30.0	28.8	30.0	30.0	32.0	20.0	24.0
Median:																						
Bachelors	11.5	12.0	13.9	14.0	16.4	16.8	20.0	20.0	22.0	23.0	24.0	24.0	25.0	25.0	26.2	26.5	26.0	26.3	26.6	26.0	21.0	22.0
Masters	13.2	14.0	15.5	16.0	17.5	18.8	21.1	22.3	22.5	24.0	26.0	27.5	26.8	27.5	26.2	28.0	27.5	29.0	30.0	30.0	22.0	24.0
Doctors	16.8	20.0	20.0	21.5	22.0	25.0	25.2	29.1	28.0	31.1	30.0	33.0	32.6	36.0	33.0	36.0	35.8	37.0	35.0	35.5	26.0	29.5
Upper 25%:																						
Bachelors	13.0	13.8	15.6	16.0	18.8	19.0	23.4	23.5	26.0	26.9	28.0	29.0	30.0	30.4	34.2	35.0	32.6	33.0	35.0	35.0	26.5	27.0
Masters	14.0	15.6	17.6	18.0	20.0	20.2	24.3	25.0	25.3	26.4	30.0	32.4	31.0	32.4	32.0	35.0	33.0	33.5	36.4	40.0	27.5	29.0
Doctors	20.0	21.0	22.0	23.1	26.0	28.4	30.0	33.6	33.7	36.3	36.0	39.0	40.0	44.0	40.0	44.0	43.0	46.0	43.0	45.0	32.5	35.0
Upper 10%:																						
Bachelors	14.5	15.3	17.0	17.4	21.0	22.0	26.0	26.0	31.0	32.0	33.0	34.6	37.0	37.0	43.0	43.0	41.7	42.5	41.7	41.7	34.0	35.0
Masters	15.9	16.4	19.5	19.5	22.1	22.6	27.5	28.1	30.0	34.7	35.0	37.0	38.5	40.0	40.0	45.0	40.0	40.0	45.0	60.0	34.0	35.0
Doctors	21.2	22.0	24.0	25.0	29.7	31.0	35.0	37.2	39.0	40.4	43.0	46.0	50.0	54.0	47.0	50.0	50.0	68.0	50.0	72.0	40.0	43.5

Source: Chem. Eng. News, June 20, 1977.

Table 8.18 Salary of chemical engineers, 1976

Median salary by year of degree (thousands)

Year of B.S.	Highest degree Bachelor	Highest degree Master	Highest degree Ph.D.	Year of B.S.	Highest degree Bachelor	Highest degree Master	Highest degree Ph.D.
1975	$15.0			1953	$30.0	$30.5	$30.0
1974	15.0	$16.7		1952	30.25	33.5	33.0
1973	16.0	17.0		1951	32.5	34.0	32.5
1972	17.0	17.5		1950	32.25	33.0	31.0
1971	17.5	18.0	$18.75	1949	30.5	30.5	30.75
1970	18.5	18.5	21.75	1948	31.0	33.0	33.0
1969	20.0	20.0	20.75	1947	34.5	31.0	30.0
1968	20.0	20.75	22.0	1946	25.0	29.75	33.0
1967	20.5	22.5	21.5	1945	27.5	40.0	34.5
1966	22.0	23.0	23.0	1944	36.0	32.5	34.0
1965	22.25	24.5	24.0	1943	33.0	38.0	37.0
1964	23.5	24.5	26.0	1942	35.0	33.5	35.75
1963	24.0	24.0	25.0	1941	35.0	30.0	47.0
1962	25.0	24.0	25.0	1940	38.5	38.0	31.5
1961	28.0	28.0	27.0	1939	35.0	43.0	36.0
1960	25.0	26.75	27.0	1938	40.0	35.0	38.0
1959	26.5	25.75	28.25	1937	37.0	39.0	39.0
1958	29.0	30.5	28.0	1936	36.5	31.5	†
1957	28.25	30.5	28.0	1935	32.5	39.5	31.0
1956	28.0	30.0	31.0	1934	50.75	39.5	33.0
1955	30.5	32.5	29.5	1933	†	36.5	†
1954	29.0	28.25	29.75	pre-1933	32.5	32.0	32.5

Compensation (thousands)

	Overall salary summary 1975	Overall salary summary 1976	Fees in addition to salary 1975	Fees in addition to salary 1976	Consultants' fees, etc., self-employment 1975	Consultants' fees, etc., self-employment 1976	Salary by sex Male	Salary by sex Female
Lower decile	14.0	16.0	0.5	0.5	10.75	4.5	16.5	14.5
Lower quartile	17.0	20.0	1.0	1.5	20.0	15.0	20.0	14.5
Median	22.0	25.0	3.0	3.0	30.0	27.5	25.0	16.0
Upper quartile	28.0	32.0	6.0	8.0	40.5	50.0	33.0	19.0
Upper decile	36.0	42.0	14.0	15.0	75.0	80.0	43.0	25.0

Salary measure by size of company (thousands)

Number of employees	Median 1975	Median 1976	Mean, 1976
1–199	21.0	25.0	28.0
200–999	21.0	24.0	25.9
1,000–4,999	21.5	25.0	27.2
5,000 and over	23.5	26.75	30.9

† Sample too small for meaningful data.
Source: AIChE survey, 1976.

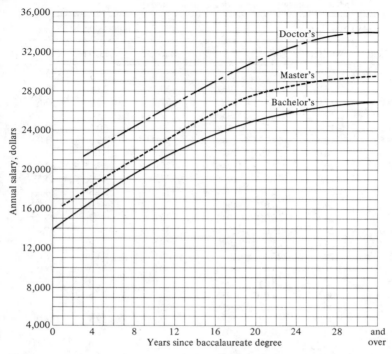

Figure 8.7 Median salaries by degree level for engineers 1976. (*Engineers' Joint Council, 1976.*)

self-employed consultants than for the employed engineers. Women engineers are a fairly recent phenomenon, and their lack of seniority probably limits their top pay.

8.3.3 Supply and Demand of Labor

The balance of supply and demand determines the numerical level of chemical professionals as well as their salary and wage level.

According to the theory of marginal productivity, a firm that wishes to maximize profit will try to compare the incremental value gained by hiring an extra employee with the incremental cost. The profit of a firm is given by

$$\pi(q) = \text{TR} - \text{TC} \qquad (2.21)$$

Two expressions have been used for total cost TC, Eqs. (2.10) and (8.16). Since Eq. (8.16) explicitly includes labor, we will use it to facilitate our discussion in this section:

$$\pi(q) = pq - K - S - L \qquad (8.24)$$

An expression for L is given by

$$L = \sum w_i x_i \qquad (8.3)$$

where x_i is the number of operators, technicians, chemists, accountants, managers, chemical engineers, etc., needed to operate the business and w_i is the wage of each type of employee.

If all else remains constant, the incremental profit of hiring an extra employee of type i is

$$\frac{\partial \pi}{\partial x_i} = \frac{\partial (pq - K - S)}{\partial x_i} - \frac{\partial (L)}{\partial x_i} \qquad (8.25)$$

since

$$\frac{\partial (L)}{\partial x_i} = \frac{\partial (w_i x_i)}{\partial x_i} = w_i$$

The marginal value of hiring the extra employee MV_i is

$$MV_i = \frac{\partial (pq - K - S)}{\partial x_i} = p \frac{\partial q}{\partial x_i} + \frac{\partial p}{\partial x_i} q - \frac{\partial K}{\partial x_i} - \frac{\partial S}{\partial x_i} = w_i \qquad (8.26)$$

The marginal value of hiring the extra employee may take any one of a number of forms:

1. An increase in reaction yield as a result of creative bench-scale chemistry. For instance, if a chemist could increase the value of the reaction rate constant in the Delos process (Example 2.1) from 0.005 to 0.006 min^{-1}, some \$200,000 per year could be saved in total costs. It would be well worthwhile to hire such a chemist!
2. An increase in sales as a result of hiring more and/or better salespersons and technical service people.
3. A decrease in plant costs as a result of hiring more and or better capital design and construction engineers.
4. An decrease in raw-material costs by innovative process design. For instance if a chemical engineer could make process changes which increase the concentration of Algol in the feed to the Delos production unit from 0.20 to 0.24 mol/l, it would lower production costs by some \$270,000.

A rational firm should hire an employee whose marginal value is greater than the wage. The estimation of probable MV_i by the plant supervision is often intuitive and inexact.

If all other factors are kept constant, the hiring of more and more employees of type i will lead sooner or later to diminished return. For a firm engaged in selling commercial catalysts, the presence of a few highly skilled specialists in catalyst preparation is essential. Their departure would bring great loss to the firm. However, doubling the number of such highly skilled specialists will generally bring the firm much less than double additional value. On the other hand, the marginal value of low-skilled day laborers may have a very flat profile. Both

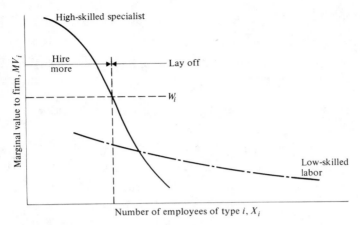

Figure 8.8 Employee demand curve.

profiles are shown in Fig. 8.8. A rational firm should keep on adding employees of type i until the MV_i falls to the value of w_i; the firm should also discharge employees of type j if MV_j is less than w_j. This process should continue till MV_j rises to w_j. Therefore, the demand schedule for employees of type i in a firm is the curve of marginal value vs. numbers, and the industry-wide demand schedule is the sum of all the curves for the individual firms.

There are several components to the marginal value of labor to a firm. It has been pointed out that a salesman may increase the sales volume q. Technical-service people can increase the convenience and confidence of customers and

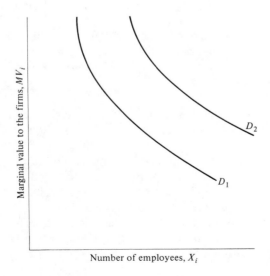

Figure 8.9 Employee demand curve.

thereby increase q. Product engineers and chemists can improve the performance and usefulness of products, thereby increasing both q and p. Manufacturing and process engineers can decrease the consumption of capital and supplies for the production of a pound of product. *An employee is worth his keep if the value of his contribution is greater than his wage.* Some firms, less concerned with profit maximization, may refrain from laying off an old and loyal employee even if his MV is less than his w.

The demand schedule for employees is not static. When there is an increase in demand for the products of the firm or an increase in product price, the marginal value of employees increases. An increase in GNP and the various sectors of final demand affects the employment of chemical professionals by increasing their marginal value MV to the CPI. The MV of chemical professionals may be increased upon the introduction of a new product that is much desired by the public or upon the introduction of a more efficient process and equipment. The demand schedule for chemical professionals would then shift from curve D_1 to curve D_2 in Fig. 8.9.

There are three main sources for the supply of chemical professionals:

1. New college graduates with degrees in chemistry and chemical engineering
2. Immigrants with chemistry and chemical engineering degrees
3. People with no college degree or with degrees in other fields such as mechanical engineering, mathematics, and physics who are willing to change their fields

Eugene Houdry, the inventor of cracking catalyst, was an immigrant from France. Thomas Midgely, the inventor of Freon and tetraethyllead, was a mechanical engineer. In a given year, many of the chemical engineering and chemistry

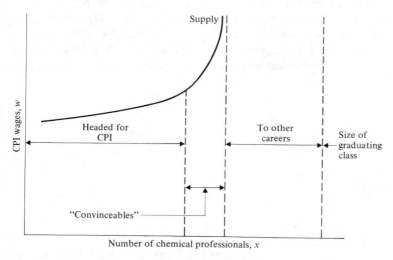

Figure 8.10 CPI supply curve for chemical professionals.

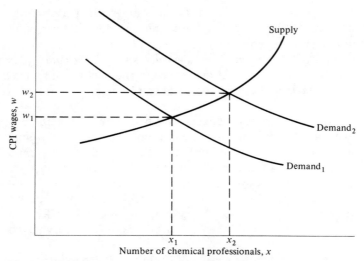

Figure 8.11 Supply and demand for chemical professionals.

graduates look for jobs in the CPI, but a significant number select other career objectives such as medicine, law, and business. Besides these two groups with their minds already made up, there are other convinceables who will work in the CPI if salaries are high enough and will do something else otherwise. The supply schedule shown in Fig. 8.10 is the relation between salary level in CPI and the number of chemical professionals willing to join the CPI.

The simple theory predicts that the market clears at the intersection of the supply and demand schedules (Fig. 8.11). Under demand schedule D_1, we have the happy situation that the intersection is at x_1, so that everyone wanting a job in the CPI can have one. If the demand schedule expands to curve D_2, a significant portion of the convinceables also enter employment in the CPI. This group includes people who might have gone to law school until they heard about the salary increase and mechanical engineers who transferred with the help of

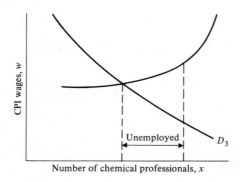

Figure 8.12 Supply and demand of chemical professionals (unemployment).

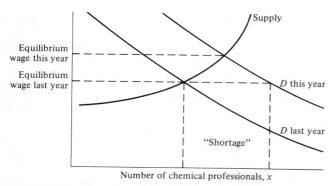

Figure 8.13 Supply and demand of chemical professionals (shortage).

evening classes and on-the-job training. On the other hand, if the demand schedule contracts to curve D_3, a significant portion of those seeking jobs in CPI are unable to find them and are unemployed (Fig. 8.12).

To this simple theory, we need to add the speed and mechanism of market adjustment to new equilibrium conditions and to consider the effects of adding a new employee on other employees. Suppose the demand schedule expands but the supply schedule remains unchanged; then the new equilibrium wage will be higher than the equilibrium wage of last year. Firms making offers at last year's wage will find that the percentage of refusals is much greater and will start to complain of a "shortage" of chemical professionals (Fig. 8.13). The reasonable interpretation of the shortage is the unavailability of sufficient numbers of engineers at last year's wage. If the firms adjust to the new realities of a higher equilibrium wage, the market is cleared and there is no longer a shortage. If the CPI thinks it is desirable to have 10,000 new chemical engineers each year and is willing to pay much higher salaries to obtain them, the supply will be limited only by the aptitude and endurance of young people for organic chemistry and transport phenomena. What is sometimes termed shortage is really a lack of demand or an announced need not backed with sufficient dollars.

Let us examine how the employment market adjusts to the new equilibrium. Information flow in the employment market of chemical professionals is very slow and uncertain, in comparison with the New York Stock Exchange and the Chicago Commodity Market. At first, a firm finds out that after making a larger number of offers to new graduates at last year's wage level, the percentage of refusals has greatly increased. This is the first indication that this year's hiring quota cannot be met at last year's wage. There are usually other hints and rumors that some firms in the CPI are offering higher salaries. A conference of college recruiters and managers coupled with telephone calls to university placement offices convinces the local management that an increase over last year's salary is necessary. Such increases must be approved by company headquarters. It takes some time to convince management and to execute the new policy. The upward adjustment of starting salary is then communicated to the students, some of whom are better informed than others. Adjustment to the new equilibrium takes place over a period of months.

The hiring of new employees at increased wage levels has an impact on existing employees. To take care of any effect on other employees a total derivative of labor cost with respect to x_i must be considered.

$$\frac{\partial L}{\partial x_i} = \frac{\partial}{\partial x_i} \left(\sum w_j x_j \right) = \frac{\partial}{\partial x_i} (w_i x_i) + \frac{\partial}{\partial x_i} \left(\sum_{j \neq i} w_j x_j \right)$$

$$= w_i + x_i \frac{\partial w_i}{\partial x_i} + \frac{\partial}{\partial x_i} \left(\sum_{j \neq i} w_j x_j \right) \tag{8.27}$$

The first term on the right side is the proposed starting wage w_i. The second term, $x_i(\partial w_i / \partial x_i)$, is the increase in starting salary needed multiplied by the number of employees x_i of type i already on the payroll. Since an increase in starting salary is proposed to win over the new employee, this news cannot be insulated from the older employees, who would certainly expect a similar increase to retain parity. If a firm is unwilling to give any increase, the older employees have the option of resigning and moving to a new firm or of remaining for nonmonetary considerations. A firm with a very large number of employees of type i already on the payroll would be reluctant to increase w_i, since the marginal cost of the new employee is not simply w_i but also the much larger $x_i(\partial w_i / \partial x_i)$. An increase in w_i may be inevitable unless all firms form a cartel to suppress wages. (A possible stay in federal penitentiaries is the risk of such a venture.) The third term on the right of Eq. (8.27) needs to be included because there is always a possibility of substitution of one type of employee for another type. For some jobs, a mechanical engineer can substitute for a chemical engineer. An increase in w_i could also lead to demand for wage increase from all the other types of employees w_j.

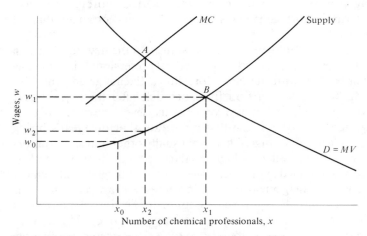

Figure 8.14 Supply and demand set by marginal cost of labor.

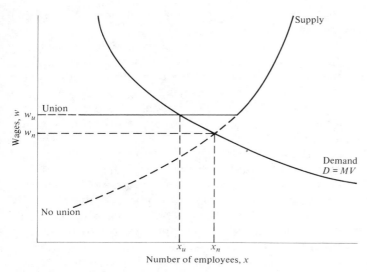

Figure 8.15 Union modified supply-demand equilibrium.

An example of the other-employee effect is given in Fig. 8.14. Suppose a firm employs x_0 employees at wage w_0. Due to business expansion, a new MV has been developed, shifting the demand curve to a new position $D = \text{MV}$. The number of employees x should be set at point A, where $\text{MC} = \text{MV}$. The marginal cost of extra labor is

$$\text{MC} = \frac{dL}{dx} = \frac{d(wx)}{dx} = w + x\frac{dw}{dx} \qquad (8.28)$$

If it were possible to keep the salary of any new employee secret, the firm could hire $x_1 - x_0$ new employees at wage w_1 (point B Fig. 8.14) and keep all old employees at a wage of w_0. This is not all acceptable practice, however, since all employees need comparable pay for comparable jobs. The firm will have to set the employment level at x_2, where $\text{MC} = \text{MV}$, and offer all employees the same wage w_2. A firm cannot consider the employment of new personnel in isolation from the needs of the existing employees.

The equilibrium theory of supply and demand applies only when there is perfect communication. Any inefficiency in information flow makes adjustment slow and uneven. Besides the reluctance of large firms to increase w_i, most firms today are unwilling to offer wages much lower than last year's to the unemployed. Having employees doing the same job but being paid at different rates invites conflict in the company and movement toward unionization. A union or the threat of unionization effectively makes the supply schedule horizontal at the low end. It may have the effect of keeping the wage level higher, but also making the employment level lower than otherwise. In the situation depicted in Fig. 8.15 a union sets a minimum wage at w_u and alters the supply schedule. The equilibrium wage w_u is higher than that without a union at w_n, but the number of employed x_n is smaller. It is sometimes argued that unions have a useful role when there is a monopsony (only one firm hiring engineers) or an oligopsony (few firms hiring engineers). Such cases do not appear to exist in the CPI, where thousands of firms bid for the services of chemical professionals. There may be few employers for very highly specialized talents, so that a union of Raman spectroscopists could conceivably develop a "code of ethics" for minimum salary and prosper. But without legal protection of exclusive job jurisdiction, chemical professionals have no impregnable barriers against entry by outsiders.

Some chemical engineers and chemists have argued that a sure way to increase professional prestige and pay would be to restrict the supply schedule by limiting enrollment in the universities and by complete exclusion of immigration. They point to the income of medical doctors and plumbers for the wisdom of contracting supply. However, the exclusive right to practice medicine and to fix plumbing are specified in law, so that control of supply can actually be achieved even to the disadvantage of the public. There are no job functions that the law recognizes as the exclusive domain of degreed and certified chemists and chemical engineers. When firms in the CPI face a shortage of chemists and chemical engineers, they may establish on-the-job training programs for ambitious young people without such degrees and defeat the purpose of supply contraction.

Of course, the salaries of chemical professionals of the same vintage are not uniform. Chemical professionals are a differentiated product, not a commodity, and some are worth more to a firm than others. Firms in the CPI are also differentiated, and starting salary is not the only factor which a prospective employee considers. Some companies are located in particularly desirable geographical areas with agreeable climate and surroundings or with outstanding cultural and educational resources. Some companies offer the opportunity of rapid advancement, and some companies challenge the entrepreneurial spirit of the graduate and offer participation in creating new businesses.

But to some extent, the salary dispersion among members of the same vintage is a manifestation of ignorance in the market. A college graduate and a firm make decisions based on incomplete information. For instance, many graduates might have taken their first jobs with some other firm except that no recruiters came at the right time. The cost of acquiring this rapidly obsolete market information can be very high and cannot be supported by an individual alone. A rational professional will continue to search for companies and better wage offers until the expected marginal return is equal to the marginal cost of search. The expected marginal return is the subjective judgment that the next company would offer more money than the best offer in hand. The expected cost of search depends on the position of the professional. The most popular market places for buyers and sellers to get together are university placement bureaus, trade magazines, professional association meetings, employment brokers, and the informal source of the grapevine. For recent graduates the expected cost of search is minimal, since they reside in a designated market. All they need do is to pay some attention to the placement-bureau bulletin board, fill out forms, be interviewed, and talk to professors and fellow students. They can search many places at very little cost, and their ignorance of the market should be minimal. It is well known that the salary distribution among new graduates is relatively narrow.

For the professional with a few years of industry experience the salary distribution is much broader, and as time goes on, large differences between the salary of one professional and another can develop. A good part of the salary dispersion can be explained by growing recognition of a dispersion of knowledge, skill, and drive among employees. Another part of this dispersion may be explained by the employee's growing ignorance of the market and by the reluctance to change jobs due to noneconomic factors. For instance, in Japan, where lifetime employment in one firm is the rule, the move from one company to another is suspiciously close to disloyalty. Older professionals in the United States occasionally talk to their former professors college placement offices and to exceptionally well-informed fellow workers. They may also advertise and hire the service of professional employment agencies. But perhaps the best method of getting themselves known is by going to meetings, publishing and presenting papers, and being active in professional societies. In any case, since their marginal cost of a search is much higher than that of a college student, they need a much higher expected marginal return to justify searching for a new position.

8.4 FINANCE

This section discusses two major financial considerations which are of singular importance to any business, profitability and capital structure. Some companies in the CPI generate an awesome flow of cash and profit, the significance of which must be analyzed by appropriate financial ratios and by comparisons with other enterprises before they can be understood. For instance, in 1975, Exxon generated a net income of $2.5 billion, a seemingly unconscionable profit in a world where poverty still runs rampant. But in comparison to its sales of $44.9 billion, there was a profit margin of only 5.6 percent, or about 1.5 cents on the 35 cents received at the refinery gate per gallon of gasoline. In comparison to its assets of $32.8 billion, it is earning 7.6 percent on its investment, which is more risky and not as profitable as long-term bank rates. About half the $32.8 billion of asset is borrowed, leaving the stockholders with an equity of $17.0 billion, so that the earning on equity is 14.7 percent, much better than bank rates.

In 1974, the profits of Occidental Petroleum increased by 269 percent over the previous year, an increase of $204 million. Some critics have called it an obscene profit. Another way of looking at this profit is through the comparison in Table 8.19. The startling increase of profit in 1974 was achieved in a recovery from a miserable performance in the previous 2 years to a more normal profit plus a 60 percent increase in sales volume. Viewed in this light, Occidental's 1974 profits appear to be much less than a windfall.

The management of a firm is entrusted with capital from stockholders and lenders, who expect their investments to produce profit at reasonable risks. The

Table 8.19 Occidental Petroleum

Year	Sales (millions)	Profit margin, %	Profit (millions)
1972	$2,721	0.7	$ 19.0
1973	3,456	2.2	76.0
1974	5,538	5.1	280.7

ultimate sources of capital are in the savings of individuals, bank deposits, and insurance and pension plans. These funds are sometimes directly invested by individuals, but investments are increasingly made indirectly by professional managers of credit unions, by pension trust officers, and by insurance and bank portfolio managers. These investors are constantly examining alternate investments in terms of yield and security and rapidly withdraw investments in firms that show symptoms of weakness. Such action on the part of investors damages a firm's future ability to raise more capital in the market when it wishes to replace worn equipment and to implement new technologies.

The capital structure is concerned with the ratio of borrowed capital to owner's equity. It is generally cheaper to use borrowed money if you can secure lenders and if the economy is going smoothly. A highly leveraged company also faces the downside risk when business is bad. Stockholders receive high dividends only when profits are good, but the interests and principals of bondholders must be paid on time, with the threat of insolvency and bankruptcy. The financial officers of the company are concerned with the optimum debt-to-equity ratio.

8.4.1 Profitability

Table 8.20 shows net sales, net income, and net income as a percentage of sales for the CPI and for all manufacturing. Excise taxes, such as gasoline tax, are not included in net sales, so that the figures reported here would be lower than those

Table 8.20 Net sales and income of the CPI, 1972–1974

Year	Net sales (millions)	Net income (millions)	Net income as percentage of sales
Chemicals and allied products (ESIC 28)			
1975	$86,935	$6,558	7.5
1974	86,805	7,246	8.3
1973	83,581	5,686	6.8
1972	70,427	4,499	6.4
Industrial chemicals and synthetics (ESIC 28.1)			
1975	$40,904	$2,794	6.8
1974	43,121	3,524	8.2
1973	39,612	2,553	6.4
1972	33,162	1,809	5.5

Table 8.20 (*continued*)

Year	Net sales (millions)	Net income (millions)	Net income as percentage of sales
		Drugs (ESIC 28.3)	
1975	$13,217	$1,563	11.8
1974	12,092	1,463	12.1
1973	15,188	1,545	10.2
1972	13,341	1,347	10.1
		Petroleum and coal products (ESIC 29)	
1975	$124,048	$ 9,229	7.4
1974	117,112	14,602	12.5
1973	97,806	7,434	7.6
1972	79,082	5,201	6.6
		Rubber and miscellaneous plastics products (ESIC 30)	
1975	$24,739	$ 767	3.1
1974	26,725	1,327	5.0
1973	26,410	1,061	4.0
1972	21,663	859	4.0
		Primary metal industries (ESIC 33)	
1975	$66,429	$2,841	4.3
1974	79,917	5,239	6.6
1973	66,284	3,046	4.6
1972	51,880	1,708	3.3
		Stone, clay, and glass products (ESIC 32)	
1975	$27,312	$ 865	3.2
1974	26,685	1,183	4.4
1973	26,063	1,263	4.8
1972	22,519	1,060	4.7
		Paper and allied products (ESIC 26)	
1975	$32,044	$1,790	5.6
1974	30,799	2,176	7.1
1973	26,503	1,441	5.4
1972	23,324	941	4.0
		All manufacturing	
1975	$1,066,660	$48,396	4.5
1974	1,060,961	58,403	5.5
1973	1,017,163	48,058	4.7
1972	849,523	36,467	4.3

Source: *Chem. Eng. News,* Facts and Figures issue June 2, 1975, p. 42; June 7, 1976, p. 47.

Table 8.21 Net income compared with net worth for the CPI, 1972–1974

Year	Net worth (millions)	Net income (millions)	Net income as percentage of net worth
Chemicals and allied products (ESIC 28)			
1975	$44,787	$6,558	14.6
1974	41,665	7,246	17.4
1973	39,910	5,686	14.2
1972	36,129	4,499	12.4
Industrial chemicals and synthetics (ESIC 28.1)			
1975	$21,898	$2,794	12.8
1974	21,405	3,524	16.5
1973	20,338	2,553	12.6
1972	18,495	1,809	9.8
Drugs (ESIC 28.3)			
1975	$9,302	$1,563	16.8
1974	8,080	1,463	18.1
1973	8,529	1,345	18.1
1972	7,729	1,347	17.4
Petroleum and coal products (ESIC 29)			
1975	$76,596	$ 9,229	12.2
1974	74,047	14,602	19.7
1973	66,592	7,434	11.2
1972	61,014	5,201	8.5
Rubber and miscellaneous plastics products (ESIC 30)			
1975	$9,562	$ 767	8.0
1974	9,452	1,327	14.0
1973	9,055	1,061	11.7
1972	8,326	859	10.3
Primary metal industries (ESIC 33)			
1975	$34,554	$2,841	8.2
1974	33,868	5,239	15.5
1973	30,943	3,046	9.8
1972	29,177	1,708	5.9
Stone, clay, and glass products (ESIC 32)			
1975	$12,130	$ 865	7.1
1974	11,623	1,183	10.2
1973	11,660	1,263	10.8
1972	10,877	1,060	9.8

Table 8.21 (*continued*)

Year	Net worth (millions)	Net income (millions)	Net income as percentage of net worth
	Paper and allied products (ESIC 26)		
1975	$14,878	$1,790	12.0
1974	12,958	2,176	16.8
1973	11,536	1,441	12.5
1972	10,615	941	8.9
	All manufacturing		
1975	$435,723	$48,396	11.1
1974	408,590	58,403	14.3
1973	386,383	48,058	12.4
1972	353,092	36,467	10.3

Source: *Chem. Eng. News*, Facts and Figures issue, June 7, 1976.

in company annual reports. For instance in 1973, the Exxon Company annual report showed a total revenue of $28,508 million, but the net sale reported by *Fortune* and the FT Commission was $25,724 million. In 1973, the FTC made several changes in accounting procedures, such as the reporting of all foreign subsidiaries on a nonconsolidated basis, so that figures after 1974 are not strictly comparable to figures before 1973.

The year 1974 is the high-water mark, with manufacturing profit margin at 5.5 percent, partly due to the Arab oil embargo and the resulting shortages and price increases. The drug companies consistently led all the other sectors of the CPI, with a double-digit profit margin. The petroleum companies jumped from a 1973 profit margin comparable to industrial chemicals to a drug-company type of profit margin in 1974, only to fall back again in 1975. Both petroleum and chemicals consistently rank 2 to 3 percentage points better than all manufacturing. Rubber and stone, clay, and glass rank as average or below average compared with all manufacturing.

Perhaps a more meaningful figure is the net income as percent of net worth, here defined as the equity of common and preferred stock, shown in Table 8.21. With this measure, the discontinuity of 1974 is still evident, followed by a severe downturn in 1975. The relative ranking of industries does not change much. Drug companies still lead the group, followed by petroleum and industrial chemicals. Rubber and stone, clay, and glass lag behind all manufacturing.

Profit is a measure of a company's efficiency in manufacturing and its correct assessment of market needs. The company that has a low or negative profit for a period of time provides bad service for its employees, its stock- and bondholders, and the government tax collectors; it cannot invest adequately for the future, and it cannot serve its customers well. Such a company eventually disappears or more commonly is absorbed by another company with more efficient management.

8.4.2 Capital Structure

Funds for capital spending needed by the CPI are generated internally, through depreciation allowances and retained earnings, and externally, by selling stocks and bonds, borrowing from banks and insurance companies, etc. Sources of capital funds for all United States nonfinancial corporations for selected years 1955 to 1974 are shown in Fig. 8.16. It is clear that United States industry is increasingly depending on external funds for its capital needs rather than on internal funds. In fact, in 1974 over half the new capital funding was supplied by debt. Table 8.22 gives the source of funds as well as application of funds for the 25 leading chemical companies (ESIC 28.1). This table identifies three significant trends in the chemical industry. Since 1972

1. Depreciation has accounted for decreasing percentages of total funds.
2. Long-term debt has increased, supplying 21.4 percent of the funds in 1976.
3. Capital expenditures have accounted for increasingly larger percentages of the total funds.

A more detailed breakdown showing effectiveness of the use of capital for various industrial segments is given in Table 8.23 which presents the debt-to-equity ratio and return on equity. As far as operating management is concerned, the task is to produce the best profit picture based on total plant and working capital. But the investor is also interested in the capital structure of a company. He wants to know how much of the return must go to debtors and what is left over for him. A company that is highly leveraged is heavily in debt, so that fluctuations in income are magnified into even greater fluctuations in return on equity.

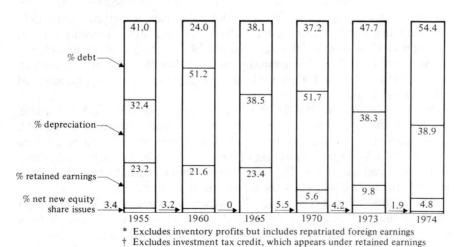

* Excludes inventory profits but includes repatriated foreign earnings
† Excludes investment tax credit, which appears under retained earnings

Figure 8.16 Sources of capital for United States, nonfinancial corporations, 1955 to 1974. [*Du Pont Manage. Bull.*, vol. 4, no. 2 (November 1975).]

Table 8.22 Sources and application of funds of the top 25 chemical companies, 1970–1976

	1976		1975		1974		1972		1970	
	Millions	Percentage of total	Millions	Percentage of total	Milions	Percentage of total	Millions	Percentage of total	Millions	Percentage of total
Sources:										
Net income	$4,334	40.6	$ 3,720	36.4	$4,008	45.5	$2,401	41.2	$1,839	35.8
Depreciation and depletion	2,729	25.6	2,431	23.8	2,224	25.2	1,888	32.4	1,692	32.9
Deferred taxes	379	3.5	412	4.0	311	3.5	80	1.4	88	1.7
Other internal sources	686	6.4	549	5.4	527	6.0	495	8.5	527	10.3
Long-term debt	2,290	21.4	2,927	28.6	1,622	18.4	811	13.9	902	17.6
Sales of stock	262	2.5	180	1.8	120	1.4	148	2.5	87	1.7
Total	$10,680	100.0	$10,219	100.0	$8,812	100.0	$5,823	100.0	$5,135	100.0
Application:										
Dividends	$1,713	16.0	$ 1,540	15.1	$1,476	16.7	$1,260	21.6	$1,180	23.0
Capital expenditures	6,186	57.9	5,933	58.1	4,953	56.2	2,448	42.0	2,788	54.3
Additions to working	1,141	10.7	1,404	13.7	1,293	14.7	1,127	19.3	283	5.5
Reduction of long-term debt	766	7.2	772	7.5	396	4.5	564	9.7	435	8.5
Other applications	874	8.2	570	5.6	694	7.9	424	7.3	449	8.7
Total	$10,680	100.0	$10,219	100.0	$8,812	100.0	$5,823	100.0	$5,135	100.0

Source: *Chem. Eng. News*, Facts and Figures issue, June 6, 1977.

**Table 8.23 Return on equity and debt-to-equity
ratio for several United States industries**

Industry	Return on equity, %	Debt-to-equity ratio
Cosmetics	14.0	0.2
Ethical drug	22.6	0.1
International oil	13.5	0.3
Coal	21.7	0.3
Diversified chemicals	13.4	0.4
Speciality chemicals	14.5	0.5
Food distribution	15.3	0.5
Computer	12.7	0.3
Electrical equipment	17.6	0.3
Utility	11.6	1.1
Auto	10.5	0.5
Railroads	5.6	0.6
All industry	11.6	0.4

Source: Compiled from company reports.

As an example of this effect, consider two companies. Company A has a debt-to-equity ratio of 0.2. Company B has a debt-to-equity ratio of 1.0. Assume that the interest rate on debts is 7 percent and that each company earns 25 cents per dollar of capital before income tax and interest. This problem is worked out by assuming that debt + equity = capital assets, which in many cases is a good assumption (Table 8.24).

Therefore, given the same gross earnings per dollar of capital as company A, company B with a heavy debt structure shows a much superior net earning on equity after tax. But suppose business is bad and that gross before-tax earnings on capital are only 2 cents on the dollar. Then the results are as shown in Table 8.25. Highly leveraged company B turned the same low gross earning into a deficit. Thus, using borrowed money for business is a two-edged sword: it is good during prosperous times but can be bad during economic downturns.

Table 8.24 Example—debt, equity

	Company A	Company B
Debt-to-equity ratio	0.2	1.0
Debt, %	16.7	50
Interest payment, cents	$0.167 \times 7\% = 1.2$	$0.50 \times 7\% = 3.5$
Equity, %	83.3	50
Gross profit before taxes, cents	$25 - 1.2 = 23.8$	$25 - 3.5 = 21.5$
Income tax (50%), cents	11.9	10.7
Net income after taxes, cents	11.9	10.8
Return on equity, %	$11.9/83.3 = 14.3$	$10.8/50.0 = 21.6$

Table 8.25 Example—debt, equity

	Company A	Company B
Debt-to-equity ratio	0.2	1.0
Interest payment, cents	$0.167 \times 7\% = 1.2$	$0.50 \times 7\% = 3.5$
Profit before taxes, cents	$2 - 1.2 = 0.8$	-1.5
Income tax, cents	0.4	
Income tax credit, cents	....	-0.7
Profit after taxes, cents	0.4	-0.8
Return on equity	$0.4/83.3 = 0.5\%$	$-0.8/50.0 = -1.5\%$

The debt-to-equity ratios of chemical and petroleum companies tend to be more conservative than the overall industrial debt-to-equity average of 0.4, but there has been an upward trend in debt-to-equity ratio for the chemical industry during the past 10 years (Table 8.26). Chemical companies are becoming increasingly dependent on external financing for plant expansions and new plant construction. For example, Du Pont has traditionally financed capital expansions from internal funds and had a debt-to-equity ratio of 0.02 in 1965. In 1976 Du Pont's debt-to-equity ratio was 0.2. Some major chemical companies have maintained high debt-to-equity ratios. For example, the ratio of long-term debt to equity for Dow Chemical was 0.66 in 1974 and above 0.8 for 1970 to 1973. Outside the CPI, industries that are heavily government-regulated monopolies, e.g., utilities, airlines, and telephone companies, tend to have high debt-to-equity ratios. Such companies can lean on the federal government as the ultimate guarantor of

Table 8.26 Leverage of the chemical and allied products industry†

Year	Long-term debt (millions)	Shareholders' equity (millions)	Debt-to-equity ratio
1975	$5,836	$13,153	0.44
1974	4,610	12,653	0.36
1973	3,826	11,119	0.34
1972	3,613	10,085	0.36
1971	3,518	9,485	0.38
1970	3,334	8,837	0.38
1969	3,066	8,587	0.36
1968	2,840	8,185	0.35
1967	2,721	7,853	0.35
1966	2,279	7,510	0.30

† Based on a composite of seven leading chemical companies.

Source: "Standard and Poor's Industry Surveys," vol. 1, January 1976, p. C40.

their debts. Since their services are essential to their customers and have no substitutes, one assumes that they cannot be permitted to fail. In Japan, where the government, the banks, and the manufacturing companies enjoy a high degree of cooperation, foreclosure of a manufacturing company is unthinkable, and a debt-to-equity ratio of 5 is customary.

Funds are generated internally from net income and depreciation and externally from new debts and selling new stocks. The major uses of funds are dividends to stockholders, capital investment and increase in working capital, and holding cash and lending out to the money market. Many companies have an annual capital-expenditure decision on how much to spend this year and which projects to fund. Each project proposed must have the projected cash flow and profit forecast for the duration of the project, which may be 20 years. The risks and consequences of adverse conditions on profit are also estimated. All projects are ranked by their projected return on investment and other financial and risk parameters. The projects with the highest merit are funded first, and then the rest in descending order till the total capital available is exhausted. Most aggressive growth-oriented companies have more worthwhile projects than available funds. A less aggressive company may have few worthwhile projects with a sufficiently high return on investment. In that case, the company is better off collecting interest by lending the funds to some other companies who have better ideas on how to invest.

8.5 ROLE IN THE NATIONAL ECONOMY

The qualitative importance of the CPI to the United States economy lies mainly in its contribution of synthetic raw materials and semifinished materials for further processing and manufacturing. It has been exceedingly successful in displacing natural products. Consider the replacement of natural dyes with synthetic dyes, cotton and silk with synthetic fibers, herbal medicine with antibiotics, smoky coal with clean-burning oil, and many others. The CPI has been a major contributor to every major sector of human need (Table 8.27). Reference 5 gives a more thorough treatment of CPI contributions in satisfying these and other needs.

Table 8.27 The CPI's contributions to society

Need	Major CPI contributions
Food	Processing: additives to prevent spoilage, improve nutritional value, and impart desired flavor and color
	New foods: margarine, edible oils, dehydrated foods Canning, frozen food, ready-to-serve food New sources, e.g., single-cell protein
Clothing	Dyes and finishes (permanent press) Synthetic fibers and nonwoven fabrics Additives to decrease flammability and soiling

Table 8.27 (*continued*)

Need	Major CPI contributions
Shelter	Paints and coatings Air purification and conditioning Plastics and other materials for structure and furniture Adhesives and sealants Heating and power
Agriculture	Fertilizers and pesticides Plant-growth regulators Nutrients and drugs for animals Fuel for tractors and drying crops
Health	Pharmaceuticals Soap and personal care Drug delivery systems
Transportation	Automobile: body, fuel, and lubricant, rubber, fabric, and seat, antifreeze, brake fluid Aircraft: aluminum
Communications	Telephone and TV: plastics, wires, copper, semiconductors Photography: silver and other chemicals, photocopy Publishing: printing ink, paper
Defense	Gunpowder, shells, rocket fuels, atomic weapons
Ecology	Air- and water-pollution control Recycle of solids

Table 8.28 Summary of the chemical and allied products industries, 1972

SIC code	Industry group	Employees (thousands)	Value added by manufacture (millions)	Value of shipments (millions)	Capital expenditures (millions)
281	Industrial chemicals	100	$ 3,343	$ 6,133	$ 333
282	Plastics materials, synthetics	162	4,935	9,796	694
283	Drugs	130	6,131	8,019	245
284	Soaps, cleaners, toilet goods	112	6,201	9,778	236
285	Paints and allied products	66	1,792	3,822	82
286	Industrial organic chemicals	137	6,073	11,605	832
287	Agricultural chemicals	48	1,737	3,929	156
289	Miscellaneous chemical products	83	2,203	4,268	151
28	Chemicals and allied products	837	32,413	57,350	2,728
	All manufacturing	19,029	354,054	756,534	24,078

Source: U.S. Bureau of the Census, *Statistical Abstract of the United States: 1975*, 96th ed., table 1266.

Table 8.29 Summary of the CPI and related industries, 1972

SIC code	Industry group	Employees (thousands)	Value added by manufacture (millions)	Value of shipments (millions)	Capital expenditures (millions)
20	Food and kindred products	1,569	$ 35,617	$115,060	$ 2,355
26	Paper and allied products	633	13,064	28,262	1,335
28	Chemicals and allied products	837	32,413	57,350	2,728
29	Petroleum and coal products	140	5,793	28,695	1,154
30	Rubber and miscellaneous plastics products	618	11,653	20,924	1,060
32	Stone, clay, glass	623	12,587	21,538	1,196
33	Primary metal industries	1,143	23,258	58,430	2,161
	All manufacturing	19,029	354,054	756,534	24,078

Source: U.S. Bureau of The Census, *Statistical Abstract of the United States:* 1975, 96th ed., table 1266.

The importance of the CPI can be discussed in terms of its contributions and size. We have already seen in Chap. 4 the importance of the CPI to other industries. In terms of net sales, SIC 28 accounts for more than 8 percent of all manufacturing sales; SIC 29 accounts for more than 9 percent. The size of the CPI in terms of employees, value added, value of shipment, and capital expenditure is

Table 8.30 Percentage of all manufacturing accounted for by various CPI sectors, 1972

SIC code	Industry	Percentage of all manufacturing, 1972			
		Employees	Value added	Value of shipments	Capital expenditures
20	Food and kindred products	8	10	15	10
26	Paper and allied products	3	4	4	6
28	Chemicals and allied products	4	9	8	11
29	Petroleum and coal products	1	2	4	5
30	Rubber and miscellaneous plastics products	3	3	3	4
32	Stone, clay, and glass products	3	4	3	5
33	Primary metal industries	6	7	8	9

Table 8.31 Percentage of all manufacturing accounted for by various important United States industries, 1972

SIC code	Industry	Percentage of all manufacturing, 1972			
		Employees	Value added	Value of shipments	Capital expenditures
23	Apparel and related products	7	4	4	2
24	Lumber and wood products	4	3	3	4
34	Fabricated metal products	8	8	7	5
35	Machinery, except electrical	10	11	9	8
36	Electrical and electronic equipment	9	9	7	6
37	Transportation equipment	9	11	13	11

indicated by Tables 8.28 and 8.29. As a percentage of all manufacturing, the various parts of the CPI are listed in Table 8.30. For comparison, Table 8.31 shows employees, value added, value of shipments, and capital expenditures all as percentages of the total for all manufacturing (1972) for several other key United States industrial sectors.

8.6 RELATION WITH GOVERNMENTS

The starting point of modern economic theory is the free market of Adam Smith, where numerous buyers and sellers meet to transact their business without government interference. Each party takes the action that will maximize his own personal gain. It is relatively easy to expound theories and to assign problems based on this free-market situation, but a modern firm in the CPI works under an enormous number of supportive and regulative actions of the government. There are few decisions that a company's management can make without permission of the government. The larger the company, the greater the influence of government.

An oil company must lease drilling rights for oil and gas from the government, pay a large bonus to acquire the lease, and pay yearly fees and royalties on oil recovered. The government decides when the leases will be available for bids, what the terms will be, and eventually whether the bids are high enough. The government grants the right of way to build pipelines and marine terminals for the movement of oil and decides on how they should be built. The government can approve or disapprove of refinery construction on a given site, decrees the permissible discharge of waste products into the air and water, regulates plant safety for employees, and may shut down a plant for noncompliance. The government decides on the price of crude oil, both from "old wells" and from newly discovered fields, and which refinery may buy how much oil from each well. The government regulates the price of refined products from gasoline to fuel oil. The government determines a minimum wage and imposes rules relating to the desired number of minorities in each labor force. The government decides on how much oil may be imported and whether domestic oil companies may get together to bargain as a single unit with foreign oil-producing countries. The government decides on the quantity and the supplier of oil for governmental and military uses. The government decides on how much to spend on education and research, which produce needed manpower and scientific knowledge that benefit the oil companies. The government may decide that a company is too big and powerful and order it to be broken up into smaller entities. The government may subsidize a company, lend money to, or guarantee the debts of, a company, and provide protection for domestic operations from foreign competition. The list can go on indefinitely. No wonder a company in the CPI is very anxious to have good relations with the government.

In a single issue of *Chemical Week* (Jan. 26, 1977) one can find the following articles about the influence of government:

Editorial, "The American Disease," on the habit of going to the law court to settle disputes. Energy policy, coal development, chemical plant siting are all pinned down by legal crossfire. The United States has twice the population of Japan, but 30 times as many lawyers.

Dow shelves $500 million petrochemical complex in California, plagued by environmental demands on siting.

Congress refuses to move control of testing new anticancer drugs from Food and Drug Administration to National Cancer Institute.

Coke and Coal Chemical Institute claim that Occupational Safety and Health Agency standards for protection of coke-oven workers for carcinogen emission cannot be met.

Food and Drug Administration rule drug-absorption rate data must be provided for new drug applications.

Environmental Protection Agency proposes to give financial aid to public interest groups to participate in hearings.

Secretary of Transportation Coleman issues license for superports in Gulf of Mexico.

Federal Power Commission is concerned about pipeline cutoff of natural gas to CPI firms, causing a switch to alternative fuels and shutdowns with layoffs.

Department of Health, Education and Welfare consider resumption of swine flu shots.

Food and Drug Administration reviews safety of 2,100 preservatives, flavors, and colors.

Occupational Safety and Health Agency publishes new guidelines on benzene exposure in workplace from 10 to 1 ppm.

U.S. District court rules that OSHA may not conduct warrantless inspection at plant sites.

Hydrocarbon aerosol propellants surge in use to replace fluorocarbons, accused of ozone depletion.

British government proposes to require formal notifications before introduction of new industrial chemicals, including test data for product safety.

Bolivia and Columbia settle dispute over pesticide plant.

Energy Research and Development Agency negotiates with Grace for coal-to-ammonia plant and with city of Memphis for low-Btu gas from coal plant.

ERDA ready to sign two high-Btu gas-from-coal plants, one with FMC at Illinois for $276 million and one with Conoco at Ohio for $2.4 million.

Environmental Protection Agency bans discharge of polychlorinated biphenyls into waterways.

Grace wins contract from Office of Water Research and Technology for desalting plant by reverse osmosis in Yuma, Arizona, for 104 million gallons per day.

EPA and ERDA support pyrolysis system for municipal and industrial waste into fuels at Garrett Research, city of Seattle, and Redwood City, California.

The power of the government to reward or to punish a company is demonstrated by these news items. It may be argued that this is a good thing or a bad thing, but it is here.

Energy supply and price is an issue that is important and pervasive and largely politically determined. Before 1973, oil from the Persian Gulf at $2 per barrel (or 34 cents per million Btu) was ousting domestic oil, at $3.25 per barrel, from the marketplace. Thus, import quotas and tickets to import (worth $1.25 per barrel, of course) were issued to protect domestic producers. This legislation denied the benefit of lower prices to domestic consumers. Since 1974, imported oil has risen to $12 per barrel, domestic oil from existing oil wells is regulated at $5 per barrel while "new" oil is permitted to be sold at $11 per barrel. This ruling denied a bigger windfall to domestic producers and assured lower average prices to domestic consumers in comparison with western European and Japanese consumers, who have little domestic oil.

A similar story applies to the federal regulation of interstate natural gas at a limit of 9 to 16 cents per thousand cubic feet (or 9 to 16 cents per million Btu), while intrastate natural gas is not regulated by the federal government. Under the cheap natural-gas policy, the producers are injured to the benefit of the consumers. When a commodity is regulated at below market price, the production will decline and consumption will rise so that shortages are created. It may seem a paradox that the importation of liquefied natural gas from Algeria is permitted at a cost of over $4 per thousand cubic feet, while domestic natural-gas producers may not market interstate natural gas above the regulated price of $1.45. In the winter of 1976, the intrastate gas that was not regulated in Texas rose to $2 per thousand cubic feet, and severe shortages were accelerated by the cold winter in the East and Midwest. Senators from the producing states of Texas, Louisiana, and Oklahoma were in favor of deregulation of gas price; senators from the consuming states of New England, the East, and Midwest were opposed. The situation has been compared to the stands of the OPEC nations vs. the industrialized OECD nations.

It is imperative that United States energy sources be secure from takeover or interruption by foreign wars or hostile acts of foreign nations. The United States has many energy resources that can be developed, i.e., coal, oil shale, tar sand, biomass, etc. At this moment, these technologies are available only at pilot-plant scale or smaller. The costs of producing synthetic oil are only estimations that may represent the optimism of the promoters. There are no creditable estimates below $20 per barrel of oil and $4 per thousand cubic feet of substitute natural gas. Should the United States produce these expensive energy sources at any cost to demonstrate independence of foreign sources? How large a premium per million Btu should be paid, and how many trillion Btu should be thus produced to demonstrate independence from blackmail? How should the subsidy be awarded without giving the undeserved a windfall? How long should the subsidy be continued to ensure the inflow of venture capital without encouraging permanent dependence?

The government and the people must wrestle with these problems and make decisions that are vital to the fortunes of the CPI and the nation.

The recent expansion of governmental powers seems inexorable and very alarming to company managers who fear that few degrees of freedom of action are left. Political power has always been supreme over economic power in the western world. In the mercantilistic days of Colbert and Louis XIV, the state exercised nearly complete control over all manufacturing and commerce. The decentralized decision making and superior economic performance of Britain were recognized and celebrated by Adam Smith in the "Wealth of Nations." Indeed, the world has witnessed no system more efficient than the decentralized decision-making process of the marketplace, where each party takes actions designed to maximize his own gain and is rapidly rewarded or punished by the marketplace. The rapid growth of total national wealth and prosperity is the best argument for the free-enterprise system. As long as the system can provide rising prosperity to all, there will be little demand for change.

In the United States of the nineteenth century there were many complaints about the monopolizing tendencies of the giant steel, oil, railroad, and other industries. But until the Great Depression, when a quarter of the labor force was out of work, state intervention in business was kept to a minimum. Since 1932, governmental power has steadily increased at the expense of economic power. It has been postulated that the American people fear bigness and concentrated power without accountability. When they fear that business is too big to be controlled and not responsive to the wishes of the public, the government and the labor unions are encouraged to form the countervailing powers. It is one person one vote in the political arena rather than the one dollar one vote in the economic arena. Those who have fewer dollars and their allies seek to overcome the advantages of wealth through the use of politics and government.

It is by no means the case that the public loves the government more than business. In fact, many public-opinion polls demonstrate that the public holds senators and congressmen in lower esteem than businessmen. The public is merely using one institution to check the power of another.

The relative importance of equality and efficiency is foremost in the national debate today. By equality, we mean not just the equality of opportunities universally espoused in decades past but the equality of results espoused by many today. It is generally agreed that higher efficiency is attained by decentralized decision makers seeking economic gain. The dynamic American economic strength is the envy of all central planners from Moscow to India. But pure economic competition would lead to a high degree of inequality that is deemed intolerable by today's ethics. Total equality damages the incentives of hard work and innovation. It may well be that equality and efficiency are irreconcilable goals, and a choice or trade-off must be made between them.

Since the government holds enormous power over the prosperity of companies, it is natural that companies try their best to influence government. Companies form trade associations to represent their interests in Washington, and bigger companies have their own registered lobbyists. They provide timely information and critical comments to key congressional members and regulatory agency officials and provide company management with advanced notice on contemplated governmental actions.

We may compare our present political-economic system to a ship with a sail and a rudder. The sail is the private economic sector that provides the driving force for economic activities and advances; the rudder is the public political sector that guides the ship toward desired goals. The government cannot provide the economic driving force, and private companies cannot satisfy the political goals of the people. Both rudder and sail are needed in the mixed economy of the United States today.

The people ultimately determine, as individual consumers, what will be produced and sold. Collectively, as voters, the people determine what institutional behavior is permissible. The public simply expects business to provide goods to consumers and profit to stockholders. Business may conform to public expectations or educate the public to expect otherwise, but business may not ignore public expectations. The growth of government "interference" in business is a direct result of the gap between public expectation and business performance. The tragedies of the tranquilizer thalidomide, of mercury poison in Minamata, Japan, of the pesticide intermediate Kepone in the James River, of oil spills off George's Bank are all instances of a lack of industrial self-regulation. The government moved in as a result of public indignation. The lesson should not be forgotten by industry.

8.7 REFERENCES

1. C. H. Kline, Maximizing Profits in Chemicals, *CHEMTECH*, February 1976.
2. C. E. Ferguson, "Microeconomic Theory," 3d ed., Irwin, Homewood, Ill., 1972.
3. John Von Neumann and Oskar Morgenstern, "Theory of Games and Economic Behavior," Princeton University Press, Princeton, N.J., 1953.
4. M. S. Peters and K. D. Timmerhaus, "Plant Design and Economics for Chemical Engineers," McGraw-Hill, New York, 1968.
5. "Chemistry in the Economy," American Chemical Society, Washington, 1974.

8.8 NOTATION

AC	average cost of producing a chemical, dollars per pound
c	constant [Eq. (8.6)]
K	cost of fixed and working capital per year, consisting of depreciation, dollars per year, return on capital (opportunity cost), and maintenance and repair
L	cost of labor, dollars per year
LRAC	long-range average cost
MC	marginal cost = incremental cost of producing product (defined by [Eq. (2.12)]
MV_i	marginal value of hiring employee of type i
p_s	unit cost of supplies per pound or product produced
q	quantity of product produced, mass per year
S	cost of supplies, dollars per year
SRAC	short-range average cost
TC	total annual production cost
w_i	wage of employee i
x_i	number of employees of type i needed

8.9 PROBLEMS

8.1 Even though the petroleum refining industry is not as concentrated as the auto and aircraft industries, there is increasing public pressure to break up the " big eighteen " oil companies. What are the reasons behind this movement, and are they justified? Why is the public less bothered by the much higher concentration in the automobile sector, consisting of the " big three " and ailing American Motors?

8.2 What type of academic training and specialization are particularly appreciated by a firm making a commodity, and why? Answer the same questions for firms making a pseudo-commodity, fine chemicals, or specialty chemicals.

8.3 What are the possible exceptions to the general observation that greater experience leads to lower cost expressed as deflated constant dollars? What are the exceptions to the general observation that a greater experience would lead to lower value added expressed as deflated constant dollars?

8.4 Construct the profit payoff matrix between two firms making Delos (Sec. 2.2.3). Firm X has a reactor of 30,000 l, and firm Y has a reactor of 50,000 l. Let the price be set at three different levels. Estimate the market shares, production levels, and profits of the two firms. Is there a dominant optimal strategy or a mixed optimal strategy?

8.5 Process engineers are concerned with the manufacturing process, and product engineers are concerned with the improvement of product properties by blending, additives, and other techniques. Which courses in the standard chemical engineering and chemistry curricula would prepare you for work in either of these branches? What elective courses can you take to further your usefulness in either branch?

8.6 Suppose a manufacturing plant's operation can be represented by a Cobb-Douglas production function of

$$q = 0.25K^{0.8}L^{0.4}$$

and suppose that the product demand over a 10-year period is given by

$$q = 0.5 + 0.05t \qquad t = 1, \ldots, 10$$

What is the optimal value of K_0 which will minimize total cost of manufacturing these products over the 10-year period?

8.7 The Trans-Alaska Pipeline is 800 mi long, serviced by a pumping station approximately every 100 mi. In the initial stages, when the oil flow is to be less than 1 million barrels per day, this density of pumping stations conserves capital and pumping cost. When the oil flow rises above 2 million barrels per day, the pumping cost rises steeply, and it would be cheaper to build more pumping stations. Sketch quantitatively the cost per barrel delivered vs. barrels per day for the SRAC of two different pumping-station densities and the LRAC curve.

8.8 Do you believe that the economic reward and social status of chemical professionals are commensurate with their contributions to society in comparison with doctors, lawyers, and plumbers? If you believe that one profession is unfairly favored over another, what prevents young people from deserting the less favored to enter the more favored profession, so as to lead to an equalization? Do you believe that the wage spread among chemical professionals within the CPI is justified and sustainable?

8.9 Why is there a larger income spread among the self-employed than the employed?

8.10 Identify the parameters in Example 2.1 which could be changed, and discuss how the chemical engineer or chemist would alter each of them to improve profit.

8.11 Relate the theory of marginal productivity and wage to your own professional life. What type of impact would you strive to make on your company profit on what time scale and would it pay for your keep? If the answer is no, what should you do to avoid being laid off? How do you plan to keep up and to expand your usefulness, and how do you plan to keep informed about the employment market? How would you find out whether you are underpaid or overpriced?

8.12 Would a professional union work to your personal advantage now and 20 years from now? If the union tends to decrease the income spread between the most and the least accomplished, is it good for the profession and is it good for you? Would a union give you greater job protection? Do you believe that a company which cannot reduce forces to survive may go out of business altogether, so that all employees lose their jobs?

8.13 Since the drugs sector is consistently more profitable than stone, clay, glass, why would investors not shift funds from one to the other until both have an equal yield? What are the barriers to entry and exit? Would they persist forever?

8.14 What would happen if a company such as Du Pont, which has a policy of paying out half its income to stockholders, suddenly reversed policy and channeled all profits back into the business? What would be the reaction of various types of stockholders? Should Du Pont do this, and if not why not?

8.15 Foreign subsidiaries of United States companies often have very high debt-to-equity ratios. Why are the parent firms less concerned about the risk for foreign subsidiaries than for the parent United States companies?

8.16 Do you believe that your relatives, friends, and neighbors are aware of the contributions of the CPI? How would you respond to the comment that Hercules is but a " hoola-hoop manufacturer " or that Colgate does nothing but "put stripes on toothpaste"? Can you defend the notion that firms in the CPI must make a reasonable profit to pay for future plants and research?

8.17 Study the contribution the CPI made to society by developing (*a*) DDT, (*b*) fertilizers, (*c*) pesticides, (*d*) penicillin. Write a short paragraph on each product, discussing the major contribution. (A good source of information is Ref. 5.)

9

INTERNATIONAL ASPECTS OF THE CPI

The chemical processing industries are worldwide in scope. Practically every nation has a chemical industry and conducts foreign trade in chemicals, chemical raw materials, and chemical products. A firm in the domestic CPI can regard all foreign nations as potential markets for manufactured chemicals, for technology licensing, and plant investment. In return, the United States is a market for the reverse flow of goods, technology, labor, and capital.

According to the theory of relative advantages, two nations trade because they possess different resources. A nation with superior crude-oil deposits might wish to trade with a country having a healthy automobile-manufacturing industry. Such a trade relationship would be to the benefit of both countries. Relative advantage is a flexible notion, and one may find that nations and people occasionally rearrange their priorities vis-à-vis "advantages." For example, in wartime, a nation with a superior automobile-manufacturing technology might prefer to import passenger cars from another nation, in order to throw its domestic manufacturing capacity into the manufacture of military vehicles. On a simpler level, a professor good at typing might hire a secretary to do his typing so that he can devote his time to preparing his lectures and doing research.

The advantages of operating in the United States for the CPI include an abundant raw-material supply from the farms and the mines, a highly skilled and diligent work force, a large body of technical knowledge in research and engineering, and abundant capital and management skills. The United States looks abroad for many things that are insufficient at home, such as crude oil, tungsten ore, and novel technologies.

Despite the obvious advantages of international commerce, various powerful forces tend to inhibit the movement of goods, technology, capital, and labor. Most nations "shelter" inefficient domestic producers and their employees from superior foreign goods, particularly if these domestic producers qualify as infant industries that require special protection and nurture during their formative periods. Another impediment to the smooth flow of international commerce may be certain national security considerations. It may be unwise to have a vitally needed raw-material supply entirely in the hands of unreliable foreign nations. A nation cannot import much more than it exports for an extended period without succumbing to balance-of-payment problems and the threat of currency devaluation. The free movement of labor may lead to a large immigrant labor force that may disrupt the homogeneity and harmony of the host country, creating unpleasant political problems. Domination of the economic life of a nation by foreign owners and managers creates envy and breeds the threat of nationalization.

The bulk of the world's chemical manufacture is accounted for by a handful of developed countries. Of the free world's 200 largest chemical producers, nine countries, the United States, West Germany, Japan, the United Kingdom, the Netherlands, France, Italy, Switzerland, and Belgium, account for over 95 percent of the total chemical sales (Table 9.1). In developing countries the CPI are generally involved in making simple products such as fertilizers, bulk inorganic chemicals, and in a few cases specialty chemicals, for which there is a clear economic advantage such as abundant raw materials and low freight for low-priced products.

This chapter concerns itself with some of the important features of the world CPI. United States involvement in foreign chemical trade and United States investment in developing nations are considered. This chapter treats industries that roughly correspond to the domestic SIC 28 classification.

Table 9.1 The leading countries in chemical sales

Country	Share of market, %† 1973	1974
United States	44.4	42.7
West Germany	16.4	16.5
Japan	11.7	11.4
United Kingdom	6.7	6.5
Netherlands	5.1	5.2
France	4.6	4.9
Italy	3.4	4.2
Switzerland	3.6	3.1
Belgium	1.7	1.7
	97.6	96.2

† As measured by percentage of the total sales of the world's 200 largest chemical producers.
Source: Chem. Age, July 22, 1975, p. 53.

9.1 UNITED STATES FOREIGN TRADE IN CHEMICALS

The United States is the largest exporter in world trade today, followed closely by West Germany, as shown in Table 9.2. However, exports play a small role in the total United States economy as they amount to only a little over 5 percent of the GNP. This is a marked contrast to a country like Belgium, where exports account for over 49 percent of the GNP. A small nation like Belgium depends on foreign nations for many of its economic needs. Larger nations, such as the United States, China, and the U.S.S.R., contain many diverse economic activities and tend to be self-sufficient *autarkies*. A country of particular interest is Japan, which despite its small area is the third largest exporter in the world. Its exports account for less than 9 percent of its GNP since Japan's domestic market is the third largest in the world.

In 1974, United States foreign trade in chemicals accounted for $8.822 billion in exports and $3.991 billion in imports. Exports in chemicals accounted for 9 percent of all United States exports in 1974. In 1975, United States chemical trade provided over $5 billion of trade surplus to the United States economy. This fact is particularly significant in view of the low overall United States trade balances and even trade deficits in recent years (Table 9.3). The United States market share of world exports in all manufacturing and in chemicals is given by Table 9.4. The United States share of world trade has declined in recent years, but this trend is expected to reverse.

In comparison with the chemical trade of other nations the United States accounted for 18.5 percent of the dollar value of world exports of chemicals in 1974; only West Germany exports more chemicals (measured in dollar value) than the United States (Table 9.5).

Table 9.2 World trade, 1973

	GNP in 1973 dollars (billion)	Exports 1973 (billion)	Exports as percentage of GNP
United States	$1,294.9	$70.2	5.4
Belgium	45.7	22.5	49.2
France	255.1	35.6	13.9
West Germany	348.2	68.6	19.7
Italy	138.3	22.2	16.1
Netherlands	59.7	24.1	40.4
Switzerland	40.9	9.5	23.2
United Kingdom	174.8	30.5	17.4
Canada	118.9	25.3	21.3
Japan	413.1	36.9	8.9
U.S.S.R.	840	21.5	2.6
China (1971)	128	2.3	1.8

Source: U.S. Bureau of the Census, *Statistical Abstract of the United States: 1975,* 96th ed., table 1403.

Table 9.3 United States trade in millions of dollars

	1964	1972	1973	1974	1975
All commodities:					
Exports†	$25,690	$49,199	$70,823	$ 97,907	$107,191
Imports‡	18,684	55,583	67,476	100,972	96,140
Trade balance	7,006	−6,384	1,347	−3,065	11,051
Chemicals:					
Exports§	2,375	4,134	5,748	8,822	8,705
Imports§	714	2,015	2,437	3,991	3,696
Trade balance	$1,661	$2,119	$3,311	$4,831	$5,009

  † Exports of domestic and foreign merchandise, excluding Department of Defense shipments.
  ‡ General imports, customs value.
  § Exports of domestic merchandise, including Department of Defense shipments.
  Source: Chem. Eng. News, Facts and Figures issue, June 2, 1975, p. 66; June 7, 1976, p. 68.

Table 9.4 United States market share of world exports in all manufacturing and chemicals†

	All manufacturing		Chemicals	
	U.S. share (millions)	Percentage of world	U.S. share (millions)	Percentage of world
1960	$12,716	25.3	$1,779	29.6
1961	12,924	24.1	1,793	28.2
1962	13,835	24.6	1,880	27.9
1963	14,459	23.6	2,013	26.9
1964	16,718	24.0	2,369	27.1
1965	17,648	22.8	2,407	24.7
1966	19,510	23.0	2,693	24.6
1967	21,090	23.3	2,812	24.2
1968	24,113	23.6	3,296	24.2
1969	27,132	22.5	3,393	21.9
1970	29,730	21.3	3,840	21.9
1971‡	30,845	20.0	8,855	20.0
1972	34,285	19.2	4,162	18.7
1973	45,574	19.5	5,781	19.0
1974	64,559	20.3	8,891	18.5
1975§	17,371	21.5	2,336	20.4

  † World exports are defined as exports from 15 major industrial countries. Percentage shares are based on values excluding shipments to the United States.
  ‡ Data in this series have been revised back to 1971 to reflect United States share based on export-weighted exchange rates.
  § First quarter only.
  Source: Chem. Eng. News, Dec. 22, 1975, p. 34.

Table 9.5 World chemical trade (millions)

	1964		1972		1973		1974	
	Exports	Imports	Exports	Imports	Exports	Imports	Exports	Imports
World	$10,910		$29,120†		$40,800†		$58,000	
United States	2,375	$ 714	4,134	$2,015	5,758	$ 2,437	8,822	$ 3,991
Canada	250	437	639	1,001	753	1,230	1,069	1,857
European Economic Community, nine countries	5,370	11,151	15,717	11,151	21,892	16,659	35,864†	25,028†
Belgium and Luxembourg	319	374	1,564	1,213	2,223	1,599	3,527†	2,679†
France	880	629	2,428	2,185	3,153	3,004	5,137†	5,009†
West Germany	1,887	673	5,416	2,509	7,576	3,410	11,918†	5,053†
Italy	490	462	1,222	1,564	1,829	2,506	3,793†	4,070†
Netherlands	536	447	2,338	1,356	2,914	1,524	4,687†	2,322†
United Kingdom	1,154	707	2,404	1,630	3,664	2,584	5,994†	4,372†
Switzerland	526	316	1,525	833	2,035	1,148	2,705	1,711
Eastern Europe	910	990	2,040	2,460	2,750	3,320	‡	‡
Japan	384	458	1,784	1,148	2,147	1,865	4,059	2,668

† *Chem. Eng. News* estimate.
‡ Not available.
Source: Chem. Eng. News, Facts and Figures issue, June 2, 1975, p. 66.

Table 9.6 United States chemical trade by world area (millions)

	1964		1972		1973		1974	
	Exports	Imports	Exports	Imports	Exports	Imports	Exports	Imports
Canada	$335	$145	$ 693	$439	$ 844	$ 554	$1,213	$ 760
Western Europe	850	285	1,434	933	1,891	1,179	2,651	1,995
European Economic Community								
six original countries	540	175	929	591	1,221	776	1,732	1,415
Nine countries	709	228	1,204	791	1,557	1,003	2,208	1,146
Eastern Europe	13	3	33	15	30	19	54	42
Japan	195	39	313	250	629	239	766	487
Rest of Asia	210	10	348	26	575	36	973	80
Middle East	40	1	80	11	119	13	181	16
Latin America	475	54	908	82	1,165	94	2,245	220
Australasia	81	9	128	99	212	151	351	195
Africa	88	6	108	17	172	22	270	29
Other areas	88	162	89	143	111	130	154	167
Total	$2,375	$714	$4,134	$2,015	$5,748	$2,437	$8,822	$3,991

Source: *Chem. Eng. News*, Facts and Figures issue, June 2, 1975, p. 66.

On the import side of the ledger, several countries import a greater dollar volume of chemicals than the United States, including West Germany, France, Italy, and the United Kingdom. The dollar volume of United States chemical trade with specific countries is shown in Table 9.6. The balance of trade with less developed nations in Asia, the Middle East, Latin America, and Africa is better than 10 : 1 in favor of the United States. The balance of trade with more developed nations in Canada, Western Europe, and Japan is closer to 1 : 1 but still in favor of the United States.

United States trade of specific product groups, as classified by SITC code, is shown in Table 9.7. Three categories account for 64 percent of United States imports: organic chemicals, inorganic chemicals, and fertilizers. Organic chemicals, synthetic resins, medicinals and pharmaceutical products, and manufactured fertilizers accounted for 65.7 percent of United States exports of chemicals in 1974.

Since 1973, the cost of oil imports has taken a dramatic leap upward and has had a major impact on the United States trade balance (Table 9.8). Foreign trade in chemicals is influenced greatly by trade tariffs. A tariff is a custom or duty charge imposed by a government on imports and occasionally on exports. Although tariffs are usually attacked with vehemence by free-market economists, they are nonetheless a fact of life and are imposed for several reasons:

1. To "keep money at home" by reducing the ability of foreign products to compete with domestically made products
2. To provide domestic wage earners by causing domestic prices to increase
3. To protect special-interest groups
4. To provide revenue

Table 9.7 Dollar volume of United States chemical trade by product classification (millions)

SITC† code	Classification	1972 Exports	1972 Imports	1973 Exports	1973 Imports	1974 Exports	1974 Imports	Major suppliers
512	Organic chemicals	$1,103	$ 509	$1,510	$ 630	$2,568	$1,380	Japan, West Germany
513	Inorganic chemical elements, oxides including hydroxides, peroxides, and halogen salts	262	348	339	429	508	614	Australia, Canada
514	Inorganic chemicals except elements, oxides, hydroxides, peroxides, and halogen salts	152	78	206	94	327	128	Canada, West Germany
515	Radioactive and associated materials	181	110	236	151	215	112	Canada, France
521	Mineral tar, tar oils, and crude chemicals from coal, petroleum, and natural gas	31	8	72	6	84	9	
531	Synthetic organic dyes, natural indigo, color lakes, and toners	53	104	86	104	117	106	West Germany, Switzerland

SITC[†]	Product							Principal sources of imports[‡]
532	Dyeing and tanning extracts, including synthetic and artificial bates	4	10	4	7	6	10	Argentina, South Africa
533	Pigments, paints, varnishes, and related materials	100	16	126	21	182	26	
541	Medicinal and pharmaceutical products	474	149	626	164	800	212	West Germany, United Kingdom
551	Essential oils, perfume, and flavor materials	60	73	84	89	110	155	France, Switzerland
553	Perfumery and cosmetics, dentifrices, and other toilet preparations, except soap	42	27	57	36	85	39	France
554	Soaps, cleansing, polishing, and finishing operations	93	14	122	18	175	27	
561	Fertilizers, manufactured	298	232	407	280	812	573	Canada, Netherlands
571	Explosives and pyrotechnic products, including hunting and sporting ammunition	28	21	31	27	50	20	
581	Synthetic resins regenerated cellulose, and plastic materials	696	177	1,028	207	1,618	316	Japan, West Germany
599	Chemical products and materials not elsewhere classified	556	140	767	174	1,165	264	
	Total	$4,134	$2,015	$5,748	$2,437	$8,822	$3,991	

† Standard International Tariff Classification.
‡ Imports are *Chem. Eng. News* estimates based on 10-month data.
Source: Chem. Eng. News, Facts and Figures issue, June 2, 1975, p. 66.

Table 9.8 Petroleum imports by the United States

Year	Volume, 10^6 bbl	Value (millions)	Unit value per barrel	Petroleum import as percentage of total import
1973	2,307	$ 7,765	$ 3.37	11
1974	2,231	24,668	11.06	24.6
1975	2,152	24,726	11.49	25.7

Source: *Chem. Eng. News*, Dec. 22, 1975, p. 33.

5. To retaliate against a foreign nation
6. To protect "essential" industries
7. To protect "new" industries until they are established

Tariffs have played an essential role in developing the United States chemical industry. In the early twentieth century, tariffs on coal-tar intermediates, manufactured dyes, and synthetic medicinals were especially vital in encouraging growth of a domestic chemical industry. In fact, to protect the infant United States chemical industry, particularly from German competition, Congress enacted the Dye and Chemical Control Act of 1921 to provide a 6-month embargo on products for which a comparable domestic product was available on reasonable terms. However, starting with the Trades Agreement Act in 1934, tariffs have been progressively lowered on chemicals and allied products.

In recent years, tariff reductions have been negotiated on an international scale by the so-called Kennedy Round of conferences on General Agreement on Tariffs and Trade (GATT) and the more recent Kennedy Round and Tokyo Round in the United States and in Europe. During the world recession of 1974 to 1975, chemical exports became vital to maintaining acceptable balance-of-trade positions for several countries. The fear of possible trade wars using tariff protection has prompted the General Agreement on Tariffs and Trade, which it is hoped will discourage destructive tariff protection.

9.2 MOVEMENT IN CAPITAL INVESTMENTS BETWEEN THE UNITED STATES AND ABROAD

Investment by CPI companies abroad, either through wholly owned subsidiaries or partnerships with local entrepreneurs, has been increasing. The primary reasons for increased foreign investment have included a wish (1) to be near important natural resources, (2) to be near important markets, (3) to avoid import tariffs and quotas, (4) to participate in local markets, and (5) to avoid shipping costs from the United States.

The book values of United States investments abroad are given in Table 9.9a. About 75 percent of the investment is in the developed nations of Canada, Europe, Japan, Australia, New Zealand, and South Africa. The investments in petroleum

Table 9.9a   Value of United States investments abroad, 1973 (billions)

	Manufacturing	Petroleum	Mining	Others	Total
Developed nations	$38.0	$16.4	$4.8	$14.9	$74.1
Less developed nations	7.8	10.4	2.7	6.9	27.9
Total	$45.8	$29.6	$7.5	$24.4	$107.3

Table 9.9b   Value of direct foreign investment in the United States, 1973 (billions)

	Manufacturing	Petroleum	Finance and insurance	Total
Canada	$2.4	$0.3	$0.4	$ 4.0
Europe	5.7	3.4	2.1	12.2
Japan	0.3	0.7	0.2	0.3
Others				1.2
All	$8.4	$4.4	$2.7	$17.7

Source: U.S. Bureau of the Census, *Statistical Abstract of the United States: 1975*, 96th ed., table 1349.

and mining are high in underdeveloped nations which have rich resources. Investments from Canada and Europe in the United States are also significant (Table 9.9b).

The annual property, plant, and equipment expenditures by majority-owned foreign affiliates of United States companies are shown in Table 9.10. The petroleum industry accounts for one-third of investment abroad. The bulk of this industry's expenditures are for exploration and drilling, refining, and marketing oil. Chemicals and allied products accounted for 8 percent of all United States capital expenditures abroad in 1974, with a total expenditure of $2.1 billion.

Table 9.10 Property, plant, and equipment expenditures by majority-owned foreign affiliates of United States companies, selected industries (billions)

	1970	1971	1972	1973	1974	1975†	1976‡
Total	$14.1	$16.3	$16.7	$20.6	$25.8	$27.0	$30.4
Petroleum	4.0	5.0	5.2	6.6	8.5	9.3	10.6
Chemicals and allied products	1.2	1.2	1.2	1.4	2.1	2.7	3.2
Rubber products	0.2	0.2	0.3	0.3	0.3	0.3	0.3
Food products	0.4	0.4	0.4	0.6	0.7	0.7	0.8
Primary and fabricated metals	0.7	0.6	0.6	0.8	0.8	0.8	0.8

† Estimated.
‡ Projected.
Source: *Surv. Curr. Bus.*, September 1975, p. 29.

Table 9.11 Property, plant, and equipment expenditures by majority-owned foreign affiliates of United States chemical and allied product companies by country (millions)

	1971	1972	1973	1974	1975	1976
Canada	$ 164	$ 311	$ 357	$ 595	$ 601	$ 656
Europe	842	626	631	1,031	1,423	1,737
Japan	62	90	91	113	162	155
Australia, New Zealand, South Africa	21	29	44	43	66	86
Latin America	124	185	195	305	410	505
Middle East	1	2	7	3	10	†
Other Africa	3	5	4	5	5	†
Other Asia and Pacific	19	31	26	29	35	47
Total	$1,235	$1,241	$1,355	$2,126	$2,712	$3,198

† Not available.

Source: *Surv. Curr. Bus.*, September 1975, pp. 31–37.

Table 9.11 lists United States capital expenditures of chemicals and allied products by country for 1971 to 1976. Most investment is in Canada, Europe, and Latin America. Since Japanese law did not permit more than 50 percent ownership of a company by foreign interests until recently, Japan has not been a traditional site for heavy United States investment. In Europe, chemical-industry investment has mostly centered in the United Kingdom, West Germany, France, Belgium, Luxembourg, Italy, and the Netherlands. The bulk of United States investment in Latin America has been concentrated in Brazil and Mexico.

Investment by chemicals and allied products abroad has been a fairly recent phenomenon. From 1957 to 1962 annual plant and equipment expenditures by chemicals and allied products abroad ranged from $234 million to $278 million. By 1964, the figure had grown to $619 million annually, and by 1968 it topped

Table 9.12 United States investment abroad by industry, 1976

Industry	Domestic investment (billions)	Investment in majority-owned foreign affiliates (billions)	Foreign Domestic + foreign,
Chemical	$ 6.67	$2.7	28.8
Food	3.92	0.7	15.2
Paper	3.33	0.6	15.3
Petroleum	11.63	9.6	45.2
Rubber	1.12	0.3	21.1
All manufacturing	51.85	11.5	18.2

Source: *Chem. Eng. News*, Facts and Figures issue, June 7, 1976, p. 46.

$1,318 million. In 1976 chemicals and allied products planned to spend in the neighborhood of $3 billion in plants and equipment abroad.

For many industries in the CPI, foreign investment is taking a large percentage of their total investment, especially in the chemical and petroleum industries. This is shown in Table 9.12.

There are several problems associated with investing in chemical plants overseas. Some of the major problems can be summarized as follows:

1. Unfamiliar laws and customs
2. Competition from local companies, including companies which are government-owned and favored
3. Political instability, including anti-American campaigns, unfair treatment, and nationalization of companies
4. Economic problems, e.g., rampant and chronic inflation, currency devaluation, and difficulty of withdrawing funds from a country once they are invested
5. Lack of necessary skilled labor and management talent; labor unrest
6. Lack of infrastructure (roads and harbors, telecommunication, electricity and water, banks and insurance, schools, parks and recreation, doctors and hospitals), especially in underdeveloped countries

In addition to these problems, United States firms investing abroad have faced difficulties from the United States government. In the past, a major problem was the government's restriction on capital outflow from the United States. Capital outflow was considered detrimental to our economy because it caused a deficit in our international balance of payments. Restriction was accomplished by voluntary programs initiated in 1965 to curtail capital outflow by the 500 largest United States corporations and by mandatory programs initiated in 1968 to limit capital outflow to fixed percentages of previous years' investments plus reinvested earnings. As a result of these measures, United States chemical companies were forced to finance many of their foreign operations by selling bonds and taking out loans abroad. Many United States chemical firms sold substantial amounts of securities in the European bond market to raise capital. This led to highly leveraged affiliates of United States companies. To alleviate some of the problems, many United States foreign investments took the form of joint ventures with foreign companies. Ownership was often on a 50-50 basis, but sometimes the foreign company held controlling interest.

The foreign company in a joint venture often provides a great deal of knowledge, experience, facilities, sales organization, and financing. A foreign partner can help with local customs, laws, building codes, hiring people, and establishing good relationships with customers, government, and lenders. In some countries, particularly the underdeveloped, joint ownership may be required by the government. Indeed the government itself may be the required partner.

In more recent years, the policy of the United States government has changed somewhat vis-à-vis capital outflow. It is generally felt that while foreign investments may initially drain capital out of the country, in the long run the capital

Table 9.13 Unit labor cost as percentage of United States unit labor cost

	1965	1970	1974
Canada	85	85	99
Japan	57	51	91
Germany	55	58	99
United Kingdom	107	84	122

Source: U.S. Department of Commerce, Foreign Direct Investment in the United States, 1976.

returning in the form of profits and foreign purchases more than offsets the initial outflow. However, recent changes in governmental policy do not change the structure of foreign investments overnight, and foreign operations of the CPI are still characterized by heavy leveraging. The shape of future ventures abroad remains to be seen.

Another difficulty the United States chemical firm has in competing with foreign companies is that the United States government and the United States firm do not always work together. Whereas the governments of Japan and West Germany are financially and legally cooperating with their CPI's overseas operations, the United States government is not. This lack of governmental cooperation may be desirable in some respects, but it also lessens the amount of protection to be expected from the government. In some instances, United States companies and the United States government play the roles of adversaries when engaged in overseas operations.

Another consideration in planning an overseas operation is the cost of labor. In the past, qualified labor has, in some instances, been cheaper abroad. However, the data in Table 9.13 indicate that labor costs in Canada, Japan, and Germany have risen to approximately the same level as United States labor costs.

The cost of labor in the United Kingdom is of particular interest, for despite the low wages in the United Kingdom, labor productivity lags behind the other nations, so that the labor cost per unit of production is higher than that of other nations. The United States has a very low degree of labor unrest and political instability, and the United States government is generally more favorable to business.

In recent years, the reverse flow of foreign investments in the United States has greatly increased. The major investors are from Canada and Europe, with rapid increases from Japan. The United States is particularly attractive to foreign investors, as it has large and secure energy resources in oil and gas and in coal and oil shale. In addition the United States has the greatest market in the world, thanks to its large GNP, and a diligent and well-educated labor force. Finally, the United States has great political stability. The wealthy nations in OPEC find the United States a favorite place to invest, although to date their investments have usually been in the form of bonds rather than equity.

Table 9.14   Foreign-controlled capacity, selected chemicals

	1975 U.S. capacity, 10^6 lb	Foreign-controlled capacity, %	Company
High-density polyethylene	6,715	13	Solvay
Ethylene oxide	5,070	12	Shell, BASF
Polypropylene	3,000	15	Shell, Montecatini
Isopropanol	2,275	35	Shell
Caprolactam	800	50	BASF, DSM

Source: U.S. Department of Commerce, *Foreign Direct Investment in the United States,* 1976.

Some of the largest investors in the United States CPI have been:

United Kingdom. Unilever investment in Lever Brothers and Lipton, British Petroleum investment in Standard Oil of Ohio, Burmah Oil investment in Signal Oil and Gas, ICI investment in Atlas
Netherlands. Royal Dutch/Shell investment in Shell Oil, Akzo investment in Akzona, Dutch State Mine in several companies
Germany. BASF investment in Wyandotte and Dow-Badische, Hoechst investment in American Hoechst and Foster Grant, Bayer investment in Mobay Chemicals and Cutter Lab
Switzerland. Nestles, Ciba-Geigy, Hoffman-LaRoche, and Sandoz

In some areas of chemical manufacturing, foreign-controlled capacity amounts to a significant percentage of total United States capacity (Table 9.14).

9.3 MOVEMENT OF TECHNOLOGY AND LABOR BETWEEN THE UNITED STATES AND ABROAD

United States technological innovations are admired around the world. Some of the most important technologies introduced after the Second World War include nuclear power, jet airplanes, digital computers, new polymers and fibers, and antibiotics. These discoveries and inventions have led to a flow of technologies being transferred abroad, earning licensing royalties and publicity.

The free flow of technologies between nations is a fairly recent phenomenon. The ancient Chinese took great pains to prevent the movement of silkworms and mulberry seeds abroad, permitting only the export of raw and finished silk. The Venetians protected their fine art of glassblowing by forbidding their artisans to leave Venice to instruct others. The current international exchange of technologies is generally regarded as beneficial to all involved.

Table 9.15 Incomes from technology transfers (millions)

Nation	1960			1970		
	Receipt	Payment	Receipt/Payment	Receipt	Payment	Receipt/Payment
Japan	$ 2.3	$ 94.9	0.02	$ 34.0	$314.0	0.11
United States	650	67	9.7	1,805	194	9.30
United Kingdom	......	......	......	175.5	164.6	1.07
France	48.1	90.8	0.53	195.0	230.0	0.85
West Germany	38.8	127.5	0.31	105.0	249.8	0.42

Source: Minister of Science and Technology, Science and Technology White Paper, Tokyo, 1970.

It is important to remember that this flow of technologies is two-way. Important technologies that the United States learned from abroad include penicillin from Fleming, Florey, and Chain in England, silica-alumina cracking catalyst from Houdry in France, the basic oxygen steel furnace from Austria, low-density polyethylene from ICI in England, high-density polyethylene from Natta in Italy and Ziegler in Germany, and Librium and Valium tranquilizers from Hoffman–La Roche of Switzerland.

One measure of this technology transfer is the flow of income from royalties; Table 9.15 shows that the United States is the dominant exporter of technology and has a receipt-to-payment ratio above 9. Both West Germany and Japan are heavily on the deficit side, but both are improving rapidly.

Part of the United States success can be explained by its vastly larger research manpower, greater than any other nation except the U.S.S.R. (Table 9.16). It must be remembered, however, that a major fraction of the United States and U.S.S.R. research efforts are concentrated in aerospace and defense projects, which have a

Table 9.16 Number of people in research and development, 1967

	People in R & D (thousands)	R & D people per 1,000 population
United States	504	2.6
U.S.S.R.	589	2.5
Japan	157	1.5
United Kingdom	59	1.1
West Germany	61	1.1
France	49	1.0
Italy	20	0.4

Source: Minister of Science and Technology, Science and Technology White Paper, Tokyo, 1970.

Table 9.17 Immigration of professionals in chemistry into the United States

	Chemical engineers	Chemists	Total scientists and engineers
1967	668	1,392	12,523
1970	908	1,495	13,337
1974	333	592	5,969

Source: U.S. Bureau of the Census, *Statistical Abstract of the United States: 1975* 96th ed., table 925,

relatively minor impact on civilian technologies that can be exported for economic gains.

Science and technology are international, and there is considerable movement of chemical professionals between nations. Immigration into the United States is monitored by the Immigration and Naturalization Service. Table 9.17 illustrates the recent history of immigration into the United States by chemical professionals. These numbers rose to a peak in 1970, with an influx rate per year approximately equal to 1 percent of the work force in chemistry and in chemical engineering. Following the recession and increased unemployment, the inflow has been reduced to about one-third of the peak value. Immigration has brought us many of the giants such as E. I. Du Pont, Leo Baekeland, Vladimir Ipatieff, Eugene Houdry, Herman Mark, and Herman Frasch.

9.4 THE CPI OF OTHER COUNTRIES

The consumption of chemical products is closely related to the GNP of a nation. In addition, chemical production has some correlation with GNP (Table 9.18). The relative wealth of nations is measured by GNP per capita. There are three indicators of national wealth, as shown in Table 9.18.

1. *Affluent* nations are those with GNPs greater than $2,000 per capita. This group includes the United States and Canada, most nations in western Europe, Japan, Australia, and New Zealand. Several of these nations have significant and powerful firms in the CPI that compete with United States firms.
2. *Coping* nations are those with GNPs between $200 and $2,000 per capita. This group includes four thriving nations on the Mediterranean, Portugal, Spain, Greece, and Turkey; the wealthier nations in Latin America, Argentina, Brazil, Chile, Mexico, Panama; and the energetic states of East Asia: Taiwan, Hong Kong, Singapore, South Korea, and Malaysia. These nations have significant manufacturing operations in the CPI and are major purchasers of technology and sophisticated equipment.

Table 9.18 Chemical product consumption, selected countries

Country	GNP per person 1972, U.S. dollars per person	Per capita production 1970 lb per year per person	
		Sulfuric acid	Plastic
United States	$5,550	289	87.7
West Germany	4,693	162	158
Canada	4,696	254	29.3
Netherlands	3,790	264	195
United Kingdom	2,714	133	58.8
South Korea	294	3	
Philippines	202	11	2.3
India	98	4	0.3

3. *Poor* nations are those with GNPs below $200 per capita. This group includes the densely populated and resource deficient nations in Asia, Bangladesh, Burma, Ceylon, India, and Pakistan, and the awakening Latin American and African states, Haiti, Ethiopia, Niger, Sudan, and Uganda. The CPI activities in these nations are understandably concentrated in fertilizers and pesticides for food production.

To these three groups, we add two other groups for special treatment:

4. *Communist* nations with centrally planned economies. This group includes the Soviet Union, the Warsaw Pact nations of Eastern Europe, China, the East Asian nations of North Korea, Vietnam, Laos, and Cambodia. Some of these

Table 9.19 Breakdown of labor force by industry

	Primary (agriculture, fishing, mining), %	Secondary (manufacturing), %	Tertiary (service, commerce, government), %
United Kingdom	3.1	46.5	50.4
United States	4.5	34.1	61.4
West Germany	9.6	48.4	42.0
France	15.4	39.1	45.4
Italy	20.8	42.0	37.2
Japan	18.8	34.5	46.7
Venezuela	32.3	21.1	46.6
Philippines	52.7	13.6	33.7
Mexico	54.2	18.9	26.9
India	72.9	11.4	15.7
Thailand	81.9	4.2	13.9

Source: United Nations, *Yearbook of Labor Statistics, 1970*, New York, 1971.

nations have huge supplies of natural resources and increasing exports of oil. China has been a large purchaser of fertilizers and entire chemical plants. The Soviet Union continues to be a major purchaser of western technologies.
5. *Oil-rich nations* of the OPEC. Several members of this group have a very high ratio of oil reserve to population, including Saudi Arabia, Kuwait, Libya, and Qatar. These nations are expected to have an enormous cash flow until the end of the century and are expected to invest heavily in modernization and in chemical plants.

An almost exclusive reliance on agriculture is necessary for the poor nations. This is seen quite clearly in Table 9.19, which gives the percent of a nation's labor force in the three major industrial groups. An increase in national wealth coincides with the movement of low-efficiency traditional agricultural labor to urban areas for employment in the more modern manufacturing and commerce.

In 1964, a meeting of the United Nations Conference on Trade Development estimated the production of chemicals by region as follows:

OECD European Members	29.2%
United States and Canada	36.8
Japan	3.4
Oceania	2.1
Latin America	3.3
Asia outside of Japan, China	3.1
Africa outside of South Africa	0.6
South Africa	0.7
U.S.S.R.	11.8
Eastern Europe	6.2
Peoples Republic of China	2.6
Middle East	0.3%

9.4.1 The Chemical Industry in Developed Countries

Specific countries to be discussed are West Germany, the United Kingdom, France, Japan, Switzerland, Italy, the Netherlands, and Belgium. The top four chemical producers, ranked by 1974 sales, for these countries are listed in Table 9.20. Also given is each company's *Chemical Age* 200 ranking for 1974 (see Chap. 5). For further comparison, economic data on research and development and capital spending as a percentage of sales, return on capital, and sales per employee are given in Table 9.21 for the top 20 chemical producers. In addition to the above-mentioned countries, the chemical industry in the U.S.S.R. and Eastern Europe will also be considered.

Table 9.20 The four largest chemical producers by country, 1974

Country	Company	Sales, 1974 (millions)	Ranking†
West Germany	BASF	$8,541.6	1
	Hoechst	7,795.2	2
	Bayer	7,180	4
	Veba-Chemie	2,006.8	20
United Kingdom	ICI	7,331.0	3
	Beecham	1,044.1	50
	BOC International	965.1	58
	British Petroleum	777.5	78
France	Rhône-Poulenc	4,426.3	9
	Pechiney-UK	1,033	52
	EMC	968.5	60
	Air Liquide	938	63
Switzerland	Ciba-Geigy	3,108	16
	Hoffmann–La Roche	1,881	24
	Sandoz AG	1,330.7	37
	Lonza AG	257	166
Japan	Mitsubishi Chemical	1,889	23
	Sumitomo Chemical	1,842	25
	Asahi Chemical	1,711.8	29
	Toray Industries	1,567	33
Netherlands and Belgium	Akzo	4,063	10
	Royal Dutch Shell	3,567.2	11
	DSM	2,644.7	17
	Solvay & Cie	2,124	19

† Among *Chem. Age* top 200.

West Germany Three firms, BASF, Hoechst AG, and Bayer AG, dominate the West German chemical scene. They also claim three of the top four spots in the 1974 *Chemical Age* top 200 ranking. All three were originally dyestuffs' manufacturers, but, as indicated by recent sales distributions, they are now extremely diversified (Table 9.22).

The three German chemical companies have had an interesting and uneven history. In an attempt to meet world competition following the First World War, these three firms merged in 1925 to form I. G. Farben, which became an important supporter of Hitler from 1932 until the end of the Second World War. During the war, I. G. Farben produced synthetic rubber, synthetic gasoline from $CO-H_2$ mixtures, explosives, methanol, poison gases, tetraethyl lead, magnesium, aluminium, and many other products for the war effort. Following the war, the firm was liquidated, and its leaders were arrested. BASF, Bayer and Hoechst were re-formed in 1953. The record of all three in both growth and profitability has been spectacular.

Table 9.21 Further economic data on the top 20 chemical companies in the world, 1974

No.	Name	Sales (millions)	R & D, %	Capital spending, %	Return on capital, %	Sales per employee (thousands)
1	BASF	$8,541.6	2.7	6.3	18.7	$ 76,958
2	Hoechst	7,795.2	4.0	8.3	17.6	43,619
3	ICI	7,331	2.8	6.5	22.7	34,909
4	Bayer	7,180	2.5	4.7	19.5	109,534
5	Du Pont	6,910	5.0	15.0	15.2	50,487
6	Montedison	6,178	0.1	7.5	12.0	
7	Union Carbide	5,320	1.8	9.7	25.8	52,157
8	Dow	4,938	3.0	17.6	34.2	92,645
9	Rhône-Poulenc	4,426.3	3.9	10.3	46.0	37,113
10	Akzo	4,063	3.3	7.4	11.7	38,548
11	Royal Dutch Shell	3,567.2	...	10.2		
12	Monsanto	3,498	3.0	8.9	26.2	57,414
13	Grace	3,472	0.9	7.9	19.2	46,417
14	Exxon	3,300	...	3.7	46.6	
15	Borden	3,264	...	...	15.7	
16	Ciba-Geigy	3,108	7.5	...	23.1	
17	DSM	2,644.7	...	5.6	35.8	89,657
18	Allied Chemical	2,216	1.4	13.8	20.5	68,890
19	Solvay	2,214	2.4	8.4	14.9	47,765
20	Veba-Chemie	2,006.8	...	4.5		

Source: Chemical Age Top 200, *Chem. Age*, July 1975.

The United Kingdom Imperial Chemical Industries (ICI) is an order of magnitude larger than the next largest British chemical producer. ICI is active in almost every segment of the chemical industry, including agricultural chemicals, fibers, paints, petrochemicals, plastics, pharmaceuticals, and metals. The company is a world leader in polyester and nylon fiber production. It is an international company, having almost 500 subsidiaries.

Throughout the 1960s and early 1970s ICI was characterized by low profitability and efficiency in comparison with its German and United States counterparts. It borrowed heavily, was poorly managed, and was plagued by technical mistakes such as the building of obsolete plants and gross overexpansion. However, in 1974 ICI ranked second among the chemical companies of the world in pretax profits. Return on capital was 22.7 percent, which was better than the large German firms and comparable to United States performance. The company has sought to increase productivity through aggressive capital investment and research and development spending.

In spite of its efforts to improve, ICI faces monumental difficulties. The British domestic market for chemical products collapsed in 1975. Furthermore, ICI must

Table 9.22 Distribution of sales by product type for the top three West German firms

	Percent
Bayer AG†:	
Chemicals	33
Plastics and surface coatings	14
Dyestuffs	13
Polyurethanes	12
Pharmaceuticals	11
Fibers	9
Rubber	8
BASF:‡	
Plastics	19.2
Oil and gas	14.4
Chemicals	11.6
Dyestuffs	8.5
Fertilizers	10.3
Potassium salts	5.3
Fibers	6.3
Dispersions	3.8
Coatings	3.4
Other	17.2
Hoechst AG:‡	
Fibers and fiber mats	11
Synthetic resin and paints	13
Pharmaceuticals	15
Chemicals	11
Film and sheeting	4
Agricultural chemicals	5
Surfactants	4
Reprographic products	3
Other	18

† As percentage of 1973 sales.
‡ As percentage of 1974 sales.
Source: "Standard and Poor's Standard Corporation Descriptions," 1975.

operate with price controls, high rate of inflation, decreasing domestic per capita GNP, devaluation of the British currency, and social and political unrest.

The other British chemical companies of major importance are Beech Chem, which manufactures proprietary medicines and canned foods; British Oxygen Company (BOC), which manufactures industrial gases, synthetic resins, and emulsions and refines tall oil; and British Petroleum (Chemicals) International, which manufactures petrochemicals and plastics.

France The two big names in French chemicals are Rhône-Poulenc and Pechiney-Ugine-Kuhlmann. Rhône-Poulenc produces a broad spectrum of chemicals including pharmaceuticals, photographic chemicals, plastics, fibers, and fertilizers. Pechiney-UK is a composite of merged companies. It is a major manufacturer of aluminum (35.3 percent of 1973 sales). Copper fabrication (22.1 percent of 1973 sales); mining and electrometallurgy (7.9 percent); specialty and stainless steels and titanium (7.4 percent) are other major Pechiney-UK businesses. Chemicals accounted for 19.5 percent of 1973 sales.

Japan The Japanese chemical industry is characterized by many small and medium-sized firms. The largest, Mitsubishi Chemical, ranks twenty-third in the *Chemical Age* top 200. Fertilizers for intensive farming on the limited land available and synthetic fibers to clothe an increasingly affluent population have been particularly important to Japan's chemical industry. Extensive innovation, intense domestic competition, United States financial and technical aid, and a rapid growth in domestic demand led to a 16 percent annual growth rate of the Japanese chemical industry from 1962 to 1968.

Obtaining adequate petrochemical feedstocks and fuel for energy are basic problems facing Japanese chemical companies. Essentially all of Japan's hydrocarbon raw materials are imported. However, the Japanese have gone to great lengths to obtain assured supplies of raw materials. In addition, the Japanese economy and society are relatively stable. Low unemployment, moderate inflation, growing increases in personal wealth, and strengthening position in world chemical trade point to a healthy Japanese CPI in coming years.

Switzerland Pharmaceuticals and other fine chemicals dominate the Swiss CPI. Hoffman–La Roche is probably the world's largest manufacturer of pharmaceuticals. Swiss firms are not required to make public much of the financial information which is required in most countries. As a result it is difficult to study the performance or prospects of the Swiss CPI. However, low domestic inflation, negligible unemployment, a strong currency, a strong world position, and an apparently strong financial position indicate a healthy future outlook for Swiss chemical companies.

The Netherlands and Belgium Because of its excellent port facilities and ability to handle large amounts of chemical imports and exports, the Netherlands is of paramount importance to the European chemical industry. The chemical industry of the Netherlands includes important joint ventures with British companies. Akzo is the largest Dutch chemical company. It is a world leader in synthetic fiber production, and in 1974 approximately 43 percent of its total sales were in fibers.

The largest Belgian chemical company is Solvay. Soda ash (calcium carbonate) manufactured by the Solvay process accounts for a large percentage of Solvay's sales, but the company also produces plastics, fertilizers, halogen derivatives, and peroxy compounds.

Italy Montedison is the largest chemical concern in Italy. The company was formed in 1966, when Edison, a former electric utility company whose utility interests were bought by the Italian government, bought Montecatini, a chemical company. Originally, the chemical company was involved in many areas, including lead and zinc mines, petrochemicals, plastics, fertilizers, and olive oil. Since 1966 the company has sold many of its unprofitable businesses, e.g., its lead and zinc mines, steel mills, aluminum operations, and food operations, to the government. In recent years it has expanded into many nonchemical areas, including retailing, engineering, banking, and even currency and commodity speculation. Presently, the Italian government owns an estimated 30 percent of Montedison. The firm has many inefficient and obsolete plants. From an overall view, strikes, chronic high inflation, lackluster management, obsolete plants, price controls, political unrest, and a weak currency cast a shadow on the future of the Italian chemical industry.

U.S.S.R. Before 1958 the chemical industry in Soviet Russia was small and by world standards obsolete. It was based on coal until the early 1960s, when the Russians began experimenting with a petrochemical industry. Early Russian attempts to build petrochemical plants were often less than successful. As a result, Russian chemical process technology has been mostly imported. Growth of the Soviet chemical industry has been rapid, averaging about 15 percent per year. In 1970 the U.S.S.R. made 45 percent as much sulfuric acid and 20 percent as much resins and plastics as the United States.

Eastern Europe The chemical industries of Bulgaria, Czechoslovakia, East Germany, Hungary, Poland, Rumania, and Yugoslavia are fairly new and modern. Soft coal from extensive domestic reserves is still used in some countries as a raw material. Little reliable data on the industry exist, and it is difficult to ascertain much about the health or direction of the CPI in these countries. However, a burgeoning demand for chemical products in the Communist bloc countries would seem to indicate a strong future for the CPI there.

China The rate of oil production in China has been estimated as 1.25 million barrels per day.[1] Substantial amounts have been exported to Japan and Southeast Asia to earn foreign exchange. Her ultimate potential as an oil exporter is controversial, ranging from the most glowing comparison with Saudi Arabia to the more modest comparison with Indonesia.

There are significant fertilizer, cement, and paper industries in China. In 1970 China imported $330 million worth of chemicals, chiefly fertilizers from Japan and Western Europe. In recent years, China has been buying entire petrochemical and fertilizer plants. In a reversal of earlier dependence on the U.S.S.R., the percentage of Chinese trade with Communist nations has dropped to below 22 percent,

[1] China: Energy Balance Projections, Central Intelligence Agency, November 1975.

and the present biggest trading partners are the developed nations of Japan and Western Europe.[1]

9.4.2 The Chemical Industry in Less Developed Countries

There is a significant CPI industry in the coping nations, producing many essential chemicals as import substitutions to save foreign exchange. They are primarily simple chemicals that have a local raw-material or labor advantage and are too low-priced to be transported over long distances. Some of the more notable products are hormones in Mexico and the Bahamas and vegetable extracts for tanning in Argentina and South Africa. Chemical mining for export is important for world trade:

Bauxite. Jamaica, Ghana, Surinam
Nuclear minerals. Congo
Phosphate. Morocco, Tunisia, Peru
Sulfur. Mexico
Tin. Malaysia, Bolivia
Silver. Mexico, Peru
Natural rubber. Malaysia, Indonesia

In the poor nations, virtually all needed chemicals are presently imported. Needless to say, the governments of several such less developed countries would like to see the CPI develop in their countries. Their people need chemical products for many reasons. Moreover, it is often a matter of national prestige to have a few nice, new, shiny plants. But realization of the CPI in underdeveloped countries can occur only with support from the world's developed countries, and the firms in developed countries need political, moral, or economic incentives to give such support.

From an economic viewpoint, there are several factors one needs to consider when surveying the potential for developing a chemical industry in an underdeveloped country. Table 9.23 lists some of the more important general factors along with some typical ranges. In addition, a country's potential for developing a chemical industry must be approached in terms of factors of production, infrastructure, market, and sociopolitical factors. Some necessary questions about each are summarized below:

1. Factors of production
   a. Is there land available for a plant site?
   b. Is there capital available?
   c. Is there a trained or trainable labor force available?
   d. Are the necessary raw materials available?

---

[1] People's Republic of China: An Economic Assessment, Joint Economic Committee, Congress of the United States, 1972.

2. Infrastructure
    a. Is there other heavy industry in the country?
    b. Are parts, machinery, and equipment available?
    c. Is there plant-construction capability?
    d. Are there ports for exports and imports?
    e. Are there established domestic outlets for products?
    f. Are transportation, communication, medical, education, banking, and other services available?
3. Market
    a. Is there a domestic need for chemical products?
    b. Do the potential customers have the ability to pay for the products?
    c. Are there nearby markets in other countries?
4. Sociopolitical factors
    a. Are foreign investment and chemical plants welcomed by the government and by the general public?
    b. Are incentives offered by the government to encourage CPI investment?
    c. Will the country's people make acceptable employees?
    d. Are they dependable and hard-working?
    e. Is the company relatively safe from foreign military intervention?

For many underdeveloped countries, answers to some of these and other pertinent questions are positive; however, this is usually balanced by several equally discouraging answers. For example, India has a large and rapidly growing population and certainly offers large potential needs for chemical products, but it has inadequate supplies of raw materials and limited capital and the general population cannot afford to buy many products. As another example, several of

Table 9.23 Important factors, selected countries

Factor	Typical value	Example
Population density, people per square mile:		
High	> 200	India
Low	< 50	Argentina
Annual population growth rate, %:		
High	> 2.2	Mexico, Thailand
Low	< 1	Greece
GNP per capita:		
High	> $1,000	Hong Kong, South Africa
Median	$200–$1,000	Egypt, Mexico
Low	< $200	India, Ethiopia
GNP and size of market (billions)		
High	> $10	India, Brazil
Low	< $1	Burundi

Table 9.24 GNP per capita growth

	Growth rate of GNP per capita, %
United States	3.3
Bolivia	3.1
Iran	6.5
Kenya	3.3
Mexico	3.8
Panama	4.6

the sparsely populated Middle East countries have sufficient raw materials and capital for a chemical industry; however, they do not have adequate infrastructure, political stability, domestic demand, or trained labor for developing a complex CPI. In fact, for most currently underdeveloped countries the prospects of developing a chemical industry in the near future are not promising because of the extraordinarily high level of risk associated with building plants. However, GNP per capita is growing rapidly in some less developed countries, indicating future opportunities for the CPI (Table 9.24).

9.4.3 The Chemical Industry of Oil-rich Nations

There are a few exceptions to the above pessimistic outlook, especially where one or two of the potential benefits far offset the problems and risks associated with such investment. The OPEC nations have been endowed with large amounts of

Table 9.25 OPEC Oil Reserves, 1974

Country	Reserves, 10^9 bbl	Population (thousands)	Reserves, 10^3 bbl per population
Saudi Arabia	132	8,706	15.2
Kuwait	64	929	69
Iran	60	32,139	1.9
Iraq	32	10,765	2.9
Libya	25.6	2,346	10.9
United Arab Emirates	25.5	215	119
Nigeria	19.9	61,270	0.33
Venezuela	14.2	11,632	1.2
Indonesia	10.5	127,586	0.08
Algeria	7.6	16,275	0.47
Qatar	6.5	89	73
Ecuador	5.7	6,951	0.82

Source: "Basic Petroleum Data Book," American Petroleum Institute, Washington, 1975; U.S. Bureau of the Census, *Statistical Abstract of the United States: 1976*, 96th ed.

petroleum reserves and hence have a strong raw-material base for a petrochemical industry (Table 9.25). Moreover, the recent quadrupling of oil prices has supplied an adequate amount of capital to build large and sophisticated petrochemical complexes and downstream processing facilities. The governments of most of these countries have been extremely active in pursuing such development for a variety of reasons:

1. To provide for large domestic demand, especially in countries like Iran and Egypt
2. To prolong oil wealth by concentrating on higher value-added products derived from oil
3. To provide non-labor-intensive business, especially in countries like Saudi Arabia, where the population is low
4. To increase national power and prestige

There are many serious and difficult problems to be faced in building a CPI in the Middle East. The more formidable are as follows:

1. There is a serious lack of technical and managerial personnel in most of the countries. Even those with such people, e.g., Iran and Egypt, do not have nearly enough. Many of the countries lack even semiskilled and unskilled labor. Indeed, the people problem may be the most limiting factor in the development of a CPI in the oil-rich nations. In some instances, petrochemical complexes would require setting up from scratch a completely new community of 20,000 to 30,000 people. Many of these people would be foreigners, which would present social problems, particularly in the countries whose own populations are small.
2. There are limited local markets in many of the countries such as Saudi Arabia and the United Arab Emirates. Thus, large quantities of chemicals would have to be exported and sold in foreign markets. The Middle East countries presently lack the marketing abilities and connections to sell large quantities of chemicals outside their borders.
3. Construction costs will be large, and building times will be long. Investment in a chemical plant may be about 30 percent more than in the United States. Projects will take 40 to 50 percent longer. In many instances there will be little economic foundation to support such large and complex construction. Almost all the necessary plant equipment and related material will have to be shipped to the plant site. There will be severe scheduling problems. Often, large stocks of spare parts, catalysts, chemicals, and other supplies will have to be shipped to the plant site and stored there.
4. Libya, Saudi Arabia, and other Persian Gulf countries lack the necessary fresh water for major petrochemical complexes. A large chemical operation requires some 50 million gallons of water daily.

In spite of the problems, many United States companies and several European countries are investigating and making plans to invest in the Middle East. Chemical-plant construction firms from around the world are actively pursuing and winning contracts to build huge and modern complexes throughout the Middle East. There is strong expectation that the Middle East will become a major area of chemical production activity in years to come.

9.5 SUGGESTED READING

International statistics of a general nature can be found in " The International Yearbook and Statesmen's Who's Who," IPC Business Press,

The Organization for Economic Cooperation and Development (OECD) publishes economic data regularly on an international basis.

The *United Nation Statistical Yearbook* and other UN publications also provide international data.

The *Statistical Abstract of the United States* provides several tables of international data.

Articles dealing with the CPI of specific world areas appear often in *Chemical and Engineering News, Chemical Week*, and *Chemical Engineering*. These are useful and should be filed for reference.

9.6 PROBLEMS

9.1 Compare Tables 9.1 and 9.2. Table 9.1 lists nine countries ranked according to chemical sales. Using Table 9.2, rank these same countries according to their exports as a percentage of GNP. Is the ranking any different? If so, explain why.

9.2 The economic performance of a country or a firm can be misrepresented through biased presentation of economic indicators. Illustrate this by using the data in Table 9.4 to draw two graphs, one showing United States income from exports vs. time and another depicting United States exports as a percentage of world exports vs. time.

9.3 Consult Table 9.21 and note the data given for two companies with comparable sales, ICI and Bayer. What are the sales for these companies? What do these companies spend on research and development? What return on capital do these companies enjoy? What are the respective sales per employee? Explain any discrepancies you find. Tables 9.16 and 9.19 and the data relating to labor costs may prove helpful in developing a credible explanation. If you were seeking a job and both ICI and Bayer made you an offer, what would you be inclined to do assuming you have found the answers to the above questions about the two firms? Why?

9.4 United States producers of color televisions claim that they have been damaged by the importing of Japanese sets and want to slow down imports by a quota. Presumably, United States consumers prefer Japanese sets because they are cheaper or of better quality. Would the following groups support the quota? Why?
1. United States producers of color television sets and labor unions
2. United States producers of picture tubes, transistors, plastics, and other supplies for television sets
3. United States consumers
4. U.S. State Department
5. U.S. Department of Commerce
Is a quota in the national interest? What could Japan do to retaliate? Which United States sector would suffer?

9.5 Is the relative decline of the United States CPI a national crisis? Is it inevitable? Is it caused by United States firms investing in plants abroad, selling technologies abroad, training foreign students in chemistry and chemical engineering? Can we stop these developments? Should we?

9.6 What is your attitude toward working for a United States company abroad or for a foreign company in the United States? What about working for a foreign national company, such as ARAMCO in Saudi Arabia? Would you have sufficient skills and career-development potential for upward movement, job security, esteem of friends and family?

9.7 What are the advantages of permitting foreign chemical professionals to emigrate to the United States, and who are the beneficiaries? What are the disadvantages, and who are the victims? On a whole, should immigration be unrestricted, restricted by quotas, or forbidden?

9.8 Less-developed countries must import high-technology products (such as cars, chemicals, computers, and airplanes) from the more developed countries to modernize. To pay the bills, they must sell things to the more developed countries to earn foreign exchange; selling raw materials is not enough. Many economists believe that they must sell low-technology products (such as shirts, shoes, and toys) to the more developed countries. Who in the more developed countries would not subscribe to this idea and why? Should this idea be carried out?

9.9 Why are the German and Japanese CPIs gaining on the United States CPI? Can and should the United States government do something to reverse this trend?

9.10 When a less developed country starts a plant to produce chemicals locally, usually imports are throttled down or shut off. Consumers complain of high prices and low quality. It has been said that in the 1800s the South would have much preferred consumer products and machinery from England and France to inferior and more expensive products from New England and the rest of the North. Is protected domestic production justified?

9.11 It is sometimes said that multinational corporations are mighty "engines of change" for less developed countries, introducing modern technology and organization, a better standard of living, and a social system that is often better than cruel and arbitrary local customs. What are the complaints against the multinational corporations and do they outweigh the advantages? Are there other "engines" that offer better alternatives?

10

FUTURE PROSPECTS: THREATS AND OPPORTUNITIES

Even in the midst of prosperity, a prudent person plans for the continuity and growth of his fortunes. We are in the midst of the most explosive rate of change in the history of mankind. Toffler [1] eloquently describes our predicament: " Rip Van Winkle found himself a stranger in his own village after a long sleep; we would feel estrangement even after a brief nap. As the Red Queen said to Alice, we have to keep on running very hard to stay at the same place."

The CPI are one of the most dynamic sectors of American economic life, responding to both external forces and internal innovations. No chemical company can feel secure for very long with an established technology or market. Examples abound of chemical processes and products which were once important but are now obsolete or dated.

At the founding of the American republic, two of the most important products of the colonial chemical industry were spermaceti candles and black gunpowder. The spermaceti candles were eventually replaced by petroleum wax candles, then by kerosene lamps, and finally by electric light. An essential ingredient in the production of black gunpowder is saltpeter (potassium nitrate). When the British naval blockade of the American colonies introduced some risk into the importation of saltpeter, Congress established a saltpeter works in Philadelphia and appointed Benjamin Rush, a chemist and signer of the Declaration of Independence, to operate it. Niter deposits were found as incrustations on the walls of cellars and stables, the result of decomposition of organic matter. The colonial chemists constructed "niter beds" consisting of layers of decayed animal and vegetable substances and mortar from old walls in a thickness of 3 to 4 ft, periodically moistened with blood or urine. Only 0.3 lb of saltpeter was recovered per cubic foot of the beds every 2 years [2]. Imported and domestic saltpeter was eventually replaced by Chilean saltpeter and subsequently by ammonia synthesis and oxidation. Finally, black powder was replaced by more modern explosives, nitroglycerin, dynamite, ammonium nitrate and fuel oil, and atomic and hydrogen bombs. The Du Pont Company, founded by a young French immigrant in 1802, manufactured black powder for the American army, hunters, and frontiersmen who needed it to clear the land as they moved west. The Du Pont Company manufactured black powder until 1973, when it sold its last black-powder operation.

A more recent example of the rise and decline of an important product is rayon. As the first mass-produced synthetic fiber, it had a phenomenal growth between the First and Second World Wars, capturing a large share of the cotton and silk markets. Competition from more modern and appealing synthetic fibers, e.g., nylon and polyesters, caused rayon's popularity to wane. Today it has a very small share of the total fiber market. Another product whose popularity grew rapidly and then declined is cellophane. Despite its early success, cellophane has lost much of its market share to the preferred polyvinyl chloride and polyethylene wrapping films.

The inorganic raw-material supply for the chemical industry comes mostly from mining. The shortage or exhaustion of one mineral requires the substitution of another. Chilean saltpeter replaced niter-bed saltpeter. The shortage of rutile ore for titanium dioxide manufacture has led to development of processes that make use of ilmenite. An even more dramatic change of raw-material supply is illustrated by organic raw materials. The CPI initially used organic materials derived from farming, forestry, fishing, and animal-husbandry sectors. Coal-tar and coke-oven products rose as the principal source following the discovery of synthetic dyes. In the decades following the Second World War, coal was virtually totally displaced by natural gas and refined petroleum products because of their lower cost and greater cleanliness. By the end of this century, with the anticipated scarcity of oil and gas and with the vastly greater resource base of coal, the CPI will probably derive most of its organic raw material from coal.

Chemical companies do not have a guaranteed place in the economy, as evidenced by the fall of once mighty companies, e.g., Virginia Carolina Chemical Company and American Viscose Company, which failed to maintain their commanding positions in a changing world and were absorbed by more adaptable and successful companies.

In addition to economic threats, companies of the twentieth century must also deal with complex sociopolitical factors which might influence their fate. The conduct of many companies has come under public attack, particularly in the areas of environmental and consumer protection, employee safety and health, and concentration of power. Increasing governmental regulation and controls, as well as threats of divestiture and confiscation, require responsible and effective business behavior. Sixty years ago, Du Pont was ordered by the courts to sell Hercules and Atlas (now part of ICI); the Standard Oil Trust was broken into many companies

Table 10.1 The CPI: Threats, needs, and opportunities

Part of CPI	Threats	Needs	Opportunities
Manufacturing plants	Deterioration Obsolescence Inadequate capacity Poor location	Capital investment	Superior technology Larger and more effective plants Better location
Technology	Replacement by improved processes Dwindling raw-material supply Inability to meet requirements vis-à-vis safety, environment, etc.	Research Development Technical service	New processes New products Substitute raw materials Solution to environmental and health problems
Market	Replacement by better products Changes in the needs of important customers Decline or disappearance of important customers Government intervention	Market surveillance Market development	Penetration of markets not previously served with existing products Invasion of existing markets with newly developed products Invention of new markets through development of new products
Employees	Obsolescence Low productivity Retirement Resignations	Recruitment Career development Continuing education Professional society meetings	Upgrading and reeducating employees Improvement in productivity
Public and government relations	Opposition to plant-site location Inability to raise capital Tax increases Divestiture, confiscation, antitrust action, nationalization Import-export control Price control Capital-flow control Inflation, war, civil unrest	Lobby Public relations Public education	Increased government-industry cooperation Better university-industry understanding Greater public acceptance Better service to the public

that survived as Exxon, Mobil, American Oil, Atlantic Richfield, Standard Oil of California, and many others. Further breakup of the oil companies is frequently debated in Congress.

In this maelstrom of changes there are many dangers to the continuity of a process, a product, or a chemical company. Some of the outstanding threats and the needed measures to combat them are listed in Table 10.1. Besides a defensive and reflective response, these changes also afford magnificent opportunities for innovation and growth.

Prudent professionals in chemistry join a company for much more than the immediate prospects, as they may spend the next 40 years of their life there and must be concerned with its future. You should study the historic growth patterns within the CPI and the external and internal factors affecting the CPI and then plan to improve its future.

10.1 GROWTH PATTERN

The CPI are characterized by growth, as exemplified by the diversity of growth rates of different products in Table 10.2. The main reasons for the growth in annual production of a chemical are:

1. Growing population
2. Growing affluence as measured by real GNP per capita growth (Chap. 2)
3. New uses for chemical products, e.g., as oxygen for steelmaking, and displacement of natural products, e.g., nylon replacing silk
4. Declining chemical prices, which cause chemicals to be used in broader markets (Chap. 2)
5. Economic growth of foreign nations and the expansion of international trade (Chap. 9)

When growth is measured in terms of dollars per year, there is an additional reason for growth:

6. Increasing prices caused by inflation or by upgrading of the product to higher specification or performance

The growth rate of a chemical measured in dollars per year can be termed *neutral* (growing at the same rate as the United States GNP), *aggressive* (growing at a much higher rate than the GNP), or *declining* (accounting for a progressively smaller share of the GNP even though it is still growing in absolute tonnage).

The growth rates in chemical sales for 1964, and 1971 to 1974 are given in Table 10.3, both in terms of value of shipments and by an industrial production index. As shown by the annual change in production index for 1964 to 1974, several segments of the CPI, e.g., plastics, synthetic fibers, drugs and medicine, have shown aggressive growth. Each of these segments has had a growth in

Table 10.2 Comparisons of United States chemical production, 1974 and 1950

Chemical	U.S. production 10^6 lb		Increase in production, %
	1950	1974	
Inorganics:			
Carbon dioxide	1,134	2,910	156
Hydrochloric acid	1,238	4,810	288
Sodium hydroxide	5,020	21,730	333
Nitric acid	2,672	16,370	513
Oxygen	1,477	32,120	2,075
Sulfuric acid	26,058	64,710	148
Sodium sulfate	2,000	2,750	37
Organics:			
Acetic acid	462	2,260	389
Acetone	482	2,060	327
Benzene	1,428	11,070	675
Ethylene	1,392	23,520	1,589
Ethylene dichloride	305	7,700	2,424
Ethylene oxide	454	3,890	756
Ethylene glycol	519	3,110	499
Formaldehyde	835	5,850	600
Isopropanol	866	1,910	121
Phenol	292	2,320	695
Propylene	1,100	9,820	793
Styrene	539	5,940	1,002
Fibers:			
Nylon	90.6	2,125	2,245
Polyester	1	1,518	151,700
Acrylic	1	634	63,300
Olefin	0.2	463	231,400
Plastics:			
Polyethylene	55	8,810	15,900
Polypropylene	0	2,249	
Polystyrene	261	3,364	1,189
GNP	355	831	134

Source: Data from miscellaneous sources.

production index of over 11 percent compounded yearly, while total manufacturing has seen a growth of 4.4 percent. On the other hand, several sectors, e.g., petroleum products, soaps, paints, and synthetic rubber, have shown below average manufacturing growth rates. The fate of individual chemical growth rates (in terms of pounds per year) is well tabulated in *Chemical and Engineering News Facts and Figures.* The stellar performance of all noncellulosic fibers, of the major thermoplastics, and of the petrochemicals (such as ethylene, propylene, methanol,

Table 10.3 Growth of the CPI

As measured by shipments

	Manufacturers' shipments (billions)					Annual change, %	
	1974	1973	1972	1971	1964	1973–1974	1964–1974
All manufacturing industries	$980.7	$856.8	$749.6	$671.0	$448.0	14.5	8.2
Chemicals and allied products	81.4	67.0	57.4	51.9	34.3	21.5	9.0
Industrial chemicals	26.6	19.4	16.7	15.9	11.5	37.1	8.7
Drugs, soaps, and toiletries	19.7	18.5	17.0	15.7	†	6.5	†
Petroleum and coal products	56.9	35.8	29.9	26.9	18.3	58.9	12.0
Rubber and plastics products	23.4	20.5	19.2	17.0	9.7	14.1	9.2
Paper and allied products	39.8	32.4	28.3	25.5	17.2	22.8	8.8

As measured by production indexes

	Industrial production indexes, 1967 = 100					Annual change, %	
	1974‡	1973	1972	1971	1964	1973–1974	1964–1974
Total index	124.8	125.6	115.2	106.8	81.7	−0.6	4.3
Manufacturing, total	124.4	125.1	114.0	105.2	81.2	−0.6	4.4
Nondurable manufacturing	129.7	129.7	122.1	113.6	84.4	0.0	4.4
Chemicals and products	154.3	150.2	139.6	126.4	73.9	2.7	7.6
Chemicals and synthetic materials	165.5	162.2	146.8	129.4	75.7	2.0	8.1
Basic chemicals	141.3	136.2	125.6	116.0	76.3	3.7	6.4
Alkalies and chlorine	122.5	120.7	117.5	112.0	81.9	1.5	4.1
Gases, coal tar, etc.	163.7	156.8	146.6	125.6	76.1	4.4	8.0
Basic organic chemicals	151.1	143.9	129.3	119.0	73.4	5.0	7.5
Inorganic chemicals, not elsewhere classified	115.0	113.7	108.0	106.1	80.0	1.1	3.7
Synthetic materials	214.7	214.9	189.7	156.6	74.5	−0.1	11.2
Plastics	217.6	213.3	192.7	155.7	74.7	2.0	11.3
Synthetic rubber	129.4	135.6	126.9	117.2	92.0	−4.6	3.5
Synthetic fibers	231.4	234.5	201.1	166.4	70.9	−1.3	12.6
Chemical products	144.1	139.0	132.8	123.6	72.3	3.7	7.1
Drugs and medicines	193.2	186.8	169.0	157.8	65.6	3.4	11.4
Soaps and toiletries	124.3	119.2	119.8	109.4	80.1	4.3	4.5
Soaps and related products	120.0	121.1	127.8	111.0	90.0	−0.9	2.9
Paints	126.3	118.9	121.8	114.1	88.5	6.2	3.6
Agricultural chemicals	109.6	106.6	103.8	96.4	67.6	2.8	5.0
Petroleum products	124.0	127.4	120.6	115.7	90.8	−2.7	3.2
Rubber and plastics products	164.4	163.8	145.5	126.0	74.4	0.4	8.2

† Not available.
‡ Preliminary.
Source: Chem. Eng. News, Facts and Figures issue, June 2, 1975, p. 59.

vinyl chloride, propylene oxide, and vinyl acetate, as well as the aromatics terephthalic acid, cumene, dimethyl terephthalate, and *p*-xylene) should especially be noted. Drugs are shown as growth chemicals. This is contrasted with the laggards in cellulosic fibers, inorganics such as sodium sulfate and calcium chloride, synthetic rubber, and coatings.

Table 10.4 Rubber and fiber use in the United States

| Year | Rubber, 10^3 long tons | | Fiber, lb per person per year | | |
	Natural	Synthetic	Cotton, wool, flax, silk	Synthetic	Total
1950	720	538	35.2	9.8	45.0
1960	479	1,079	25.6	10.0	35.0
1970	559	1,918	19.8	26.2	46.0
1974	687	2,393	16.0	35.3	51.3

It is well known that the growth segments represent dynamic advances in technology, increase in end uses, and heavy investment in research and new plants. The production rates of noninnovative chemicals, such as sulfuric acid, manage to keep pace with GNP growth and overall manufacturing growth. The declining cellulosic fibers are not keeping pace with GNP growth, as they are being replaced by newer products having better performance and lower price. The growth of some chemical products can be attributed to the growth of total use, e.g., synthetic rubber slowing the growth of natural rubber and synthetic fibers replacing cotton, wool, flax, and silk (Table 10.4).

A chemical may show above-average growth if it serves an industrial customer who has experienced above-average growth or has changed to a new technology requiring the chemical. An example of new technology is the shift of the steel industry to oxygen-blown steel mills, which caused the boom in oxygen consumption. We also need to investigate segments of our economy growing at faster than average rates. Noninnovative chemicals may grow rapidly if their customers are growing, e.g., indigo dye for blue jeans. On the other hand, dwindling numbers of customers can sound the death knell for even the most innovative of chemicals or plants. The information in Table 10.5 summarizes United States growth from 1950

Table 10.5 Measures of U.S. growth

	Value in 1974 / Value in 1950
Population	1.39
GNP, current dollars	4.91
Constant 1958 dollars	2.31
Per capita, constant 1958 dollars	1.65
Production index, industrial	2.78
Chemicals and products	6.16
Petroleum products	2.58
Rubber and plastics products	4.82
Paper and products	3.02

Source: U.S. Bureau of the Census, *Statistical Abstract of the United States 1975.*

Table 10.6 Growth of selected sectors

	Ratio of production index 1974/1950
Transportation equipment	2.57
Furniture	2.44
Apparel	1.64
New construction	3.30

to 1974. During this period, chemicals and rubber and plastics have had superior increases in production index compared with increases in the overall industrial production index. Petroleum and paper have just kept up. The fact that rubber and chemical growth has outstripped much of manufacturing points toward new-use and replacement-of-older-product roles. These roles are sustained by aggressive research and development and marketing efforts. Several of the key customers of chemicals and rubber have not grown any faster than industrial production (Table 10.6).

It would be instructive to look at an assortment of growth figures for the United States during this period. Table 10.7 shows the growth of durable goods, nondurable goods, and services in the United States. The increased percentage devoted to service is characteristic of advanced societies. Table 10.8 shows the growth of the contribution to GNP by industry. Between 1950 and 1974 the GNP has increased by a factor of 4.6. It is apparent that service is growing much faster than durable goods or nondurable goods. In the industrial sectors, rapid growth is seen in communications, utility, finance, services, and government sectors, while agriculture and mining lag behind. In an assortment of figures (Table 10.9) it is seen that the fast growers are:

Airline revenue
National health
Schools and universities
Foreign travel
Federal, state, and local government budgets
Defense

Table 10.7 Growth in personal consumption in the United States, 1950–1974 (billions of current dollars)

Personal consumption	1950	1960	1970	1974	$\frac{1974}{1950}$
Durable goods	$30.5	$ 45.3	$ 91.3	$127.5	4.2
Nondurable goods	98.1	151.3	263.8	380.2	3.9
Services	62.4	128.7	262.6	369.0	5.9

Table 10.8 Growth in contribution to GNP by industry, 1950–1974 (billions of current dollars)

Industry	1950	1960	1970	1974	$\frac{1974}{1950}$
Agriculture	$20.8	$21.7	$31.6	$60.1	2.9
Mining	9.2	12.7	16.9	19.5	2.1
Construction	12.7	22.7	46.6	61.8	4.9
Manufacturing	83.8	144.4	282.3	325.2	3.9
Transportation	16.0	22.5	38.5	50.9	3.2
Communications	4.5	10.4	22.7	30.4	6.8
Utilities	5.3	12.7	22.6	29.9	5.6
Trade	51.3	84.3	166.4	218.9	4.3
Finance industries	30.7	67.5	137.8	177.8	5.8
Services	24.3	49.9	114.0	148.6	6.1
Government	23.7	53.7	129.4	167.9	7.1
GNP	284.8	503.7	977.1	1,294.9	4.6

Table 10.9 United States trends, 1950–1974

Item	Spending (billions)				$\frac{1974}{1950}$	Source†
	1950	1960	1970	1974		
National health	$ 12.0	$ 25.9	$ 69.2	$ 104.2	8.7	100
School expenditures	8.8	24.7	70.2	98.8	11.2	176
Recreation	11.1	18.3	40.7	52.8	4.7	360
Foreign travel	0.68	2.6	6.2	8.4	12.3	366
Federal budget	42	92.2	196.6	268.4	6.4	370
State and local government	28	61	148	189	6.8	414
Defense	12.4	45.2	79.3	78.6	6.3	505
Railroad revenue	9.6	9.6	12.2	15.2	1.6	974
Airline revenue	0.6	2.1	7.1	11.5	19.2	989
Car, truck, bus sales	8.0	7.8	8.2	10.0	1.25	953
Food energy, kcal per person per day	3,260	3,140	3,300	3,350	1.03	148
Beef consumption, lb per person per year	63.4	85.1	113.7	116.5	1.84	150
Pork consumption, lb per person per year	69.2	64.9	66.4	66.5	0.96	150
College enrollment (millions)	2.66	3.22	7.14	7.80	2.93	175
Motor vehicle registration (millions)	49.3	73.8	108.4	130.8	2.70	955
Federal civilian employees (millions)	2.12	2.43	2.93	2.86	1.35	402
State and local government employees (millions)	4.29	6.39	10.2	11.8	2.75	440

† Number is that of table in U.S. Bureau of the Census, *Statistical Abstract of the United States: 1975*, 96th ed., from which data were taken.

Past behavior is no guarantee of future performance, but the trend is clear: United States consumers are continuing to have greater relative utility for services over goods and for luxury items having high income elasticity. There have been particularly large growths in government services and in government expenditures. Firms in the CPI must become cognizant of these trends and gear their markets toward these growing needs if they are to participate in future growth in a better than average fashion.

10.2 INNOVATION AND RESEARCH

Technical and marketing innovations are the most important driving forces for economic and social progress in the world today. Some impressive innovations which have had a major impact are the development of high-yield and high-protein corn and rice for the " green revolution," the development of oral contraceptives for better family planning, the desalination of seawater for parched lands, and the ever-increasing gain in the productivity of chemical plants.

Until the rise of the modern research laboratory as a permanent institution, invention was the lonely pursuit of isolated individuals. There is a strong correlation between the expenditure for research and development and the rate of growth

Table 10.10 Industrial R & D spending, 1972

| Industry | 1972 R & D spending† (billions) | | | R & D spending as percentage of value added by manufacturer‡ |
	Total	Federally funded	Privately funded	
Electrical equipment and communication	$4.92	$2.49	$2.43	16
Aircraft and missiles	4.99	4.04	0.95	38
Motor vehicles and other transportation equipment	1.98	0.30	1.68	7
Machinery	1.96	0.35	1.61	5
Chemicals and allied products	1.90	0.19	1.71	6
Petroleum refining and extraction	0.47	0.015	0.46	10
Rubber products	0.26	0.03	0.23	5
Primary metals	0.26	0.01	0.25	1
Food and kindred products	0.26	0.001	0.259	1
Paper and allied products	0.19	0.002	0.188	1

† U.S. Bureau of the Census, *Statistical Abstract of the United States: 1975*, 96th ed., table 914.
‡ Value added by manufacturer from ibid., table 1266.

of industries. High-technology industries devote a large percentage of their income to research and development, as shown in Table 10.10. The chemical and petroleum industries are among the leaders in their reliance on technological innovations to improve and change products and processes. Product innovation includes both new products and new uses for existing products. Process innovation has led to lower operating costs and lower product prices and has permitted changes to different raw materials. Among the leaders in research and development only a few industries spend more than chemicals and petroleum. Much of the research and development funding in electrical equipment and aerospace industries is from the government, while only a small percentage of chemical and petroleum industry research and development is government-funded. Outside the two main sectors, drugs (SIC 283, not shown in Table 10.10) is a very heavy spender on research and development in synthetic organic chemistry and pharmacology. Research and development expenditures in the other sectors of the CPI are only modest.

After the Russians launched Sputnik in 1957, United States expenditures for research and development began increasing dramatically, at an annual compounded rate of 10–15 percent until 1968. Accompanying this aggressive funding of research and development was a sense of euphoria—all the problems of humanity could be dispelled through heavy expenditures on research. Total research and development funding increased in this period from 1.5 to 3 percent of the United States GNP. In the recession following 1968, the public became disenchanted with the inability of research and technology to deliver on all the miracles promised or implied, and hence the national research budget shrank both in terms of constant dollars and as a percentage of the GNP. Research programs in industry and universities were critically examined to determine their short-term usefulness. Companies became increasingly concerned with obtaining exclusive patents and competitive advantages over other companies.

The benefits of research and innovation are widely distributed, and the public usually benefits far more than the inventors. We live in an era of abundant and cheap technology both domestically and abroad. A nation that spends about 1 percent of its GNP on research, such as Italy or Japan, can have a GNP growth

Table 10.11 Growth of various types of firms

	Annual growth rate in sales, %	Sales in 1974 (billions)	Annual growth rate in jobs, %	Gain in jobs
Five mature companies, e.g., Bethlehem Steel	11.4	$36	0.6	25,000
Five innovative companies, e.g., Polaroid, IBM	13.2	21	4.3	106,000
Five young high-technology companies, e.g., Data General	42.0	0.86	40.7	35,000

rate equal to or greater than that of nations spending 3 percent on research, such as the United Kingdom and the United States. The growth of high-research aerospace and electronics industries was partly responsible for the growth of banking and insurance industries. Decades of research in fertilizers and pesticides resulted in the tremendous growth of productivity on the farms. However, among United States chemical companies and pharmaceutical companies, there is real evidence that the companies with higher research-and-development–to–sales ratios have higher profit-to-sale ratios [3], as shown in Table 10.11 for 1969 to 1974. It has been suggested that innovation in large corporations is devoted mainly to cost reduction and increased productivity, but in some small, technically based, new companies innovation is necessary for survival [4].

A high rate of expenditure on research is a necessary but not a sufficient condition for growth and profitability. At its conception, an innovation is simply an idea. This idea must be nurtured and developed until it reaches maturity as a product that can be placed on the market to generate a new cash flow. If the idea is to develop successfully, there must be close coordination and cooperation between manufacturing and marketing. Research is a risky undertaking, and its rewards are not always guaranteed. The rewards of research must be great enough to justify its cost. Innumerable factors can contribute to (or even cause) the failure of an attempted innovation. For example, Sun Oil invested $300 million in a project aimed at converting the tar sands of Alberta, Canada into oil. This pioneering venture promised to furnish a large, new, and secure source of energy, but it ran into a host of political and technical problems and has yet to make any profit [5]. New and more stringent standards on drug approval by the Food and Drug Administration (FDA) have dramatically increased the cost of innovation and consequently have lowered the rate at which new drugs reach the marketplace.

Research can be classified as *proprietary research* or as *cooperative research;* the former is performed by a firm in an attempt to gain a competitive advantage over rival firms, and the latter is performed on behalf of a group of firms to solve common problems.

Proprietary research is carried out only by individuals and firms in an oligopoly, with the aim of developing more desirable products and more efficient processes. The results are guarded by trade secrets and patents. It has been argued that a monopoly does not need to do proprietary research and a firm in atomistic competition cannot afford to. Proprietary research has been responsible for most of the important technical innovations which have enriched our lives, from Perkin's discovery of mauve dye and Haber's synthesis of ammonia to the modern successes in nylon and cracking catalysts. This type of research is expensive, and the payoffs are uncertain. Adequate rewards must be probable before it will be undertaken, and the firm must be able to recoup the research cost by exclusive exploitation of the market for a limited time. When Watt invented his improved steam engine, he offered it to mine operators to pump water at a royalty equivalent to one-third of the savings in fuel. He was plagued with piracy and hired detectives to catch cheaters, but eventually he had to lower the royalty to 15 percent. Ever since then it has been customary for the inventor to assume full responsibility for the cost and risk associated with research and innovation. The fruits of his labor accrue, in large part, to the public and the licensees, who have borne no risk.

Cooperative research is funded jointly by many firms, by nonprofit organizations, and by governments. The results are available to all sponsors, and often to the public, in publications. Even monopolies like the public-regulated utilities band together to form organizations like the Electric Power Research Institute to solve energy-supply problems. The atomistic farmers have their research done by the U.S. Department of Agriculture and the various state agricultural experimental stations. Firms in the CPI often form research organizations to solve common problems that may not be proprietary: the Fractionation Research Institute and Heat Transfer Research Institute answer needs for engineering design data, and the Institute of Toxicology Research studies the toxicity of chemicals. Unless results are freely published and available to subscribers and nonsubscribers alike, such institutes may face questioning from the United States antitrust division of the Justice Department since they may be giving the subscriber firms an advantage over the nonsubscribers.

10.3 CAPITAL INVESTMENT

The CPI are among the leaders in industrial capital spending. Table 10.12 shows annual total capital spending for several CPI sectors, and Table 10.13 gives the capital spending per company for the 10 largest chemical companies (ESIC 28.1). The ratio of capital expenditure to net plant and equipment gives the rate of renewal. These ratios for 1975 are shown in Table 10.14. This capital renewal takes care of both replacement and expansion of capacity. A 20 percent capital renewal rate indicates a 5-year turnover for the chemical industry. Such a turnover rate keeps equipment modern and efficient, in contrast to many sectors, such as textiles.

Table 10.12 Capital spending in the United States by the CPI (billions)

Industry	1971	1972	1973	1974	1975
Chemicals	$ 3.44	$ 3.45	$ 4.46	$ 5.69	$ 6.31
Food and beverage	2.69	2.55	3.11	3.25	3.46
Paper	1.25	1.38	1.86	2.58	2.98
Petroleum	5.85	5.25	5.45	8.00	10.19
Rubber	0.84	1.08	1.56	1.47	1.41
Textiles	0.61	0.73	0.77	0.84	0.70
All manufacturing	29.99	31.35	38.01	46.01	49.30

Source: Chem. Eng. News, Facts and Figures issue, June 2, 1975, p. 38.

Table 10.13 Capital spending of the top 10 United States chemical companies (ESIC 28.1), 1970–1975 (millions)

Company	1975	1974	1973	1972	1971	1970
Du Pont	$1,000	$1,038	$781	$461	$474	$499
Dow Chemical	940	870	402	359	365	348
Union Carbide	800	517	289	244	335	394
Monsanto	525	313	205	168	205	301
Celanese	250	220	159	128	169	135
W. R. Grace	290	277	157	133	98	116
Allied Chemical	306	306	185	128	132	139
Hercules	160	217	144	80	53	91
American Cyanamid	250	138	64	72	109	91
Rohm & Haas	160	141	92	73	99	86

Source: Chem. Eng. News, Facts and Figures issue, June 2, 1975, p. 38.

The CPI annual capital expenditures have increased by a factor of 2 since 1972. The chemical industry is expected to continue its surge in capital spending, reaching almost $8 billion in 1976. There are several major reasons for this growth in capital spending:

1. In the late 1960s and early 1970s, the basic chemicals market was characterized by low prices and overcapacity. Such a situation made capital expansion highly inappropriate. Many companies were losing money or at best operating marginally. Then in 1973 to 1974 shortages developed for many chemicals, and consequently prices rose. However, chemical companies, remembering the recent burden of overcapacity, were hesitant to add new capacity. It has been only within the past couple of years that continuing high prices have motivated companies to expand their facilities.
2. Inflation has rendered capital-depreciation allowances insufficient to cover actual capital-replacement needs. In particular, inflation of construction costs has in many instances doubled replacement costs for a particular facility by the time it has been fully depreciated.

Table 10.14 Renewal rates

	Rate of renewal, %		Rate of renewal, %
Chemicals and allied products	20.1	Textile mills	10.9
Petroleum and coal products	18.6	Stone, clay, and glass	13.6
Rubber	15.7	Primary metal	19.1
Paper	21.4	All manufacturing	16.9
Food	12.8		

Source: Chem. Eng. News,

3. Expensive antipollution equipment required by stringent legislation is requiring increasing amounts of capital. For example, Du Pont planned to spend $80 million (15 percent of its domestic construction budget) on pollution-abatement facilities in 1976.

Chemical companies are scrambling to secure their needed raw materials, and this accounts for large capital expenditures. For example, Dow Chemical expects its expenditures for oil and gas exploration to approach $200 million annually during the next several years. Du Pont is actively pursuing a joint venture with Atlantic Richfield. Union Carbide is spending heavily on its process for converting the entire barrel of crude oil into petrochemical feedstocks.

Thus it appears that chemical companies are spending more on capital expenditures and that debt is becoming more important in financing such expenditures. It is therefore important for CPI companies to maintain the confidence of investors and debtors, who are wooed by many other fund-hungry customers, i.e., federal government bonds and paper, state and local government bonds, other industries' stocks and bonds, home mortgage and consumer credit companies, etc. This makes it increasingly important for the CPI to earn a good profit in order to pay high interest and attractive dividends.

The two principal uses of economic goods and services are current consumption and capital investment for the future. Modern industry requires enormous investments in plants and equipment. To ensure continued growth of profits and production, a substantial percentage of industrial profits must be ploughed back into the production operation. Without the reinvestment of a portion of today's profits, there will be obsolete facilities and lower profits tomorrow.

There is a correlation between investment and growth of GNP among nations, as shown in Table 10.15. The United States has not been a thrifty reinvestor and consequently has not had as impressive an economic growth rate as Japan, West Germany, or France.

Table 10.15 Investment and growth

	Nonresidential fixed investment as percentage of GNP, 1960–1973	Growth rate of constant-dollar GNP 1960–1973, %
Japan	29.0	10.8
West Germany	20.0	5.9
France	18.2	5.5
Canada	17.4	5.4
United Kingdom	15.2	5.2
Italy	14.4	4.1
United States	13.6	2.9

Source: Du Pont Manage. Bull., vol. 4, no. 3, November 1975.

10.4 PRODUCTIVITY

Productivity may be defined as the measure of an industry's efficiency in using capital, people, and natural resources. A dramatic example of an increase in productivity is provided by the case of penicillin, a drug discovered in 1928 by Alexander Fleming. During the Second World War, it was produced in several hundred thousand shaker flasks. One innovation followed another—deep-tank fermentation, extraction with pH gradient, freeze drying, etc. The price decline by a factor of 10,000 between 1943 and 1965 (Table 10.16) is most impressive.

The driving forces behind productivity increases are complex. Thurow gives the breakdown in Table 10.17 for the causes of the increase in productivity in the United States.

Measurements of productivity are often given in terms of ratios of outputs to inputs. For example, productivity might be measured as:

1. Dollar output per employee
2. Dollar output per production worker
3. Dollar output per worker-hour
4. Value added per employee
5. Dollar output per dollar assets
6. Dollar output per dollar of raw materials

Measures 1 to 4 indicate efficiency in use of people; measure 5 indicates efficiency in use of capital; and 6 indicates the efficiency in use of raw materials. These are partial-productivity measures. Although any one ratio gives an idea of the efficiency in using one particular input, all ratios must be considered to get an overall idea of total productivity. There are trade-offs such as the substitution of operators by automatic machinery. An industry may be very efficient in its use of people but not as efficient in its use of capital. Usually, trends in productivity ratios rather than absolute values are important for a particular industry. Rising

Table 10.16 Price of penicillin

Year	Production, 10^9 units/yr	Treatment, patients per month	Average value per 10^9 units
1943	2	200	$200,000
1944	2,489	248,900	21,900
1946	27,415	....	4,400
1948	92,945	....	1,600
1950	219,902	21,990,200	509
1965	....	....	20

Source: A. L. Elder, This History of Penicillin Production, *CEP Symp. Ser.* 100, 1976.

Table 10.17 Productivity increase

	Percent
More people in labor forces	20
Better educated labor forces	34
Increase in quantity of plants	3
Increase in quality of plants	12
Economy of scale	11
More efficient market	1
Increase in knowledge	20
	100

Source: L. C. Thurow, *Tech. Rev.*, March 1971, p. 45.

productivity is the key to economic growth, and the increase of output per employee pays for increases in salaries and wages.

Table 10.18 gives value added per employee for SIC 28 and 291 for 1963, 1967, and 1972. Also given is the value added per employee index and its compound annual growth rate for 1963 to 1972. In relative terms, this ratio for SIC 28 and 291 has been more than double that of all manufacturing. In terms of growth, chemicals and allied products and petroleum refining have grown at about the same rate as all manufacturing, at 6 to 6.5 percent annually. However, specific industry groups within SIC 28 have shown notable differences in the growth rate

Table 10.18 Value added per employee in the United States chemical and petroleum refining industries

		Value added per employee						
		Dollars per employee			Index (1967 = 100)			Annual growth rate, %
SIC code	Industry	1963	1967	1972	1963	1967	1972	1963–1972
	All manufacturing	$11,327	$13,558	$18,606	84	100	137	6
28	Chemicals and allied products	23,861	28,002	38,725	85	100	138	6
281	Industrial chemicals	26,038	31,198	33,430	83	100	107	3
282	Plastics materials, synthetics	19,896	22,087	30,463	90	100	138	5
283	Drugs	28,353	34,517	47,162	82	100	137	6
284	Soap, cleaners, toilet goods	33,326	40,515	55,366	82	100	137	6
285	Paints, allied products	18,229	19,985	27,151	91	100	136	4.5
286	Industrial organics chemicals	†	33,634	44,328	†	100	132	3
287	Agricultural chemicals	14,605	21,869	36,187	67	100	165	10.5
291	Petroleum refining	26,369	44,346	45,495	59	100	103	6.5

† Not available.

Source: Value added and employee data from U.S. Bureau of the Census, *Statistical Abstract of the United States: 1975*, 96th ed., table 1266.

of value added per employee. In particular, industrial chemicals (SIC 281) and industrial organic chemicals (SIC 286) have grown at only 3 percent annually. Agricultural chemicals have grown much faster, at 10.5 percent annually.

Table 10.19 gives the value added per employee for several additional CPI and other manufacturing industries. In absolute terms, the value added per employee for the industries listed has been about the same or only slightly higher than for all manufacturing. The growth rates of the ratio for all but primary metal industries have kept pace with all manufacturing, growing at 6.0 percent annually. Primary metals has grown at 4.5 percent annually.

Table 10.19 Value added per employee for CPI and other industries, United States, 1963–1972

		Value added per employee						
		Dollars per employee			Index (1967 = 100)			Annual growth rate, %
SIC code	Industry	1963	1967	1972	1963	1967	1972	1963–1972
20	Food and kindred products	$13,283	$16,134	$22,700	82	100	141	6
26	Paper, allied products	12,578	15,268	20,638	82	100	135	6
30	Rubber, miscellaneous plastic products	11,241	13,153	18,856	85	100	143	6
32	Stone, clay, glass	12,272	14,124	20,204	87	100	143	6
33	Primary metal industries	13,381	15,596	20,348	86	100	130	4.5
37	Transportation equipment	14,094	15,362	23,152	92	100	151	6
27	Printing, publishing	11,474	13,923	19,126	82	100	137	6
	All manufacturing	11,327	13,558	18,606	84	100	137	6

Source: Value added and employee data from U.S. Bureau of the Census, *Statistical Abstract of the United States: 1975*, 96th ed., table 1266.

Although not readily available on an industry-wide scale, the dollar output per dollar of capital can be approximated by dollar sales per dollar of total assets. This ratio is shown for several companies in Table 10.20 for 1974. As shown, this ratio ranges from about 1 to 2. For the ESIC 28.1 companies the ratio ranges from 0.98 to 1.19. For the large oil companies the ratio ranges from 1.32 to 1.48.

The productivity of an employee depends heavily on the existence of sophisticated machinery and an up-to-date plant. Industry variations in capital invested per production worker were discussed in Chap. 8.

The savings that result due to increases in productivity benefit the stockholders by increasing profits, the employees by increasing salaries and wages, and the consumers by decreasing prices. The experience and learning curves, which are measures of productivity, were treated in Chaps. 2 and 8.

Table 10.20 Sales per total assets for selected companies, 1974

Company	Sales per assets	Company	Sales per assets
Allied	1.18	Procter and Gamble	1.60
Celanese	1.03	Colgate-Palmolive	1.93
Du Pont	1.17	Goodyear Tire	1.24
Hercules	1.15	Firestone Tire	1.23
Monsanto	1.19	Uniroyal Tire	1.40
Dow	0.98	American Home Products	1.65
Union Carbide	1.09	Pfizer	0.92
Exxon	1.34	Bristol-Myers	1.53
Texaco	1.35	Owens-Illinois	1.15
Mobil	1.34	PPG Industries	1.03
Standard Oil (California)	1.48	Johns-Manville	1.12
Gulf	1.32		

Source: Data from *Fortune*, May 1975.

10.5 FUTURE PROSPECTS

The future is unpredictable, but prudent men and women plan ahead to exploit new opportunities and to avoid new threats. The CPI are capital intensive and require sophisticated processes; 3 to 10 years may elapse between process conception and plant start-up. A plant may be expected to be productive from 10 to 30 years, with the necessary maintenance and minor changes. It is therefore necessary to attempt to predict the social and economic conditions which will affect technical operations 10 to 30 years in the future. Futurology, usually based on a small amount of scientific methodology and a great deal of imagination, is a thriving business in the United States.[1]

The basic facts needed to assess the market in the future are:

1. The population of the United States, of the industrially developed countries in Western Europe and Japan, of the communist nations, and of the Third World
2. The total buying power of these markets, measured as GNP and GNP per capita
3. The changing market demand for specific products due to product competition, substitution, changes in needs and tastes, and changes in life style
4. The social and political climates for industrial activities, the movement of products and capital across national boundaries, and the profitability of chemical processing in comparison to alternative forms of investment

---

[1] Some of the better-known books on the subject are Herman Kahn, "The Next 200 Years," Morrow, New York, 1976; Herman Kahn and Anthony J. Wiener, "The Year 2000," Macmillan, New York, 1967; J. R. Bright, "Technological Forecasting," Prentice-Hall, Englewood Cliffs, N.J., 1968; J. W. Forrester, "World Dynamics," Wright-Allen Press, Cambridge, Mass., 1971; D. H. Meadows et al., "The Limits to Growth," Potomac Associates for the Club of Rome, Universe Books, New York,

Possible future developments which would necessitate technological changes are:

1. The emergence of completely new sciences and technologies to open up possibilities that are presently nonexistent
2. The exhaustion of traditional raw-material sources and the discovery of new resources
3. The development of superior processing technologies and of better products
4. The impact of new government regulations requiring novel solutions

An American Institute of Chemical Engineers study [6] discusses a number of probable environments and challenges for the upcoming decade:

1. The United States and the world will continue to face shortages in energy, food, and materials. Due mostly to a lack of political leadership, these problems will be poorly understood by the public, and the solutions will be piecemeal rather than bold steps forward.
2. There will be an appreciable shift in the United States population, with a decline in the absolute number of 15- to 19-year-olds and an increase in the number of 25- to 45-year-olds.
3. There will be a shift in manpower from the older industrial Northeast to the Southwest, where energy is cheaper, and to foreign energy-rich nations.
4. The role of government in the CPI, particularly in the oil industries, will continue to increase. Government will impose performance standards, import quotas, production quotas, prices, and distribution of products.
5. Pollution control and the environmental impact of products will continue to be important issues. There will be more specific pollution-abatement projects as we learn more about environmental science and engineering. The attack on the CPI will probably intensify as it is the producer of many products having unknown and potentially serious effects.
6. The United States and the developed world will continue in the trend toward a postindustrial society, in which the growth sectors will not be in the production of nondurable or durable goods but in the providing of services.
7. The demand for energy will slow down, but its cost will go up. Construction of conventional oil refineries will be static, but there will be an accelerated growth in petrochemicals. We will also see the construction of massive coal and oil-shale conversion plants to provide clean oil and gas.

If this scenario is taken to be accurate, what will its impact on the CPI be, and how should the CPI respond? We can only question, ponder, and speculate. For instance, let us consider trend 2, the shift in population away from the 15 to 24 age group to the 25 to 45 group (Table 10.21). What do people in these two age groups normally do? What do they normally demand in goods and services? According to input-output analysis, what sectors of the CPI might prosper or languish because of it? What might it mean to the chemical professional's personal career plans?

Table 10.21 Estimated and projected United States population by age group (millions)

	Age									
Year	Under 5	5–13	14–17	18–21	22–24	25–34	35–44	45–54	55–64	65 and over
1950	16.4	22.4	8.4	8.9	7.1	24.0	21.6	17.5	13.4	12.4
1960	20.3	33.0	11.2	9.6	6.6	22.9	24.2	20.5	15.6	16.7
1970	17.1	36.6	15.9	14.7	9.9	25.3	23.1	23.3	18.7	20.1
1974	16.3	34.1	16.9	16.1	10.8	29.8	22.8	23.8	19.5	21.8
1980	17.3	30.2	15.8†	17.1†	12.3†	36.2†	25.7†	22.6†	21.0†	24.5†
1990	20.1	34.6	12.9	14.5†	10.6†	41.1†	36.5†	25.2†	20.5†	28.9†
2000	18.4	36.0	16.8	16.0	10.3	34.5	41.3†	35.7†	22.9†	30.6†

† Series II-2.1 lifetime births per 1,000 women assumed.

Source: U.S. Bureau of the Census, *Statistical Abstract of the United States: 1975*, 96th ed., table 3.

The notion of economic growth has come under attack as being wasteful of limited resources, unnecessary to the "good life," destructive of the environment, and a major contributor to the uneven distribution of income and wealth. It is sometimes considered to be at the root of both antitechnology and antiestablishment attitudes and a prime cause of the phenomenon called "rich man's guilt." Large corporations in the CPI have been particular objects of scorn because of their alleged power, insufficient regard for environmental and consumer interests, and inadequate concern for employee health and safety. It cannot be denied that some members of the CPI have exhibited less than exemplary conduct. The industry's credibility was badly damaged by irresponsible handling of such problems as the vinyl chloride levels in plants and inadequate safety precautions in the manufacture of the pesticide Kepone.

Distrust of large corporations can be seen even among the elites of doctors, lawyers, engineers, and MBAs. In a survey of 6,000 such people the following percentages agreed with these statements:[1]

Existence of large corporations is essential to our economic growth. 73%
Many of the largest companies should be broken up for the good of the country. 37%
Large corporations should be forced to fight pollution more aggressively. 73%
Corporations fairly represent quality of their products and services. 49%
(Doctors somewhat more critical than lawyers and engineers; MBAs are the least critical.)

[1] R. D. Fierro, *MBA*, April 1976, p. 18.

Table 10.22 Current rates of population increase

Continent	Annual increase, %	Years to double population
North America	1.3	54
South America	2.9	24
Europe	0.8	88
U.S.S.R.	1.1	64
Asia	2.3	30
Africa	2.6	27
Oceania	2.1	33
World	2.0	35

On the other hand, the vital role of economic growth in relieving poverty is defended by Rustin [7]; he quoted J. F. Kennedy, who said, "A rising tide lifts all the boats." Rustin says, "To those who insist that we can no longer tolerate economic growth, my response is simply we cannot afford to do without it." This is supported by Kahn[1] who estimates that there are more than enough earth resources for 200 years of growth.

An anticipated shortage of food will be one of the most important issues facing the United States and the world as population increases dramatically. In a traditional undeveloped society, birth and death rates are more or less in balance at a yearly rate of about 50 per 1,000 members in the population. With the intervention of better hygiene and medical care, death rates have dropped to approximately 10 per 1,000 in the developed countries. The gap between birth and death rates has been the cause of the population explosion in recent years. People are now beginning to realize that it is no longer necessary to have five children to make sure that one will survive to adulthood. With the improvement of income and education, the birth rates in developed countries range between 10 to 15 per 1,000. The current rates of population increase for the various continents are shown in Table 10.22. In 1976, there were 4 billion people on earth. At the present rate of 2.0 percent increase compounded, in 11.2 years (1987) there will be 1 billion more mouths to feed.

This extra billion people will need food before anything else. The United Nations Food and Agriculture Organization estimates that an average person needs 2,400 kcal of food per day, including 100 g of protein. The current world food supply is already significantly below that. How will these new mouths be fed? Modern agriculture uses enormous quantities of fertilizers and pesticides, as well as farm machinery to till the soil, harvest the crops, dry the crops, store the crops away from pests, and transport the crops to market. Enormous quantities of irrigation water must also be provided. The high-yield crops of the green revolution have a particular need for extra irrigation and fertilizers. This means a great

[1] Op. cit.

Table 10.23 1973 production of cereal crops and energy values

	Production, 10^6 t			Export, 10^6 t			
	U.S.	World	$\dfrac{\text{U.S.}}{\text{World}}$	U.S.	World	$\dfrac{\text{U.S.}}{\text{World}}$	Energy, kcal/g
Wheat	46.6	367	12.7	31.7	72.2	43.9	3.6
Corn	143.3	313	45.8	32.0	42.2	75.8	1.1†
Soya	42.6	58	73.8	13.2	15.5	85.2	3.5
Rice	4.2	309	1.4	1.8	6.5	27.7	3.5

† Due to 74 percent moisture content.

demand for capital, management, and technical expertise, all of which are found mainly in the developed countries and very difficult to transfer.

A review of some of the major food crops in the world reveals that the United States is a major food producer and the dominant food exporter (Table 10.23). China and India may produce more rice, and Russia may produce more wheat, but they are all consumed domestically and additional imports from the United States are required.

The extra food energy needed by the anticipated 1 billion additional people is

$$[2{,}400 \text{ kcal/(person)(day)}](365 \text{ day/yr})(1 \times 10^9 \text{ people}) = 876 \times 10^{12} \text{ kcal}$$

In wheat equivalent this is

$$(876 \times 10^{12} \text{ kcal})\frac{2 \text{ g}}{3.6 \text{ kcal}}\frac{1 \text{ t}}{10^6 \text{ g}} = 243 \text{ million metric tons}$$

By way of comparison, the wheat equivalent of United States crop production in 1973 was

$$46.6 + 143.3 \times \frac{1.1}{3.6} + 42.6 + 4.2 = 137 \text{ million tons}$$

Thus the billion new mouths will require an amount much more than the entire current United States output. Where will this new food come from?

These calculations are not new. In the early 1960s many farm machinery and fertilizer companies were convinced that a big food crunch was approaching and geared up plant capacity in anticipation of the new needs. However, the market demand did not materialize. These companies made the classic mistake of confusing need (what people would like to have or must have to sustain a life style) with demand (market order attached to hard dollars). Since the less developed countries were unable to pay for the food purchases, the only possible buyers were the governments of the more developed countries, who were urged to spend 1 percent of their GNP on foreign aid. As it turned out, the more developed nations were not in such a generous mood. Thus the profits for farm machinery and fertilizer companies plummeted for 10 years.

Now this scenario is being played once again, as market demand for fertilizer is very high. This is not due to a moral commitment on the part of the more developed countries to pay the food bill for the less developed countries. It is due to the fact that with improved income and standard of living in Western Europe and Japan, people are eating vegetables less and demanding more animal products, such as meat, eggs, and milk. It takes about 3 lb of grain to produce 1 lb of chicken, and the ratio for beef is closer to 8. Therefore, the growth is in the upgrading of the food habit in the more developed countries.

What will the future bring? We have to ponder whether the population will increase as expected, whether the appetite for grain-consuming meat products in the more developed countries will increase, and whether charitable feelings of world brotherhood will make a sudden leap upward.

Now consider the predicted shortages of oil and gas. Such shortages will encourage:

1. Curtailment of consumption
2. Increase of imports from the Middle East
3. Substitution with synthetic oil and gas

What would each of these points mean in terms of CPI industrial activities? In what sectors would these impacts be felt the most? What types of jobs will be needed in the future, and in which part of the country or of the world will they be located? What types of skills would be most appreciated? What research and engineering problems must be solved? What does all this mean to the chemical professional's own personal upward mobility?

Finally, let us consider the threat from the environmental issue. A recent study of chemical engineers who have been in industry for the last 10 years showed that they wish to know more about the environmental impact of their jobs. The CPI has been the target of several environmentalists. Commoner [8] accuses the CPI of being the principal producer of new and menacing materials with unknown environmental impact. The Clean Air Act, the zero-discharge requirements of the Clean Water Act, the recent Toxic Substance Act—all are aimed directly at the CPI to assure that (1) all the old abuses are cleaned up so that there will be no hazards in factories, in transportation, in use, and in disposal of chemical materials and that (2) no new substances can be made and used unless they can be proved to be nontoxic, either in the short or long run.

Critics of the environmental movement say that although these are noble goals, we cannot pursue them to the exclusion of other important goals. Regulations to achieve the above goals would cause the closing of plants, creating unemployment and hardship as well as harming the overall economy; condemn invested plants and equipment as well as patents and technologies to the scrap heap; stifle innovation and prevent consumers from using highly useful new products; and promote the use of substitutes which may be even more harmful than the banned substances.

The above regulations would be particularly unfortunate especially in view of the fact that it is impossible to design technologies for zero discharge and it is impossible to prove, via accelerated test methods, that a new substance will neither accumulate in the environment nor be harmful 50 years hence. However, proceeding on the assumption that such regulations will be enacted, we must ask several questions. What will such regulations do to the innovation processes of chemical companies who try to deliver better living through chemistry? Will there be less innovation and therefore less need for research and development people, or will quite the opposite be true? What skills will be needed for chemical professionals if environmental issues continue to be important in the coming decade? How do these issues relate to the chemical professional's personal career plans?

We have attempted in this chapter to raise only some of the major points and questions concerning current trends and their effects on the future of the CPI and on the chemical professionals employed by these industries. It is important to realize that many of the major issues confronting our society and the world have strong implications for the future well-being of the CPI and for the people they employ. But it is also important to realize that predicting the future is often for naught; trends can change suddenly, and surprises abound.

No book can teach the "sixth sense" of business acumen for anticipating the future. Foresight, however, can be obtained through experience. Throughout this text we have sought to impart some of the tools and insights necessary for intelligent speculating, pondering, and planning toward the future. The future belongs to those who understand both the present and the past, for they will be those most able to adapt and prosper.

10.6 REFERENCES

1. Alvin Toffler, "Future Shock," Random House, New York, 1970.
2. J. F. Henahan, 200 Years of American Chemicals, *Chem. Week*, Feb. 18, 1976, p. 26; T. H. Chilton, "Strong Water," MIT Press, Cambridge, Mass., 1968.
3. J. Wei, Planning and Marketing of Research, *Chem. Eng. Prog.*, March 1971, p. 22.
4. *Science*, July 2, 1976, p. 34; D. M. Kiefier, *Chem. Eng. News*, Dec. 15, 1975, p. 38.
5. *Forbes*, Apr. 15, 1975, p. 65.
6. American Institute of Chemical Engineering, 1976–86 Dynamic Objectives for Chemical Engineering,
7. Bayard Rustin, *The New York Times*, May 2, 1976, p. 13.
8. Barry Commoner, "The Closing Circle," Bantam Books Inc., New York, 1972.

10.7 PROBLEMS

These problems require the reader to use material from all chapters in the book and from outside sources.

10.1 Would you agree with the following statements, and if not, why not?

(*a*) To improve the economic security and job security of chemical engineers and chemists, we should limit enrollment in universities to a minimum and completely exclude immigration.

(*b*) There are 800 million Chinese, forming the greatest possible market in the world. If they would buy a stick of chewing gum per person per day, plants to manufacture this gum could be increased in size 100 times.

(c) The smart course of action is to let other nations invent the new processes and products, take the risk, and have the start-up problems. When the process and product is commercially viable, we can then license them pretty cheaply.

10.2 Will the high growth of fibers and plastics continue in the future? Can we extrapolate present growth trends into the future, or must we modify them for various powerful reasons?

10.3 Will tomorrow's world be more concerned with the basic necessities of food and fuel or with leisure and life-enrichment luxuries? What products of the CPI will support these two divergent trends? What talents should chemical professionals have to satisfy these needs?

10.4 If better relations between the government and the CPI and between the public and the CPI are of increasing importance to firms in the CPI, what should chemical professionals in the CPI do to prepare themselves to help better such relations?

10.5 There appears to be a trend away from product innovations and toward process innovations. Should chemical professionals try to follow this shift in emphasis, or should they retain their "professional integrity"? How should the chemical professionals adapt to this trend?

10.6 It is often said that the CPI will be unable to raise the capital needed for plant expansion in the future unless it can generate more profit. Social critics dismiss such reasoning. Can you construct a set of cogent arguments to support the critics and to support the CPI?

10.7 Unions often fear that changes directed toward increasing productivity mean fewer jobs, and they often fight such changes bitterly. Is their fear justified? Is it true that industries with high gains in productivity have falling payrolls and that industries with low gains in productivity have stationary payrolls?

10.8 What will the change in age structure of the population in the United States mean to you in your career development?

10.9 Are the environmentalists, consumer advocates, and antiestablishment critics helpful or harmful to firms in the CPI? What is their impact on chemical professionals? Who eventually has to pay the cost of clean air, safer products, and better workplaces? Is there a degree of environmental protection that we should not go beyond, and how do we determine that point?

10.10 In an article in *Forbes*, June 15, 1976, Monsanto was reported to have obtained 50 percent of its operating earnings from agricultural chemicals, even though this division accounts for only 15 percent of sales. The agricultural-chemicals division also yields a 52 percent profit margin before tax. Many companies such as Stauffer, Ciba-Geigy, Shell, and Eli Lilly would like to compete for the same business. Monsanto's next priority for the 1980s is plant-growth chemicals based on concepts such as whole fields of lettuce maturing at the same time. The next generation of agricultural chemicals will be based on developments in cell biology and basic genetics, " plants that can grow in saline soil because their roots extract salt and tomatoes shaped like cucumbers that can be packed and shipped easily." Are such products commodities or specialty chemicals? How did Monsanto price its products? What barriers to entry has Monsanto, and are they stable in the long run?

10.11 Indigo is the essential dye for blue denim. It is in very short supply due to the sudden worldwide craze for jeans. Chemical professionals are puzzled, since they have labored to develop superior nonfading dyes and increased plant capacity for them, only to have them spurned in favor of the older and supposedly obsolete indigo. Should a firm start a plant to increase indigo production capacity? What types of information does the organization need before it can justify such an expansion, and how would it obtain such information?

11.12 (*Forbes*, June 1, 1976.) Zoltan Merszei, the Hungarian-born Canadian citizen who recently became president of Dow Chemical, was instrumental in getting Dow started in Japan and Europe. Now 44 percent of Dow's sales are outside the United States market. Merszei supports protective tariffs. Are these consistent facts? He will only put capital investment in a part of the world where he does not encounter environmentalists or governmental obstacles. What is to be gained and what may be lost by this approach?

10.13 The video-disc for the television industry is about to be born. (*Forbes*, June, 1976.) The main contenders are the Philips/MCA system with a 12-in 30-min LP disc of aluminum-coated vinyl and the RCA system with a 12-in 60-min LP disc of metal-coated vinyl. Estimated prices are $10 for a disc and

$500 for a record-player attachment for a home color television. One can then play first-run movies, concerts, operas, and broadway shows at home. The laser arm of the Philips/MCA system assures that a record will last forever, but the RCA system with a stylus is predicted to allow a record to last only 500 plays. For reference, Americans last year spent $2.5 billion on phonograph records and $1.9 billion on movie admissions. How would you estimate the vinyl polymer production needed to support this industry? Would it be a significant plant expansion?

10.14 (*Forbes*, June 15, 1976.) Frank Reichel sold the once mighty American Viscose Co.'s operating assets in rayon and acetate fibers in 1963 to the FMC Corp. and gave the proceeds of $400 million back to the stockholders. In the last 2 years, FMC has lost $45 million on the fiber business it bought from American Viscose. Why did FMC buy American Viscose in 1963? What should they have done in the meantime? Should FMC sell Viscose now? How should the assets on sale be priced? (See *Chem. Week*, July 7, 1976.)

10.15 Analyze the following situations, and suggest solutions:

(*a*) In an article Hens Are Willing but People Aren't in *The New York Times* (Sunday, July 11, 1976) the reporter said that modern technology has dramatically reduced the number of egg farmers while raising laying capacity of hens. With an artificially lighted 16-h day, most hens lay 250 to 270 eggs a year. Farmers with a lighted hen house can increase production 20 to 30 percent in 9 months. But with the hurried breakfasts and cholesterol scare, Americans are eating fewer eggs, down from 400 eggs per person per year in 1945 to 275 in 1975. The egg farmers are forming a National Egg Board, collecting $\frac{1}{6}$ cent per dozen eggs sold to raise $6 million to defend their $3 billion a year business. What should they do with the money?

(*b*) (*Fortune*, April 1976.) Since 1950, the United States home building industry has been gradually increasing the number of multifamily homes (apartments, condominiums, and row houses) and mobile homes (trailers) at the expense of single-family homes. How do the needs of the multifamily and mobile homes differ from the single-family homes? How does this affect the various sectors in the CPI?

(*c*) Polychlorinated biphenyl (PCB) is widely used as a transformer oil. In recent years, it has been suggested that it is toxic to man and animals and that it should be banned. What characteristics make PCB particularly desirable in use? What is a reasonably good substitute, and are there any undesirable features in the use of this substitute? Is it possible to use existing plants to manufacture this substitute?

10.16 (*Chem. Week*, July 7, 1976.) "The Environmental Protection Agency has authorized the use of DDT in six Colorado counties, where rodent fleas are carrying bubonic plague." DDT has been banned in the United States since 1972. Where did the EPA obtain the DDT? Does any firm in the United States now make DDT? If so, how profitable is the business? What are the pros and cons of DDT use? Can you suggest a rational policy?

SIC CODES FOR
CHEMICALS AND ALLIED PRODUCTS

Major Group 28.—CHEMICALS AND ALLIED PRODUCTS

The Major Group as a Whole

This major group includes establishments producing basic chemicals, and establishments manufacturing products by predominantly chemical processes. Establishments classified in this major group manufacture three general classes of products: (1) basic chemicals such as acids, alkalies, salts, and organic chemicals; (2) chemical products to be used in further manufacture such as synthetic fibers, plastics materials, dry colors, and pigments; (3) finished chemical products to be used for ultimate consumption such as drugs, cosmetics, and soaps; or to be used as materials or supplies in other industries such as paints, fertilizers, and explosives. The mining of natural rock salt is classified in mining industries. Establishments primarily engaged in manufacturing nonferrous metals and high percentage ferroalloys are classified in Major Group 33; silicon carbide in Major Group 32; baking powder, other leavening compounds, and starches in Major Group 20; and artists' colors in Major Group 39. Establishments primarily engaged in packaging, repackaging, and bottling of purchased chemical products, but not engaged in manufacturing chemicals and allied products, are classified in trade industries.

Group No. / Industry No.

281 **INDUSTRIAL INORGANIC CHEMICALS**

This group includes establishments primarily engaged in manufacturing basic industrial inorganic chemicals. Establishments primarily engaged in manufacturing formulated agricultural pesticides are classified in Industry 2879; medicinal chemicals, drugs and medicines in Industry 2833; and soap and cosmetics in Group 284.

2812 Alkalies and Chlorine

Establishments primarily engaged in manufacturing alkalies and chlorine.

Alkalies	Potassium hydroxide
Carbonates, potassium and sodium	Sal soda
Caustic potash	Soda ash
Caustic soda	Sodium bicarbonate
Chlorine, compressed or liquefied	Sodium carbonate (soda ash)
Potassium carbonate	Sodium hydroxide (caustic soda)

2813 Industrial Gases

Establishments primarily engaged in manufacturing gases for sale in compressed, liquid, and solid forms. Establishments primarily engaged in manufacturing fluorine and sulfur dioxide are classified in Industry 2819; household ammonia in Industry 2842, and other ammonia in Industry 2873; and chlorine in Industry 2812. Distributors of industrial gases and establishments primarily engaged in shipping liquid oxygen are classified in trade.

Acetylene	Helium
Argon	Hydrogen
Carbon dioxide	Neon
Dry ice (solid carbon dioxide)	Nitrogen
Gases, industrial: compressed, liquefied, or solid—*mfpm*	Nitrous oxide
	Oxygen, compressed and liquefied

2816 Inorganic Pigments

Establishments primarily engaged in manufacturing inorganic pigments. Important products of this industry include black pigments (except carbon black, Industry 2895), white pigments and color pigments. Organic color pigments, except animal black and bone black, are classified in Industry 2865.

Animal black	Lithopone
Barium sulfate, precipitated (blanc fixé)	Metallic pigments, inorganic
Barytes pigments	Mineral colors and pigments
Black pigments, except carbon black	Minium (pigment)
Blanc fixé (barium sulfate, precipitated)	Ochers
Bone black	Paint pigments, inorganic
Chrome pigments: chrome green, chrome yellow, chrome orange, zinc yellow	Pearl essence
	Pigments, inorganic
Color pigments, inorganic	Prussian blue pigments
Iron blue pigment	Red lead pigment
Iron colors	Satin white pigment
Iron oxide, black	Siennas
Iron oxide, magnetic	Titanium pigments
Iron oxide, yellow	Ultramarine pigment
Lamp black	Umbers
Lead oxide pigments	Vermilion pigment
Lead pigments	White lead pigments
Litharge	Whiting
	Zinc oxide pigments
	Zinc pigments: zinc yellow and zinc sulphide

Group   Industry
No.   No.
281   **INDUSTRIAL INORGANIC CHEMICALS—Continued**

2819 Industrial Inorganic Chemicals, Not Elsewhere Classified

Establishments primarily engaged in manufacturing industrial inorganic chemicals, not elsewhere classified. Important products of this industry include inorganic salts of sodium (excluding refined sodium chloride), potassium, aluminum, calcium, chromium, magnesium, mercury, nickel, silver, tin; inorganic compounds such as alums, calcium carbide, hydrogen peroxide, sodium silicate, ammonia compounds (except fertilizers), rare earth metal salts and elemental bromine, fluorine, iodine, phosphorus, and alkali metals (sodium, potassium, lithium, etc.). Establishments primarily engaged in mining, milling, or otherwise preparing natural potassium, sodium, or boron compounds (other than common salt) are classified in Industry 1474. Establishments primarily engaged in manufacturing household bleaches are classified in Industry 2842; phosphoric acid in Industry 2874; and nitric acid, anhydrous ammonia and other nitrogenous fertilizer materials in Industry 2873.

Activated carbon and charcoal
Alkali metals
Alumina
Aluminum chloride
Aluminum compounds
Aluminum hydroxide (alumina trihydrate)
Aluminum oxide
Aluminum sulfate
Alums
Ammonia alum
Ammonium chloride, hydroxide, and molybdate
Ammonium compounds, except for fertilizer
Ammonium perchlorate
Ammonium thiosulfate
Barium compounds
Bauxite, refined
Beryllium oxide
Bleaching powder
Borax (sodium tetraborate)
Boric acid
Boron compounds, not produced at mines
Borosilicate
Brine
Bromine, elemental
Caesium metal
Calcium carbide, chloride, and hypochlorite
Calcium compounds, inorganic
Calcium metal
Calomel
Carbide
Catalysts, chemical
Cerium salts
Charcoal, activated
Chlorosulfonic acid
Chromates and bichromates
Chromic acid
Chromium compounds, inorganic
Chromium salts
Cobalt chloride
Cobalt 60 (radioactive)
Cobalt sulfate
Copper chloride
Copper iodide and oxide
Copper sulfate
Cyanides
Desiccants, activated : silica gel
Dichromates
Ferric chloride
Ferrocyanides
Fissionable material production
Fluorine, elemental
Fuel propellants, solid : inorganic
Fuels, high energy : inorganic
Glauber's salt
Heavy water
High purity grade chemicals, inorganic : refined from technical grades
Hydrated alumina silicate powder
Hydrochloric acid
Hydrocyanic acid
Hydrofluoric acid
Hydrogen peroxide
Hydrogen sulfide
Hydrosulfites
Hypophosphites
Indium chloride
Inorganic acids, except nitric or phosphoric
Iodides
Iodine, elemental
Iodine, resublimed
Iron sulphate

Isotopes, radioactive
Laboratory chemicals, inorganic
Lead oxides, other than pigments
Lead silicate
Lime bleaching compounds
Lithium compounds
Lithium metal
Luminous compounds, radium
Magnesium carbonate
Magnesium chloride
Magnesium compounds, inorganic
Manganese dioxide powder, synthetic
Mercury chlorides (calomel, corrosive, sublimate), except U.S.P.
Mercury compounds, inorganic
Mercury oxides
Mercury, redistilled
Metals, liquid
Mixed acid
Muriate of potash, not produced at mines
Nickel ammonium sulfate
Nickel carbonate
Nickel compounds, inorganic
Nickel sulfate
Nuclear cores, inorganic
Nuclear fuel reactor cores, inorganic
Nuclear fuel scrap reprocessing
Oleum (fuming sulfuric acid)
Oxidation catalyst made from porcelain
Perchloric acid
Peroxides, inorganic
Phosphates, except defluorinated and ammoniated
Phosphorus and phosphorus oxychloride
Potash alum
Potassium aluminum sulfate
Potassium bichromate and chromate
Potassium bromide
Potassium chlorate
Potassium chloride and cyanide
Potassium compounds, inorganic : except potassium hydroxide and carbonate
Potassium cyanide
Potassium hypochlorate
Potassium iodide
Potassium metal
Potassium nitrate and sulfate
Potassium permanganate
Propellants for missiles, solid : inorganic
Radium chloride
Radium luminous compounds
Rare earth metal salts
Reagent grade chemicals, inorganic : refined from technical grades
Rubidium metal
Salt cake (sodium sulfate)
Salts of rare earth metals
Scandium
Silica, amorphous
Silica gel
Silicofluorides
Silver bromide, chloride, and nitrate
Silver compounds, inorganic
Soda alum
Sodium aluminate
Sodium aluminum sulfate
Sodium antimoniate
Sodium bichromate and chromate
Sodium borates
Sodium borohydride
Sodium bromide, not produced at mines
Sodium chlorate

Group No.   Industry No.

281   INDUSTRIAL INORGANIC CHEMICALS—Continued

     2819   Industrial Inorganic Chemicals, Not Elsewhere Classified—Continued

Sodium compounds, inorganic
Sodium cyanide
Sodium hydrosulfite
Sodium, metallic
Sodium molybdate
Sodium perborate
Sodium peroxide
Sodium phosphate
Sodium polyphosphate
Sodium silicate
Sodium silicofluoride
Sodium stannate
Sodium sulfate—bulk or tablets
Sodium tetraborate, not produced at mines
Sodium thiosulfate
Sodium tungstate
Sodium uranate
Stannic and stannous chloride
Strontium carbonate, precipitated, and oxide

Strontium nitrate
Sublimate, corrosive
Sulfate of potash and potash magnesia, not produced at mines
Sulfides and sulfites
Sulfocyanides
Sulfur chloride
Sulfur dioxide
Sulfur hexafluoride gas
Sulfur, recovered or refined, including from sour natural gas
Sulfuric acid
Tanning agents, synthetic inorganic
Thiocyanates, inorganic
Tin chloride
Tin compounds, inorganic
Tin oxide
Tin salts
Uranium slug, radioactive
Water glass
Zinc chloride

282   PLASTICS MATERIALS AND SYNTHETIC RESINS, SYNTHETIC RUBBER, SYNTHETIC AND OTHER MAN-MADE FIBERS, EXCEPT GLASS

This group includes chemical establishments primarily engaged in manufacturing plastics materials and synthetic resins, synthetic rubbers, and cellulosic and man-made organic fibers. Establishments primarily engaged in the manufacture of rubber products, and those primarily engaged in the compounding of purchased resins or the fabrication of plastics sheets, rods, and miscellaneous plastics products, are classified in Major Group 30; and textile mills primarily engaged in throwing, spinning, weaving, or knitting textile products from manufactured fibers are classified in Major Group 22.

     2821   Plastics Materials, Synthetic Resins, and Nonvulcanizable Elastomers

Establishments primarily engaged in manufacturing synthetic resins, plastics materials, and nonvulcanizable elastomers. Important products of this industry include: cellulose plastic materials; phenolic and other tar acid resins; urea and melamine resins; vinyl resins; styrene resins; alkyd resins; acrylic resins; polyethylene resins; polypropylene resins; rosin modified resins; coumarone-indene and petroleum polymer resins; and miscellaneous resins including polyamide resins, silicones, polyisobutylenes, polyesters, polycarbonate resins, acetal resins, fluorohydrocarbon resins; and casein plastics. Establishments primarily engaged in manufacturing fabricated plastics products or plastics film, sheet, rod, nontextile monofilaments and regenerated cellulose products, and vulcanized fiber are classified in Industry 3079, whether from purchased resins or from resins produced in the same plant. Establishments primarily engaged in compounding purchased resins are also classified in Industry 3079. Establishments primarily manufacturing adhesives are classified in Industry 2891.

Acetal resins
Acetate, cellulose (plastics)
Acrylic resins
Acrylonitrile-butadiene-styrene resins
Alcohol resins, polyvinyl
Alkyd resins
Allyl resins
Butadiene copolymers, containing less than 50% butadiene
Carbohydrate plastics
Casein plastics
Cellulose nitrate resins
Cellulose propionate (plastics)
Coal tar resins
Condensation plastics
Coumarone-indene resins
Cresol-furfural resins
Cresol resins
Dicyandiamine resins
Diisocyanate resins
Elastomers, nonvulcanizable (plastics)
Epichlorohydrin bisphenol
Epichlorohydrin diphenol
Epoxy resins
Ester gum
Ethyl cellulose plastics
Ethylene-vinyl acetate resins
Fluorohydrocarbon resins
Ion exchange resins
Ionomer resins
Isobutylene polymers
Lignin plastics
Melamine resins
Methyl acrylate resins
Methyl cellulose plastics
Methyl methacrylate resins
Molding compounds, plastics
Nitrocellulose plastics (pyroxylin)

Nylon resins
Petroleum polymer resins
Phenol-furfural resins
Phenolic resins
Phenoxy resins
Phthalic alkyd resins
Phthalic anhydride resins
Polyacrylonitrile resins
Polyamide resins
Polycarbonate resins
Polyesters
Polyethylene resins
Polyhexamethylenediamine adipamide resins
Polyisobutylenes
Polymerization plastics, except fibers
Polypropylene resins
Polystyrene resins
Polyurethane resins
Polyvinyl chloride resins
Polyvinyl halide resins
Polyvinyl resins
Protein plastics
Pyroxylin
Resins, phenolic
Resins, synthetic: coal tar and non-coal tar
Rosin modified resins
Silicone fluid solution (fluid for sonar transducers)
Silicone resins
Soybean plastics
Styrene resins
Styrene-acrylonitrile resins
Tar acid resins
Urea resins
Vinyl resins

Group Industry
No. No.

282 **PLASTICS MATERIALS AND SYNTHETIC RESINS, SYNTHETIC RUBBER, SYNTHETIC AND OTHER MAN-MADE FIBERS, EXCEPT GLASS—Continued**

2822 Synthetic Rubber (Vulcanizable Elastomers)

Establishments primarily engaged in manufacturing synthetic rubber by polymerization or copolymerization. An elastomer for the purpose of this classification is a rubber-like material capable of vulcanization, such as copolymers of butadiene and styrene, or butadiene and acrylonitrile, polybutadienes, chloroprene rubbers, and isobutylene-isoprene copolymers. Butadiene copolymers containing less than 50% butadiene are classified in Industry 2821. Natural chlorinated rubbers and cyclized rubbers are considered as semifinished products and are classified in Industry 3069.

Acrylate type rubbers
Acrylate-butadiene rubbers
Acrylic rubbers
Adiprene
Butadiene-acrylonitrile copolymers (over 50% butadiene)
Butadiene rubbers
Butadiene-styrene copolymers (over 50% butadiene)
Butyl rubber
Chlorinated rubbers, synthetic
Chloroprene type rubbers
Chlorosulfonated polyethylenes
Cyclo rubbers, synthetic
EPDM polymers
Elastomers, vulcanizable (synthetic rubber)
Epichlorohydrin elastomers
Estane
Ethylene-propylene rubbers
Fluoro rubbers
Fluorocarbon derivative rubbers
Hypalon
Isobutylene-isoprene rubbers
Isocyanate type rubber

Isoprene rubbers, synthetic
Neoprene
Nitrile-butadiene rubbers
Nitrile-chloroprene rubbers
Nitrile type rubber
N-type rubber
Polybutadienes
Polyethylenes, chlorosulfonated
Polyisobutylene-isoprene elastomers
Polyisobutylene (synthetic rubber)
Polymethylene rubbers
Polysulfides
Pyridine-butadiene copolymers
Pyridine-butadiene rubbers
Rubber, synthetic
Silicone rubbers
S-type rubber
Stereo regular elastomers
Styrene-butadiene rubbers (50% or less styrene content)
Styrene-chloroprene rubbers
Styrene-isoprene rubbers
Thiol rubbers
Urethane rubbers
Vulcanized oils

2823 Cellulosic Man-Made Fibers

Establishments primarily engaged in manufacturing cellulosic fibers (including cellulose acetate and regenerated cellulose such as rayon by the viscose or cuprammonium process) in the form of monofilament, yarn, staple or tow suitable for further manufacturing on spindles, looms, knitting machines or other textile processing equipment. Establishments primarily engaged in manufacturing textile glass fibers are classified in Industry 3229.

Acetate fibers
Cellulose acetate monofilament, yarn, staple, or tow
Cellulose fibers, man-made
Cigarette tow, cellulosic fiber
Cuprammonium fibers
Fibers, cellulose man-made
Fibers, rayon
Horsehair, artificial : rayon
Nitrocellulose fibers

Rayon primary products : fibers, straw, strips, and yarn
Rayon yarn, made in chemical plants (primary products)
Regenerated cellulose fibers
Triacetate fibers
Viscose fibers, bands, strips, and yarn
Yarn, cellulosic : made in chemical plants (primary products)

2824 Synthetic Organic Fibers, Except Cellulosic

Establishments primarily engaged in manufacturing synthetic organic fibers, except cellulosic (including those of regenerated proteins, and of polymers or copolymers of such components as vinyl chloride, vinylidene chloride, linear esters, vinyl alcohols, acrylonitrile, ethylenes, amides, and related polymeric materials) in the form of monofilament, yarn, staple or tow suitable for further manufacturing on spindles, looms, knitting machines or other textile processing equipment. Establishments primarily engaged in manufacturing textile glass fibers are classified in Industry 3229.

Acrylic fibers
Acrylonitrile fibers
Anidex fibers
Casein fibers
Elastomeric fibers
Fibers, man-made : except cellulosic
Fluorocarbon fibers
Horsehair, artificial : nylon
Linear esters fibers
Modacrylic fibers
Nylon fibers and bristles
Olefin fibers
Organic fibers, synthetic : except cellulosic

Polyester fibers
Polyvinyl ester fibers
Polyvinylidene chloride fibers
Protein fibers
Saran fibers
Soybean fibers (man-made textile materials)
Vinal fibers
Vinylidene chloride fibers
Yarn, organic man-made fiber except cellulosic
Zein fibers

Group   Industry
No.   No.

283   DRUGS

This group includes establishments primarily engaged in manufacturing, fabricating, or processing medicinal chemicals and pharmaceutical products. Also included in this group are establishments primarily engaged in the grading, grinding, and milling of botanicals.

2831   Biological Products

Establishments primarily engaged in the production of bacterial and virus vaccine, toxoids and analogous products (such as allergenic extracts), serums, plasmas, and other blood derivatives for human or veterinary use.

Agar culture media	Culture media or concentrates
Aggressins	Diagnostic agents, biological
Allergenic extracts	Diphtheria toxin
Allergens	Plasmas
Antigens	Pollen extracts
Anti-hog-cholera serums	Serobacterins
Antiserums	Serums
Antitoxins	Toxins
Antivenom	Toxoids
Bacterial vaccines	Tuberculins
Bacterins	Vaccines
Bacteriological media	Venoms
Biological and allied products: antitoxins, bacterins, vaccines, viruses	Viruses
Blood derivatives, for human or veterinary use	

2833   Medicinal Chemicals and Botanical Products

Establishments primarily engaged in (1) manufacturing bulk organic and inorganic medicinal chemicals and their derivatives; and (2) processing (grading, grinding, and milling) bulk botanical drugs and herbs. Establishments primarily engaged in manufacturing agar-agar and similar products of natural origin, endocrine products, manufacturing or isolating basic vitamins, and isolating active medicinal principals such as alkaloids from botanical drugs and herbs are also included in this industry.

Adrenal derivatives: bulk, uncompounded	Kelp plants
Agar-agar (ground)	Mercury chlorides, U.S.P.
Alkaloids and salts	Mercury compounds, medicinal: organic and inorganic
Anesthetics, in bulk form	Morphine and derivatives
Antibiotics: bulk uncompounded	N-methylpiperazine
Atropine and derivatives	Oils, vegetable and animal: medicinal grade—refined and concentrated
Barbituric acid and derivatives: bulk, uncompounded	Opium derivatives
Botanical products, medicinal: ground, graded, and milled	Ox bile salts and derivatives: bulk, uncompounded
Brucine and derivatives	Penicillin: bulk, uncompounded
Caffeine and derivatives	Physostigmine and derivatives
Chemicals, medicinal: organic and inorganic—bulk, uncompounded	Pituitary gland derivatives: bulk, uncompounded
Cinchona and derivatives	Procaine and derivatives: bulk, uncompounded
Cocaine and derivatives	Quinine and derivatives
Codeine and derivatives	Reserpines
Digitoxin	Salicylic acid derivatives, medicinal grade
Drug grading, grinding, and milling	Strychnine and derivatives
Endocrine products	Sulfa drugs
Ephedrine and derivatives	Sulfonamides
Ergot alkaloids	Theobromine
Fish liver oils, refined and concentrated for medicinal use	Vegetable gelatin (agar-agar)
Gland derivatives: bulk, uncompounded	Vegetable oils, medicinal grade: refined and concentrated
Herb grinding, grading, and milling	Vitamins, natural and synthetic: bulk, uncompounded
Hormones and derivatives	
Insulin: bulk, uncompounded	

2834   Pharmaceutical Preparations

Establishments primarily engaged in manufacturing, fabricating, or processing drugs in pharmaceutical preparations for human or veterinary use. The greater part of the products of these establishments are finished in the form intended for final consumption, such as ampuls, tablets, capsules, vials, ointments, medicinal powders, solutions, and suspensions. Products of this industry consist of two important lines, namely: (1) pharmaceutical preparations promoted primarily to the dental, medical, or veterinary professions; and (2) pharmaceutical preparations promoted primarily to the public.

Adrenal pharmaceutical preparations	Barbituric acid pharmaceutical preparations
Analgesics	Belladonna pharmaceutical preparations
Anesthetics, packaged	Botanical extracts: powdered, pilular, solid, and fluid
Antacids	Chapsticks
Anthelmintics	Chlorination tablets and kits (water purification)
Antibiotics, packaged	
Antihistamine preparations	
Antipyretics	
Antiseptics, medicinal	
Astringents, medicinal	

Group No.	Industry No.	
283		**DRUGS—Continued**

2834 Pharmaceutical Preparations—Continued

Cold remedies
Cough medicines
Cyclopropane for anesthetic use (U.S.P. par N.F.), packaged
Dextrose and sodium chloride injection, mixed
Dextrose injection
Digitalis pharmaceutical preparations
Diuretics
Druggists' preparations (pharmaceuticals)
Effervescent salts
Emulsifiers, fluorescent inspection
Emulsions, pharmaceutical
Ether for anesthetic use
Fever remedies
Galenical preparations
Hormone preparations
Insulin preparations
Intravenous solutions
Iodine, tincture of
Laxatives
Liniments
Lozenges, pharmaceutical
Medicines, capsuled or ampuled
Nitrofuran preparations
Nitrous oxide for anesthetic use
Ointments
Parenteral solutions
Penicillin preparations

Pharmaceuticals
Pills, pharmaceutical
Pituitary gland pharmaceutical preparations
Poultry and animal remedies
Powders, pharmaceutical
Procaine pharmaceutical preparations
Proprietary drug products
Remedies, human and animal
Sirups, pharmaceutical
Sodium chloride solution for injection. U.S.P.
Sodium salicylate tablets
Solutions, pharmaceutical
Spirits, pharmaceutical
Suppositories
Tablets, pharmaceutical
Thyroid preparations
Tinctures, pharmaceutical
Tranquilizers and mental drug preparations
Vermifuges
Veterinary pharmaceutical preparations
Vitamin preparations
Water decontamination or purification tablets
Water, sterile : for injections
Zinc ointment

284 SOAP, DETERGENTS, AND CLEANING PREPARATIONS, PERFUMES, COSMETICS, AND OTHER TOILET PREPARATIONS

This group includes establishments primarily engaged in manufacturing soap and other detergents and in producing glycerin from vegetable and animal fats and oils; specialty cleaning, polishing, and sanitation preparations; and surface active preparations used as emulsifiers, wetting agents, and finishing agents, including sulfonated oils; and perfumes, cosmetics, and other toilet preparations.

2841 Soap and Other Detergents, Except Specialty Cleaners

Establishments primarily engaged in manufacturing soap, synthetic organic detergents, inorganic alkaline detergents, or any combination thereof, and establishments producing crude and refined glycerin from vegetable and animal fats and oils. Establishments primarily engaged in manufacturing shampoos or shaving products, whether from soap or synthetic detergents, are classified in Industry 2844; and synthetic glycerin in Industry 2869.

Detergents. synthetic organic and inorganic alkaline
Dye removing cream, soap base
Foots soap
Glycerin, crude and refined : from fats—except synthetic

Mechanics' paste
Scouring compounds
Soap : granulated, liquid, cake, flaked, and chip
Textile soap
Washing compounds

2842 Specialty Cleaning, Polishing, and Sanitation Preparations

Establishments primarily engaged in manufacturing furniture, metal, and other polishes; waxes and dressings for fabricated leather and other materials; household, institutional and industrial plant disinfectants, deodorants; dry cleaning preparations; household bleaches; and other sanitation preparations. Establishments primarily manufacturing household pesticidal preparations are classified in Industry 2879.

Ammonia, household
Aqua ammonia, household
Beeswax, processing of
Belt dressing
Blackings
Bleaches, household : liquid or dry
Burnishing ink
Chlorine bleaching compounds, household : liquid or dry
Cleaning and polishing preparations
Cloths, dusting and polishing : chemically treated
Degreasing solvent
Deodorants, nonpersonal
Disinfectants, household and industrial plant
Drain pipe solvents and cleaners
Dressings for fabricated leather and other materials
Dry cleaning preparations
Dust mats, gelatin
Dusting cloths, chemically treated
Dye removing cream, petroleum base
Floor wax emulsion
Floor waxes
Furniture polish and wax
Harness dressing

Household bleaches, dry or liquid
Industrial plant disinfectants and deodorants
Ink, burnishing
Ink eradicators
Leather dressings and finishes
Lye, household
Paint and wallpaper cleaners
Polishes : furniture, automobile, metal, shoe, and stove
Polishing and cleaning preparations
Re-refining dry-cleaning fluid
Rug, upholstery, and dry cleaning detergents and spotters
Rust removers
Saddle soap
Sanitation preparations
Shoe cleaners and polishes
Sodium hypochlorite
Stain removers
Starches, plastic
Sweeping compounds, oil and water absorbent, clay or sawdust
Wallpaper cleaners
Wax removers
Waxes for wood, fabricated leather, and other materials

Group No.	Industry No.	

284 SOAP, DETERGENTS, AND CLEANING PREPARATIONS, PERFUMES, COS-
METICS, AND OTHER TOILET PREPARATIONS—Continued

2843 Surface Active Agents, Finishing Agents, Sulfonated Oils and Assistants

Establishments primarily engaged in producing surface active preparations for use as
wetting agents, emulsifiers, and penetrants. Establishments engaged in producing
sulfonated oils and fats and related products are also included.

Assistants, textile and leather
   processing
Calcium salts of sulfonated oils, fats, or
   greases
Cod oil, sulfonated
Emulsifiers, except food and
   pharmaceutical
Finishing agents, textile and leather
Leather finishing agents
Mordants
Oil, turkey re..
Oils, soluble (textile assistants)

Penetrants
Sodium salts of sulfonated oils, fats, or
   greases
Softeners (textile assistants)
Soluble oils and greases
Sulfonated oils, fats and greases
Surface active agents
Textile processing assistants
Textile scouring compounds and wet-
   ting agents
Thin water (admixture)

2844 Perfumes, Cosmetics, and Other Toilet Preparations

Establishments primarily engaged in manufacturing perfumes (natural and synthetic), cosmetics, and other toilet preparations. This industry also includes establishments primarily engaged in blending and compounding perfume bases; and those
manufacturing shampoos and shaving products, whether from soap or synthetic detergents. Establishments primarily engaged in manufacturing synthetic perfume and
flavoring materials are classified in Industry 2869, and essential oils in Industry 2899.

Bath salts
Bay rum
Body powder
Colognes
Concentrates, perfume
Cosmetic creams
Cosmetic lotions and oils
Cosmetics
Cupranol
Dentifrices
Denture cleaners
Deodorants, personal
Depilatories (cosmetic)
Dressings, cosmetic
Face creams and lotions
Face powders
Home permanent kits

Lipsticks
Manicure preparations
Mouth washes
Perfume bases, blending and
   compounding
Perfumes, natural and synthetic
Powder : baby, face, talcum, and toilet
Rouge, cosmetic
Sachet
Shampoos
Shaving preparations : cakes, creams,
   lotions, powders, tablets, etc.
Talcum powders
Toilet creams, powders, and waters
Toilet preparations
Tooth pastes and powders
Washes, cosmetic

285 PAINTS, VARNISHES, LACQUERS, ENAMELS, AND ALLIED PRODUCTS

2851 Paints, Varnishes, Lacquers, Enamels, and Allied Products

Establishments primarily engaged in manufacturing paints (in paste and ready mixed
form); varnishes; lacquers; enamels and shellac; putties, wood fillers and sealers;
paint and varnish removers; paint brush cleaners and allied paint products. Establishments primarily engaged in manufacturing carbon black are classified in Industry 2895;
bone black, lamp black, and inorganic color pigments in Industry 2816; organic color
pigments in Industry 2865; plastics materials in Industry 2821; printing ink in Industry
2893; calking compounds and sealants in Industry 2891; and artists' paints in Industry
3952.

Calcimines, dry and paste
Cleaners, paint brush
Coating, air curing
Colors in oil, except artists'
Dispersions, thermoplastic and col-
   loidal : paint
Dopes (paint)
Driers, paint
Enamels, except dental and china
   painting
Epoxy coatings, made from purchased
   resin
Fillers, wood : dry, liquid, and paste
Intaglio ink vehicle
Japans, baking and drying
Kalsomines, dry or paste
Lacquer bases and dopes
Lacquer, clear and pigmented
Lacquer thinner
Lacquers, plastic
Lead-in-oil paints
Linoleates (paint driers)
Lithographic varnishes
Marine paints
Naphthanate driers
Oleate driers
Paint brush cleaners
Paint driers

Paint removers
Paints, asphalt and bituminous
Paints : oil and alkyd vehicle, and
   water thinned
Paints, plastic texture : paste and dry
Paints, waterproof
Phenol formaldehyde coatings, baking
   and air curing
Plastics base paints and varnishes
Plastisol coating compound
Polyurethane coatings
Primers, paint
Putty
Resinate driers
Shellac (protective coating)
Soyate driers
Stains : varnish, oil, and wax
Tallate driers
Undercoatings, paint
Varnish removers
Varnishes
Vinyl coatings, strippable
Vinyl plastisol
Water paints
Wood fillers and sealers
Wood stains
Zinc oxide in oil (paint)

Group Industry
No.   No.

286   **INDUSTRIAL ORGANIC CHEMICALS**

Establishments primarily engaged in manufacturing industrial organic chemicals. Important products of this group include: (1) non-cyclic organic chemicals such as acetic, chloroacetic, adipic, formic, oxalic and tartaric acids and their metallic salts; chloral, formaldehyde and methylamine; (2) solvents such as amyl, butyl, and ethyl alcohols; methanol; amyl, butyl and ethyl acetates; ethel ether, ethylene glycol ether and diethylene glycol ether; acetone, carbon disulfide and chlorinated solvents such as carbon tetrachloride, perchloroethylene and trichloroethylene; (3) polyhydric alcohols such as ethylene glycol, sorbitol, pentaerythritol, synthetic glycerin; (4) synthetic perfume and flavoring materials such as coumarin, methyl salicylate, saccharin, citral, citronellal, synthetic geraniol, ionone, terpineol, and synthetic vanillin; (5) rubber processing chemicals such as accelerators and antioxidants, both cyclic and acyclic; (6) plasticizers, both cyclic and acyclic, such as esters of phosphoric acid, phthalic anhydride, adipic acid, lauric acid, oleic acid, sebacic acid, and stearic acid; (7) synthetic tanning agents such as naphthalene sulfonic acid condensates; (8) chemical warfare gases; (9) esters, amines, etc. of polyhydric alcohols and fatty and other acids; (10) cyclic crudes and intermediates; (11) cyclic dyes and organic pigments; and (12) natural gum and wood chemicals. Establishments primarily engaged in manufacturing plastics materials and nonvulcanizable elastomers are classified in Industry 2821; synthetic rubber in Industry 2822; essential oils in Industry 2899; rayon and other synthetic fibers in Industries 2823 and 2824; specialty cleaning, polishing and sanitation preparations in Industry 2842; paints in Industry 2851; and inorganic pigments in Industry 2816. Distilleries engaged in the manufacture of grain alcohol for beverage purposes are classified in Industry 2085.

2861   **Gum and Wood Chemicals**

Establishments primarily engaged in manufacturing hardwood and softwood distillation products, wood and gum naval stores, charcoal, natural dyestuffs, and natural tanning materials. Establishments primarily engaged in manufacturing synthetic tanning materials and synthetic organic chemicals are classified in Industry 2869, and synthetic organic dyes in Industry 2865.

Acetate of lime, natural	Naval stores, wood
Acetone, natural	Oak extract
Annato extract	Oil, pine : produced by distillation of
Brazilwood extract	pine gum or pine wood
Brewers' pitch, product of softwood	Oils, wood : product of hardwood
distillation	distillation
Calcium acetate, product of hardwood	Pine oil, produced by distillation of
distillation	pine gum or pine wood
Charcoal, except activated	Pit charcoal
Chestnut extract	Pitch, wood
Dragon's blood	Pyroligneous acid
Dyeing materials, natural	Quebracho extract
Dyestuffs, natural	Quercitron extract
Ethyl acetate, natural	Rosin, produced by distillation of pine
Extracts, dyeing and tanning : natural	gum or pine wood
Fustic wood extract	Softwood distillates
Gambier extract	Sumac extract
Gum naval stores, processing but not	Tall oil, except skimmings
gathering or warehousing	Tanning extracts and materials,
Hardwood distillates	natural
Hemlock extract	Tar and tar oils, products of wood
Logwood extract	distillation
Mangrove extract	Turpentine, produced by distillation of
Methanol, natural (wood alcohol)	pine gum or pine wood
Methyl acetone	Valonia extract
Methyl alcohol, natural (wood alcohol)	Wattle extract
Myrobalans extract	Wood alcohol, natural
Naval stores, gum : processing but not	Wood creosote
gathering or warehousing	Wood distillates

2865   **Cyclic (Coal Tar) Crudes, and Cyclic Intermediates, Dyes, and Organic Pigments (Lakes and Toners)**

Establishments primarily engaged in manufacturing coal tar crudes and cyclic organic intermediates, dyes, color lakes and toners. Important products of this industry include: (1) derivatives of benzene, toluene, naphthalene, anthracene, pyridine, carbazole, and other cyclic chemical products; (2) synthetic organic dyes; (3) synthetic organic pigments; and (4) cyclic (coal tar) crudes, such as light oils and light oil products; coal tar acids; and products of medium and heavy oil such as creosote oil, naphthalene, anthracene, and their higher homologues, and tar. Establishments primarily engaged in manufacturing coal tar crudes in chemical recovery ovens are classified in Industry 3312, and petroleum refineries which produce such products in Industry 2911.

Group Industry
No. No.

286   INDUSTRIAL ORGANIC CHEMICALS—Continued

2865   Cyclic (Coal Tar) Crudes, and Cyclic Intermediates, Dyes, and Organic Pigments
(Lakes and Toners)—Continued

Acid dyes, synthetic
Acids, coal tar : derived from coal tar
distillation
Alkylated diphenylamines, mixed
Alkylated phenol, mixed
Aminoanthraquinone
Aminoazobenzene
Aminoazotoluene
Aminophenol
Aniline
Aniline oil
Anthracene
Anthraquinone dyes
Azine dyes
Azo dyes
Azobenzene
Azoic dyes
Benzaldehyde
Ben:ene hexachloride (BHC)
Benzene, product of coal tar distillation
Benzoic acid
Benzol, product of coal tar distillation
Biological stains
Chemical indicators
Chlorobenzene
Chloronaphthalene
Chlorophenol
Chlorotoluene
Coal tar crudes, derived from coal tar
distillation
Coal tar distillates
Coal tar intermediates
Color lakes and toners
Color pigments, organic : except animal
black and bone black
Colors, dry : lakes, toners, or full
strength organic colors
Colors, extended (color lakes)
Cosmetic dyes, synthetic
Creosote oil, product of coal tar dis-
tillation
Cresols, product of coal tar distillation
Cresylic acid, product of coal tar dis-
tillation
Cyclic crudes, coal tar : product of coal
tar distillation
Cyclic intermediates
Cyclohexane
Diphenylamine
Drug dyes, synthetic
Dye (cyclic) intermediates
Dyes, food : synthetic
Dyes, synthetic organic

Eosine toners
Ethylbenzene
Hydroquinone
Isocyanates
Lake red C toners
Leather dyes and stains, synthetic
Lithol rubine lakes and toners
Maleic anhydride
Methyl violet toners
Naphtha, solvent : product of coal tar
distillation
Naphthalene chips and flakes
Naphthalene, product of coal tar dis-
tillation
Naphthol, alpha and beta
Nitro dyes
Nitroaniline
Nitrobenzene
Nitrophenol
Nitroso dyes
Oil, aniline
Oils : light, medium, and heavy—prod-
uct of coal tar distillation
Organic pigments (lakes and toners)
Orthodichlorobenzene
Paint pigments, organic
Peacock blue lake
Pentachlorophenol
Persian orange lake
Phenol
Phloxine toners
Phosphomolybdic acid lakes and toners
Phosphotungstic acid lakes and toners
Phthalic anhydride
Phthalocyanine toners
Pigment scarlet lake
Pitch, product of coal tar distillation
Pulp colors, organic
Quinoline dyes
Resorcinol
Scarlet 2 R lake
Stains for leather
Stilbene dyes
Styrene
Styrene monomer
Tar, product of coal tar distillation
Toluene, product of coal tar distilla-
tion
Toluidines
Toluol, product of coal tar distillation
Vat dyes, synthetic
Xylene, product of coal tar distillation
Xylol, product of coal tar distillation

2869   Industrial Organic Chemicals, Not Elsewhere Classified

Establishments primarily engaged in manufacturing industrial organic chemicals,
not elsewhere classified. Important products of this industry include: (1) non-cyclic
organic chemicals such as acetic, chloroacetic, adipic, formic, oxalic and tartaric acids
and their metallic salts; chloral, formaldehyde and methylamine; (2) solvents such as
amyl, butyl, and ethyl alcohols; methanol; amyl, butyl and ethyl acetates; ethel ether,
ethylene glycol ether and diethylene glycol ether; acetone, carbon disulfide and chlorinated solvents such as carbon tetrachloride, perchloroethylene and trichloroethylene;
(3) polyhydric alcohols such as ethylene glycol, sorbitol, pentaerythritol, synthetic
glycerin; (4) synthetic perfume and flavoring materials such as coumarin, methyl
salicylate, saccharin, citral, citronellal, synthetic geraniol, ionone, terpineol, and synthetic vanillin; (5) rubber processing chemicals such as accelerators and antioxidants,
both cyclic and acyclic; (6) plasticizers, both cyclic and acyclic, such as esters of phosphoric acid, phthalic anhydride, adipic acid, lauric acid, oleic acid, sebacic acid, and
stearic acid; (7) synthetic tanning agents such as naphthalene sulfonic acid condensates;
(8) chemical warfare gases; and (9) esters, amines, etc. of polyhydric alcohols and fatty
and other acids. Establishments primarily engaged in manufacturing plastics materials
and nonvulcanizable elastomers are classified in Industry 2821; synthetic rubber in
Industry 2822; essential oils in Industry 2899; wood distillation products, naval stores,
and natural dyeing and tanning materials in Industry 2861; rayon and other synthetic
fibers in Industries 2823 and 2824; specialty cleaning, polishing and sanitation preparations in Industry 2842; paints in Industry 2851; urea in Industry 2873; organic
pigments in Industry 2865; and inorganic pigments in Industry 2816. Distilleries engaged in the manufacture of grain alcohol for beverage purposes are classified in Industry 2085.

Group Industry
No.   No.
286

INDUSTRIAL ORGANIC CHEMICALS—Continued

2869 Industrial Organic Chemicals, Not Elsewhere Classified—Continued

Accelerators, rubber processing : cyclic
 and acyclic
Acetaldehyde
Acetates, except natural acetate of
 lime
Acetic acid, synthetic
Acetic anhydride
Acetin
Acetone, synthetic
Acid esters, amines, etc.
Acids, organic
Acrolein
Acrylonitrile
Adipic acid
Adipic acid esters
Adiponitrile
Alcohol, aromatic
Alcohol, fatty : powdered
Alcohol, methyl : synthetic (methanol)
Alcohols, industrial : denatured (non-
 beverage)
Algin products
Amyl acetate and alcohol
Antioxidants, rubber processing : cyclic
 and acyclic
Bromochloromethane
Butadiene, from alcohol
Butyl acetate, alcohol, and propionate
Butyl ester solution of 2, 4-D
Calcium oxalate
Camphor, synthetic
Carbon bisulfide (disulfide)
Carbon tetrachloride
Casing fluids, for curing fruits, spices,
 tobacco, etc.
Cellulose acetate, unplasticized
Chemical warfare gases
Chloral
Chlorinated solvents
Chloroacetic acid and metallic salts
Chloroform
Chloropicrin
Citral
Citrates
Citric acid
Citronellal
Coumarin
Cream of tartar
Cyclopropane
DDT, technical
Decahydronaphthalene
Dichlorodifluoromethane
Diethylcyclohexane (mixed isomers)
Diethylene glycol ether
Dimethyl divinyl acetylene (di-isopro-
 penyl acetylene)
Dimethylhydrazine, unsymmetrical
Embalming fluids
Enzymes
Esters of phosphoric, adipic, lauric,
 oleic, sebacic, and stearic acids
Esters of phthalic anhydride
Ethanol, industrial
Ether
Ethyl acetate, synthetic
Ethyl alcohol, industrial (non-
 beverage)
Ethyl butyrate
Ethyl cellulose, unplasticized
Ethyl chloride
Ethyl ether
Ethyl formate
Ethyl nitrite
Ethyl perhydrophenanthrene
Ethylene
Ethylene glycol
Ethylene glycol ether
Ethylene glycol, inhibited
Ethylene oxide
Fatty acid esters, amines, etc.
Ferric ammonium oxalate
Flavors and flavoring materials, syn-
 thetic
Fluorinated hydrocarbon gases
Formaldehyde (formalin)
Formic acid and metallic salts
Freon
Fuel propellants, solid : organic
Fuels, high energy : organic
Geraniol, synthetic
Glycerin, except from fats (synthetic)
Grain alcohol, industrial (nonbever-
 age)
Hexamethylenediamine

Hexamethylenetetramine
High purity grade chemicals, organic :
 refined from technical grades
Hydraulic fluids, synthetic base
Hydrazine
Industrial organic cyclic compounds
Ionone
Isopropyl alcohol
Ketone, methyl ethyl
Ketone, methyl isobutyl
Laboratory chemicals, organic
Lauric acid esters
Lime citrate
Malononitrile, technical grade
Metallic salts of acyclic organic chem-
 icals
Metallic stearate
Methanol, synthetic (methyl alcohol)
Methyl chloride
Methyl perhydrofluorine
Methyl salicylate
Methylamine
Methylene chloride
Monochlorodifluoromethane
Monomethylparaminophenol sulfate
Monosodium glutamate
Mustard gas
Naphthalene sulfonic acid condensates
Naphthenic acid soaps
Normal hexyl decalin
Nuclear fuels, organic
Oleic acid esters
Organic acid esters
Organic chemicals, acyclic
Oxalates
Oxalic acid and metallic salts
Pentaerythritol
Perchloroethylene
Perfume materials, synthetic
Phosgene
Phthalates
Plasticizers, organic : cyclic and acyclic
Polyhydric alcohol esters, amines, etc.
Polyhydric alcohols
Potassium bitartrate
Propellants for missiles, solid : organic
Propylene
Propylene glycol
Quinuclidinol ester of benzylic acid
Reagent grade chemicals, organic : re-
 fined from technical grades
Rocket engine fuel, organic
Rubber processing chemicals, organic :
 accelerators and antioxidants
Saccharin
Sebacic acid
Silicones
Soaps, naphthenic acid
Sodium acetate
Sodium alginate
Sodium benzoate
Sodium glutamate
Sodium pentachlorophenate
Sodium sulfoxalate formaldehyde
Solvents, organic
Sorbitol
Stearic acid salts
Sulfonated naphthalene
Tackifiers, organic
Tannic acid
Tanning agents, synthetic organic
Tartaric acid and metallic salts
Tartrates
Tear gas
Terpineol
Tert-butylated bis (p-phenoxyphenyl)
 ether fluid
Tetrachloroethylene
Tetraethyl lead
Thioglycolic acid, for permanent wave
 lotions
Trichloroethylene
Trichloroethylene stabilized, degreas-
 ing
Trichlorophenoxyacetic acid
Trichlorotrifluoroethane tetrachlorodi-
 fluoroethane isopropyl alcohol
Tricresyl phosphate
Tridecyl alcohol
Trimethyltrithiophosphite (rocket pro-
 pellants)
Triphenyl phosphate
Vanillin, synthetic
Vinyl acetate

Group Industry
No.   No.

287   AGRICULTURAL CHEMICALS

This group includes establishments primarily engaged in manufacturing nitrogenous and phosphatic basic fertilizers, mixed fertilizers, pesticides, and other agricultural chemicals. Establishments primarily engaged in manufacturing basic chemicals, which require further processing or formulation before use as agricultural pest control agents, are classified in Group 281 or 286.

2873   Nitrogenous Fertilizers

Establishments primarily engaged in manufacturing nitrogenous fertilizer materials or mixed fertilizers from nitrogenous materials produced in the same establishment. Included are ammonia fertilizer compounds and anhydrous ammonia, nitric acid, ammonium nitrate, ammonium sulfate and nitrogen solutions, urea, and natural organic fertilizers (except compost) and mixtures.

Ammonia liquor
Ammonium nitrate and sulfate
Anhydrous ammonia
Aqua ammonia, made in ammonia plants
Fertilizers: natural (organic), except compost

Nitric acid
Nitrogen solutions (fertilizer)
Plant foods, mixed: made in plants producing nitrogenous fertilizer
Urea

2874   Phosphatic Fertilizers

Establishments primarily engaged in manufacturing phosphatic fertilizer materials, or mixed fertilizers from phosphatic materials produced in the same establishment. Included are phosphoric acid; normal, enriched, and concentrated superphosphates; ammonium phosphates; nitro-phosphates; and calcium meta-phosphates.

Ammonium phosphate
Calcium meta-phosphate
Defluorinated phosphate
Diammonium phosphate
Fertilizers, mixed: made in plants producing phosphatic fertilizer materials

Phosphoric acid
Plant foods, mixed: made in plants producing phosphatic fertilizer
Superphosphates, ammoniated and not ammoniated

2875   Fertilizers, Mixing Only

Establishments primarily engaged in mixing fertilizers from purchased fertilizer materials.

Compost
Fertilizers, mixed: made in plants not manufacturing fertilizer materials

Potting soil, mixed

2879   Pesticides and Agricultural Chemicals, Not Elsewhere Classified

Establishments primarily engaged in the formulation and preparation of ready-to-use agricultural and household pest control chemicals, including insecticides, fungicides and herbicides from technical chemicals or concentrates; and the production of concentrates which require further processing before use as agricultural pesticides. This industry also includes establishments primarily engaged in manufacturing or formulating agricultural chemicals, not elsewhere classified, such as minor or trace elements and soil conditioners. Establishments primarily engaged in manufacturing basic or technical agricultural pest control chemicals including insecticides, fungicides, and herbicides such as lead and calcium arsenates, and copper sulfate are classified in Group 281, and DDT, BHC, 2,4-D carbamates, etc., in Group 286. Establishments primarily engaged in manufacturing agricultural lime products are classified in Major Group 32.

Agricultural disinfectants
Agricultural pesticides
Arsenates: calcium, copper, and lead— formulated
Arsenites, formulated
Bordeaux mixture
Calcium arsenate and arsenite, formulated
Cattle dips
Copper arsenate, formulated
DDT (insecticide), formulated
Defoliants
Elements, minor or trace (agricultural chemicals)
Exterminating products, for household and industrial use
Fly sprays
Fungicides
Growth regulants, agricultural
Herbicides
Hormones, plant
Household insecticides
Insect powder, household
Insecticides, agricultural
Lead arsenate, formulated

Lime-sulfur, dry and solution
Lindane, formulated
Moth repellants
Nicotine and salts
Nicotine bearing insecticides
Paris green (insecticide)
Pesticides, household
Phytoactin
Plant hormones
Poison: ant, rat, roach, and rodent— household
Pyrethrin bearing preparations
Pyrethrin concentrates
Rodenticides
Rotenone bearing preparations
Rotenone concentrates
Sheep dips, chemical
Sodium arsenite (formulated)
Soil conditioners
Sulfur dust (insecticide)
Thiocyanates, organic (formulated)
Trace elements (agricultural chemicals)
Xanthone (formulated)

Group   Industry
No.   No.

289   **MISCELLANEOUS CHEMICAL PRODUCTS**

2891 Adhesives and Sealants

Establishments primarily engaged in manufacturing industrial and household adhesives, glues, calking compounds, sealants, and linoleum, tile, and rubber cements from vegetable, animal, or synthetic plastics materials, purchased or produced in the same establishment. Establishments primarily engaged in manufacturing gelatin and sizes are classified in Industry 2899, and vegetable gelatin or agar-agar in Industry 2833.

Adhesives	Laminating compounds
Adhesives, plastic	Mucilage
Calking compounds	Paste, adhesive
Cement (cellulose nitrate base)	Porcelain cement, household
Cement, linoleum	Rubber cement
Cement, mending	Sealing compounds for pipe threads
Cement, rubber	and joints
Epoxy adhesives	Sealing compounds, synthetic rubber
Glue, except dental : animal, vegetable,	and plastic
fish, casein, and synthetic resin	Wax, sealing
Iron cement, household	

2892 Explosives

Establishments primarily engaged in manufacturing explosives. Establishments primarily engaged in manufacturing ammunition for small arms are classified in Industry 3482 and fireworks in Industry 2899.

Amatol (explosive)	Lead azide (explosive)
Azides (explosives)	Mercury azide (explosive)
Blasting powder and blasting caps	Nitrocellulose powder (explosive)
Carbohydrates, nitrated (explosives)	Nitroglycerin (explosive)
Cordeau detonant (explosive)	Nitromannitol (explosive)
Cordite (explosive)	Nitrostarch (explosive)
Detonating caps for safety fuses	Nitrosugars (explosives)
Detonators (explosive compounds)	Pentolite (explosive)
Dynamite	Permissible explosives
Explosive cartridges for concussion	Picric acid (explosive)
forming of metal	Powder : pellet, smokeless, and sport-
Explosive compounds	ing (explosive)
Explosives	RDX (explosive)
Fulminate of mercury (explosive com-	Squibbs, electric
pound)	Styphnic acid
Fuse powder	Tetryl (explosive)
Fuses, safety	TNT (trinitrotoluene)
Gunpowder	Well shooting torpedoes (explosives)
High explosives	

2893 Printing Ink

Establishments primarily engaged in manufacturing printing ink, gravure ink, screen process ink, and lithographic ink.

Bronze ink	Ink, printing : base or finished
Gold ink	Lithographic ink
Gravure ink	Printing ink
Ink, duplicating	Screen process ink

2895 Carbon Black

Establishments primarily engaged in manufacturing carbon black (channel and furnace black).

Carbon black	Furnace black
Channel black	

2899 Chemicals and Chemical Preparations, Not Elsewhere Classified

Establishments primarily engaged in manufacturing miscellaneous chemical preparations, not elsewhere classified, such as fatty acids, essential oils, gelatin (except vegetable), sizes, bluing, laundry sours, writing and stamp pad inks; industrial compounds, such as boiler and heat insulating compounds, metal, oil and water treating compounds, water-proofing compounds and chemical supplies for foundries. Establishments primarily engaged in manufacturing vegetable gelatin (agar-agar) are classified in Industry 2833; and dessert preparations based on gelatin in Industry 2099.

Acid, battery	Chemical supplies for foundries
Acid resist for etching	Citronella oil
Anise oil	Concrete curing compounds (blends of
Antifreeze compounds, except indus-	pigments, waxes, and resins)
trial alcohol	Concrete hardening compounds
Bay oil	Core oil and binders
Binders (chemical foundry supplies)	Core wash
Bluing	Core wax
Boiler compounds, antiscaling	Corrosion preventive lubricant, syn-
Bombs, flashlight	thetic base : for jet engines
Caps, for toy pistols	Defrosting fluid
Carbon removing solvent	De-icing fluid
Chemical cotton (processed cotton	Dextrine sizes
linters)	Desalter kits, sea water

Group No. 289
Industry No.

MISCELLANEOUS CHEMICAL PRODUCTS—Continued

2899 Chemicals and Chemical Preparations, Not Elsewhere Classified—Continued

Drilling mud
Dyes, household
Essential oils
Eucalyptus oil
Exothermics for metal industries
Facings (chemical foundry supplies)
Fatty acids: margaric, oleic, and stearic
Fire extinguisher chargers
Fire retardant chemicals
Fireworks
Flares (all kinds)
Fluidifier (retarder) for concrete
Fluorescent inspection oil
Fluxes: brazing, soldering, galvanizing, and welding
Foam charge mixtures
Food contamination testing and screening kits
Foundry supplies
Frit
Fuel tank and engine cleaning chemicals, automotive and aircraft
Fusees: highway, marine, and railroad
Gelatin capsules, empty
Gelatin: edible, technical, photographic, and pharmaceutical
Glue size
Gum sizes
Grapefruit oil
Grouting material (concrete mending compound)
Gun slushing compounds
Heat insulating compounds
Heat treating salts
Hydrofluoric acid compound, for etching and polishing glass
Igniter grains, boron potassium nitrate
Incense
Industrial sizes
Ink and writing fluids, except printing
Inspection oil, fluorescent
Insulating compounds
Jet fuel igniters
Laundry sours
Lemon oil
Lighter fluid
Magnetic inspection oil and powder

Margaric acid
Metal drawing compound lubricants
Metal treating compounds
Military pyrotechnics
Napalm
Oil, red (oleic acid)
Oil treating compounds
Oleic acid (red oil)
Orange oil
Orris oil
Ossein
Oxidizers, inorganic
Packers' salt
Parting compounds (chemical foundry supplies)
Patching plaster, household
Penetrants, inspection
Peppermint oil
Plastic wood
Plating compounds
Pyrotechnic ammunition: flares, signals, flashlight bombs, and rockets
Railroad torpedoes
Red oil (oleic acid)
Rifle bore cleaning compounds
Rosin sizes
Rust resisting compounds
Salt
Signal flares, marine
Sizes: animal, vegetable, and synthetic plastics materials
Sodium chloride, refined
Soil testing kits
Spearmint oil
Spirit duplicating fluid
Stearic acid
Stencil correction compounds
Tints and dyes, household
Torches (fireworks)
Torpedoes, railroad
Vegetable oils, vulcanized or sulfurized
Water, distilled
Water treating compounds
Waterproofing compounds
Wax, core
Wintergreen oil
Writing ink and fluids

CHEMICAL COMPANIES LISTED ON THE NEW YORK, AMERICAN, AND OVER-THE-COUNTER EXCHANGES[1]

Table B.1 New York Stock Exchange

Name of firm	Ticker symbol	Principal business
Abbott Laboratories	ABT	Diversified health-care products
Airco Inc.	AN	Industrial gases and equipment, ferroalloys
Air Products & Chemicals Inc.	APD	Industrial gases and equipment, chemicals
Akzona, Inc.	AXO	Synthetic fiber, cable, salt, chemicals
Alberto-Culver	ACV	Cosmetics
Alco Standard	ASN	
Alcon Laboratories	ALB	Eye and nose pharmaceuticals
Allied Chemical	ACD	Basic chemicals, plastics, fibers
Amerace Corp.	AAE	Rubber, plastics, chemicals
American Cyanamid Corp.	ACY	Chemicals, drugs, agricultural, and consumer products
American Home Products	AHP	Drugs, cosmetics, foods
American Hospital Supply	AHS	Pharmaceuticals
Ansul Co.	AFX	Specialty chemicals
Archer-Daniels-Midland	ADM	Food processing
Armstrong Cork	ACK	Interior furnishings
Ashland Oil Inc.	ASH	Oil refiner, asphalt, resins, chemicals
Atlantic Richfield Co.	ARC	Oil and gas
Avon Products	AVP	Cosmetics
Basic Inc.	BAI	Refractories; steel-industry specialty chemicals

(*continued*)

Table B.1—*continued*

Name of firm	Ticker symbol	Principal business
Baxter Travenol Laboratories Inc.	BAX	Medical-care products, enzymes
Beatrice Foods	BRY	Dairy and grocery products, chemicals
Beker Industries Corp.	BKI	Chemical fertilizers
Big Three Industries Inc.	BIG	Industrial gases; welding equipment
Borden, Inc.	BN	Dairy and food products, chemicals
Borg-Warner	BOR	Transport equipment, chemicals
Bristol-Meyers Co.	BMY	Toiletries, ethical drugs
British Petroleum Co., Ltd.	BP	Oil (sixth largest in world)
Cabot Corp.	CBT	Carbon black, oil and gas machinery
Carlisle Corp.	CSL	Rubber, plastics, tires, wire
Carter Wallace, Inc.	CAR	Drug and toiletry products
Celanese Corp.	CZ	Fibers, chemicals, plastics
Central Soya	CSY	Soya processing
Chelsea Industries	CHD	Textiles, shoes, plastic, food
Chemetron Corp.	CTN	Industrial and medical gas, chemicals
Chesebrough-Pond's	CBM	Cosmetics
Cris-Craft Industries	CCN	Chemicals, plastics, foam, rubber, TV stations, boats
Cities Service Co.	CS	Integrated oil enterprise
Clorox Co.	CLX	Soap products, cleaning agents
Coastal States Gas	CGP	Natural gas, petrochemicals
Colgate Palmolive Co.	CL	Soap, detergents, drugs, foods, toiletries
Commonwealth Oil Refining Co., Inc.	CWO	Offshore refinery, Puerto Rico petrochemical products
Consolidated Foods	CFD	Brand foods
Continental Oil Co.	CLL	Integrated enterprise, oil, chemicals, coal
Cooper Laboratories	COO	Pharmaceuticals
CPC International	CPC	Corn products, food
Crompton & Knowles	CNK	Specialty chemicals, textile machinery
Dart Industries	D	Chemical products
Dayco Corp.	DAY	Plastic, rubber, chemicals, consumer products
Desoto Inc.	DSO	Paints, detergents
Dexter Corp.	DEX	Chemical materials, industrial web producer
Diamond Shamrock	DIA	Chemicals, oil and gas, resins, plastics
Diversified Industries	DMC	
Dow Chemical	DOW	Large diversified chemical company
Dresser Industries	DI	Industrial equipment, oil, gas chemicals
Du Pont, E.I., de Nemours & Co.	DD	Large chemical producer
Eagle-Picher Industries	EPI	Industrial products,
Eastman Kodak Co.	EK	Photograph apparatus, chemicals
El Paso Co.	ELG	Natural gas
Emery Industries	EI	Oleochemical products
Englehard Minerals & Chemicals	ENG	Minerals and chemicals (international)
Enserch Corp.	ENS	Natural gas, chemical fertilizer, plastic pipe

Table B.1—*continued*

Name of firm	Ticker symbol	Principal business
Esmark, Inc.	ESM	Swift, Playtex, agricultural chemicals, energy
Ethyl Corp.	EY	Petroleum and industrial chemicals
Exxon Corp.	XON	Chemicals, gas, oil, etc. (world's leading oil company)
Faberge, Inc.	FBG	Cosmetics
Ferro Corp.	FOE	Chemical specialties, plastics
Filtrol Corp.	FLT	Catalysts, absorbents, cement
First Mississippi Corp.	FRM	Chemicals, fertilizer, land
FMC Corp.	FMC	Machinery, chemicals, rayon
Foremost-McKesson	FOR	Drugs and liquor
Freeport Minerals	FT	Sulfur, oil, and natural gas
GAF Corp.	GAF	Building products, chemicals, photo equipment, business systems
General American Oil Co. of Texas	GAO	Crude oil, gas, hydrocarbons
General Electric	GE	Electric products, specialty chemicals
General Mills	GIS	Food
General Tire & Rubber	GY	Tires, chemicals, plastics
Gillette Co.	GS	Shaving needs, cosmetics, toiletries
Goodrich, B. F.	GR	Tires, rubber products, chemicals, plastic materials
Grace, W. R., & Co.	GRA	Chemicals, food, paper, oil
Gulf Oil Corp.	GO	Oil (fifth largest company)
Gulf Resources & Chemical Corp.	GRE	Metals, coal, lithium, fertilizers, mining
Gulf States Utilities	GTU	Chemical manufacturing, oil, electric power in Texas and Louisiana
Gulf & Western	GW	Conglomerate
Helene Curtis Industries	HC	Cosmetics
Helmerich & Payne	HP	Oil and gas, chemicals, drilling
Hercules Inc.	HPC	Chemical and plastics
Hoover Ball & Bearing	HBB	Ball bearings
Houston Natural Gas	HNG	Natural gas
Hunt, Philip A., Chemical	HCC	Photochemical processing system, chemicals
ICN Pharmaceuticals	ICN	Pharmaceuticals
Inmont Corp.	IKN	Printing inks, chemicals
International Flavors & Fragrances	IFF	Speciality chemicals
International Minerals & Chemicals	IGL	Fertilizer, metals, potash, phosphate rock
International Tel. & Tel.	ITT	Telecommunication equipment
Ipco Hospital Supply Corp.	IHS	Hospital supplies
Johnson & Johnson	JNJ	Surgical dressings and pharmaceuticals
Kerr-McGee Corp.	KMG	Oil, uranium, contract drilling
Koppers Co., Inc.	KOP	Forest products, chemicals
Kraftco Corp.	KRA	Food products
Lilly, Eli, & Co.	LLY	Ethical drugs, agrichemicals, cosmetics
Lubrizol Corp.	LZ	Chemical additives for lubricants
Marathon Oil Co.	MRO	Medium-sized integrated oil nit

(*continued*)

Table B.1—*continued*

Name of firm	Ticker symbol	Principal business
Marion Laboratories Inc.	MKC	Pharmaceuticals
Martin Marietta	ML	Aerospace, chemicals, construction materials
Merck & Co. Inc.	MRK	Ethical drugs and fine chemicals
Miles Laboratories	MIL	Alka-Seltzer, health care
Minnesota Mining & Mfg. Co.	MMM	Scotch tapes, coated abrasives
Mobil Corp.	MOB	Oil (third largest in world), chemicals, plastics
Molycorp. Inc.	MLY	Molybdenum and rare earths
Monsanto Co.	MTC	Diversified chemical products, fibers, plastics
Morton-Norwich Products Inc.	MNP	Drugs, food, household products
Murphy Oil Corp.	MUR	Integrated oil company, contract drilling
Nalco Chemical Co.	NLC	Specialty chemicals
National Chemsearch Corp.	NCH	Cleaning and other chemicals
National Distillers & Chemical Corp.	DR	Major distiller, chemicals, plastics, metals
National Starch & Chemical Corp.	NSC	Starches, adhesives, and chemicals
NL Industries Inc.	NL	Chemicals, paint, metals
North American Philips	NPH	Chemicals
Northern Natural Gas	NNG	Natural gas
Northwest Industries	NWT	Chemicals
Oakite Products	OKT	Cleaning and conditioning chemicals
Occidental Petroleum Corp.	OXY	Oil and gas, sulfur, fertilizers
Olin Corp.	OLN	Chemicals, brass, guns
Pennwalt Corp.	PSM	Chemicals, specialized equipment
Pfizer Corp.	PFE	Drugs, chemicals
Phillips Petroleum Co.	P	Domestic integrated oil, chemicals
PPG Industries	PPG	Glass, paint, chemicals
Procter & Gamble, Co.	PG	Leading soapmaker, food
Products Research & Chemical Corp.	PRC	Sealants, coatings, specialty chemicals
Publicker Industries	PUL	Distiller, chemicals
Purex Corp.	PRX	Bleaches, detergents, steel wool
Quaker Oats	OAT	Food processer, chemicals, toys pet foods and products, restaurants
Quaker State Oil Refining Co.	KSF	Motor oil, lubricants, waxes, chemicals
Reichhold Chemicals	RCI	Synthetic resins, chemicals
Revlon, Inc.	REV	Cosmetics, ethical drugs
Richardson Co.	RCS	Battery parts, chemicals
Richardson-Merrell	RXM	Proprietary and ethical drugs
Robins, A. H., Co., Inc.	RAH	Pharmaceuticals
Rohm & Haas Co.	ROH	Chemical producer
Rorer-Amchem, Inc.	ROR	Health-care products, specialty chemicals
Royal Dutch Petroleum Co.	RD	Oil (second largest international)
Schering-Plough Corp.	SEP	Drugs, toiletries, cosmetics
SCM Corp.	SCM	Coatings, office equipment, appliances, food

Table B.1—*continued*

Name of firm	Ticker symbol	Principal business
Seagrave Corp.	SVE	
Searle, G. D., & Co.	SRL	Ethical drugs, health-care equipment
Shell Oil Co.	SUO	Oil (second largest domestic refiner)
Shell Transport & Trading Co.	SC	Owns 40% Royal-Dutch Shell
Sherwin-Williams	SHW	Paint and varnish (largest manufacturer)
Skelly Oil Co.	SYE	Crude producer
Smithkline Corp.	SKL	Ethical drugs, consumer products
Squibb Corp.	SQB	Drugs, cosmetics, food, candy
Staley, A. E., Mfg.	STA	Corn products
Standard Brands Paint	SBP	Discount stores, manufactures own paint
Standard Oil of California	SD	Oil, gas, plastics, petrochemicals
Standard Oil of Indiana	SN	Oil, gas, plastics, petrochemicals
Standard Oil of Ohio	SOH	Oil, gas, plastics, petrochemicals
Stauffer Chemical Co.	STF	Industrial, agricultural, and specialty chemicals
Sterling Drug, Inc.	STY	Proprietary drugs and others
Sun Chemical Corp.	SNL	Printing inks, chemicals, packaging materials
Sun Co., Inc.	SUN	Large integrated oil company
Sybron Corp.	SYB	
Tenneco, Inc.	TGT	Natural gas, chemicals, land, ship building
Tesoro Petroleum Corp.	TSO	Integrated oil company
Texaco, Inc.	TX	Oil (second largest in world)
Texfi Industries	TXF	Knitted apparel and fabrics
Textron, Inc.	TXT	Diversified manufacturing concern
Thiokol Corp.	THI	Chemicals
Unilever N.V.	UN	Vast international enterprise, soaps, detergents
Union Camp	UCC	Paper, chemicals, residential development, building materials
Union Carbide Corp.	UK	Ranks second in chemical industry
Union Oil Co. of California	UCL	Integrated domestic oil
Uniroyal, Inc.	R	Rubber, tires, chemicals
United Merchants & Mfrs.	UMM	Textiles, Robert Hall Chain
Univar Corp.	UVX	Food and chemicals
UOP, Inc.	UOP	Refining processes, engineering
Upjohn Co.	UPS	Drugs, chemicals, agricultural products
Vulcan Materials	VMC	
Warner-Lambert Co.	WLA	Drugs, cosmetics, candy, gum
Wheelabrator-Frye	WFI	
Whittaker Corp.	WKR	Metals, textiles, chemicals
Williams Cos.	WMB	Fertilizers, energy, metals
Witco Chemical Corp.	WIT	Organic chemicals, motor oil, detergents, asphalts

[1] Nearly all the pertinent stocks on the New York and American Stock Exchanges are listed; the OTC list (Table B.3), for various reasons, is only a partial one.

Table B.2 American Stock Exchange

Name of firm	Ticker symbol	Principal business
A & E Plastik Pak	AE	Fully integrated plastics, manufacturer
Alcolac, Inc.	ALC	Specialty organic chemicals
American Maize-Prod	AZE.A	
American Petrofina	API.A	Integrated oil and petrochemical
Anglo Co. Ltd.	AGO.A	Contract drilling, chemicals, auto parts
Ati, Inc.	ATQ	
Canadian Occidental Petroleum	CXY	Chemical, oil, gas, sulfur
Canadian Superior Oil	CDS	Crude oil, natural gas, sulfur
Cominco, Ltd.	CLT	Lead, zinc mines, fertilizer
Conchemco, Inc.	CKC	Mobile homes, surface coatings
Cook Paint & Varnish	COK	Industrial coatings, paint stores
Corenco Corp.	CCR	Oil, fertilizer, and feeds
Courtaulds Ltd.	COU	Textiles, rayon yarn
Crest-Foam Corp.	CFO	Polyester foam and apparel, shoes
Diversey Corp.	DIV	Cleaning and sanitation chemicals
Essex Chemical	ESX	Sealants, coatings, adhesives
Fields Plastics & Chemicals	FLP	Vinyl and plastic sheeting
Foote Mineral	FTE	Ferroalloys and lithium compounds
Forest Laboratories	FRX	Pharmaceuticals
Glasrock Products	GLA	Plastics and magnesium oxide
Great Lakes Chemical	GLK	Bromine and brominated chemicals
Grow Chemical	GRO	Specialty coatings, chemical products
Guardsman Chemicals	GRV	Varnishes, lacquers, paints
Gulf Oil Canada, Ltd.	GOC	Oil (second largest Canadian)
Imperial Chemical Industries, Ltd.	IMP	World's largest chemical (Great Britain)
Imperial Oil, Ltd.	IMO	Subsidiary of Exxon
Indian Head	IHD	
Inolex Corp.	ILX	Food, cosmetics, chemicals
Ionics, Inc.	ION	Electrical chemical processing equipment, desalination
Kewanee Industries	KOC	Crude oil, gas, chemicals
New England Nuclear	NNC	Radioactive chemicals, nuclides
Pantasote Co.	PNT	Plastic and rubber products
Park Chemical	PAK	Industrial and auto products
Park Electrochemical	PKE	Laminates, aluminum trim
Pentron Industries	PEN	Housewares, cabinets, plastics
Pratt & Lambert	PM	Paints and varnishes, industrials
Purepac Laboratories	PUR	Drugs, medical devices
Raycon, Inc.	RAC	Fluorocarbon gas
Remington Arms Co.	REM	Guns, chemicals for guns
Robintech, Inc.	ROB	PVC resin and pipe
Stepan Chemical	SCL	Organic chemicals
Supronics Corp.	SU	Women's cosmetics, coatings
Synalloy Corp.	SYO	Chemicals, dyes, machinery, metals
Syntex Corp.	SYN	Pharmaceuticals, agribusiness
Terra Chemicals	TCI	Chemical fertilizers

Table B.2—*continued*

Name of firm	Ticker symbol	Principal business
Total Petroleum, Ltd.	TPN	Oil and gas exploration and production, Canada refining and marketing in midwest U.S.
U.S. Filter	UFT	Polution-control systems, chemicals
U.S. Radium	URD	Luminous chemicals, x-ray, etc.
Valspar Corp.	VAL	Paint, varnish, ink, plastics
Verit Industries	VER	Meat processing, mobile homes, chemicals
Volpex Corp.	VOT	Plastics, auto items
West Chemical Products	WCP	Sanitation and health products

Table B.3 Over-the-counter stocks

Name of firm	Ticker symbol	Principal business
Aceto Chemical	ACET	Chemical distributor and manufacturer
Bayer AG	BAYRY	Large German chemical company
Betz Laboratories	BETZ	Water-treatment chemicals
Bio-Rad Laboratories	BRLS	Research chemicals for medical tests
Buckeye International	BEYE	Plastics, castings
Burdox, Inc.	BDOX	Compressed and liquid gases
Calbiochem	CALB	Biochemicals
Carboline Co.	CARB	Industrial synthetic linings, coatings
Chattem Drug & Chemical	CHTT	Proprietary medicines, chemicals
Chemed Corp.	CMED	Specialty medical chemicals
Chemplast, Inc.	CPLS	Plastic industrial products
Detrex Chemical Industries	DTRX	Chemical specialties
Diagnostic Data	DIAG	Drug development
Early California Industries	ERLY	Rice, specialty foods, chemicals
Economics Laboratory, Inc.	ECON	Cleaning and sanitation products
Exolon Co.		Silicon carbide, aluminum oxide
Fuller, H. B., Co.	FULL	Industrial adhesives
Guardian Chemical	GCHM	Pharmaceuticals, fine chemicals
Hexcel Corp.	HEXC	Plastics, honeycomb cores
Interplastic Corp.	INPL	Synthetic resins, plastics
K-V Pharmaceutical	KVPH	Drugs
Liquid Air of North America	LANA	Industrial gases and equipment
Loctite Corp.	LCTE	Chemical sealants, adhesives
Macdermid, Inc.	MACD	Metal-finishing chemicals
Mallinckrodt, Inc.	MALL	Chemicals and pharmaceuticals
Morgan Adhesives	MRGA	Self-adhesive papers, films, foils
Mylan Laboratories	MYLN	Drugs for others, capsules
Na-Churs International	NACHF	Liquid fertilizer

(*continued*)

Table B.3—*continued*

Name of firm	Ticker symbol	Principal business
Noxell Corp.	NOXLB	Medicated skin creams, cosmetics
O'Neal, Jones & Feldman	OJFC	Ethical pharmaceuticals
Ormont Drug & Chemical	ORMT	Pharmaceuticals
Petrolite Corp.	PLIT	Specialty chemicals, equipment, waxes
PVO International	PVOC	
Quaker Chemical	QCHM	Specialty chemicals
Realex Corp.	RELX	Plastics, insecticides
Reid Prov. Labs	REID	Pharmaceuticals
Reliance Universal	RELI	Industrial chemical coatings
REX Plastics	RXPL	Polyethylene film
Ring Around Products	RING	Seed, spray, equipment, chemicals
Royster Co.	ROYS	Mixed fertilizers
RPM, Inc.	RPOW	Heavy-duty paints and chemicals
Rucker Pharmacal	RUCK	Pharmaceuticals
Sigma-Aldrich	SIAL	Biochemical and organic products
Sonoco Products	SONO	Industrial paper products, chemicals
Southwest Petro-Chem	SWPC	Lubricating greases
Sperti Drug Products	SPER	Pharmaceuticals, sun lamps
Stanley Home Products	STHP	Household items, detergents, sanitation products
Swedlow, Inc.	SWEDD	Acrylic sheet, jet windows
Tenneco		Oil, chemicals, packaging
Tipperary Corp.	TIPR	Oil, gas, fertilizers
Tutag, S. J., & Co.	TUTG	Pharmaceutical and generic drugs
Ventron Corp.	VTRN	Chemical and metal hydrides
Virginia Chemicals	VCHM	Industrial chemicals, refrigerants
Zenith Laboratories	ZENI	Generic drugs

LIST OF TABLES

INDEX